EVERY SCIENCE IS, AMONG OTHER THI

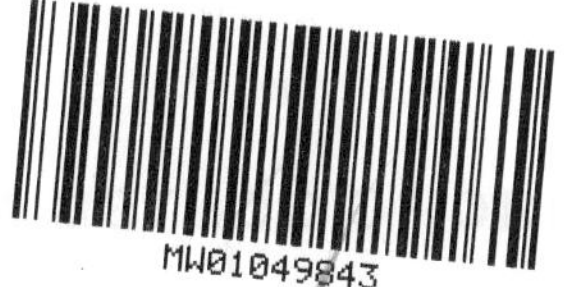

ING, SIMPLIFYING, MAKING THE INDIGESTIBLE DIGESTIBLE TO THE MIND.

HERMANN HESSE

PHYSICS IS THAT SUBSET OF HUMAN EXPERIENCE WHICH CAN BE REDUCED TO COUPLED HARMONIC OSCILLATORS.

MICHAEL PESKIN

THE GOAL SHOULD BE, NOT TO IMPLANT IN THE STUDENTS' MIND EVERY FACT THAT THE TEACHER KNOWS NOW; BUT RATHER TO IMPLANT A WAY OF THINKING THAT ENABLES THE STUDENT, IN THE FUTURE, TO LEARN IN ONE YEAR WHAT THE TEACHER LEARNED IN TWO YEARS. ONLY IN THAT WAY CAN WE CONTINUE TO ADVANCE FROM ONE GENERATION TO THE NEXT.

EDWIN JAYNES

JAKOB SCHWICHTENBERG

NO-NONSENSE QUANTUM FIELD THEORY

NO-NONSENSE BOOKS

First printing, September 2020

With illustrations by Corina Wieber

BOOK EDITION: 1.4

Dedicated to my parents

Preface

When I tried to learn quantum field theory, it was a frustrating experience. When I read the standard textbooks, I felt as if I had hired a climbing coach to show me how to get to the top of Mt. Everest and right after the start he would take my hand, say: "Watch this!", and then make a huge jump upwards. From one moment to the next I was 100 meters above the ground but had no idea how I got there.

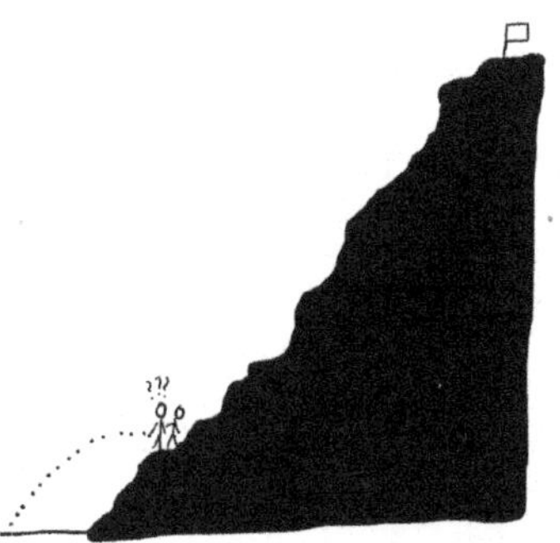

There were no retrospective explanations either, just more and more jumps upwards accompanied by "encouraging" statements that everything is "obvious" or "easy". It was puzzling and frustrating.

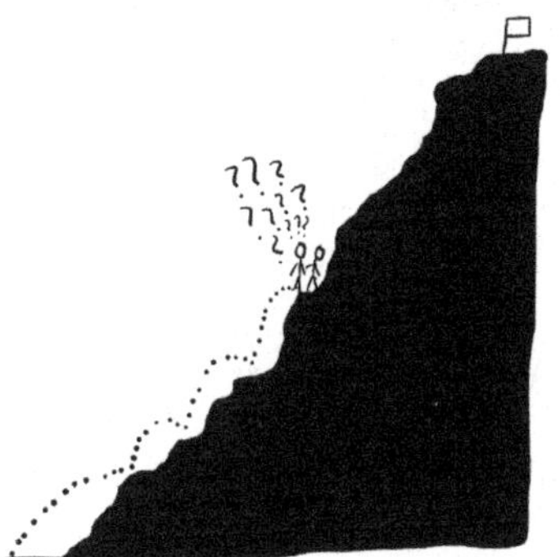

Most physicists will tell you that it *has* to be this way. That this is the only way to understand. I'm convinced that this is nonsense.

Using our Mt. Everest analogy, who do you think will learn more effectively:

▷ Someone who has watched a world-class climber make incredible moves for a few hours and afterwards tries to do them himself,

▷ or someone who has a coach who takes him through the motions step by step?

I'm not saying that the first approach doesn't work. It's obviously extremely popular and currently the standard approach in universities all around the world. But my goal with this book is to provide an alternative that takes an approach which is closer to the second scenario.

In fact, I eventually discovered a textbook that convinced me that a step-by-step approach may not only be possible but can be also enjoyable and effective. The book is called Student Friendly Quantum Field Theory by Robert D. Klauber. It's a fantastic book and remains to this day my favorite textbook.

Klauber's book motivated me to write student-friendly textbooks on all kinds of topics ranging from classical mechanics[1] to gauge theory[2]. But it also discouraged me from writing a quantum field theory textbook. Instead, I recommended Klauber's book at every possible occasion to everyone who would listen. I still do.

[1] Jakob Schwichtenberg. *No-Nonsense Classical Mechanics : a student-friendly introduction*. No-Nonsense Books, Karlsruhe, Germany, 2019b. ISBN 9781096195382

[2] Jakob Schwichtenberg. *Physics from Finance*. No-Nonsense Books, Karlsruhe, Germany, 2019c. ISBN 978-1795882415

So why did I eventually write a quantum field theory textbook nevertheless?

I learned a lot about quantum field theory in the past few years and slowly but steadily realized that I would explain most concepts completely differently than Klauber does in his book. Not necessarily better, but different.[3] Therefore, I figured that it won't hurt anyone if there is a second student-friendly introduction to quantum field theory on the market. The readers can still decide which book they prefer and since the books are quite different, it's possible to read both without getting bored. Every author is able to provide a unique perspective and for any topic you need multiple perspectives to grasp the whole picture.

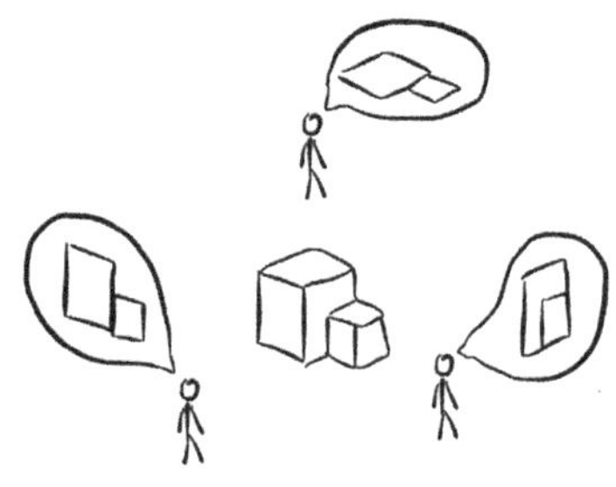

[3] It's, in fact, impossible to say in general terms which explanation is the best since the effectiveness of an explanation always depends on the reader's interests and background.

With that said, let me explain in a bit more detail what makes this book different.

- ▷ First, it wasn't written by a professor. As a result, this book is by no means an authoritative reference. Instead, this book is written like a casual conversation with a more experienced student who shares with you everything he wishes he had known earlier. I'm convinced that someone who has just recently learned the topic can explain it much better than someone who learned it decades ago. Many textbooks are hard to understand, not because the subject is difficult, but because the author can't remember what it's like to be a beginner[4].

[4] This is known as the "Curse of Knowledge."

▷ Second, this book is unique in that it contains lots of idiosyncratic hand-drawn illustrations. Usually, textbooks include very few pictures since drawing them is either a lot of work or expensive. However, drawing figures is only a lot of work if you are a perfectionist. The images in this book are not as pretty as the pictures in a typical textbook since I firmly believe that *lots* of imperfect illustrations are much better than a few perfect ones. The goal of this book, after all, is to help you understand quantum field theory and not to win prizes for my pretty illustrations.

▷ Finally, my only goal with this book was to write the most student-friendly quantum field theory textbook and not, for example, to build my reputation. Too many books are unnecessarily complicated because if a book is hard to understand it makes the author appear smarter.[5] To give a concrete example, nothing in this book is assumed to be "obvious" or "easy to see". Moreover, calculations are done step-by-step and are annotated to help you understand faster.

[5] To quote C. Lanczos: "Many of the scientific treatises of today are formulated in a half-mystical language, as though to impress the reader with the uncomfortable feeling that he is in the permanent presence of a superman."

However, this book is certainly not a good fit for everyone. In particular, a necessary byproduct of the slower step-by-step approach is that we won't get as far as most other books. Instead of talking about dozens of advanced topics, we will only discuss the fundamental ideas at the heart of quantum field theory in detail. Secondly, by reading this book you will not become a skillful practitioner. The main focus is on understanding the basic concepts and not on how to calculate cross sections.[6] Of course, you can learn about advanced concepts and how to calculate cross sections by consulting other textbooks after reading this book. I'm convinced that this book will provide you with a solid foundation for such further studies.

[6] I'm not a fan of books that try to achieve various things at once since it means that they won't do any of them particularly well. In particular, I think it's annoying when important ideas are "left for the reader as an exercise".

Without any further ado, let's dive in. I hope you enjoy reading this book as much as I have enjoyed writing it.

Karlsruhe, December 2019 *Jakob Schwichtenberg*

PS: If you find an error, I would appreciate a short email to errors@jakobschwichtenberg.com.

PPS: You can discuss the content of the book with other readers, ask questions and find bonus material at:
`www.nononsensebooks.com/qft/bonus`.

Acknowledgments

Special thanks to Dr. Florian Colbatzky whose comments, ideas and corrections have made this book so much better. Moreover, I want to thank Fabian Waetermans and Jacob Ayres for carefully proofreading the manuscript and Anne van Rossum, Jay Bhambure, Robert Welters, Adam Brown, John O'Neall, Eran Zamir, Ashwin Balaji, Andreas Pargner, Namkyu Park, John P. Rickert, Ronald Legere, Luis Odin Estrada Ramos, Don Washburn, Phil Hystad, and Joey Ooi for reporting several typos.

Before we discuss any details, we need to talk about three things. First, a crucial question:

Why should you care about quantum field theory?

Quantum field theory is the best theory of elementary particles and their interactions that we have. Using quite a small set of input parameters, quantum field theory allows us to make an extremely large number of wide ranging predictions.

Most importantly, all predictions made using it so far have proved to be correct. In fact, the predictions made using quantum field theory have resulted in some of the most spectacular agreements with experiment imaginable. Famously, the quantum field theoretical prediction and measurements of the electron anomalous magnetic dipole moment are in agreement within ten parts in a billion (10^{-8}).

But quantum field theory is not only amazing because it allows us to *describe* lots of phenomena, but also because it allows us to actually *understand* them. A few examples:

▷ Quantum field theory allows us to understand the common origin and properties of three of the four known fundamental forces. Electrogmagnetic interactions, strong interactions and weak interactions can all be understood and described perfectly within the framework of quantum field theory.[7]

▷ Quantum field theory also offers an intriguing perspective on the origin of the masses of elementary particles. According to our present understanding, all known massive elementary particles are inherently massless and only acquire the property that we call mass dynamically through the Higgs mechanism.

[7] The fourth known fundamental force, gravity, is described by Einstein's theory of general relativity. Currently, there exists no entirely satisfactory model that incorporates gravity into the framework of quantum field theory. This is known as the problem of quantum gravity.

▷ Quantum field theory explains why all electrons that we've observed so far have exactly the same properties.[8]Quantum field theory allows us to understand why different, yet indistinguishable, copies of elementary particles exist.

[8] In fact, this is true for all elementary particles.

Motivated by these phenomenal results, some physicists like David Tong, just to name one example, go even as far to declare that "*quantum field theory is literally the language in which the laws of Nature are written.*"

I'm personally not that optimistic that we've already found the ultimate framework to describe nature for reasons that are discussed in Chapter 18. But what is unquestionable is that quantum field theory represents the present frontier in theoretical physics. It's the "ultimate" theory that we currently know about and thus, anyone who wants to explore new territory needs a solid understanding of it.

And even though quantum field theory represents the cumulative result of the works of thousands of physicist over hundreds of years, it is beautiful and simple at it's core. This is astonishing if you think about it. There is no reason why nature should behave according to a small set of simple rules that can be derived from a few basic principles. It's this fact which makes many physicists optimistic that we've indeed revealed something deep about nature.

In addition, it's also worth mentioning that there are also more pragmatic reasons to learn about quantum field theory. It's an extremely versatile tool and can also be used to describe, for example, condensed matter systems or financial markets. Famously, we can use quantum field theory to explain unexpected phenomena such as the fractional quantum Hall effect, or superconductivity.

With all of this in mind, I'm confident to declare that you won't regret any minute you spend learning about quantum field theory. At the very least, your perspective on how nature works will be permanently changed.

Preliminaries

Almost everybody will tell you that you need a solid grasp of

▷ the Lagrangian formalism,

▷ special relativity,

▷ and quantum mechanics

to properly understand quantum field theory. This is certainly not completely wrong. If you know the fundamentals of these three topics you will find it much easier to understand the main ideas of quantum field theory.

On the other hand, however, it's certainly not impossible to get some understanding of what quantum field theory is all about without having studied the Lagrangian formalism, special relativity and quantum mechanics in detail. Moreover, I'm not a fan of just-in-case learning and find a just-in-time approach much more effective (especially for self-learners).[9] So if your main goal is to understand quantum field theory, I don't think it's very smart to spend years preparing for this goal by learning other topics. How can you know in advance which aspects of other topics are really relevant for your goals? Moreover, it's really hard to stay motivated if your real goal always seems incredibly far away.

[9] I'm not saying that just-in-case learning is wrong. There is no wrong approach. Different methods work for different people and ultimately you need to figure out for yourself what works best for you. If you're unsure, my suggestion would be that you give the more direct, dive-right-in approach a go. If it doesn't work out, you can still revert to a more traditional approach.

Instead, it's far more effective to dive right in. Once you actually start learning quantum field theory, you will quickly notice which aspects of other topics are really relevant. You can then close gaps in your knowledge on a case-by-case basis as you move along. If you follow such an aggressive learning approach, you will not only know what exactly you should learn more about, but you will also be extremely motivated to do so.

Motivated by this general philosophy, I try to keep all my books as self-contained as possible. For the book you're reading right now this means that we will discuss just enough special relativity, quantum mechanics and of the general ideas behind the Lagrangian formalism to understand what is going on in quantum field theory. Moreover, I will freely refer you to other resources such that you can always catch up on the details whenever you feel like a deeper discussion is necessary.

The third thing we need to talk about is the meaning of a few special symbols which we will use in the following chapters.

Notation

▷ Three horizontal lines $\equiv$ indicate that we are dealing with a definition.

▷ The symbol $\stackrel{!}{=}$ means "has to be", i.e., indicates that we are dealing with a condition.

▷ The most important equations, statements and results are highlighted like this:

$$\boxed{\frac{\partial L}{\partial q} - \frac{d}{dt}\left(\frac{\partial L}{\partial \dot{q}}\right) = 0} \tag{1}$$

▷ $\frac{\partial f(x,y,z,t)}{\partial t}$ denotes the derivative with respect to t.

▷ A dot above a function denotes the derivative with respect to time $\dot{q}(t) \equiv \frac{dq(t)}{dt}$ and $\ddot{q}(t) \equiv \frac{d^2q(t)}{dt^2}$.

▷ We sometimes use the shorthand notation $\partial_i \equiv \frac{\partial}{\partial i}$ for the partial derivative where $i \in \{x, y, z\}$ and ∂_μ for $\mu \in \{t, x, y, z\}$.

▷ Greek indices like μ, ν or σ, are always summed from 0 to 3:

$$x_\mu y_\mu = \sum_{\mu=0}^{3} x_\mu y_\mu .$$

- ▷ In contrast, Latin indices like i, j, k are always summed from 1 to 3:

$$x_i x_i \equiv \sum_{i=1}^{3} x_i x_i.$$

- ▷ δ_{ij} denotes the Kronecker delta, which is defined as follows:

$$\delta_{ij} = \begin{cases} 1 & \text{if } i = j \\ 0 & \text{if } i \neq j \end{cases}$$

- ▷ ϵ_{ijk} denotes the three-dimensional Levi-Civita symbol:

$$\epsilon_{ijk} = \begin{cases} 1 & \text{if } (i,j,k) \in \{(1,2,3),(2,3,1),(3,1,2)\} \\ 0 & \text{if } i = j \text{ or } j = k \text{ or } k = i \\ -1 & \text{if } (i,j,k) \in \{(1,3,2),(3,2,1),(2,1,3)\} \end{cases}$$

- ▷ To avoid that the layout breaks, column vectors are often written as a transposed row vector. For example

$$\vec{v} = (0,1,0)^T = \begin{pmatrix} 0 \\ 1 \\ 0 \end{pmatrix}$$

- ▷ $\dagger$ denotes the Hermitian conjugate which is a composition of complex conjugation and transposition: $A^\dagger = A^{T\star}$. For ordinary functions, the transposition makes no difference and hence we have $f^\dagger = f^\star$.
- ▷ An expression of the form $A \ll B$ means that A is much smaller than B. Similarly $B \gg A$ means that B is much larger than A.
- ▷ The notation $0_{2\times 2}$ is used for the (2×2) matrix that only contains zeroes. Moreover, , $1_{2\times 2}$ denotes the (2×2) unit matrix.

Although not notational issues, but nevertheless important, the following two comments on the word usage in this book:

- ▷ By coordinate transformation I always mean rotations, boosts, translations or mirroring transformations. There are lots of additional coordinate transformations (diffeomorphisms) that are important in other contexts which aren't discussed in this book.

- ▷ The word fundamental in this book means "fundamental as far as we know". Quantum field theory is not necessarily the end of the story, but it's still useful to speak of fundamental fields and elementary particles.

That's it. We are ready to dive in (after a short look at the table of contents).

Contents

1 **Bird's-Eye View of Quantum Field Theory** 23

Part 0 Preliminaries

2 **Spacetime** 37
- 2.1 The Arena of Physics 38
- 2.2 Maximum Speed 41
- 2.3 The Speed of Light 43
- 2.4 Time Dilation 45
- 2.5 Proper Time 48
- 2.6 The Minkowski Metric and Four-Vectors 51
- 2.7 The Relativistic Energy-Momentum Relation 57
- 2.8 Lorentz and Poincaré Transformations 62
- 2.9 Summary 67

3 **Fields** 69
- 3.1 Scalar Fields 72
- 3.2 Vector Fields 74
  - 3.2.1 Polarization 75
- 3.3 Scalars, Vectors, Tensors, and Spinors 80
- 3.4 Spinor Fields 94
  - 3.4.1 Spinor Formalism 96
  - 3.4.2 Spin 100
  - 3.4.3 Chirality 106
- 3.5 Field Dynamics 108
- 3.6 Waves 112
  - 3.6.1 Wave Packets 117
- 3.7 Field Spaces 122

3.8 Local Coordinate Systems . . . 125
3.9 Gauge Fields . . . 129

4 The Lagrangian Formalism 137
4.1 The Euler-Lagrange Equation . . . 141
4.1.1 Intermezzo: Variational Calculus . . . 142
4.1.2 Deriving the Euler-Lagrange Equation . . . 146
4.1.3 The Meaning of the Euler-Lagrange Equation 150
4.2 The Lagrangian Formalism in Field Theory . . . 153
4.3 Noether's Theorem . . . 155
4.3.1 Spacetime Symmetries . . . 157
4.3.2 Internal Symmetries . . . 161

5 The Behavior of Free Fields 167
5.1 Free Scalar fields and the Klein Gordon Equation . 170
5.1.1 The Meaning of the Klein-Gordon Equation 171
5.1.2 The Meaning of the Klein-Gordon Lagrangian 181
5.1.3 Solutions of the Klein-Gordon Equation . . . 189
5.1.4 General Solution of the Klein-Gordon Equation . . . 192
5.2 Free Spinor Fields and the Dirac Equation . . . 195
5.2.1 The Meaning of the Dirac Equation . . . 199
5.2.2 Solutions of the Dirac Equation . . . 205
5.2.3 The Mass Basis . . . 211
5.2.4 General Solution of the Dirac Equation . . . 214
5.3 Free Gauge Fields and the Proca/Maxwell equations 214
5.3.1 Meaning of the Proca and Maxwell Equations 216
5.3.2 Solutions of the Proca Equation . . . 218
5.3.3 Solutions of the Maxwell Equation . . . 225
5.3.4 General Solution of the Proca and Maxwell equation . . . 233

6 Interacting Classical Fields 235
6.1 Green's Functions . . . 236
6.1.1 Delta Decomposition . . . 237
6.1.2 Green's Function of the Klein-Gordon Equation . . . 240
6.1.3 Summary . . . 245
6.2 Self-Interactions . . . 246
6.3 Yukawa Interactions . . . 253

6.3.1 Scalar Field in the Presence of Yukawa Interactions 255
6.3.2 Green's Function of the Dirac Equation . . . 257
6.3.3 Spinor Field in the Presence of Yukawa Interactions 260
6.4 Gauge Interactions 264
6.4.1 Green's Function of the Maxwell Equation . 266

Part I What Everybody Ought to Know About Quantum Field Theory

7 Quantum Mechanics 273
7.1 The Quantum Formalism 273
7.1.1 Group Theory 276
7.1.2 Quantum Operators 280
7.1.3 The Canonical Commutation Relation 282
7.1.4 The Schrödinger Equation 283
7.1.5 Time Evolution 286
7.1.6 Quantum Waves 287
7.1.7 de Broglie Relations 292
7.1.8 The Stationary Schrödinger Equation 292
7.2 The Quantum Harmonic Oscillator 294

8 Quantum Fields 301
8.1 Quantum Fields vs. Classical Fields 304
8.2 The Canonical Commutation Relations 307
8.3 Field Operators 309
8.3.1 Creation and Annihilation Operators 313
8.4 Particle States 322
8.4.1 Plane Waves 324
8.4.2 The Uncertainty Relation 327
8.4.3 Dealing with Non-Normalizable States . . . 330
8.4.4 Wave Packets 332
8.5 Propagators 334
8.5.1 Dynamical Propagators 336
8.5.2 Advanced and Retarded Propagators 338
8.5.3 The Feynman Propagator 341
8.5.4 Summary 349
8.6 Complex Scalar Fields 351

8.6.1 Antiparticles 353
8.6.2 Complex Scalar Field Propagators 355
8.7 Quantized Spinor Fields 358
8.7.1 Spinor Hamiltonian 362
8.7.2 Spinor Particles 363
8.7.3 Spinor Propagator 365
8.8 Quantized Gauge Fields 367
8.8.1 Quantized Massive Gauge Fields 367
8.8.2 Quantized Massless Gauge Fields 372

9 Interacting Quantum Fields 379
9.1 Transition Amplitudes and Time Evolution 380
9.2 The Interaction Picture 382
9.3 The Dyson Series 384
9.3.1 Time-Ordering 387
9.4 Ground State Energy in the Presence of Interactions 394

Part II Essential Applications

10 Scattering - a First Look 407
10.1 Zeroth-Order Approximation 409
10.2 First-Order Approximation 412

11 Amplitude Technology 421
11.1 Contractions 423
11.2 Wick's Theorem 428
11.3 Important Contractions 430
11.4 Scattering - a Second Look 437
11.4.1 Zeroth-Order Approximation 437
11.4.2 First Order Approximation 438
11.5 Feynman Diagrams 441
11.6 Scattering - a Third Look 448
11.6.1 Zeroth order Approximation 448
11.6.2 First order Approximation 450
11.6.3 Second-Order Approximation 451
11.7 Summary 459

12 Elementary Models 465
12.1 Yukawa Interactions 467
12.1.1 Important Contractions 468

12.1.2 Zeroth-Order Approximation 470
12.1.3 First-Order Approximation 471
12.1.4 Second-Order Approximation 472
12.1.5 The Non-Relativistic Limit 476
12.1.6 Further Comments 477
12.2 Gauge Interactions 481
12.2.1 The Non-Relativistic Limit 483
12.2.2 Further Examples 486

13 Scattered Comments **487**
13.1 Virtual Particles 488
13.2 Loops and Legs 491
13.3 Scattering Conventions 492
13.4 Regularization 493
13.5 The Renormalization Group 498
13.5.1 The Meaning of the Renormalization Group Equation 502

Part III Get an Understanding of Quantum Field Theory You Can Be Proud Of

14 The Living Vacuum **513**
14.1 Symmetry Breaking 517
14.2 Explicit Symmetry Breaking 519
14.3 Spontaneous Symmetry Breaking 521
14.4 Spontaneous Mass Generation 529

15 The Path Integral Formulation **535**
15.1 The Path Integral in Quantum Mechanics 536
15.1.1 The Classical Path 546
15.2 The Path Integral in Quantum Field Theory 549

16 Non-Perturbative Phenomena **553**
16.1 Instantons 556

17 Effective Field Models and the Origin of Simplicity **565**
17.1 Dimensional Analysis 568
17.2 The Origin of "Fundamental" Lagrangians 572

18 Outlook **577**

19 Further Reading Recommendations 581

Part IV Appendices

A Cumbersome Calculations from Part 0 and Part I 589
A.1 Rewriting the Proca Lagrangian 590
A.2 Noether Current for a Complex Field 591
A.3 Rewriting the General Solution of the Klein-Gordon Equation 592
A.4 Verifying the $a(k)$, $a^\dagger(k)$ commutation relations . . 595
A.5 Rewriting the Scalar Field Energy 597
A.6 Rewriting the Scalar Field Momentum 599
A.7 Demonstration that the Feynman Propagator is a Green's Function 601
A.8 Total Charge in Terms of Creation and Annihilation Operators 606

B Cumbersome Calculations from Part II and Part III 611
B.1 Validating Wick's Theorem For Three Field Products 611
B.2 Work in the Vicinity of an Infinitely Long Wire . . . 614
B.3 Fourier Transform of the Yukawa Potential 616

C Wave Properties 619
C.1 Advanced properties 624

D Gauge Symmetry in Classical Electrodynamics 627
D.1 Partial Gauge Fixing 629

E Delta Distribution 631
E.1 Integral Representation of the Delta Distribution . . 634

F Statistics 635
F.1 Mean 635

Bibliography 637

Index 639

1

Bird's-Eye View of Quantum Field Theory

Quantum field theory is, at its heart, quite simple. However, specific applications can be extremely complicated and confusing. For this reason it's easy to lose the forest for the trees. To prevent this, we start this book with a quick overview. Afterwards, we will talk about the various concepts in more detail and gradually refine our understanding until we are ready for applications.

So don't worry if not everything is immediately clear in this chapter. Our goal is solely to get an overview and each idea mentioned here will be discussed later in more detail.

The most basic objects in quantum field theory are fields. A field is a mathematical object that assigns a value (or a more complicated object) to every point in space at every moment in time.

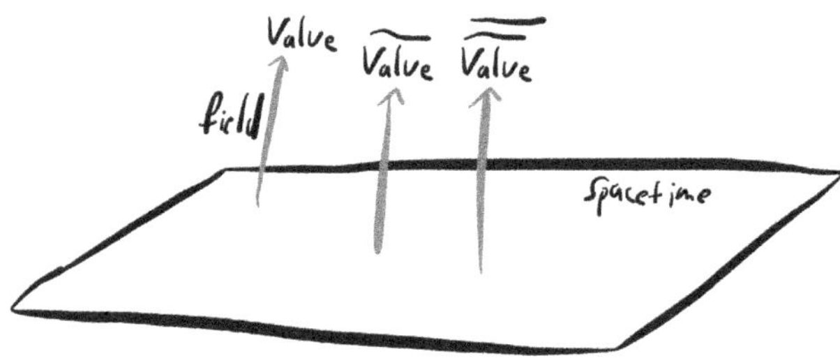

In quantum field theory, we describe nature by imagining that there are various fields stacked upon each other at each spacetime point.

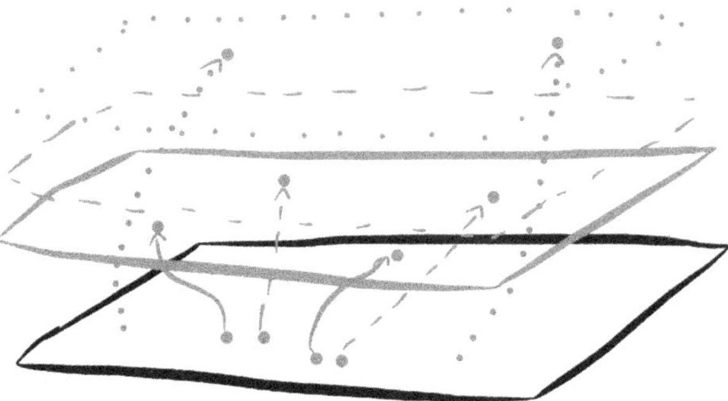

Moreover, we interpret specific field excitations as elementary particles. For example, an elementary excitation of the electron field is what we call an electron.

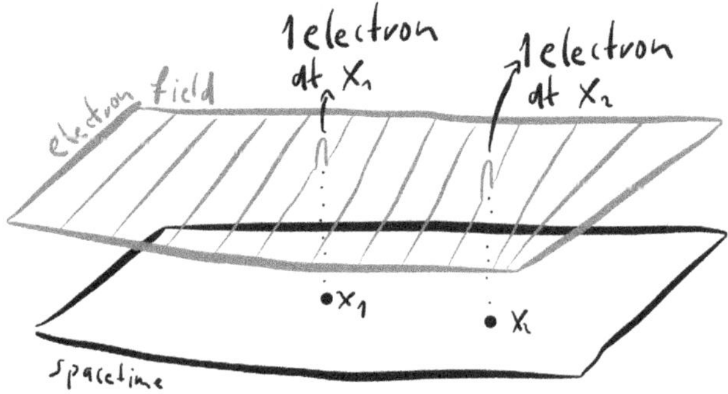

The most important kinds of fields in modern physics are scalar fields, spinor fields and vector fields. A scalar field assigns a scalar to each spacetime point, a spinor field a spinor and a vector field a vector. For each kind of a field there is a different equation of motion that tells us how it evolves in time. For example, the Klein-Gordon equation[1]

$$(\partial_\mu \partial^\mu + m^2)\phi(x) = 0\,, \tag{1.1}$$

is the equation of motion for scalar fields. Its general solution reads[2]

$$\phi(x) = \int \mathrm{d}k^3 \frac{1}{(2\pi)^3\sqrt{2\omega_k}} \left(a(\vec{k})\mathrm{e}^{-ikx} + a^\dagger(\vec{k})\mathrm{e}^{ikx} \right) . \tag{1.2}$$

[1] To unclutter the notation we use x as a short-hand notation for x_μ.

[2] Here we use the short-hand notation $k^\mu x_\mu = kx$.

In quantum field theory, fields are no longer ordinary functions but operators. This is encoded in the canonical commutation relation

$$[\phi(t,\vec{x}), \pi(t,\vec{y})] = i\delta(\vec{x} - \vec{y})\,, \tag{1.3}$$

where $\pi \equiv \frac{\partial \mathcal{L}}{\partial(\partial_0 \phi)}$ is the conjugate momentum density. If we plug the general solution of the Klein-Gordon equation into the canonical commutation relation, we find

$$\begin{aligned}[]
[a(\vec{k}), a^\dagger(\vec{k}')] &= (2\pi)^3 \delta(\vec{k} - \vec{k}')\,, \\
[a(\vec{k}), a(\vec{k}')] = 0\,, &\quad [a^\dagger(\vec{k}), a^\dagger(\vec{k}')] = 0\,.
\end{aligned} \tag{1.4}$$

This tells us that $a^\dagger(\vec{k}')$ is a creation operator, while $a(\vec{k})$ is an annihilation operator. We say that when $a^\dagger(\vec{k})$ acts on the ground state of the field $|0\rangle$, the result is a state that describes a single particle with momentum $\vec{k}$:

$$a^\dagger(\vec{k})\,|0\rangle \equiv |1_{\vec{k}}\rangle\ . \tag{1.5}$$

Analogously, we can describe field configurations that contain multiple particles. For example,

$$a^\dagger(\vec{q})a^\dagger(\vec{k})\,|0\rangle \equiv |1_{\vec{k}}, 1_{\vec{q}}\rangle \tag{1.6}$$

is a state that describes two particles, one with momentum $\vec{k}$ and one with momentum $\vec{q}$. Moreover, it follows from the commutation relations that when $a(\vec{k})$ acts on a state, a particle with momentum $\vec{k}$ is annihilated

$$a(\vec{k})\,|1_{\vec{k}}, 1_{\vec{q}}\rangle = |1_{\vec{q}}\rangle\ . \tag{1.7}$$

Similarly, we can interpret the coefficients that appear in the general solution of the Dirac equation which describes spinor fields and in the general solution of the Proca equation which describes gauge fields.[3]

[3] There are important but subtle differences in how we interpret scalar fields, spinor fields and gauge fields in a quantum context. We will discuss them in detail in Part I.

One of the most important aspects of quantum field theory is that it allows us to describe scattering processes. In particular, we find the probability amplitude that a specific initial configuration $|i\rangle$ (for example, two electrons) evolves into a final configuration $\langle f|$ (for example, two electrons with different momenta) by evaluating

$$\begin{aligned} A(i \to f) &= \langle f|\hat{S}|i\rangle \\ &= \langle f|i\rangle - i\langle f| \int_{-\infty}^{\infty} dt_1 H_i(t_1)|i\rangle \\ &\quad - \frac{1}{2!}\langle f|T\left(\int_{-\infty}^{\infty} dt_1 H_i(t_1)\right)\left(\int_{-\infty}^{\infty} dt_2 H_i(t_2)\right)|i\rangle - \ldots \\ &\qquad \text{(definitions)} \\ &= A^{(0)} + A^{(1)} + A^{(2)} + \ldots, \end{aligned} \tag{1.8}$$

where H_i denotes the interaction Hamiltonian. This is known as the Dyson series. Probability amplitudes can not usually be calculated in closed form and a perturbative approach is necessary. We evaluate each term in the Dyson series individually for each given scattering process and include as many terms as necessary to match the experimental accuracy. Moreover, the zeroth term is only important if no change happens.

As an example, let's consider how two particles that we call pions, π^0, which are associated with a single scalar field ϕ interact.

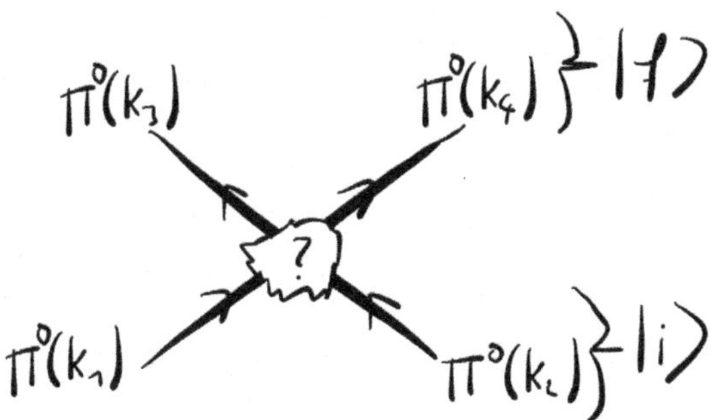

The dominant contribution to the Dyson series reads

$$A^{(1)} \equiv -i \langle \pi^0_{k_3}, \pi^0_{k_4} | i \int_{-\infty}^{\infty} dt_1 H_i(t_1) | \pi^0_{k_1}, \pi^0_{k_2} \rangle$$

$$= \frac{-\lambda}{24} \int_{-\infty}^{\infty} d^4x \, \langle \pi^0_{k_3}, \pi^0_{k_4} | \phi^4(x) | \pi^0_{k_1}, \pi^0_{k_2} \rangle \, . \tag{1.9}$$

We then use that we can understand a field as an integral over creation and annihilation operators

$$\phi(x) = \int dk^3 \frac{1}{(2\pi)^3 \sqrt{2\omega_k}} \left(a(\vec{k}) e^{-i(kx)} + a^\dagger(\vec{k}) e^{i(kx)} \right)$$

definitions

$$= \phi_-(x) + \phi_+(x) \, , \tag{1.10}$$

where ϕ_- is an integral over annihilation operators, while ϕ_+ is an integral over creation operators.

If we plug this into the formula for the probability amplitude (Eq. 1.9) we find many, many terms. For simplicity, let's consider just one of them: $\phi_+\phi_+\phi_-\phi_-$. The corresponding contribution to the Dyson series reads

$$\frac{-\lambda}{24} \int_{-\infty}^{\infty} d^4x \, \langle \pi^0_{k_3}, \pi^0_{k_4} | \phi_+(x)\phi_+(x)\phi_-(x)\phi_-(x) | \pi^0_{k_1}, \pi^0_{k_2} \rangle \, . \tag{1.11}$$

The factor $\phi_-(x)\phi_-(x)$ acts on the initial state $|\pi^0_{k_1}, \pi^0_{k_2}\rangle$ first. The result is the ground state $|0\rangle$ multiplied by some numerical factors:

$$\phi_-(x)\phi_-(x) \, |\pi^0_{k_1}, \pi^0_{k_2}\rangle = \text{numerical factor} \times |0\rangle \, . \tag{1.12}$$

Afterwards, $\phi_+(x)\phi_+(x)$ acts on the ground state $|0\rangle$. This yields a superposition of two-particle states with different momenta:

$$\phi_+(x)\phi_+(x)\,|0\rangle = \text{numerical factor} \times \int d^3k\, d^3q\, |\pi^0_q, \pi^0_k\rangle \ . \quad (1.13)$$

Since we are interested in a specific final state, we then act with $\langle \pi^0_{k_3}, \pi^0_{k_4}|$ on this superposition which projects out the numerical factor that we are really interested in;

$$\begin{aligned}\int d^3k\, d^3q\, \langle \pi^0_{k_3}, \pi^0_{k_4}|\pi^0_q, \pi^0_k\rangle &= \text{numerical factor} \times \int d^3k\, d^3q \delta(k-k_3)\delta(q-k_4) \\ &= \text{different numerical factor.} \end{aligned} \quad (1.14)$$

The final step is to integrate over the volume of the system that we are considering to take into account that the interaction can happen, in principle, everywhere.[4]

[4] This is necessary because we consider initial and final state with exactly known momenta. In a quantum context this implies that the corresponding particles are delocalized completely in space. (This is a result of the Heisenberg uncertainty relation.) Hence, we must take all possible interaction points into account.

In summary, we can describe this contribution to the total probability amplitude as follows. Two particles with momenta k_1 and k_2 enter the system. They interact at a location x at which they annihilate. But at the same moment in time and at the same location two new particles emerge with possibly different momenta k_3, k_4. This is illustrated in the following figure, which is known as a Feynman diagram.

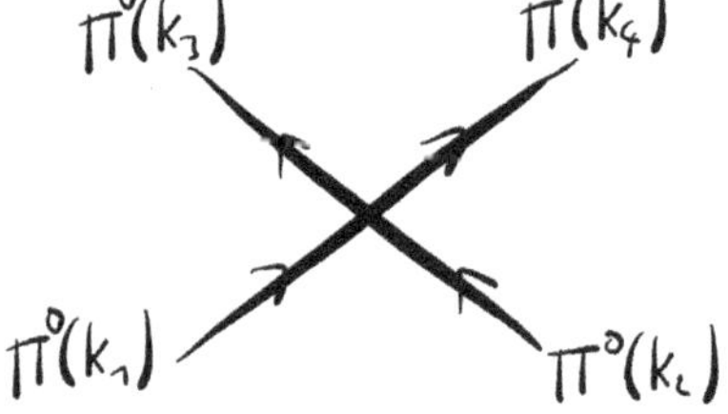

$\pi^0(k_3)$ $\pi^0(k_4)$

$\pi^0(k_1)$ $\pi^0(k_2)$

Additional terms in the Dyson series describe different ways in which the two particles can interact with each other. The total probability amplitude is the sum over all the contributions from processes that start with two particles with momenta k_1, k_2 and end with two particles with momenta k_3, k_4. An example of a higher order contribution is shown in the following figure.

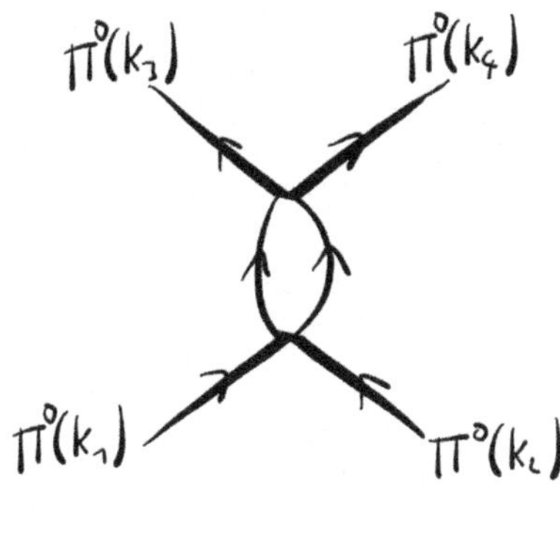

This was, of course, just a quick glimpse at what lays ahead of us. In the following chapters we will discuss all of the concepts introduced here (and many others) multiple times from various perspectives.

We will start by talking about fields in an entirely classical context. This will allow us to develop some understanding of how fields behave when they are alone and how they interact. Afterwards, we will discuss how we can interpret fields in a quantum context. The third step is to discuss applications of quantum field theory with a special focus on scattering processes. In the final part of the book, we will then discuss various slightly more advanced ideas like symmetry breaking, the path integral formulation, and non-perturbative phenomena.

Part 0
Foundations

"He who can go to the fountain does not go to the water-jar."

Leonardo da Vinci

PS: You can discuss the content of Part 0 with other readers and give feedback at `www.nononsensebooks.com/qft/bonus`.

In any physical theory, there are various actors and there are rules that describe how they behave. In addition, there is a stage on which all the drama unfolds.

Our main goal in this first part of the book is to become familiar with the actors, the rules and the stage that are most relevant for quantum field theory. To simplify the discussion, we will discuss them in this part of the book entirely in a classical context. However, we will see in the next part that almost all lessons that we learn in a classical context remain relevant for quantum field theory.

My hope is that a separation into "what?", "how?", and "why?" will help you to understand the internal structure of quantum field theory and its underlying assumptions as clearly as possible. Most importantly, I hope that you'll be able to recognize that neither the actors, nor the rules or the underlying assumptions are particularly difficult to grasp. All the confusing stuff typically only appears when we try to describe the various actors in specific situations. A useful analogy is chess. The game itself is simple, but specific matches and situations within a match can be incredibly complicated to analyze. Analogously, quantum field theory is simple but certain applications of it can be extremely difficult.

With that said, let's discuss our plan in this part of the book in a bit more detail.

The first thing we need to talk about is the stage on which quantum field theory takes place. The total stage consists of a "floor" that we call Minkowski spacetime plus abstract field spaces that are attached to spacetime.

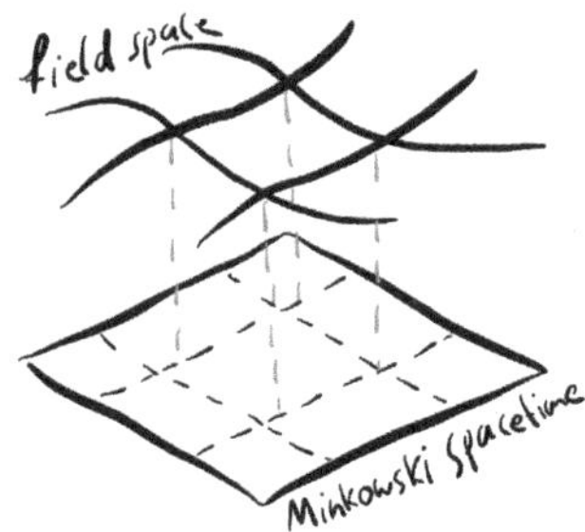

To understand the general structure of this stage, we start by talking about Einstein's theory of special relativity. Afterwards, we talk about the main actors who dance on the stage that we call Minkowski spacetime. In a field theory, as the name already suggests, the main actors are fields. So the first questions that we need to answer are:

- ▷ What is a field?
- ▷ What types of fields exist?
- ▷ Which mathematical objects can we use to describes these different kinds of fields?
- ▷ In which mathematical arena do fields operate?

Then we'll talk about the most basic rules that describe how the different kinds of fields behave when left alone. Speaking a bit more technically, we will talk about the equations that describe free fields.[5]

[5] The adjective "free" in this context always means "non-interacting".

Once we've understood the equations that describe free fields, it's only a small step to understand how fields interact with each other. Thus, this is what we will talk about afterwards.

Maybe the chess analogy helps again. First of all, there are rules that describe what you can do with a certain playing figure. These rules determine, for example, how fast this figure can move around. In chess, for example, a pawn can only move forward one field at a time. In addition, there are rules that describe how the various figures can interact with others. These rules are, of course, closely connected to all other rules and must be compatible with them. For example, a pawn can only destroy another playing figure if it is standing on a diagonal field immediately in front of it.

The following diagrams summarize our plan up to this point:

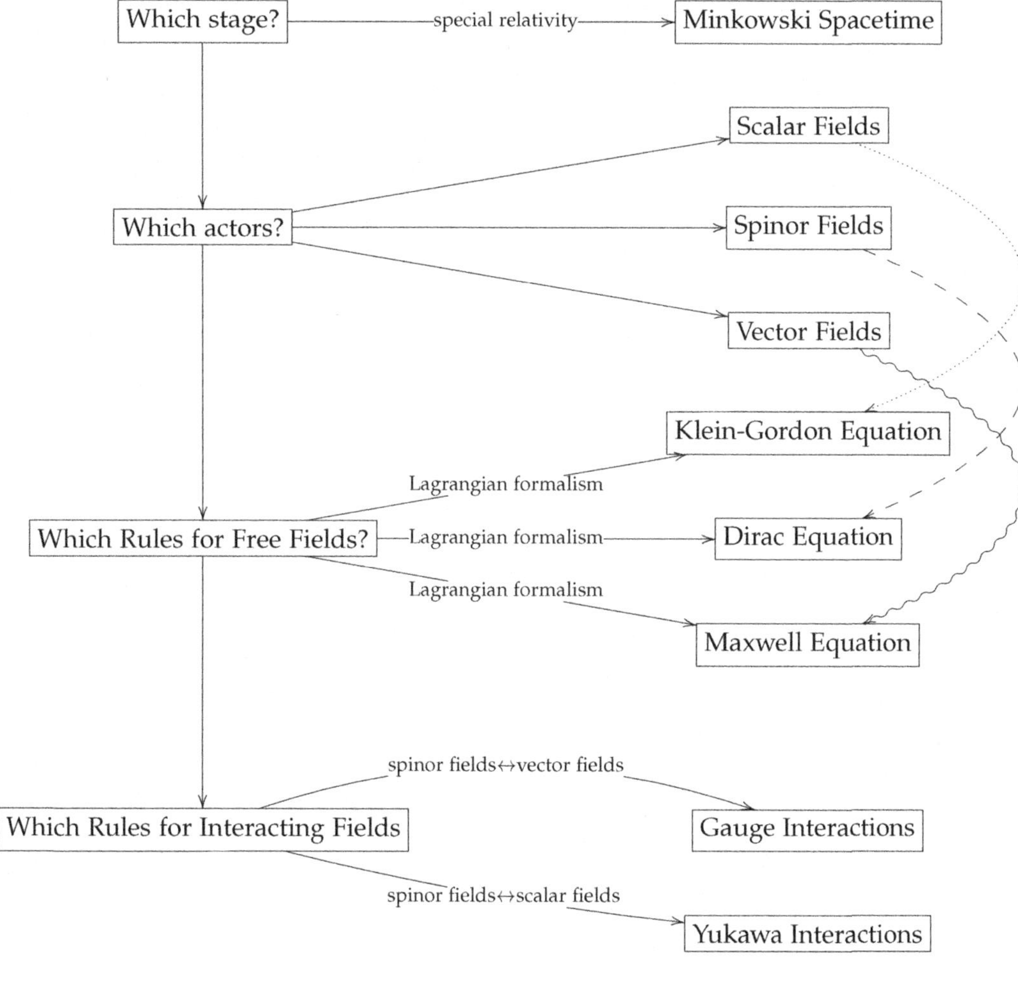

Once we've discussed all of this, we are ready to move on to Part II of the book. In this second part, we discuss in more detail how Feynman diagrams can be used to describe real-world systems. But now, let's start by talking about fields in quite general terms.

2

Spacetime

Historically, physicists didn't pay much attention to the stage on which physical processes happen. Space and time were simply featureless background structures.[1]

This changed when Einstein figured out that the structure of space and time is highly non-trivial if we look close enough.[2]

But before we can discuss how this came about, we need to cast Einstein's idea into a mathematical form and then take a step back and talk about a few essential ideas. Here's our plan in this chapter:

[1] If you're already familiar with the basics of special relativity, four-vectors, the Minkowski metric and Lorentz transformations in particular, feel free to skip this chapter.

[2] In fact, Einstein discovered not only that the structure of space and time is non-trivial but also that spacetime itself is a physical actor that changes dynamically. The correct theory that describes spacetime as a dynamical actor is Einstein's theory of general relativity.

▷ We will start by discussing spacetime in general terms.

▷ Then we will discuss how Einstein's discovery that the structure of spacetime is nontrivial can be described in mathematical terms.

▷ Afterwards, we will derive that there is an upper speed limit for all physical processes, which is a direct consequence of the nontrivial spacetime structure.

▷ Once we have understood what it means that there is a nontrivial spacetime structure, we can start discussing how

Einstein discovered it. Our journey will start with the experimental fact that all (inertial) observers always measure exactly the same value for the speed of light.

▷ This curious fact leads to many surprising consequences like, for example, that observers that move relative to each other do not agree on the time interval between two events.

▷ In addition, the constancy of the speed of light implies that the structure of spacetime is nontrivial. This is what Einstein discovered.

▷ We will then finish this chapter by recasting everything we learned in mathematical terms. In particular, we will talk about the Minkowksi metric, four-vectors and Lorentz transformations.

Let's get started.

2.1 The Arena of Physics

We usually still think of the space that we live in as a relatively boring arena. To describe the location of an object, we introduce a coordinate system. Each location is then described by three numbers (x, y, z).

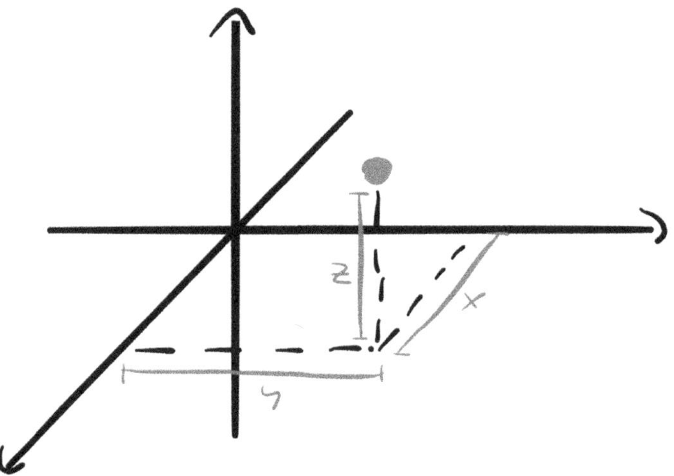

Since we need, in general, three such numbers we say that space is three-dimensional. And as you can easily check with a ruler, the distance Δs between any two objects in this three-dimensional space can be calculated using the Pythagorean theorem[3]

$$\Delta s^2 = \Delta x^2 + \Delta y^2 + \Delta z^2 . \tag{2.1}$$

Since we can calculate distances like this, we say that the space we live in is Euclidean.[4]

Now, in physics we are not only interested in knowing *where* something happens but also *when*. After all, one of our main goals in physics is to describe how objects move around. This requires that we take time into account.

Therefore, to properly describe an object in physics, we actually need four numbers (t, x, y, z). The time coordinate t tells us the time at which the object is located at (x, y, z). This means we add a fourth axis to our coordinate system. In other words, we now not only use a spatial coordinate system, but a **spacetime** coordinate system.

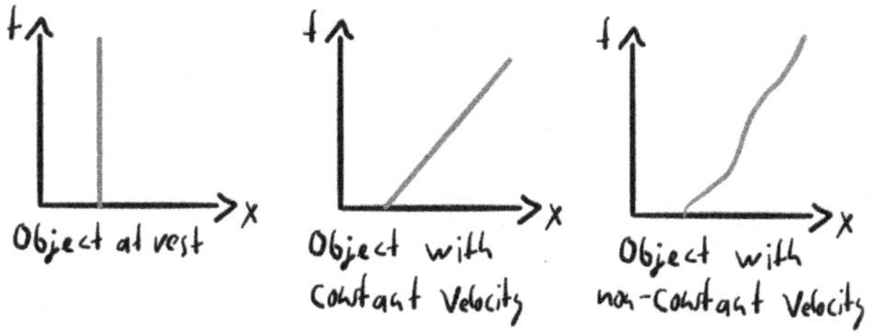

While (x, y, z) describes the location of an object in space, we say that (t, x, y, z) describes the location of an **event** in spacetime. An event is, for example, the arrival of an object at a specific location. Since we need four numbers to describe an event, we say that spacetime is four-dimensional.

[3] From another perspective, we can say that we calculate the length of the vector

$$\vec{v} = \begin{pmatrix} \Delta x \\ \Delta y \\ \Delta z \end{pmatrix}$$

which points from one point to another:

$$\begin{aligned} |\vec{v}|^2 &= \vec{v} \cdot \vec{v} \\ &= \Delta x^2 + \Delta y^2 + \Delta z^2 . \end{aligned}$$

[4] Maybe you wonder why we care about such a trivial fact and even introduce a special name? We will see in a moment that the above relation is not always true, i.e. there can be non-Euclidean spaces.

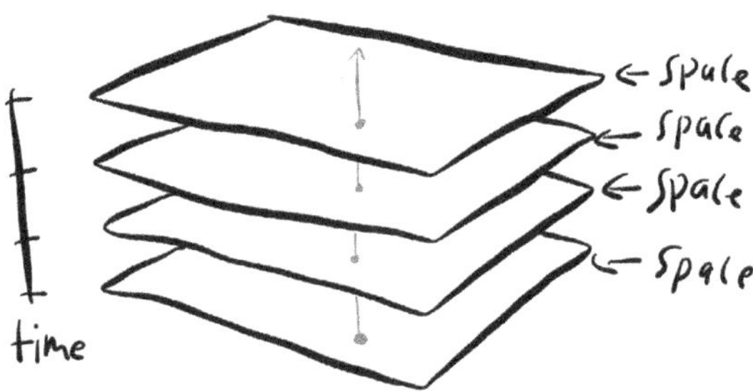

Hopefully you are not too bored or confused by these lines of thought because things are about to get really interesting.

Above, we defined the spatial distance between two objects (Eq. 2.1). Now that we've added time to our coordinate system, we can ask: what's the distance between two events in spacetime? Naively, we might write down

$$\Delta s^2 = \Delta t^2 + \Delta x^2 + \Delta y^2 + \Delta z^2 \tag{2.2}$$

but this doesn't make any sense. The differences in the spatial components $(\Delta x, \Delta y, \Delta z)$ are measured in meters, while Δt is measured in seconds. Therefore, we are comparing apples with oranges in Eq. 2.2. To fix this problem we introduce a new constant c which has units of meters per second:[5]

[5] We will talk about the meaning of this constant in a moment.

$$\Delta s^2 = c^2 \Delta t^2 + \Delta x^2 + \Delta y^2 + \Delta z^2 \,. \tag{2.3}$$

Now, the first term in the sum on the right-hand side has units $\left(\frac{\text{meters}}{\text{second}}\right)^2 \text{seconds}^2 = \text{meters}^2$ as it should be.

One of the big discoveries in physics was that this formula is *not* the relevant one. This is what Einstein figured out.

Instead, the correct expression for the (squared) distance between events is[6]

[6] We will discuss below how Einstein figured this out.

$$\Delta s^2 = c^2 \Delta t^2 - \Delta x^2 - \Delta y^2 - \Delta z^2 \,. \tag{2.4}$$

In words, this means there is a relative minus sign between the (squared) spatial distance $\Delta x^2 + \Delta y^2 + \Delta z^2$ and the (squared) temporal distance Δt^2.[7] While this formula may look extremely strange, from a mathematical perspective, it simply tells us that the local structure of spacetime is not what we would've naively expected. In technical terms, we say that the local structure of spacetime is not Euclidean (Eq. 2.3) but Minkowskian (Eq. 2.4). What makes Minkowski space different from Euclidean space is the way we define distances in it. Mathematically, we denote the four-dimensional Euclidean space as $\mathbb{R}^4$ and the four-dimensional Minkwoski space as $\mathbb{R}^{1,3}$.[8]

[7] We will talk about the physical meaning of the minus sign in Eq. 2.4 in a moment.

[8] We are talking about *a* Minkowski space and *a* Euclidean space because there are different Minkwoski spaces and different Euclidean spaces. For example, we can equally consider a two-dimensional Minkowski space $\mathbb{R}^{1,1}$ or a three-dimensional Minkowski space $\mathbb{R}^{1,2}$. These mathematical constructs with only one or two spatial dimensions are useful in certain applications or in toy models.

2.2 Maximum Speed

The minus sign not only encodes an important fact about the local structure of spacetime, it also has extremely important physical implications.

To understand this, let's consider two events that we call A and B which are spatially separated by 3 meters. Moreover, we assume that B is caused by A. For example, we can imagine that event A is the emission of a light pulse and event B is the detection at a location that is 3 meters away.

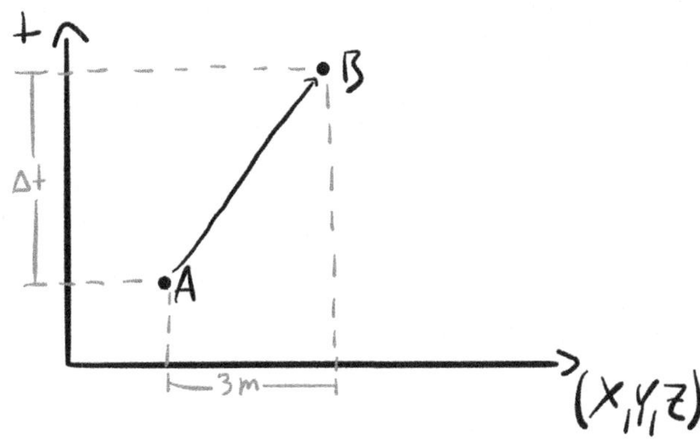

How soon after A can B happen? In other words, what's the minimum temporal distance Δt between the two events?

We can answer this question by looking at Eq. 2.4. The (squared) spatial distance between the two events $\Delta x^2 + \Delta y^2 + \Delta z^2 = (3 \text{ meters})^2$ is fixed. Therefore

$$\begin{aligned} \Delta s^2 &= c^2 \Delta t^2 - \Delta x^2 - \Delta y^2 - \Delta z^2 \\ &= c^2 \Delta t^2 - (3 \text{ meters})^2 . \end{aligned} \tag{2.5}$$

If Δt^2 is too small Δs^2 becomes negative. This would imply that Δs is imaginary ($i^2 = -1$). We therefore propose that the minimum allowed value of Δt is precisely the value for which Δs^2 is zero:

$$\Delta s^2_{\text{min}} = 0 . \tag{2.6}$$

This means that there is a *non-zero* minimum time period, Δt^2_{min}, between two events which happen at two different locations. From a slightly different perspective we can therefore say that there is a **maximum speed** at which a signal or object can travel from one point to another.

Using Eq. 2.4 we can learn something important about this maximum speed. A signal which travels at the maximum speed between the two events needs the minimum time interval Δt_{min} to travel the distance $\sqrt{\Delta x^2 + \Delta y^2 + \Delta z^2}$. Above, we argued that the minimum time interval Δt_{min} corresponds to $\Delta s_{\text{min}} = 0$. Putting this into Eq. 2.4 yields

$$\begin{aligned} \Delta s^2_{\text{min}} &= c^2 \Delta t^2_{\text{min}} - \Delta x^2 - \Delta y^2 - \Delta z^2 \\ &\quad \text{(Eq. 2.6)} \\ 0 &= c^2 \Delta t^2_{\text{min}} - \Delta x^2 - \Delta y^2 - \Delta z^2 \\ &\quad \text{(rearranging)} \\ c^2 &= \frac{\Delta x^2 + \Delta y^2 + \Delta z^2}{\Delta t^2_{\text{min}}} . \end{aligned} \tag{2.7}$$

This is interesting because

$$v \equiv \frac{\sqrt{\Delta x^2 + \Delta y^2 + \Delta z^2}}{\Delta t} \tag{2.8}$$

is exactly the speed at which a signal travels the distance $\sqrt{\Delta x^2 + \Delta y^2 + \Delta z^2}$.[9] Therefore, Eq. 2.7 tells us that a signal or

[9] Speed is always defined as a spatial distance divided by the time interval Δt needed to travel the distance.

object which needs the minimum amount of time Δt_{min} travels at speed c.

The constant c, which we introduced to get the same units for all terms in Eq. 2.4, encodes the maximum speed at which anything can travel in spacetime. In some sense, this fact is hard-coded into the structure of spacetime, as indicated by the minus sign in Eq. 2.4.

The constant c is commonly called the **speed of light** because, well, light travels at this maximum speed.[10]

[10] Take note that c is a general constant which often appears in contexts which have nothing to do with light. The name "speed of light" is only used for historic reasons. In general, c is an upper speed limit for everything in physics and all massless particles travel at speed c.

2.3 The Speed of Light

From experiments we know that while c is incredibly large, it's not infinite. The experimental value of c is

$$2.9979 \times 10^8 \,\frac{\text{meters}}{\text{second}}.$$

The fact that there is a maximum speed which is valid for anyone and anything is one of the most astonishing consequences of Einstein's theory of special relativity.

You might be wondering how Einstein figured out that the structure of spacetime is nontrivial and can be described by Eq. 2.4.

The first experimental hint that paved the way for what is now known as Einstein's theory of special relativity was the discovery by Michelson and Morley that the speed of light has exactly the same value for all inertial observers.[11]

[11] The notion of an "inertial observer" describes someone who is not accelerating. If someone accelerates it means that a force acts on him and this force necessarily plays a role in how he sees a given experiment. Thus we cannot expect that the same physical laws still apply. In contrast, inertial observers move with a constant velocity relative to each other and for them the same physical laws apply.

This is a truly mind-boggling discovery. The speed of all objects that we know from our everyday experiences depends on how we move relative to it. For example, imagine that an observer *standing* at a train station measures that a train moves at 50 $\frac{\text{km}}{\text{h}}$:

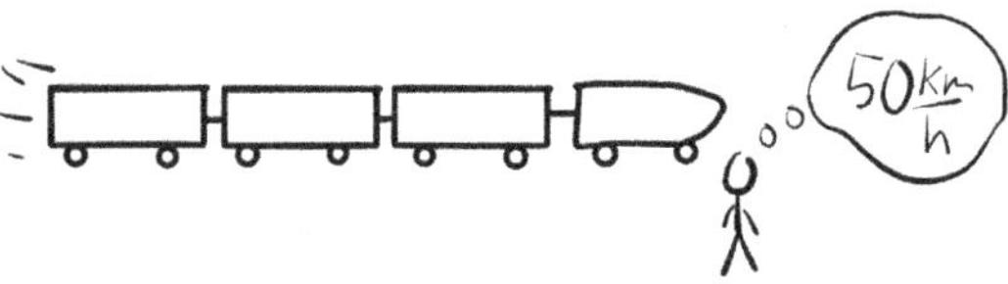

A second observer who runs at 15 $\frac{\text{km}}{\text{h}}$ parallel to the same train, measures that the train moves at 35 $\frac{\text{km}}{\text{h}}$.

Curiously, this does not happen for electromagnetic waves (i.e. light). Electromagnetic waves always travel at speed $c = 2.9979 \times 10^8$ m/s, no matter how you move.[12]

[12] A caveat: the speed of light only has this value in free space and not if our wave moves in matter. The speed of electromagnetic waves in matter is lower.

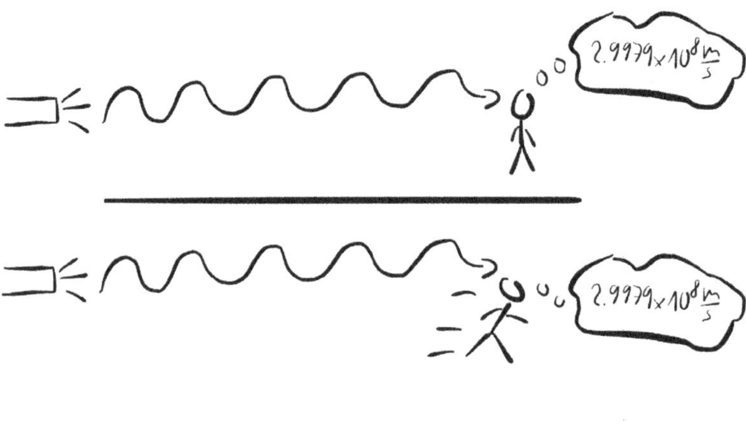

Before we can discuss why a constant speed of light for all (inertial) observers implies that Eq. 2.4 is the correct formula to describe the distance between events, we need to talk about a more direct consequence.[13]

[13] Reminder: Eq. 2.4 reads

$$\Delta s^2 = c^2\Delta t^2 - \Delta x^2 - \Delta y^2 - \Delta z^2 .$$

2.4 Time Dilation

Imagine that a person, let's call him Tom, sends a light pulse straight up where it is reflected by a mirror and eventually arrives at the point from where it originated:

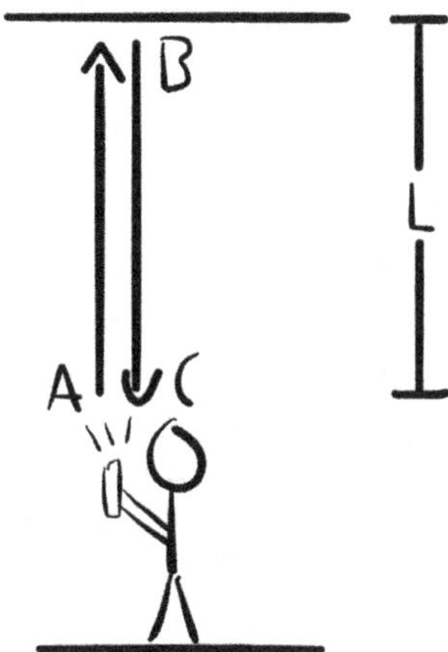

We record three important events:

▷ **A** : the light pulse leaves the starting point

▷ **B** : the light pulse is reflected by the mirror

▷ **C** : the light pulse returns to the starting point.

The time-interval between the two events **A** and **C** is[14]

$$\Delta t = t_C - t_A = \frac{2L}{c}, \tag{2.9}$$

[14] Reminder: for a constant speed v we have $v = \frac{\Delta s}{\Delta t}$, where Δs is the distance and Δt the time interval. Therefore, we have $\Delta t = \frac{\Delta s}{v}$.

where L denotes the distance between the person and the mirror.

So far, nothing interesting has happened. But this changes as soon as we consider how a second person, let's call her Sarah, observes exactly the same situation.

We imagine that Sarah moves with some constant speed u relative to Tom. For simplicity, we assume that the origins of their coordinate systems coincide when the light pulse is sent off (t_A). Moreover, we assume that Tom and Sarah pass each other at the origin of their coordinate systems.

A first crucial observation is that the starting and end points of the light pulse have different coordinates for Sarah:

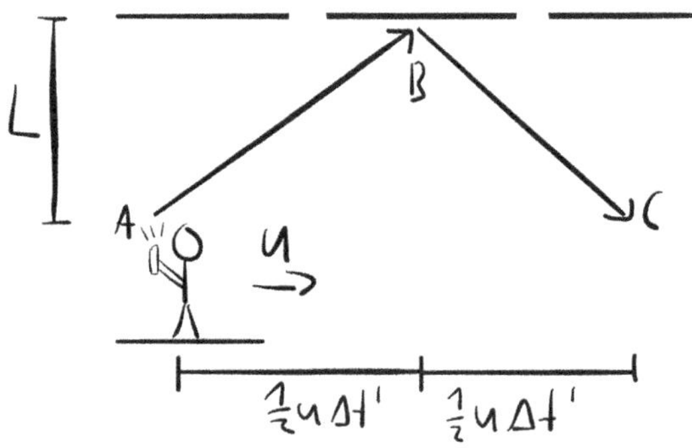

Mathematically, we have

$$x'_A = 0 \neq x'_C = u\Delta t' \qquad \rightarrow \qquad \Delta x' = u\Delta t', \tag{2.10}$$

where we use primed coordinates for Sarah's coordinate system. This means that for Sarah the light has moved in the x-direction. In contrast, for Tom

$$x_A = x_C \qquad \rightarrow \qquad \Delta x = 0. \tag{2.11}$$

What's the time interval that Sarah measures between the event **A** and the event **C**?[15]

[15] It will become clear in a moment, why this is an interesting question.

As usual the time interval $\Delta t' = t'_C - t'_A$ can be calculated as the distance l traveled by the light pulse divided by its speed c.

$$\Delta t' = \frac{l}{c} \tag{2.12}$$

For Sarah, the distance l is no longer simply L, but we can calculate it by using the Pythagorean theorem[16]

$$l = 2\sqrt{\left(\frac{1}{2}u\Delta t'\right)^2 + L^2}. \tag{2.13}$$

[16] See the two triangles in the figure above.

We can therefore calculate the time interval measured by Sarah as follows:

$$l = 2\sqrt{\left(\frac{1}{2}u\Delta t'\right)^2 + L^2} \qquad \text{this is Eq. 2.13}$$

$$\text{↷ Eq. 2.12}$$

$$c\Delta t' = 2\sqrt{\left(\frac{1}{2}u\Delta t'\right)^2 + L^2}$$

$$\text{↷ squaring}$$

$$c^2\Delta t'^2 = 4\left(\left(\frac{1}{2}u\Delta t'\right)^2 + L^2\right)$$

$$\text{↷ rearranging}$$

$$\frac{c^2\Delta t'^2}{4} - \left(\frac{1}{2}u\Delta t'\right)^2 = L^2$$

$$\text{↷ rearranging}$$

$$\Delta t'^2\left(\frac{c^2}{4} - \left(\frac{1}{2}u\right)^2\right) = L^2$$

$$\text{↷ rearranging}$$

$$\Delta t'^2 = \frac{L^2}{\left(\frac{c^2}{4} - \left(\frac{1}{2}u\right)^2\right)}$$

$$\text{↷ rearranging}$$

$$\Delta t'^2 = \frac{\frac{(2L)^2}{c^2}}{1 - \frac{u^2}{c^2}}$$

$$\text{↷ } \Delta t = \frac{2L}{c}, \text{ Eq. 2.9}$$

$$\Delta t'^2 = \frac{\Delta t^2}{1 - \frac{u^2}{c^2}}$$

$$\text{↷ } \sqrt{}$$

$$\Delta t' = \frac{\Delta t}{\sqrt{1 - \frac{u^2}{c^2}}}. \tag{2.14}$$

We can see here that for $u \neq 0$, we have $\Delta t' \neq \Delta t$. In words, this means that two observers moving relative to each other do not agree on the time interval between the two events **A** and **C**!

This phenomenon is usually called **time-dilation** since for $u \neq 0$, we have $\Delta t' > \Delta t$, which means that a time interval appears longer for a moving observer. Clocks tick differently for different observers and they count a different number of ticks between two events.

Analogously, it's possible to derive that different observers do not necessarily agree on the length of objects. This is known as **length contraction** and is another famous consequence of the constant speed of light.

With this in mind, we can finally understand why there is a minus sign between the spatial coordinates and the time coordinate in the formula that describes the distance between events (Eq. 2.4), as shown in the next section.

2.5 Proper Time

In the previous section, we calculated the time intervals between two events for two observers, Tom and Sarah, who move relative to each other. For the following calculations, it's convenient to rewrite the time interval measured by Sarah as follows

$$\begin{aligned} c\Delta t' &= 2\sqrt{\left(\frac{1}{2}u\Delta t'\right)^2 + L^2} && \text{this is the second line in Eq. 2.14} \\ &&& \curvearrowright \ \Delta x' = u\Delta t',\ \text{Eq. 2.10} \\ &= 2\sqrt{\left(\frac{1}{2}\Delta x'\right)^2 + L^2} \\ \therefore \quad \Delta t' &= \frac{2\sqrt{\left(\frac{1}{2}\Delta x'\right)^2 + L^2}}{c} \end{aligned} \tag{2.15}$$

Using these results, let's calculate the total distance between the two events (denoted **A** and **C** above) for both observers.

To start with, we use the "wrong" formula that would correspond to a trivial spacetime structure (Eq. 2.3):

$$\Delta s^2 = c^2\Delta t^2 + \Delta x^2 + \Delta y^2 + \Delta z^2 . \tag{2.16}$$

For our two observers introduced in the previous section, this formula yields[17]

[17] We use here that neither Tom nor Sarah move in the y- or z-direction and therefore $\Delta y = \Delta z = 0$ and $\Delta y' = \Delta z' = 0$.

$$\begin{aligned}
\text{Tom:}\quad \Delta s^2 &= c^2\Delta t^2 + \Delta x^2 + \Delta y^2 + \Delta z^2 && \rightarrow \Delta t = \frac{2L}{c} \text{ (Eq. 2.9)}, \Delta x = \Delta y = \Delta z = 0 \text{ (Eq. 2.11)}\\
&= c^2\left(\frac{2L}{c}\right)^2 + (0)^2 + (0)^2 + (0)^2 && \rightarrow \cancel{c^2}\\
&= 4L^2\\
\text{Sarah:}\quad \Delta s'^2 &= c^2\Delta t'^2 + \Delta x'^2 + \Delta y'^2 + \Delta z'^2 && \rightarrow \Delta t' = \frac{2\sqrt{\left(\frac{1}{2}\Delta x'\right)^2 + L^2}}{c} \text{ (Eq. 2.15), , } \Delta y = \Delta z = 0\\
&= c^2\left(\frac{2\sqrt{\left(\frac{1}{2}\Delta x'\right)^2 + L^2}}{c}\right)^2 + \Delta x'^2 + (0)^2 + (0)^2 && \rightarrow \cancel{c^2}\\
&= \Delta x'^2 + 4L^2 + \Delta x'^2 .
\end{aligned} \tag{2.17}$$

By looking at this result you can maybe already anticipate what happens when we use the alternative formula (Eq. 2.4):

$$\Delta s^2 = c^2\Delta t^2 - \Delta x^2 - \Delta y^2 - \Delta z^2 . \tag{2.18}$$

Let's calculate it explicitly:

$$\begin{aligned}
\text{Tom:}\quad \Delta s^2 &= c^2\Delta t^2 - \Delta x^2 - \Delta y^2 - \Delta z^2 && \rightarrow \Delta t = \frac{2L}{c} \text{ (Eq. 2.9)}, \Delta x = \Delta y = \Delta z = 0 \text{ (Eq. 2.11)}\\
&= c^2\left(\frac{2L}{c}\right)^2 - (0)^2 - (0)^2 - (0)^2 && \rightarrow \cancel{c^2}\\
&= 4L^2\\
\text{Sarah:}\quad \Delta s'^2 &= c^2\Delta t'^2 - \Delta x'^2 - \Delta y'^2 - \Delta z'^2 && \rightarrow \Delta t' = \frac{2\sqrt{\left(\frac{1}{2}\Delta x'\right)^2 + L^2}}{c} \text{ (Eq. 2.15), , } \Delta y = \Delta z = 0\\
&= c^2\left(\frac{2\sqrt{\left(\frac{1}{2}\Delta x'\right)^2 + L^2}}{c}\right)^2 - \Delta x'^2 - (0)^2 - (0)^2 && \rightarrow \cancel{c^2}\\
&= \Delta x'^2 + 4L^2 - \Delta x'^2 && \rightarrow \cancel{\Delta x'^2}\\
&= 4L^2 .
\end{aligned} \tag{2.19}$$

We learn here that if we use the alternative formula with a relative minus sign between the spatial coordinates and the time coordinate, we find the same total spacetime distance for Sarah and Tom. This means that if we use Eq. 2.4 instead of Eq. 2.3, we find that the total distance between events is the same for different observers. That's why Eq. 2.4 is the correct formula in a universe (like ours) with a constant speed of light.

You're probably still not convinced. Sure it would be nice to have the same total distance for all observers, but is it really mandatory?

To answer this question, we need to understand the physical meaning of the total distance between two events. In short, the total distance between two events describes (up to a constant) the time interval that an observer who travels with the object in question would measure. Just imagine a person with a watch on top of the object you want to describe.[18]

[18] A real person would, of course, influence the object. But here we are talking about an imaginary observer who has no effect on the object.

To understand the connection between the total distance and the time interval measured by this special observer take note that for him, the object always appears at rest. Mathematically, this means

$$\Delta x = \Delta y = \Delta z = 0 . \tag{2.20}$$

If we plug this into either Eq. 2.3 or Eq. 2.4, we find

$$\begin{aligned}\Delta s^2 &= c^2\Delta t^2 \pm \Delta x^2 \pm \Delta y^2 \pm \Delta z^2 \\ &\quad \text{Eq. 2.20} \\ &= c^2\Delta t^2 \pm 0 \pm 0 \pm 0 \\ &= c^2\Delta t^2 .\end{aligned} \tag{2.21}$$

Therefore, the total distance Δs^2 is equal to the (squared) time interval measured by an observer for whom the object appears at rest (times the constant c^2). Since this time interval is quite special, it is conventional to denote it by a special symbol τ and call it **proper time.**

The key idea is that while different observers do not necessarily agree on the values of time intervals, they will agree if they use exactly the same frame of reference. In our example above, for example, Tom would measure the same interval as Sarah if he starts moving with the same velocity as Sarah. Similarly, Sarah measures the same time interval as Tom if she doesn't move. The history of an observer doesn't matter.[19] If they are in the same frame of reference (move with the same velocity), they will measure the same time interval.

[19] In technical terms, we say that there is no path dependence that somehow influences what different observers measure. From a purely mathematical point of view this *could* be the case, but as far as we know it isn't in our universe.

Therefore, Sarah, Tom and all other possible observers will agree on the time interval that someone measures for whom the object in question is at rest. This follows because all observers could simply also start moving with the object in question and measure the time interval themselves.

So yes, it really is mandatory that all observers agree on the total distance between two events and therefore, the correct formula is Eq. 2.4.[20]

[20] Reminder: we saw above that different observers agree on the value of Δs only if there is a relative minus sign between the time interval Δt^2 and the spatial distances Δx^2 etc.

2.6 The Minkowski Metric and Four-Vectors

Before we move on, it makes sense to refine our notation a little bit. In particular, not every object moves with a constant velocity and thus it is not immediately clear how we can define the proper time for these objects. This can be achieved by noting that during a short enough time interval, every object appears to be moving with a constant velocity. Mathematically, this means that if we switch from our finite intervals Δt, Δx etc. to infinitesimal intervals dt, dx etc., our equations will be correct.

The correct (infinitesimal, squared) total distance reads

$$\boxed{ds^2 = (cdt)^2 - dx^2 - dy^2 - dz^2} \tag{2.22}$$

and is commonly called the **spacetime interval**.

If we want to calculate the total distance between two events, we need to sum over the contributions during all infinitesimal time intervals. Mathematically, this means that we need to integrate over ds^2:

$$\Delta s = \int ds\,. \tag{2.23}$$

Analogously, we define the proper time τ by using infinitesimal intervals:

$$\boxed{ds^2 = c^2 d\tau^2\,.}$$

Next, let's discuss how we can understand the spacetime interval in Eq. 2.22 in more mathematical terms.

In general, the mathematical tool which allows us to calculate the distance between two points in a given space is called the **metric**. In general, a metric encodes important information about the structure of the space.

For example, the mathematical relations to calculate the distance between two points A and B on a Euclidean plane and between two points C and D on a sphere are different. In the first case, the distance is given by the familiar Pythagorean formula, irrespective of the actual distance between the points, while in the second case, this formula is only (approximately) valid for points which are close to each other on the surface of the sphere. It is the metric that encodes how distance between points can be calculated in a given space.

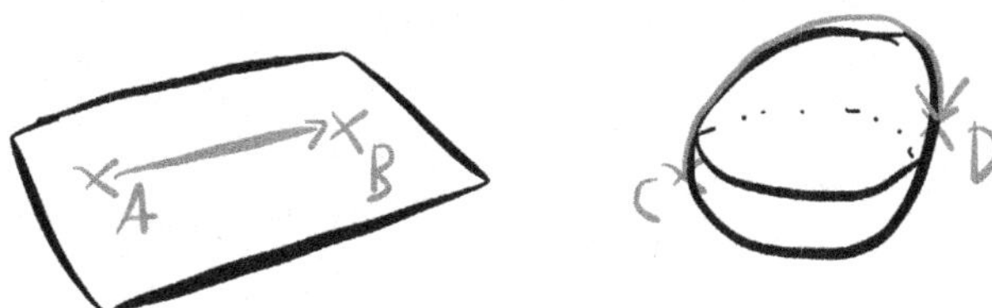

The best way to understand what a metric is, is to consider explicit examples. We can calculate the distance between two points

$$A = \begin{pmatrix} x_0 \\ x_1 \\ x_2 \\ x_3 \end{pmatrix}, \quad B = \begin{pmatrix} \tilde{x}_0 \\ \tilde{x}_1 \\ \tilde{x}_2 \\ \tilde{x}_3 \end{pmatrix} \tag{2.24}$$

by calculating the length of the vector

$$\vec{v} \equiv \begin{pmatrix} \Delta x_0 \\ \Delta x_1 \\ \Delta x_2 \\ \Delta x_3 \end{pmatrix} = \begin{pmatrix} \tilde{x}_0 - x_0 \\ \tilde{x}_1 - x_1 \\ \tilde{x}_2 - x_2 \\ \tilde{x}_3 - x_3 \end{pmatrix} \tag{2.25}$$

which connects them. In a four-dimensional Euclidean space, we find[21]

$$d(A,B) = \vec{v} \cdot \vec{v} = \Delta x_0^2 + \Delta x_1^2 + \Delta x_2^2 + \Delta x_3^2 \,. \tag{2.26}$$

But in Minkowski space, we find

$$d(A,B) = \vec{v} \cdot \vec{v} = \Delta x_0^2 - \Delta x_1^2 - \Delta x_2^2 - \Delta x_3^2 \,. \tag{2.27}$$

We describe this fact by saying that a Euclidean space and a Minkowski space have a different metric g and write the scalar product as $\vec{v}^T g \vec{v}$.

[21] Technically, we are calculating the scalar product of the vector with itself.

For

$$g_E = \begin{pmatrix} 1 & 0 & 0 & 0 \\ 0 & 1 & 0 & 0 \\ 0 & 0 & 1 & 0 \\ 0 & 0 & 0 & 1 \end{pmatrix} \tag{2.28}$$

we find the correct scalar product of a Euclidean space

$$\begin{aligned} \vec{v}^T g_E \vec{v} &= \begin{pmatrix} \Delta x_0 & \Delta x_1 & \Delta x_2 & \Delta x_3 \end{pmatrix} \begin{pmatrix} 1 & 0 & 0 & 0 \\ 0 & 1 & 0 & 0 \\ 0 & 0 & 1 & 0 \\ 0 & 0 & 0 & 1 \end{pmatrix} \begin{pmatrix} \Delta x_0 \\ \Delta x_1 \\ \Delta x_2 \\ \Delta x_3 \end{pmatrix} \\ &= \Delta x_0^2 + \Delta x_1^2 + \Delta x_2^2 + \Delta x_3^2 \,. \end{aligned} \tag{2.29}$$

And for

$$g_M = \begin{pmatrix} 1 & 0 & 0 & 0 \\ 0 & -1 & 0 & 0 \\ 0 & 0 & -1 & 0 \\ 0 & 0 & 0 & -1 \end{pmatrix} \tag{2.30}$$

we find the correct scalar product of Minkowski space[22]

$$\begin{aligned} \vec{v}^T g_M \vec{v} &= \begin{pmatrix} \Delta x_0 & \Delta x_1 & \Delta x_2 & \Delta x_3 \end{pmatrix} \begin{pmatrix} 1 & 0 & 0 & 0 \\ 0 & -1 & 0 & 0 \\ 0 & 0 & -1 & 0 \\ 0 & 0 & 0 & -1 \end{pmatrix} \begin{pmatrix} \Delta x_0 \\ \Delta x_1 \\ \Delta x_2 \\ \Delta x_3 \end{pmatrix} \\ &= \Delta x_0^2 - \Delta x_1^2 - \Delta x_2^2 - \Delta x_3^2 \,. \end{aligned} \tag{2.31}$$

[22] This is equivalent to Eq. 2.4. The only difference is that now we use a different vector and don't interpret the zeroth component as time.

We call g_E the **Euclidean metric** and g_M the **Minkowski metric**. However, it is conventional to use the symbol η for the Minkowski metric and thus we will use this notation in the following.

In index notation, we write the scalar product in Minkowski space as:

$$\begin{aligned} (\Delta s)^2 &= v_\mu \eta^{\mu\nu} v_\nu \\ &= \begin{pmatrix} \Delta x_0 & \Delta x_1 & \Delta x_2 & \Delta x_3 \end{pmatrix} \begin{pmatrix} 1 & 0 & 0 & 0 \\ 0 & -1 & 0 & 0 \\ 0 & 0 & -1 & 0 \\ 0 & 0 & 0 & -1 \end{pmatrix} \begin{pmatrix} \Delta x_0 \\ \Delta x_1 \\ \Delta x_2 \\ \Delta x_3 \end{pmatrix} \\ &= \Delta x_0^2 - \Delta x_1^2 - \Delta x_2^2 - \Delta x_3^2 \,. \end{aligned} \tag{2.32}$$

Take note that we have denoted the zeroth component by x_0 here. In physics, by convention we typically choose to interpret the zeroth component as the time component.[23] But since time and space intervals are measured using different units, we then need to introduce an additional constant that makes sure that all components have the same units.[24] We stumbled already upon this issue at the beginning of this chapter and concluded in Eq. 2.4 that the correct solution is to introduce a constant c with units meters per second. By comparing Eq. 2.4 with Eq. 2.32 we can conclude that $\Delta x_0 = ct$.[25] This implies that our **four-vectors** necessarily include the constant c in their zeroth component:

$$x_\mu = \begin{pmatrix} ct \\ x \\ y \\ z \end{pmatrix} . \tag{2.33}$$

The constant c here is essential because, as we've seen in Section 2.4, time and space components possibly get mixed if we change the coordinate system.[26] Since t is measured in seconds, we multiply it by the only fundamental velocity that we have: c. The result ct has units $\frac{\text{meters}}{\text{second}}$seconds $=$ meters which is the same as for the other components.

In addition, take note that it's conventional (but somewhat unfortunate) to denote four-vectors simply by a subscript Greek letter.[27] This can be confusing at times because exactly the same symbol, x_μ, is used for the vector and its components. In contrast, the usual three-component vectors that denote the location of an object in space (not spacetime) are conventionally denoted by a little arrow on top of them, $\vec{v}$. Moreover, the components of such a three-vector are denoted by the same symbol without the arrow but with a subscript Latin letter, v_i.

It is conventional to introduce superscript indices to avoid writing the Minkowski metric all the time:

$$x^\mu \equiv \eta^{\mu\nu} x_\nu \tag{2.34}$$

[23] This is a completely arbitrary choice and we could equally use the second or fourth component as the time coordinate.

[24] In natural units, we have by definition $c = 1$ and there is no longer any such obvious distinction between the time component and all other components.

[25] For your convenience, Eq. 2.4 reads

$$\Delta s^2 = c^2 \Delta t^2 - \Delta x^2 - \Delta y^2 - \Delta z^2 .$$

[26] Reminder: in Section 2.4 we discovered that for a moving observer a little bit of space can look like a little bit of time and vice versa. These phenomena are known as time dilation and space contraction.

[27] Reminder: by convention Greek indices run from 0 to 3.

or equally

$$y^\nu \equiv \eta^{\nu\mu} y_\mu \underbrace{=}_{\text{the Minkowski metric is symmetric } \eta^{\mu\nu}=\eta^{\nu\mu}} \eta^{\mu\nu} y_\mu \,. \tag{2.35}$$

This allows us to write the scalar product as follows:

$$x \cdot y \equiv x_\mu \eta^{\mu\nu} y_\nu = x_\mu y^\mu = x^\nu y_\nu . \tag{2.36}$$

The bottom line is that whenever you see a superscript Greek index in physics, you should remember that this is usually a short-hand notation for the Minkowski metric.[28]

[28] There are also superscript Latin indices, and we will talk about their meaning in Section 3.4.1.

Another somewhat subtle aspect of the Minkowski notation is how we define the four-vector derivative $\partial_\mu = \frac{\partial}{\partial x^\mu}$. As usual, we want that all the components of this vector have the same units. But ∂t and ∂x have different units. We can understand this as follows.

Since ∂t basically means "a little bit of t", the expression $\frac{\partial}{\partial t}$ has units $1/\text{s}$. Similarly, ∂x means "a little bit of x" and therefore $\frac{\partial}{\partial x}$ has units $1/\text{m}$.

We can achieve that $\frac{\partial}{\partial t}$ and $\frac{\partial}{\partial x}$ have the same units, by multiplying the former by $1/c$.[29] Moreover, it is conventional to introduce an additional minus sign for the spatial component.[30] The four-vector gradient ∂_μ then reads

[29] This is exactly the same trick that we used for a position four-vector in Eq. 2.33.

[30] This is useful because it allows us to calculate the dimensions of spacetime using the general formula $\partial_\mu x^\mu = 4$.

$$\partial_\mu = \frac{\partial}{\partial x^\mu} = \begin{pmatrix} \frac{\partial}{c\partial t} \\ -\frac{\partial}{\partial x} \\ -\frac{\partial}{\partial y} \\ -\frac{\partial}{\partial z} \end{pmatrix} . \tag{2.37}$$

The divergence of a four-vector, $\partial_\mu A^\mu$, therefore reads

$$\begin{aligned} \partial_\mu A^\mu &= \begin{pmatrix} \frac{\partial}{c\partial t} & -\frac{\partial}{\partial x} & -\frac{\partial}{\partial y} & -\frac{\partial}{\partial z} \end{pmatrix} \begin{pmatrix} 1 & 0 & 0 & 0 \\ 0 & -1 & 0 & 0 \\ 0 & 0 & -1 & 0 \\ 0 & 0 & 0 & -1 \end{pmatrix} \begin{pmatrix} A_0 \\ A_1 \\ A_2 \\ A_3 \end{pmatrix} \\ &= \frac{\partial}{c\partial t} A_0 + \frac{\partial}{\partial x} A_1 + \frac{\partial}{\partial y} A_2 + \frac{\partial}{\partial z} A_3 . \end{aligned} \tag{2.38}$$

Similarly, the square of the gradient of an ordinary function reads

$$\partial_\mu \phi \partial^\mu \phi = \begin{pmatrix} \frac{\partial \phi}{c\partial t} & -\frac{\partial \phi}{\partial x} & -\frac{\partial \phi}{\partial y} & -\frac{\partial \phi}{\partial z} \end{pmatrix} \begin{pmatrix} 1 & 0 & 0 & 0 \\ 0 & -1 & 0 & 0 \\ 0 & 0 & -1 & 0 \\ 0 & 0 & 0 & -1 \end{pmatrix} \begin{pmatrix} \frac{\partial \phi}{c\partial t} \\ -\frac{\partial \phi}{\partial x} \\ -\frac{\partial \phi}{\partial y} \\ -\frac{\partial \phi}{\partial z} \end{pmatrix}$$

$$= \left(\frac{\partial \phi}{c\partial t}\right)^2 - \left(\frac{\partial \phi}{\partial x}\right)^2 - \left(\frac{\partial \phi}{\partial y}\right)^2 - \left(\frac{\partial \phi}{\partial z}\right)^2 . \tag{2.39}$$

2.7 The Relativistic Energy-Momentum Relation

We have seen in Section 2.4 that time and space get mixed in special relativity. This observation motivates us to introduce four-vectors that combine spatial coordinates and the time coordinate into a single object (Eq. 2.33). A quite similar interplay also happens between different quantities. For example, we can imagine that one observer sees a moving object while a second observer who moves relative to the first observer, sees the object at rest. Therefore, the first observer will describe the object using a non-zero momentum, while for the second observer the object's momentum is zero.

A smart idea in special relativity is that we can keep track of the descriptions of different observers, by inventing a momentum four-vector p_μ. If we do this and want to find out how a different observer sees the system, we simply need to transform the momentum four-vectors p_μ in addition to the location four-vectors x_μ.[31]

[31] We will discuss transformations of four-vectors in more detail in the following section.

The only question we then need to answer is: how does a momentum four-vector p_μ actually look like? The usual momentum vector $\vec{p} = (p_1, p_2, p_3)^T$ has only three components, so what's the fourth component of p_μ?

We can answer this question by doing some dimensional analysis. First of all, we note that the length of a four-vector, which can be calculated as the scalar product of the four-vector with itself ($p_\mu p^\mu$), is an important quantity that remains unchanged if we switch between observers.[32] Therefore, we introduce a special symbol for the length of our momentum four-vector:

[32] We saw this in Section 2.5 and also will discuss this fact in more explicit terms in the following section.

$$
\begin{aligned}
X &\equiv p_\mu p^\mu \\
&= p_\mu \eta^{\mu\nu} p_\nu \\
&= \begin{pmatrix} p_0 & p_1 & p_2 & p_3 \end{pmatrix} \begin{pmatrix} 1 & 0 & 0 & 0 \\ 0 & -1 & 0 & 0 \\ 0 & 0 & -1 & 0 \\ 0 & 0 & 0 & -1 \end{pmatrix} \begin{pmatrix} p_0 \\ p_1 \\ p_2 \\ p_3 \end{pmatrix} \\
&= p_0 p_0 - p_1 p_1 - p_2 p_2 - p_3 p_3 \\
&= p_0 p_0 - \vec{p} \cdot \vec{p} \,.
\end{aligned}
\tag{2.40}
$$

(Eq. 2.36; matrix notation; $p_1 p_1 + p_2 p_2 + p_3 p_3 \equiv \vec{p} \cdot \vec{p}$)

We know that momentum is measured in $\frac{\text{kg}\cdot\text{m}}{\text{s}}$.[33] Therefore, the constant on the left-hand side is measured in $\frac{\text{kg}^2\text{m}^2}{\text{s}^2}$. All the terms in an equation must have the same units because otherwise we are comparing apples to oranges. Therefore, the zeroth component of the momentum four-vector p_0 must have units $\frac{\text{kg}\cdot\text{m}}{\text{s}}$, too.

[33] This follows from the standard formula $p = mv$ where m is measured in kilograms, and v in meters per second.

With this in mind, let's take a step back and think about which puzzle pieces possibly play a role here. We already learned above that the speed of light c plays an important role in special relativity. In particular, we saw that we need c to combine space and time coordinates into a single four-vector (Eq. 2.33).[34] The constant c describes a velocity and is therefore measured in meters per second. Moreover, a quantity that is always closely connected to the momentum of an object is its mass. Since a mass is measured in kilograms, we can combine the constant c and the mass of the object m to get a term that has exactly the

[34] For your convenience: Eq. 2.33 reads

$$x_\mu = \begin{pmatrix} ct \\ x \\ y \\ z \end{pmatrix} .$$

units that allows it to play a role in our formula:

$$\text{units of: } (mc)^2 = \left(\text{kg}\frac{\text{m}}{\text{s}}\right)^2 = \frac{\text{kg}^2\text{m}^2}{\text{s}^2} . \tag{2.41}$$

Another closely related quantity with almost exactly the right units is the energy of the object. Energy is measured in[35] $\frac{\text{kg}\cdot\text{m}^2}{\text{s}^2}$. Therefore, if we divide the energy by c and then square the resulting expression, we find another quantity with exactly the right units:

[35] Recall the formula for the classical kinetic energy $T = \frac{1}{2}mv^2$, where m is measured in kilograms and v in meters per second.

$$\text{units of: } \left(\frac{E}{c}\right)^2 = \left(\frac{\text{kg}\cdot\text{m}^2}{\text{s}^2}\frac{1}{\frac{\text{m}}{\text{s}}}\right)^2 = \frac{\text{kg}^2\text{m}^2}{\text{s}^2} . \tag{2.42}$$

The final key idea that allows us to identify which of the quantities we just constructed goes where in Eq. 2.40 is that mass is an *intrinsic* property of objects and therefore is equal for all observers. This implies that the constant m^2c^2 belongs on the left-hand side in Eq. 2.40, i.e. $X = m^2c^2$. Therefore, we put the remaining puzzle piece on the right-hand side, i.e $p_0 = E/c$, and then find

$$X \equiv p_0 p_0 - \vec{p}\cdot\vec{p} \qquad \text{this is Eq. 2.40}$$

$$\curvearrowright \quad X = m^2c^2 \text{ and } p_0 = E/c$$

$$m^2c^2 = \frac{E^2}{c^2} - \vec{p}\cdot\vec{p} . \tag{2.43}$$

This formula is famously known as the **relativistic energy-momentum relation.**[36]

[36] The "derivation" presented here is, of course, by no means rigorous and there are better but also more complicated ways to derive the relativistic energy-momentum relation. A particularly nice way to see why energy and momentum go together in a four-vector starts with the observation that momentum is the generator of spatial translations while energy is the generator of temporal translations. Thus, just as space and time get unified in a four-vector, the corresponding generators need to be unified too.

Another thing that we can learn from our dimensional analysis is that the momentum four-vector reads:

$$p_\mu = \begin{pmatrix} p_0 \\ p_1 \\ p_2 \\ p_3 \end{pmatrix} = \begin{pmatrix} \frac{E}{c} \\ p_1 \\ p_2 \\ p_3 \end{pmatrix} = \begin{pmatrix} \frac{E}{c} \\ \vec{p} \end{pmatrix} . \tag{2.44}$$

It is quite instructive to analyze the relationship between this relativistic relation and the more familiar non-relativistic relation $E = \frac{1}{2}mv^2 = \frac{p^2}{2m}$.[37] We can understand this relationship by

[37] Using $p = mv$, we find $E = \frac{p^2}{2m} = \frac{(mv)^2}{2m} = \frac{mv^2}{2}$ which is the usual kinetic energy formula.

rewriting the relativistic relation as follows:

$$
\begin{aligned}
m^2c^2 &= \frac{E^2}{c^2} - \vec{p}\cdot\vec{p} && \text{this is Eq. 2.43} \\
&&& \text{rearranging} \\
\frac{E^2}{c^2} &= m^2c^2 + \vec{p}\cdot\vec{p} \\
&&& \times c^2 \\
E^2 &= m^2c^4 + \vec{p}\cdot\vec{p}c^2 \\
&&& \sqrt{} \\
E &= \sqrt{m^2c^4 + \vec{p}\cdot\vec{p}c^2} \\
E &= \sqrt{m^2c^4\left(1 + \frac{\vec{p}\cdot\vec{p}c^2}{m^2c^4}\right)} \\
E &= mc^2\sqrt{1 + \frac{\vec{p}\cdot\vec{p}}{m^2c^2}} \,. && (2.45)
\end{aligned}
$$

If we now assume that we consider an object that moves at a speed that is far slower than the speed of light, $v \ll c$, we can use the usual formula $\vec{p}\cdot\vec{p} = m^2v^2$ and a Taylor expansion to approximate the square root:

$$
\begin{aligned}
E &= mc^2\sqrt{1 + \frac{\vec{p}\cdot\vec{p}}{m^2c^2}} \\
&&& \vec{p}\cdot\vec{p} = m^2v^2 \\
&= mc^2\sqrt{1 + \frac{m^2v^2}{m^2c^2}} \\
&&& \sqrt{1+x^2} \approx 1 + \frac{x^2}{2} \text{ for } x \ll 1 \\
&\approx mc^2\left(1 + \frac{m^2v^2}{2m^2c^2}\right) \\
&= mc^2 + \frac{1}{2}mv^2 \,. && (2.46)
\end{aligned}
$$

We can therefore conclude that in the non-relativistic limit $v \ll c$ we find almost exactly the non-relativistic energy momentum relation $E = \frac{1}{2}mv^2$. The only difference is an additional constant term mc^2 which, however, makes no difference in a classical context since it represents a constant energy offset. The calculation in Eq. 2.46 is an important cross-check that hopefully will give you some confidence in the validity of the relativistic formula (Eq. 2.43).

An important consequence of the relativistic energy-momentum relation is that a massless particle ($m = 0$) can never be at rest

($\vec{p} = 0$). This follows if we consider the relativistic energy-momentum relation (Eq. 2.43) for $m = 0$:

$$\begin{aligned}\frac{E^2}{c^2} &= m^2c^2 + \vec{p}\cdot\vec{p} \\ &\quad \text{↷ } m = 0 \\ &= \vec{p}\cdot\vec{p}\,. \end{aligned} \tag{2.47}$$

This implies that either there is no particle at all, $E = 0$, or we have a particle, $E \neq 0$, and therefore $\vec{p} \neq 0$. In contrast, for a particle of mass m, we can have $E \neq 0$ and $\vec{p} = 0$ at the same time:

$$\begin{aligned}\frac{E^2}{c^2} &= m^2c^2 + \vec{p}\cdot\vec{p} \\ &\quad \text{↷ } \vec{p} = 0 \\ &= m^2c^2\,. \end{aligned} \tag{2.48}$$

There is one final aspect of special relativity that we should discuss before we finally dive into field theory.

2.8 Lorentz and Poincaré Transformations

Since the structure of spacetime is nontrivial, we need to be careful when we want to switch coordinate systems. If we do it wrong, we might violate the fundamental postulate of special relativity that the speed of light is constant for all inertial observers. Somehow this fact needs to be reflected in the formulas that describe transformations between different coordinate systems. In particular, the formulas that describe a switch to a coordinate system that moves with a constant velocity relative to the original coordinate system, somehow need to include the fact that the speed of any object can not be faster than c.

The correct formulas can be derived using the idea that allowed transformations need to respect the laws of special relativity and hence must leave the spacetime interval ds^2 unchanged. Discussing this in detail, however, would lead us too far astray, so let me simply give you the correct formulas.[38] There are three kinds of allowed transformations: rotations, boosts and translations.

[38] You can find a detailed derivation, for example, in my book

Jakob Schwichtenberg. *Physics from Symmetry*. Springer, Cham, Switzerland, 2018b. ISBN 978-3319666303

▷ A rotation is a switch to a new coordinate system that is oriented differently with respect to the original coordinate system.

▷ A boost is a switch to a coordinate system that is moving with a different constant velocity with respect to the original coordinate system.

▷ A translation is a switch to a shifted coordinate system. Since we are dealing with spacetime coordinate systems, we can consider temporal shifts $t \to t + a$ or spatial shifts $x \to x + b$.

We call boosts, rotations and all transformations that are possible by combining them, **Lorentz transformations**. Moreover, we call boosts, rotations, translations and all transformations that are possible by combining them **Poincaré transformations**. In particular, this means that Lorentz transformations are a subset of Poincaré transformations.

Rotations only affect the spatial components of a four vector (1,2,3 but not 0) and can be described by the three basis matrices

$$R^{(vx)}_{\mu\nu}(\theta) = \begin{pmatrix} 1 & 0 & 0 & 0 \\ 0 & 1 & 0 & 0 \\ 0 & 0 & \cos(\theta) & -\sin(\theta) \\ 0 & 0 & \sin(\theta) & \cos(\theta) \end{pmatrix},$$

$$R^{(vy)}_{\mu\nu}(\theta) = \begin{pmatrix} 1 & 0 & 0 & 0 \\ 0 & \cos(\theta) & 0 & \sin(\theta) \\ 0 & 0 & 1 & 0 \\ 0 & -\sin(\theta) & 0 & \cos(\theta) \end{pmatrix},$$

$$R^{(vz)}_{\mu\nu}(\theta) = \begin{pmatrix} 1 & 0 & 0 & 0 \\ 0 & \cos(\theta) & \sin(\theta) & 0 \\ 0 & \sin(\theta) & \cos(\theta) & 0 \\ 0 & 0 & 0 & 1 \end{pmatrix}, \qquad (2.49)$$

where $R^{(vx)}_{\mu\nu}$ describes a rotation around the x-axis, $R^{(vy)}_{\mu\nu}$ describes a rotation around the y-axis, $R^{(vz)}_{\mu\nu}$ describes a rotation around the z-axis, and θ is the angle of rotation.[39] These three matrices are sufficient since any rotation can be thought of as a combination of rotations around the three coordinate axes.

[39] The small superscript v indicates that these matrices act on vectors. This will become important later when we learn that there are additional kinds of objects that are affected differently by rotations. Thus, we need different rotation matrices to rotate them properly.

As an example, let's rotate the prototypical four-vector x_μ, which describes a specific point in spacetime:

$$x_\mu \to x'_\mu = R^{vx}_{\mu\nu}(\theta)x^\nu$$

↷ Eq. 2.49, Eq. 2.33

$$= \begin{pmatrix} 1 & 0 & 0 & 0 \\ 0 & 1 & 0 & 0 \\ 0 & 0 & \cos(\theta) & -\sin(\theta) \\ 0 & 0 & \sin(\theta) & \cos(\theta) \end{pmatrix} \begin{pmatrix} ct \\ x \\ y \\ z \end{pmatrix}$$

↷

$$= \begin{pmatrix} ct \\ x \\ \cos(\theta)y - \sin(\theta)z \\ \sin(\theta)y + \cos(\theta)z \end{pmatrix}. \qquad (2.50)$$

We can see here that the temporal component, ct, and the x-component indeed remain unaffected, while the y-component and the z-coordinate get mixed appropriately.[40]

[40] As mentioned above, the temporal component ct is never affected by rotations, only by boosts and shifts to a different point in time. Moreover, we consider a rotation around the x-axis and therefore, the x-component remains unaffected.

Next, let's talk about boosts. We can describe boosts using (4×4) matrices that act on four-vectors. The main difference to the rotation matrices is that a boost also affects the time component.[41] There are three basis boost matrices since we can boost in the x-direction, y-direction or z-direction:

[41] We've discovered in Section 2.4 that observers that move relative to each other (i.e. who are related by a boost transformation) do not agree on the time interval between two events. This phenomenon is known as time dilation and implies that a boost must affect the temporal components.

$$B^{(vx)}_{\mu\nu}(v) = \begin{pmatrix} \gamma(v) & -\gamma(v)\beta(v) & 0 & 0 \\ -\gamma(v)\beta(v) & \gamma(v) & 0 & 0 \\ 0 & 0 & 1 & 0 \\ 0 & 0 & 0 & 1 \end{pmatrix},$$
$$B^{(vy)}_{\mu\nu}(v) = \begin{pmatrix} \gamma(v) & 0 & -\gamma(v)\beta(v) & 0 \\ 0 & 1 & 0 & 0 \\ -\gamma(v)\beta(v) & 0 & \gamma(v) & 0 \\ 0 & 0 & 0 & 1 \end{pmatrix},$$
$$B^{(vz)}_{\mu\nu}(v) = \begin{pmatrix} \gamma(v) & 0 & 0 & -\gamma(v)\beta(v) \\ 0 & 1 & 0 & 0 \\ 0 & 0 & 1 & 0 \\ -\gamma(v)\beta(v) & 0 & 0 & \gamma(v) \end{pmatrix}, \tag{2.51}$$

where

$$\beta(v) \equiv \frac{v}{c},$$
$$\gamma(v) \equiv \frac{1}{\sqrt{1-\frac{v^2}{c^2}}} = \frac{1}{\sqrt{1-\beta^2(v)}} \tag{2.52}$$

and v denotes the boost velocity.

As an example, let's boost the four-vector

$$\Delta x_\mu = \begin{pmatrix} c\Delta t \\ 0 \\ 0 \\ 0 \end{pmatrix} \overset{\text{Eq. 2.9}}{=} \begin{pmatrix} c\frac{2L}{c} \\ 0 \\ 0 \\ 0 \end{pmatrix} = \begin{pmatrix} 2L \\ 0 \\ 0 \\ 0 \end{pmatrix} \tag{2.53}$$

that describes the time-interval our observer Tom measures in the thought experiment discussed in Section 2.4. We are interested in a switch into a coordinate system that moves with velocity u in the x-direction:

$$\Delta x_\mu \to \Delta x'_\mu = B^{vx}_{\mu\nu}(u)\Delta x^\nu$$

↷ Eq. 2.51, Eq. 2.53

$$\begin{pmatrix} c\Delta t' \\ \Delta x' \\ \Delta y' \\ \Delta z' \end{pmatrix} = \begin{pmatrix} \gamma(u) & -\gamma(u)\beta(u) & 0 & 0 \\ -\gamma(u)\beta(u) & \gamma(u) & 0 & 0 \\ 0 & 0 & 1 & 0 \\ 0 & 0 & 0 & 1 \end{pmatrix} \begin{pmatrix} c\Delta t \\ 0 \\ 0 \\ 0 \end{pmatrix}$$

↷

$$= \begin{pmatrix} \gamma(u)c\Delta t \\ -\gamma(u)\beta(u)c\Delta t \\ 0 \\ 0 \end{pmatrix}$$

↷ Eq. 2.52

$$= \begin{pmatrix} \frac{1}{\sqrt{1-\frac{u^2}{c^2}}}c\Delta t \\ -\frac{1}{\sqrt{1-\frac{u^2}{c^2}}}\frac{u}{c}c\Delta t \\ 0 \\ 0 \end{pmatrix} . \qquad (2.54)$$

By comparing the left-hand side with the right-hand side, we can conclude

$$\Delta t' = \frac{1}{\sqrt{1-\frac{u^2}{c^2}}}\Delta t \, . \qquad (2.55)$$

This is exactly the same result (Eq. 2.15) that we calculated for our second observer, Sarah, in Section 2.4. So while we do not prove with any generality that the matrices given in Eq. 2.51 are the right ones, this cross check will hopefully give you some confidence in their validity.

With the explicit transformation matrices at hand, we can test if the scalar product given in Eq. 2.36 indeed remains unchanged.[42] For example, under a rotation

$$A_\mu \to A'_\mu = R^{(vx)}_{\mu\sigma}A^\sigma \qquad (2.56)$$

we find

[42] The defining property of a scalar is that it's unchanged by transformations. This explains the name scalar product. We will discuss scalars in more detail below.

$$
\begin{aligned}
A'_\mu A'^\mu &\overset{\text{Eq. 2.34}}{=} A'_\mu \eta^{\mu\nu} A_\nu && \text{↓ Eq. 3.22} \\
&= R^{(vx)}_{\mu\sigma} A^\sigma \eta^{\mu\nu} R^{(vx)}_{\nu\rho} A^\rho && \text{↓ Eq. 2.49, Eq. 2.30} \\
&= A^\sigma \begin{pmatrix} 1 & 0 & 0 & 0 \\ 0 & 1 & 0 & 0 \\ 0 & 0 & \cos(\theta) & -\sin(\theta) \\ 0 & 0 & \sin(\theta) & \cos(\theta) \end{pmatrix}_{\mu\sigma} \begin{pmatrix} 1 & 0 & 0 & 0 \\ 0 & -1 & 0 & 0 \\ 0 & 0 & -1 & 0 \\ 0 & 0 & 0 & -1 \end{pmatrix}^{\mu\nu} \begin{pmatrix} 1 & 0 & 0 & 0 \\ 0 & 1 & 0 & 0 \\ 0 & 0 & \cos(\theta) & -\sin(\theta) \\ 0 & 0 & \sin(\theta) & \cos(\theta) \end{pmatrix}_{\nu\rho} A^\rho && \text{↓ transposing} \\
&= A^\sigma \begin{pmatrix} 1 & 0 & 0 & 0 \\ 0 & 1 & 0 & 0 \\ 0 & 0 & \cos(\theta) & \sin(\theta) \\ 0 & 0 & -\sin(\theta) & \cos(\theta) \end{pmatrix}_{\sigma\mu} \begin{pmatrix} 1 & 0 & 0 & 0 \\ 0 & -1 & 0 & 0 \\ 0 & 0 & -1 & 0 \\ 0 & 0 & 0 & -1 \end{pmatrix}^{\mu\nu} \begin{pmatrix} 1 & 0 & 0 & 0 \\ 0 & 1 & 0 & 0 \\ 0 & 0 & \cos(\theta) & -\sin(\theta) \\ 0 & 0 & \sin(\theta) & \cos(\theta) \end{pmatrix}_{\nu\rho} A^\rho && \text{↓ matrix product} \\
&= A^\sigma \begin{pmatrix} 1 & 0 & 0 & 0 \\ 0 & 1 & 0 & 0 \\ 0 & 0 & \cos(\theta) & \sin(\theta) \\ 0 & 0 & -\sin(\theta) & \cos(\theta) \end{pmatrix}_{\sigma\mu} \begin{pmatrix} 1 & 0 & 0 & 0 \\ 0 & -1 & 0 & 0 \\ 0 & 0 & -\cos(\theta) & \sin(\theta) \\ 0 & 0 & -\sin(\theta) & -\cos(\theta) \end{pmatrix}^{\mu}{}_{\rho} A^\rho && \text{↓ matrix product} \\
&= A^\sigma \begin{pmatrix} 1 & 0 & 0 & 0 \\ 0 & -1 & 0 & 0 \\ 0 & 0 & -\cos^2(\theta) - \sin^2(\theta) & \cos(\theta)\sin(\theta) - \sin(\theta)cos(\theta) \\ 0 & 0 & \sin(\theta)\cos(\theta) - cos(\theta)\sin(\theta) & -\sin^2(\theta) - \cos^2(\theta) \end{pmatrix}_{\sigma\rho} A^\rho && \text{↓ } c^2(x) + s^2(x) = 1 \\
&= A^\sigma \begin{pmatrix} 1 & 0 & 0 & 0 \\ 0 & -1 & 0 & 0 \\ 0 & 0 & -1 & 0 \\ 0 & 0 & 0 & -1 \end{pmatrix}_{\sigma\rho} A^\rho && \text{↓ Eq. 2.30} \\
&= A^\sigma \eta_{\sigma\rho} A^\rho
\end{aligned} \tag{2.57}
$$

So the scalar product is indeed left unchanged by a rotation around the x-axis. Analogously, it can be checked that the scalar product is unchanged by other rotations and boosts. Take note that here we used that the indices of the left transformation matrix must be swapped to get the proper matrix product between the three matrices. For a matrix, this means that it gets transposed. We can also understand this by noting that the vector to the left in a scalar product always needs to be transposed. Therefore, the corresponding rotation matrix also appears transposed.[43]

[43] $\vec{A}'^T = (R\vec{A})^T = \vec{A}^T R^T$

2.9 Summary

In the previous sections, we've talked about lots of important ideas that are all directly related to special relativity. Let's recap the main lessons to make sure the bigger picture is clear.

The experimental fact at the heart of special relativity is that all (inertial) observers measure exactly the same value for the speed of light. This is surprising because the speed of objects in everyday life depends upon how we are moving relative to them.

In mathematical terms, this fact can be incorporated by using vectors in Minkowski space to describe events instead of vectors in Euclidean space. In particular, this means that the correct formula to calculate the total spacetime distance between two events reads (Eq. 2.22)

$$\boxed{ds^2 = (cdt)^2 - dx^2 - dy^2 - dz^2 .} \tag{2.58}$$

We discovered that this formula is the right one because if the speed of light is constant, two observers only agree on the proper time interval between two events if there is a relative minus sign between dt and the spatial components (dx, dy, dz). Proper time describes the time measured by an observer who sees the object in question at rest.

One important consequence of the non-trivial spacetime structure is that observers who move relative to each other measure different time intervals between two events. In physical terms, this means that time appears delayed for a moving observer. Another important consequence is that there is an upper speed limit (c) for all physical processes.

We describe events in Minkowski spacetime using four-vectors. The tool that allows us to calculate the spacetime interval between two events (described by two four-vectors) is the

Minkowski metric η (Eq. 2.30):

$$\eta = \begin{pmatrix} 1 & 0 & 0 & 0 \\ 0 & -1 & 0 & 0 \\ 0 & 0 & -1 & 0 \\ 0 & 0 & 0 & -1 \end{pmatrix}. \tag{2.59}$$

Two four-vectors with the Minkowski metric in between them yields the scalar product in Minkowski space: $x_\mu \eta^{\mu\nu} y_\nu$. We call transformations that leave this scalar product unchanged (and hence respect the laws of special relativity) Lorentz transformations. In physical terms, Lorentz transformations allow us to switch between allowed coordinate systems and include rotations and boosts.[44]

[44] As mentioned above, another allowed kind of transformation are translations. We will discuss translations in Chapter 4.3.

Now that we have set the stage, it's time to introduce the main actors.

3

Fields

When it comes to fundamental physics, the most important types of fields are scalar fields, spinor fields and vector fields.[1] In this chapter, we will discuss these mathematical objects one after another. We start with the simplest type of field: scalar fields. In short:

[1] It might be helpful to look again at the diagram on page 35 to understand how the concepts discussed in this chapter fit into the bigger picture.

> A scalar field S is a mathematical object that eats a spacetime point x_μ and spits out a number, $S(x_\mu)$.

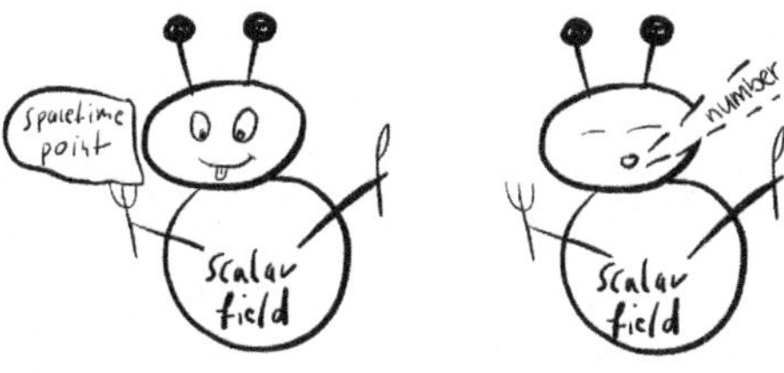

Since we get a specific number for each spacetime point, the following picture emerges.[2]

[2] Take note that although spacetime is four-dimensional, we will draw it as a two-dimensional object in all of the pictures drawn below. This is useful because it allows us to draw fields as things that live "above" this two-dimensional structure. Since spacetime, as the name suggests, already contains all of space and time, fields do not really live above it, at least not in any spatial sense. It's just that this is a helpful way to visualize the interplay between spacetime and fields.

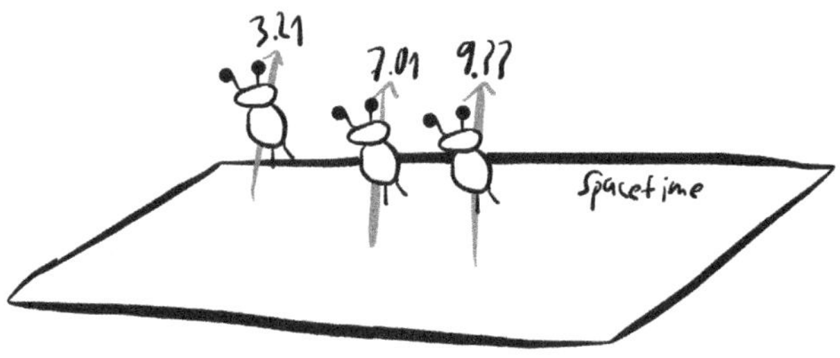

Moreover, if we assume that spacetime is continuous (which is a standard assumption), our field will also be continuous.

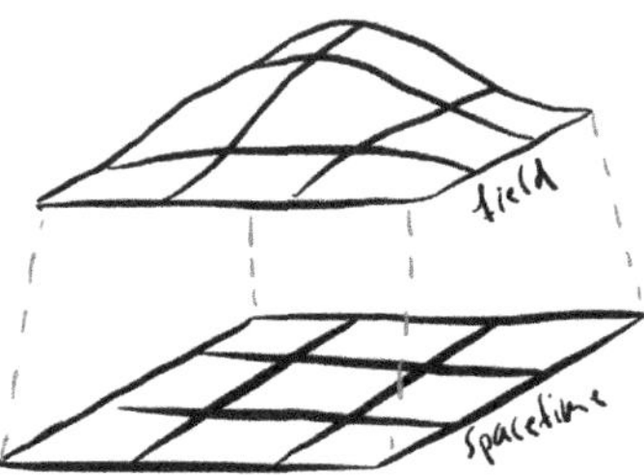

Similarly:[3]

> A vector field V_μ is a mathematical object that eats a spacetime point x_μ and spits out a vector, $V_\mu(x_\mu)$.

[3] Recall from the discussion in the previous section that V_μ is the somewhat confusing standard way to denote a four-vector. The four-vector notation is somewhat confusing because we use the same symbol for the whole vector and its components. In contrast, a three-vector (a vector with three components) is denoted by a little arrow, $\vec{v}$ and its components by using a Latin index v_i.

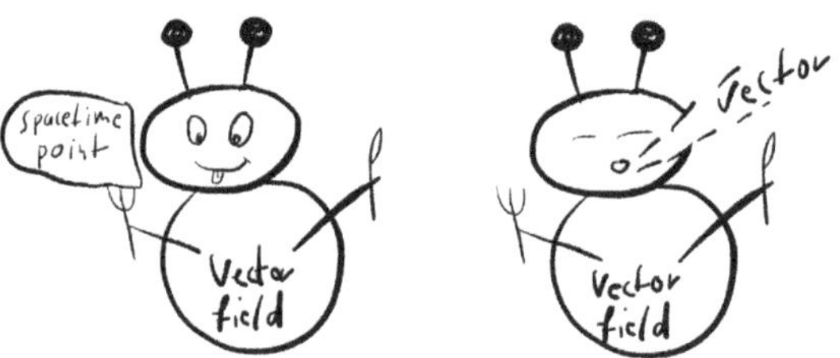

Again, we get a vector for each spacetime point:

Moreover, for our continuous spacetime we get, in principle, infinitely many arrows and therefore any attempt to draw this situation would certainly only be more confusing than helpful.

From a mathematical point of view, scalar fields and vector fields are not that special. We can, completely analogously, construct all kinds of fields. For our purposes, a field is a mathematical object F that eats a spacetime point and spits out a specific kind of mathematical object $F(x_\mu)$. For example, we can equally introduce a matrix field M which eats a spacetime point x_μ and spits out a matrix $M(x_\mu)$.[4] In fact, we can introduce a field for any kind of mathematical object you can imagine. A field is then simply the machine that is responsible for gluing one copy of this mathematical object to each spacetime point. As long as we stick to mathematics, we are always free to introduce any kind of object we want. It's only when we turn to physics that some of the concepts turn out to be more useful than others for our pursuit to describe Nature.

[4] Take note that we could also introduce fields that eat spacetime points and spit out two-component vectors, three-component vectors or even twenty-one-component vectors instead of the four-component vectors we talked about so far. From a mathematical point of view this would be perfectly reasonable and in fact, three-component vector fields are exactly what we need to describe the electric and magnetic fields. But in this book, whenever we talk about a vector field, we mean an object that spits out four-vectors.

Luckily, the fields that we need to describe Nature at fundamental scales are not terribly complicated. Scalar fields and vector fields are already two of the three main actors that we need in quantum field. The third kind is known as spinor fields and the main idea is exactly the same again:

> A spinor field ψ is a mathematical object that eats a spacetime point x_μ and spits out a spinor, $\psi(x_\mu)$.

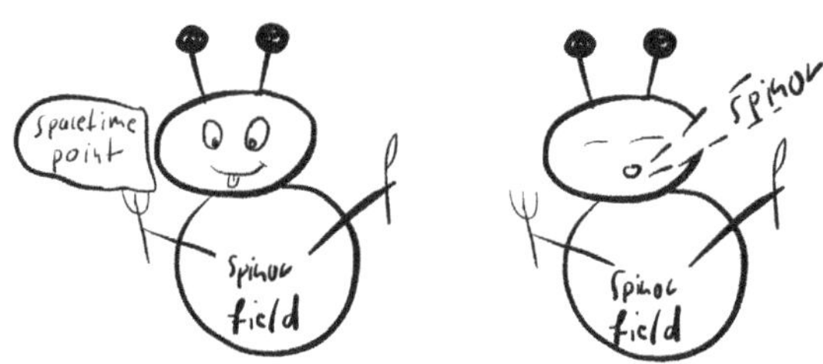

Spinors are, unlike vectors and scalars, unintuitive objects so we will discuss them in detail below. But for the moment, it's only important to keep in mind that the general idea behind spinor fields is exactly the same as for all other fields. Some kind of mathematical object (a spinor in this case) is attached to each spacetime point through a machine that we call a field (a spinor field here). The only missing puzzle piece is that we need to understand what a spinor is.

But before we explore this exciting topic, I want to quickly finish our general discussion of fields by talking about a few concrete examples.

3.1 Scalar Fields

As an example of a scalar field, let's consider

$$S(x_\mu) = x_\mu x^\mu = x_0^2 - x_1^2 - x_2^2 - x_3^2 \,. \tag{3.1}$$

The defining feature of a scalar field is that we get an ordinary number if we plug in a spacetime location. We can check this here explicitly. For example, for $x_\mu = (2,1,1,1)^T$ we find[5]

$$S\big((2,1,1,1)^T\big) = 2^2 - 1^2 - 1^2 - 1^2 = 4 - 1 - 1 - 1 = 1 \,, \tag{3.2}$$

which is a number and not, for example, a vector or a matrix. The same is true for any spacetime point which, of course, isn't too surprising since $x_\mu x^\mu$ is the scalar product in Minkowski spacetime.[6]

Nevertheless, let's check it for one more spacetime point. For $x_\mu = (3.1, 2, 0.12, 0)^T$, we find[7]

[5] Reminder: the superscript "T" denotes transposition and means

$$x_\mu = (2,1,1,1)^T = \begin{pmatrix} 2 \\ 1 \\ 1 \\ 1 \end{pmatrix}.$$

Moreover, take note that to unclutter the notation I'm suppressing all units in the following formulas.

[6] The scalar product in Minkowski spacetime was discussed in the previous chapter.

[7] I included this second example to emphasize that there is no reason why our spacetime coordinate should only take on integer values (as it was the case for $x_\mu = (2,1,1,1)^T$). The only reason why I often use integers in explicit examples is that it unclutters our calculations.

$$S\big((3.1,2,0.12,0)^T\big) = 3.1^2 - 2^2 - 0.12^2 - 0^2$$
$$= 9.61 - 4 - 0.0144 - 0 = 5.5956\,, \qquad (3.3)$$

which is an ordinary number.

The name *scalar* field indicates that this kind of object only spits out boring numbers. Scalar, in this context, is another name for an ordinary number.[8]

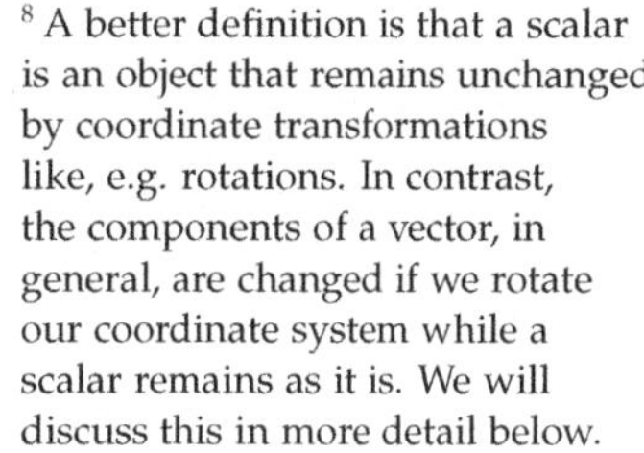
[8] A better definition is that a scalar is an object that remains unchanged by coordinate transformations like, e.g. rotations. In contrast, the components of a vector, in general, are changed if we rotate our coordinate system while a scalar remains as it is. We will discuss this in more detail below.

We call the number a scalar field assigns to each location its **field strength**. The scalar field defined in Eq. 3.1, for example, has a large field strength ($S\big((3.1,2,0.12,0)^T\big) = 5.5956$) at $x_\mu = (3.1,2,0.12,0)^T$ and a comparatively small field strength ($S\big((2,1,1,1)^T\big) = 1$) at $x_\mu = (2,1,1,1)^T$. We say, the field is *strong* at $x_\mu = (3.1,2,0.12,0)^T$ and *weak* at $x_\mu = (2,1,1,1)^T$.

A scalar field is the proper mathematical tool to describe, for example, temperature. The value of the temperature field at each point is simply the temperature there.

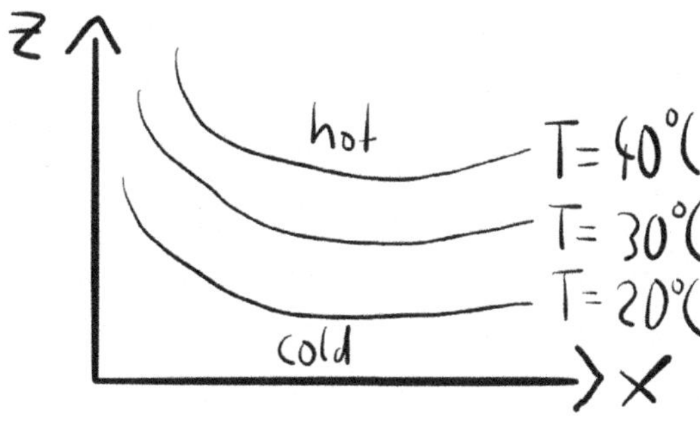

Another example of a scalar field is your cell phone's signal strength. At each point on the earth's surface (or really, anywhere in the universe) and at each moment in time your cell phone's signal strength has a particular value. This value is an ordinary number, and therefore, we are dealing with a scalar field.[9]

[9] As an aside: the only known *fundamental* scalar field is the Higgs field.

3.2 Vector Fields

The simplest example of a vector field we can come up with is

$$V_\mu(x_\mu) = x_\mu \,. \tag{3.4}$$

In words, this means that this vector field eats a spacetime point x_μ and then simply spits it out again without any modification. So for example, if we plug in $x_\mu = (2,1,1,1)^T$, we find

$$V_\mu((2,1,1,1)^T) = \begin{pmatrix} 2 \\ 1 \\ 1 \\ 1 \end{pmatrix} . \tag{3.5}$$

This is indeed a four-vector and thus we're really dealing with a vector field.

To make things slightly more interesting, let's have a look at the vector field

$$V_\mu(x_\mu) = 2x_\mu + y_\mu \,, \tag{3.6}$$

where $y_\mu = (1,0,0,0)^T$. This vector field modifies the four-vector x_μ that we put into it at least a little bit. Let's try this for an explicit spacetime point. For $x_\mu = (2,1,1,1)^T$ we find

$$V_\mu = 2 \begin{pmatrix} 2 \\ 1 \\ 1 \\ 1 \end{pmatrix} + \begin{pmatrix} 1 \\ 0 \\ 0 \\ 0 \end{pmatrix} = \begin{pmatrix} 4 \\ 2 \\ 2 \\ 2 \end{pmatrix} + \begin{pmatrix} 1 \\ 0 \\ 0 \\ 0 \end{pmatrix} = \begin{pmatrix} 5 \\ 2 \\ 2 \\ 2 \end{pmatrix} \tag{3.7}$$

Four-vector fields aren't particularly easy to imagine, just like four-dimensional spacetime itself. Thus it may be helpful to understand vector fields in general by thinking about three-component vector fields instead.

For example, a three-component vector field is the proper mathematical tool to describe the flow of air. The field strength (vector length) at each point represents the speed of the air molecules. Moreover, the direction in which the vector points at each location encodes in which direction the air molecules flow. Similarly, we need a three-component vector field, $\vec{E}$, to describe the electric field. In this case, the vectors this field assigns to each location tell us in which direction a test charge is pushed and how much it's pushed.[10]

[10] In classical electrodynamics, the force that acts on a test charge q which is located at $\vec{x}$ at time t, is directly proportional to the electric field at this point

$$\vec{F} = q\vec{E}(t, \vec{x}).$$

The field strength determines the magnitude of the force and the field orientation determines the direction of the force.

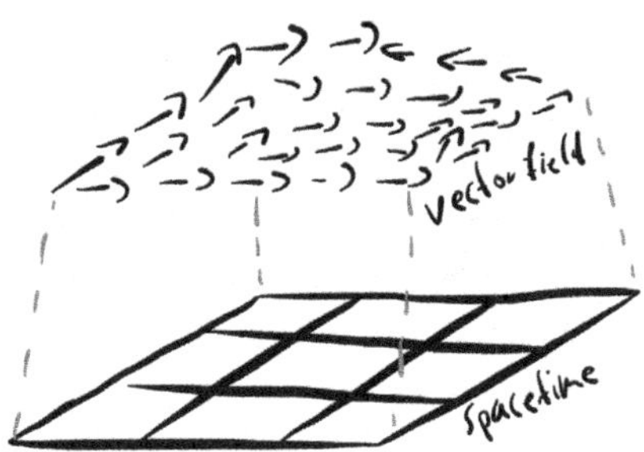

Similarly, we can imagine that a four-vector field pushes a test object in a particular direction in spacetime. This is quite hard to imagine. What does it really mean that an object is pushed in a temporal direction? Just as with the mixing of time and space that happens through boost transformations, four-vector fields and their actions need some time getting used to.

In the following section, we will discuss in a bit more detail how we typically interpret four-vector fields.

3.2.1 Polarization

A scalar field describes, for example, how energy is distributed in space and time in the form of a non-zero field strength. While a vector field is also characterized by a field strength, it possesses additional internal structure. This is what it means physically that a scalar field assigns a simple number to each space-time point, while a vector field assigns a vector. In the simplest case, you can imagine that a scalar field is only able to add or remove energy from another object, but a vector field is additionally able to change the direction or internal state of another object.[11] For example, a vector field (like the one that

[11] In some sense, a scalar field can also change the direction of objects. Mathematically, we describe this by using the gradient of a scalar field, which is a vector field. This gradient vector field is not fundamental since its structure follows directly from the structure of the underlying scalar field. So fundamentally, it's the scalar field that is responsible for directional changes. But mathematically we describe them using the corresponding gradient vector field.

we use to describe air) is able to stop a ball from rotating.

It is convenient to separate the spacetime structure and the internal structure of a vector field by writing[12]

$$A_\mu(x_\mu) = \underbrace{\epsilon_\mu}_{\text{internal structure}} \times \underbrace{f(x_\mu)}_{\text{spacetime structure}} . \tag{3.8}$$

The function $f(x_\mu)$ contains information about the field strength at different locations, while the four-vector ϵ_μ encodes the internal structure. It is conventional in this context to use four-vectors that fulfill the normalization condition[13]

$$\epsilon_\mu \epsilon^\mu = -1 . \tag{3.9}$$

In principle, there are infinitely many possible internal structures of a vector field at each spacetime point. It is, however, extremely convenient to describe these infinitely many possibilities by using a few basic building blocks. This is possible because we can write any four-vector ϵ_μ as a linear combination of four basis vectors. A simple basis vector choice is[14]

$$\epsilon^0_\mu \equiv \begin{pmatrix} i \\ 0 \\ 0 \\ 0 \end{pmatrix}, \quad \epsilon^1_\mu \equiv \begin{pmatrix} 0 \\ 1 \\ 0 \\ 0 \end{pmatrix}, \quad \epsilon^2_\mu \equiv \begin{pmatrix} 0 \\ 0 \\ 1 \\ 0 \end{pmatrix}, \quad \epsilon^3_\mu \equiv \begin{pmatrix} 0 \\ 0 \\ 0 \\ 1 \end{pmatrix} . \tag{3.10}$$

We can check that these vectors fulfill the normalization condition (Eq. 3.9). For example,

$$\begin{aligned} \epsilon^0_\mu (\epsilon^0)^\mu &= \begin{pmatrix} i & 0 & 0 & 0 \end{pmatrix} \begin{pmatrix} 1 & 0 & 0 & 0 \\ 0 & -1 & 0 & 0 \\ 0 & 0 & -1 & 0 \\ 0 & 0 & 0 & -1 \end{pmatrix} \begin{pmatrix} i \\ 0 \\ 0 \\ 0 \end{pmatrix} \\ &= i^2 = -1 \checkmark \end{aligned} \tag{3.11}$$

[12] Take note that we assume here that the internal structure is everywhere the same. This is, of course, rarely the case. We will learn later that analogous to how there are basis vectors, there are basis solutions (plane wave solutions) to our equation of motion for vector fields. Any solution can be understood in terms of these basis solutions. Moreover, these basis solutions are characterized by an internal structure that is indeed completely frozen in space and time. Thus, to unclutter the notation, we will assume here implicitly that we are dealing with such a basis solution. In addition, to unclutter the notation we ignore that both factors here depend, in general, on the four-momentum p_μ of the corresponding wave excitation. In particular, the spacetime structure of a basis solution reads, in general $f(x_\mu, p_\mu) = e^{ip_\mu x^\mu}$.

[13] We will check later that if this condition is fulfilled, the vector ϵ_μ in the expansion of $A_\mu(x_\mu)$ indeed contributes nothing to the total field strength.

[14] Take note that any four linearly-independent vectors can be used as basis vectors. However, our choice here is one of the simplest ones. Moreover, don't let yourself get confused by the fact that ϵ^0_μ contains the imaginary unit i. We will learn later that for physical fields ϵ^0_μ plays no role.

Analogously, we find

$$\epsilon^2_\mu(\epsilon^2)^\mu = \begin{pmatrix} 0 & 0 & 1 & 0 \end{pmatrix} \begin{pmatrix} 1 & 0 & 0 & 0 \\ 0 & -1 & 0 & 0 \\ 0 & 0 & -1 & 0 \\ 0 & 0 & 0 & -1 \end{pmatrix} \begin{pmatrix} 0 \\ 0 \\ 1 \\ 0 \end{pmatrix}$$

$$= -1 \quad \checkmark \tag{3.12}$$

With a basis at hand, we can write any vector a_μ as

$$a_\mu = a^0\epsilon^0_\mu + a^1\epsilon^1_\mu + a^2\epsilon^2_\mu + a^3\epsilon^3_\mu$$

Eq. 3.10

$$= a^0 \begin{pmatrix} i \\ 0 \\ 0 \\ 0 \end{pmatrix} + a^1 \begin{pmatrix} 0 \\ 1 \\ 0 \\ 0 \end{pmatrix} + a^2 \begin{pmatrix} 0 \\ 0 \\ 1 \\ 0 \end{pmatrix} + a^3 \begin{pmatrix} 0 \\ 0 \\ 0 \\ 1 \end{pmatrix}$$

$$= \begin{pmatrix} ia^0 \\ a^1 \\ a^2 \\ a^3 \end{pmatrix}, \tag{3.13}$$

where a^μ are coefficients that encode how much the vector spreads out in the four basis directions.

Analogous to how it doesn't matter which basis vectors we use for our coordinate system, it doesn't matter which basis vectors we use to describe the internal structure of vector fields. However, since we are always free to choose a convenient coordinate system, it often makes sense to align the basis vectors ϵ^i_μ (for $i = \{0, 1, 2, 3\}$) and the coordinate axes, as we do it in Eq. 3.10.

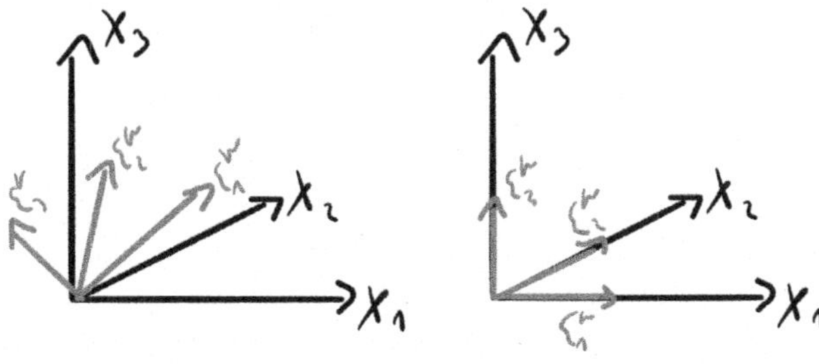

As mentioned above, somewhat naively we can imagine that the internal structure encodes in which spacetime direction an object gets pushed by our vector field. It is conventional to describe the internal structure of a vector field by using the word **polarization**. In particular, the vectors ϵ_μ that encode the internal structure in Eq. 3.8 are commonly known as **polarization vectors**. The basis vectors in Eq. 3.10 describe configurations in which the field is linearly polarized in the direction of one of the coordinate axis. By using appropriate linear combinations of them, it is also possible to write down four-vectors that describe any possible polarization.[15]

[15] One important but quite complicated example are circularly polarized field configurations. The polarization vectors that describe circularly polarized field configurations are complex. A detailed discussion of these more advanced topics would lead us too far astray here.

To understand a little better what it really means to say that a field is polarized, let's imagine a wave-like field excitation that travels along the x_3-axis.[16] This property of the field excitation is encoded by the second factor, $f(x_\mu)$, in Eq. 3.8. [17] Moreover, let's assume that the internal structure can be described by ϵ^1_μ. The situation then looks as follows:

[16] We will discover later that field excitations typically behave like waves.

[17] For your convenience: Eq. 3.8 reads

$$A_\mu(x_\mu) \propto \epsilon_\mu \times f(x_\mu).$$

If we are dealing with a wave-like structure that moves in the z-direction, the second factor here reads

$$f(x_\mu) = e^{ip_\mu x^\mu},$$

where $p_\mu = (E_p, \vec{p})^T$ is the four-momentum (Eq. 2.44) associated with the field excitation, and $\vec{p} = (0, 0, p)$ is the three-momentum of a wave that travels in the z-direction.

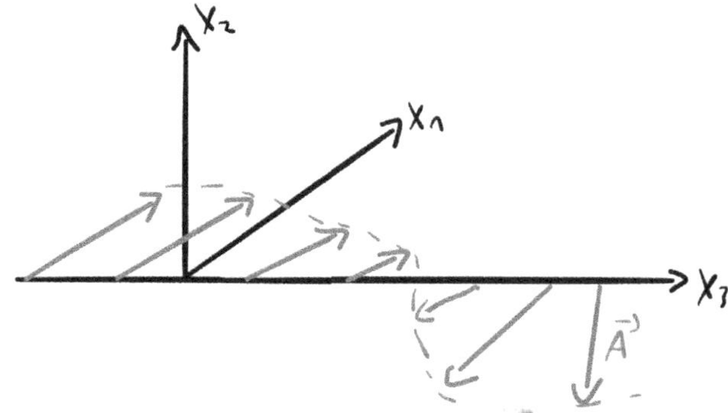

We can see here that while the field excitation travels in the x_3-direction, it oscillates in the x_1-direction. This is what we mean when we say that a field is linearly polarized.

An important but quite subtle point is that not all polarizations that we can write down mathematically, describe situations that we can observe in real world experiments. In general, only field configurations that are solutions of the equations of motion for the system at hand are physical configurations, i.e. something that we can observe in the real world. In other words, an equation of motion not only tells us how a given field configuration evolves in time, but also which configurations are physically realizable.

This is especially important because in fundamental physics we are not that interested in general vector fields. Instead, we usually only consider models that involve **gauge fields** which are a special kind of vector fields.

A defining feature of a *massive* gauge field is that there are only three linearly-independent internal structures.[18] For example, for a field excitation at rest ($\vec{p} = 0$), we can describe them using the basis vectors

$$\epsilon^1_\mu \equiv \begin{pmatrix} 0 \\ 1 \\ 0 \\ 0 \end{pmatrix}, \quad \epsilon^2_\mu \equiv \begin{pmatrix} 0 \\ 0 \\ 1 \\ 0 \end{pmatrix}, \quad \epsilon^3_\mu \equiv \begin{pmatrix} 0 \\ 0 \\ 0 \\ 1 \end{pmatrix}. \tag{3.14}$$

In other words, for a field excitation at rest configurations of the form

$$A_\mu \propto \epsilon^0_\mu = \begin{pmatrix} i \\ 0 \\ 0 \\ 0 \end{pmatrix} \tag{3.15}$$

are not physical.

For a *massless* gauge field, there are only two linearly-independent internal structures. For a field excitation that moves in the x_3-direction, we can describe them by using the basis polarization vectors[19]

$$\epsilon^1_\mu \equiv \begin{pmatrix} 0 \\ 1 \\ 0 \\ 0 \end{pmatrix}, \quad \epsilon^2_\mu \equiv \begin{pmatrix} 0 \\ 0 \\ 1 \\ 0 \end{pmatrix}. \tag{3.16}$$

[18] For a massive vector field a mass parameter m plays a role in the equations of motion. In a quantum context this implies that the elementary particle associated with the field is massive (e.g. the W-boson). For a massless vector field, there is no mass parameter in the equation of motion and the corresponding elementary particle (e.g. the photon or gluon) is massless.

[19] We discussed in Section 2.7 that all field excitations of a massless vector field (massless particles) can never be at rest. Therefore, one of the simplest situations that we can consider is an excitation that moves in the x_3-direction.

In words, this means that an excitation of a massless vector field can never be polarized in the direction of its movement.[20] Here's a somewhat naive but nevertheless helpful way to remember this curious fact of Nature. A field polarization in the x_3-direction implies that the field oscillates back and forth in the x_3-direction. But excitations of massless vector fields always travel at speed c. Therefore, if there were an excitation of a massless vector field that moves in the x_3-direction and is polarized in the z-direction, parts of the field would have a velocity faster than c. But this is in conflict with the fact that the speed of light is an upper speed limit for everything in physics.

[20] In technical terms we say that massless gauge fields cannot have a longitudinal polarization. Only transverse polarizations (i.e. polarizations perpendicular to the direction of motion) are allowed.

3.3 Scalars, Vectors, Tensors, and Spinors

A useful way to think about scalars, vectors and tensors is in terms of how they react to transformations of our coordinate system.

- ▷ A scalar remains completely unchanged.
- ▷ A vector transforms exactly like a position vector $\vec{r}$. For example, if we rotate our coordinate system using a rotation matrix R, i.e. $\vec{r} \to R\vec{r}$, any vector $\vec{v}$ gets rotated analogous to how $\vec{r}$ gets rotated: $\vec{v} \to R\vec{v}$.

The second statement may seem strange or even trivial. However, this definition is actually useful since, in principle, we can write any three quantities below each other between two big brackets. For example, we could write the pressure P, temperature T and entropy E of a gas between two big brackets

$$\begin{pmatrix} P \\ T \\ E \end{pmatrix} .$$

But even if we group these quantities together like this, the resulting object is not a vector since it doesn't transform like a position vector.

These kinds of thoughts are especially important in the context of special relativity. In special relativity our main focus are events in spacetime, which we can describe using four-vectors $x_\mu = (ct, x_1, x_2, x_3)^T$.[21]

[21] Reminder: the speed of light c appears here and in other four-vectors since all components of a vector must have the same units since otherwise we can't mix them. Since t has units [s], we multiply it by the only fundamental velocity that we have: c. The result ct has units $[\frac{\text{m}}{\text{s}}\,\text{s}]=[\text{m}]$ which is the same as the other components.

An event is characterized by a location (x_1, x_2, x_3) and a point in time t. It makes sense to define four-vectors in special relativity since t and (x_1, x_2, x_3) are mixed through transformations of our coordinate system ("boosts"). As discussed in the previous chapter, this means that two observers that are boosted relative to each other, do not agree on the time that has elapsed between two events. The mixing is analogous to how (x_1, x_2, x_3) are mixed through rotations but is a bit harder to grasp since time and space coordinates are mixed. Nevertheless, the mixing implies that we should write time and space coordinates together as a vector.

Once we've understood this, the next crucial task in any theory that respects the rules of special relativity is to find quantities that transform together like the prototypical four-vector $x_\mu = (ct, x_1, x_2, x_3)^T$. A famous example is the four-momentum vector $p_\mu = (E/c, p_1, p_2, p_3)$, where $\vec{p} = (p_1, p_2, p_3)$ is the ordinary, three-dimensional momentum vector, E the energy and c, as always, denotes the speed of light. Energy and momentum get mixed in exactly the same way as space and time coordinates. Another example is the electromagnetic potential $A_\mu = (\phi/c, A_1, A_2, A_3)$, where ϕ denotes the electric potential and $\vec{A} = (A_1, A_2, A_3)$ the magnetic vector potential.

The electromagnetic potential is a perfect example to understand why four-vectors are useful, so let's go on a short tangent here.[22]

[22] If you're not yet familiar with electrodynamics, feel free to skip this tangent. Our return to the main story is marked by a horizontal line.

The introduction of the electromagnetic potential A_μ is motivated by the observation that two observers do not necessarily agree whether or not there is a non-zero magnetic field present in a system or not.[23] Whenever there is an electric charge in a system, the electric field is non-zero. Moreover, whenever there is a *moving* charge, the magnetic field is non-zero. The crux is now that two observers do not necessarily agree whether a given charge is moving or not.

[23] Strictly speaking, there is just one magnetic field and one electric field which are present everywhere. However, their field strengths are in many regions zero or so tiny that we can treat it as zero. Nevertheless, especially in the context of classical electrodynamics, it is often convenient to act as if each object creates its own electric field and then add these contributions to find the total electric field. A more mature view, however, is that each charge leaves a specific imprint on the one electric field that is present everywhere. The overall structure of this electric field is the result of the contributions from all the individual charges.

Just imagine that there is one observer, let's call her Sarah, who sees a charge at rest and a second observer, let's call him Tom, who moves relative to Sarah. Tom sees a moving charge.

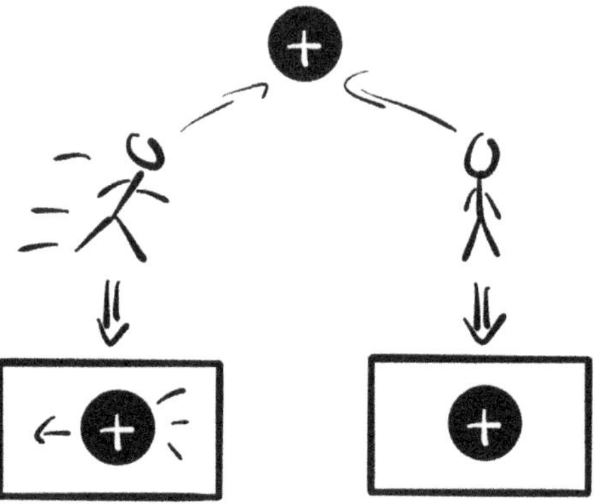

Therefore, Tom will declare that the resulting magnetic field is non-zero. In contrast, Sarah will not include a magnetic field since she sees the charge at rest.

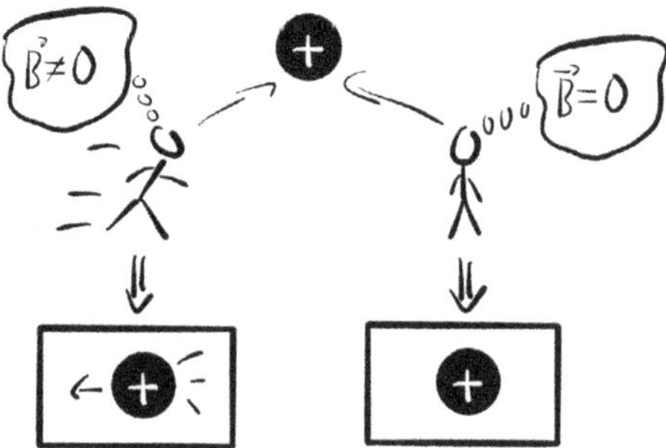

The trick that allows us to develop a consistent description that is valid for all observers is to allow that the electric and magnetic field components get mixed through coordinate transformations. In other words, just as for temporal and spatial coordinates, we combine the magnetic and electric field into a single object. The appropriate object that does the job is known as the electromagnetic field tensor $F_{\mu\nu}$.[24] Moreover, an even more convenient description is possible if we introduce the four-vector A_μ which combines the electric and magnetic potentials into a single object. The relationship between the electromagnetic field tensor $F_{\mu\nu}$ and the electromagnetic potential A_μ is[25]

$$F_{\mu\nu} = \partial_\mu A_\nu - \partial_\nu A_\mu \,. \tag{3.17}$$

The connection between the field-strength tensor $F_{\mu\nu}$, the four-vector field A_μ, the electric field $\vec{E}$ and the magnetic field $\vec{B}$ is summarized in the following diagram:

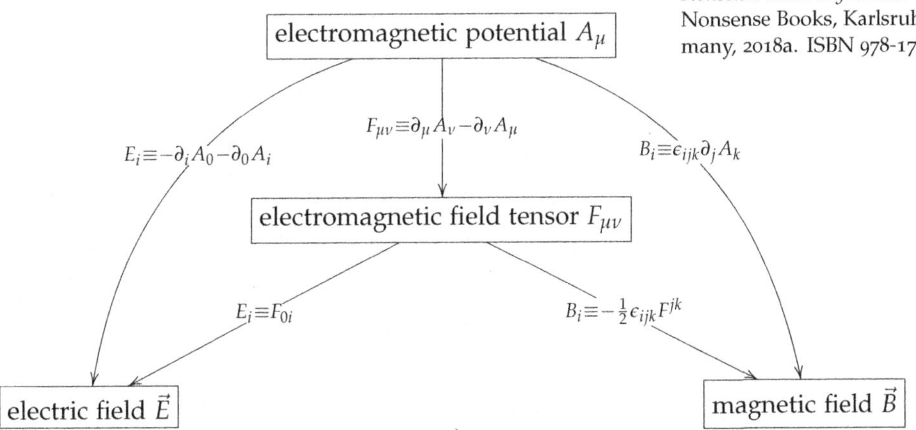

Now back to our main story.

The message to take away so far is:

> Mathematical objects like a scalar or four-vector are defined by their behavior under coordinate transformations.

24

$$F_{\mu\nu} = \begin{pmatrix} F_{00} & F_{01} & F_{02} & F_{03} \\ F_{10} & F_{11} & F_{12} & F_{13} \\ F_{20} & F_{21} & F_{22} & F_{23} \\ F_{30} & F_{31} & F_{32} & F_{33} \end{pmatrix} = \begin{pmatrix} 0 & -E_1/c & -E_2/c & -E_3/c \\ E_1/c & 0 & -B_3 & B_2 \\ E_2/c & B_3 & 0 & -B_1 \\ E_3/c & -B_2 & B_1 & 0 \end{pmatrix}$$

25 You can find a more detailed discussion of the interplay between the electric field, magnetic field, electromagnetic field tensor and the electromagnetic potential in my book:

Jakob Schwichtenberg. *No-Nonsense Electrodynamics*. No-Nonsense Books, Karlsruhe, Germany, 2018a. ISBN 978-1790842117

A scalar doesn't change at all, while a four-vector transforms exactly like the prototypical four-vector $x_\mu = (ct, x_1, x_2, x_3)^T$. Completely analogously, we can introduce additional objects that are also defined by their transformation behavior.[26]

[26] For example, the defining property of a (rank 2) tensor is that it transforms like two four-vectors at once. Let's denote the transformation of a four-vector v_μ by

$$v_\mu \to R_{\mu\nu} v^\mu .$$

A (rank 2) tensor then transforms under this transformation as

$$F_{\mu\nu} \to R_{\mu\sigma} R_{\rho\nu} F^{\sigma\rho} .$$

This is exactly how the composition $v_\mu w_\nu$ of two arbitrary four-vectors transforms. (Take note that this is not the scalar product since the indices are different. The scalar product $v_\mu w^\mu$ yields, as the name suggests, a scalar which doesn't change under coordinate transformations.

This is exactly how spinors, arguably the most mysterious objects in modern physics, enter the game. A spinor is a mathematical object that transforms non-trivially under coordinate transformations but not like a vector. Of course, as mentioned above, as long as we stick to mathematics we are always free to introduce new objects with incredibly weird or incredibly simple transformation rules. But spinors are different since they are absolutely essential for our description of Nature at fundamental scales. For example, we need spinors to describe electrons or quarks. Thus, they are not just some mathematical gimmick and it makes sense to learn about their somewhat strange transformation behavior.

Before we talk about spinors, it makes sense to recap how scalars and vectors transform.

A scalar remains unchanged by coordinate transformations. Another way to express this is by saying that all coordinate transformations look to a scalar like multiplication by the number 1, which leaves all objects unchanged. Thus under a rotation around the x-axis a scalar ϕ transforms as[27]

[27] The superscript s denotes "scalar" and the superscript x indicates that we rotate around the x-axis. The notation here may look somewhat awkward. I included an explicit notation for the trivial transformations $R^{(sx)}$, $B^{(sz)}$ because this helps to keep in mind that there is really a transformation going on. It's just that this transformation looks trivial when it acts on a scalar. But if other objects, like a vector, live in the same system, they are indeed affected by the transformation. This is discussed in more detail below.

$$\phi \to R^{(sx)} \phi , \qquad (3.18)$$

where

$$R^{(sx)} = 1 . \qquad (3.19)$$

Analogously, under a boost along the z-axis, a scalar transforms as

$$\phi \to B^{(sz)} \phi , \qquad (3.20)$$

where again

$$B^{(sz)} = 1 . \qquad (3.21)$$

In contrast, a vector sees coordinate transformations as (4×4) matrices. For example, the four-vector x_μ transforms under a rotation around the x-axis as

$$x_\mu \to R^{(vx)}_{\mu\nu} x^\nu \,, \tag{3.22}$$

where[28]

$$R^{(vx)}_{\mu\nu}(\theta) = \begin{pmatrix} 1 & 0 & 0 & 0 \\ 0 & 1 & 0 & 0 \\ 0 & 0 & \cos(\theta) & -\sin(\theta) \\ 0 & 0 & \sin(\theta) & \cos(\theta) \end{pmatrix} . \tag{3.23}$$

[28] This is the ordinary (3×3) matrix that describes a rotation around the x axis supplemented by an additional row on top since time coordinates are not affected by rotations. (We have only zeroes and a single 1 in the second row because a rotation around the x-axis leaves the x-coordinate of a vector unchanged.)

Moreover, under a boost along the z-axis a four-vector transforms as

$$x_\mu \to B^{(vz)}_{\mu\nu} x^\nu \,, \tag{3.24}$$

where (Eq. 2.51)

$$B^{(vz)}_{\mu\nu}(v) = \begin{pmatrix} \gamma(v) & 0 & 0 & -\gamma(v)\beta(v) \\ 0 & 1 & 0 & 0 \\ 0 & 0 & 1 & 0 \\ -\gamma(v)\beta(v) & 0 & 0 & \gamma(v) \end{pmatrix} . \tag{3.25}$$

With this in mind, we are ready to talk about spinors. Spinors live somewhere in between a scalar and a vector.[29]

[29] One thing that can be *extremely* confusing is that mathematicians use the word vector quite differently. For them, any element of a vector space is a vector. The defining characteristic of elements of a vector space is that they follow the same rules (axioms) as the little arrows that we use to illustrate three-component vectors. You can find a complete list of all axioms that define a vector space, for example, at Wikipedia (`https://en.wikipedia.org/wiki/Vector_space`). Thus to them, spinors are a special kind of vector since spinors can be added and multiplied by real numbers just as the arrows you know from highschool. In other words, mathematicians call spinors vectors since they live in a vector space. (The vector space spinors live in is called $\mathbb{C}^2$. The elements of $\mathbb{C}^2$ are complex column vectors with two entries.) By vector, however, we mean (unless otherwise stated) a four-vector that transforms under coordinate transformations exactly like x_μ.

A fundamental spinor, often called a **Weyl spinor**, has two-components. This implies that all fundamental spinors see coordinate transformations as (2×2) matrices. Formulated differently, when we want to calculate how a spinor looks like after a rotation or boost, we can no longer use the (4×4) matrices that work so nicely for four-vectors. Instead, we need (2×2) matrices.

One small but important detail is that there are two kinds of fundamental spinor. Both are two-component objects but behave slightly differently under coordinate transformations.

The first kind is known as **left-chiral spinors** χ and transforms, for example, under rotations around the x-axis as[30]

[30] For now, the names left-chiral and right-chiral are just names that we use to label certain objects that transform similarly but differently under Lorentz transformations. We will later fill these names with physical content.

$$\chi_a \to R^{(\chi x)}_{ab} \chi_b \,, \tag{3.26}$$

where[31]

$$R^{(\chi x)}_{ab}(\theta) = \begin{pmatrix} \cos(\frac{\theta}{2}) & i\sin(\frac{\theta}{2}) \\ i\sin(\frac{\theta}{2}) & \cos(\frac{\theta}{2}) \end{pmatrix} . \tag{3.27}$$

[31] A noteworthy detail here is that the correct (2×2) matrix that describes how a left-chiral spinor transforms under rotations contains complex entries.

Moreover, under a boost along the z-axis, a left-chiral spinor transforms as

$$\chi_a \to B^{(\chi z)}_{ab} \chi_b \,, \tag{3.28}$$

where

$$B^{(\chi z)}_{ab}(\phi) = \begin{pmatrix} e^{\frac{\phi}{2}} & 0 \\ 0 & e^{-\frac{\phi}{2}} \end{pmatrix} , \tag{3.29}$$

and ϕ denotes the rapidity of the boost which is directly related to the velocity[32]

$$\tanh(\phi) = \beta(v) = \frac{v}{c}$$

$$\Rightarrow$$

$$\phi = \text{artanh}\left(\frac{v}{c}\right) . \tag{3.30}$$

[32] Rapidity is a parameter that is used quite often in special relativity. The strange definition of ϕ given here often helps to simplify calculations. Moreover, the boost matrices for vectors can also be rewritten in terms of the rapidity:

$$B^{(vy)}_{\mu\nu}(\phi) = \begin{pmatrix} \cosh(\phi) & -\sinh(\phi) & 0 & 0 \\ -\sinh(\phi) & \cosh(\phi) & 0 & 0 \\ 0 & 0 & 1 & 0 \\ 0 & 0 & 0 & 1 \end{pmatrix},$$

$$B^{(vy)}_{\mu\nu}(\theta) = \begin{pmatrix} \cosh(\phi) & 0 & -\sinh(\phi) & 0 \\ 0 & 1 & 0 & 0 \\ -\sinh(\phi) & 0 & \cosh(\phi) & 0 \\ 0 & 0 & 0 & 1 \end{pmatrix},$$

$$R^{(vz)}_{\mu\nu}(\theta) = \begin{pmatrix} \cosh(\phi) & 0 & 0 & -\sinh(\phi) \\ 0 & 1 & 0 & 0 \\ 0 & 0 & 1 & 0 \\ -\sinh(\phi) & 0 & 0 & \cosh(\phi) \end{pmatrix},$$

where

$$\cosh(\phi) = \gamma(v)$$
$$\sinh(\phi) = \gamma(v)\beta(v) .$$

Similarly, a **right-chiral spinor** ξ transforms under rotations around the x-axis as

$$\xi_a \to R^{(\xi x)}_{ab} \xi_b \,, \tag{3.31}$$

where

$$R^{(\xi x)}_{ab}(\theta) = \begin{pmatrix} \cos(\frac{\theta}{2}) & i\sin(\frac{\theta}{2}) \\ i\sin(\frac{\theta}{2}) & \cos(\frac{\theta}{2}) \end{pmatrix} . \tag{3.32}$$

This is exactly the same matrix as in Eq. 3.27. Moreover, under a boost along the z-axis, a right-chiral spinor transforms as

$$\xi_a \to B^{(\xi z)}_{ab} \xi_b \,, \tag{3.33}$$

where

$$B^{(\xi z)}_{ab}(\phi) = \begin{pmatrix} e^{-\frac{\phi}{2}} & 0 \\ 0 & e^{\frac{\phi}{2}} \end{pmatrix} . \tag{3.34}$$

In general, left-chiral spinors and right-chiral spinors transform equally under rotations but slightly differently under boosts. The only difference in the transformation rules for boosts are the swapped positions of minus signs.

There is also a third kind of spinor which, however, is not something fundamentally new but simply a combination of the two kinds of spinors that we introduced above. A **Dirac spinor** is a left-chiral and right-chiral spinor written below each other between two big brackets:

$$\Psi = \begin{pmatrix} \chi \\ \xi \end{pmatrix} . \tag{3.35}$$

It is extremely convenient to introduce Dirac spinors for exactly the same reasons that we introduced four-vectors. We introduced four-vectors because time and space coordinates are mixed under coordinate transformations. Similarly, we introduce Dirac spinors because left-chiral and right-chiral coordinates are mixed under coordinate transformations. However, the analogy is not exactly one-to-one. For four-vectors the mixing between space and time coordinates happens under boost. In contrast, the mixing of left-chiral and right-chiral spinors happens when we mirror a system.

In general, transformations that mirror coordinate axes are known as parity transformations.[33] Mathematically, we have[34]

$$\vec{x} \overset{\text{parity}}{\longrightarrow} -\vec{x} . \tag{3.36}$$

[33] Take note that parity transformations are a completely new type of transformation. In particular, a parity transformation cannot be rewritten in terms of rotations.

[34] The transformation $t \rightarrow -t$ is known as time reversal.

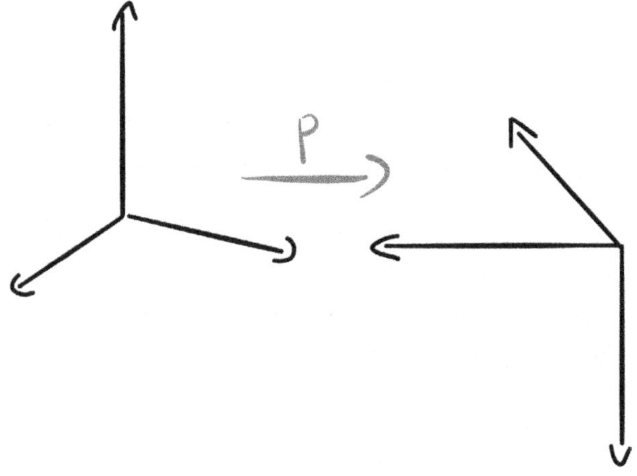

Using this new terminology we can say that left-chiral and right-chiral spinors are mixed under parity transformations.[35]

[35] Mixed is not really the right word here since a parity transformation is a discrete transformation. We will discuss below in more explicit terms what is really meant here.

We can understand this by recalling that left-chiral spinors and right-chiral spinors transform equally under rotations but slightly differently under boosts. Moreover, if we mirror our coordinate axes, a boost in the positive z-direction becomes a boost in the negative z-direction. The key observation is that if we consider the transformation law for a right-chiral spinor in a mirrored coordinate system, we find exactly the transformation law of a left-chiral spinor.

Let's make this more concrete. The transformation laws for left-chiral and right-chiral spinors under boosts (Eq. 3.29, Eq. 3.34) are related by a flip of the sign of the boost parameter ϕ. Mathematically, a boost of a right-chiral spinor along the positive z-direction is described by (Eq. 3.34)

$$B_{ab}^{(\xi z)}(\phi) = \begin{pmatrix} e^{-\frac{\phi}{2}} & 0 \\ 0 & e^{\frac{\phi}{2}} \end{pmatrix} , \tag{3.37}$$

while the same boost in a mirrored coordinate system reads

$$\begin{aligned} B_{ab}^{(\xi z)}(-\phi) &= \begin{pmatrix} e^{-\frac{-\phi}{2}} & 0 \\ 0 & e^{\frac{-\phi}{2}} \end{pmatrix} \\ &= \begin{pmatrix} e^{\frac{\phi}{2}} & 0 \\ 0 & e^{-\frac{\phi}{2}} \end{pmatrix} = B_{ab}^{(\chi z)}(\phi) \end{aligned} \tag{3.38}$$

where in both cases ϕ is a positive number that describes how much we boost our coordinate system. The key observation is that Eq. 3.38 is exactly the matrix that describes the boost of a left-chiral spinor in the z-direction. In other words, before the parity transformation the transformation behavior of a right-chiral spinor under a boost in the z-direction is described by Eq. 3.34. But after the parity transformation, the transformation is described by Eq. 3.38.

Therefore, analogously to how we always need to consider space and time coordinates simultaneously to develop a description that remains valid for all inertial observers no matter how they are boosted relative to each other, we always need to consider left-chiral and right-chiral spinors at the same time if we want a description that remains valid under parity transformations. This is why we introduce Dirac spinors.

In particular, a Dirac spinor under a parity transformation transforms as

$$\Psi = \begin{pmatrix} \chi \\ \xi \end{pmatrix} \rightarrow \Psi' = \begin{pmatrix} \xi \\ \chi \end{pmatrix} . \tag{3.39}$$

To understand why, let's consider the transformation behavior of a Dirac spinor explicitly. Since a Dirac spinor consists of a left-chiral and right-chiral spinor below each other, we can construct the correct transformation matrix by combining the transformation matrices for left-chiral and right-chiral spinors. For example, under a boost in z-direction, a Dirac spinor transforms as

$$\Psi \rightarrow \begin{pmatrix} B^{(\chi z)}(\phi) & 0 \\ 0 & B^{(\xi z)}(\phi) \end{pmatrix} \Psi$$

$$\curvearrowright \quad \Psi = \begin{pmatrix} \chi \\ \xi \end{pmatrix}$$

$$\begin{pmatrix} \chi \\ \xi \end{pmatrix} \rightarrow \begin{pmatrix} B^{(\chi z)}(\phi) & 0 \\ 0 & B^{(\xi z)}(\phi) \end{pmatrix} \begin{pmatrix} \chi \\ \xi \end{pmatrix} \tag{3.40}$$

$$= \begin{pmatrix} B^{(\chi z)}(\phi)\chi \\ B^{(\xi z)}(\phi)\xi \end{pmatrix} . \tag{3.41}$$

We can see here that if we combine the transformation matrices for right-chiral and left-chiral spinors into one big matrix, we indeed get the correct transformation behaviors:

$$\begin{aligned} \chi \rightarrow B^{(\chi z)}(\phi)\chi \quad &\hat{=} \quad \text{Eq. 3.28} \\ \xi \rightarrow B^{(\xi z)}(\phi)\xi \quad &\hat{=} \quad \text{Eq. 3.33} . \end{aligned} \tag{3.42}$$

The question we want to answer is: how does a Dirac spinor transform under parity transformations? We discovered in Eq. 3.38 that $B^{(\xi z)}(\phi) \rightarrow B^{(\xi z)}(-\phi) = B^{(\chi z)}(\phi)$ under parity transformations. Analogously, we have $B^{(\chi z)}(\phi) \rightarrow B^{(\chi z)}(-\phi) = B^{(\xi z)}(\phi)$. Therefore, the transformation law of a Dirac spinor under a boost along the z-axis (Eq. 3.40) becomes

$$\Psi \rightarrow \begin{pmatrix} B^{(\xi z)}(\phi) & 0 \\ 0 & B^{(\chi z)}(\phi) \end{pmatrix} \Psi' . \tag{3.43}$$

Since the positions of $B^{(\chi z)}(\phi)$ and $B^{(\xi z)}(\phi)$ are swapped if we mirror our coordinate axis, we need to swap the positions ξ and χ too. This is exactly the transformation behavior given in Eq. 3.39.[36]

[36] This is not some deep revelation. Instead, we are simply setting up our formalism such that it remains consistent under parity transformations.

There is one final thing I want to emphasize before we move on: Dirac spinors are not four-vectors even though they both have four components. Four-vectors and Dirac spinors are both defined by their transformation behavior and the way they transform, for example, under a boost along the z-axis are completely different.

The transformation law for a four-vector is given in Eq. 3.25, while the transformation law for a Dirac spinor is given in Eq. 3.40 and reads in more explicit terms[37]

[37] For your convenience: Eq. 3.25 reads

$$\Lambda^{Bz}_{\mu\nu}(\phi) = \begin{pmatrix} \cosh(\phi) & 0 & 0 & i\sinh(\phi) \\ 0 & 1 & 0 & 0 \\ 0 & 0 & 1 & 0 \\ i\sinh(\phi) & 0 & 0 & \cosh(\phi) \end{pmatrix}.$$

$$\Psi \to \begin{pmatrix} B^{(\chi z)}(\phi) & 0 \\ 0 & B^{(\xi z)}(\phi) \end{pmatrix} \Psi$$

∂ Eq. 3.29, Eq. 3.34

$$= \begin{pmatrix} e^{\frac{\phi}{2}} & 0 & 0 & 0 \\ 0 & e^{\frac{-\phi}{2}} & 0 & 0 \\ 0 & 0 & e^{\frac{-\phi}{2}} & 0 \\ 0 & 0 & 0 & e^{\frac{\phi}{2}} \end{pmatrix} \Psi . \tag{3.44}$$

Spinors and vectors are completely different kinds of objects. Another way to see this is by considering a rotation by $360° = 2\pi$ around some arbitrary axis. A vector, of course, remains completely unchanged by such a full rotation. We can check this explicitly by using, for example, Eq. 3.23 which describes a rotation around the x-axis:

$$R^{(vx)}_{\mu\nu}(2\pi) = \begin{pmatrix} 1 & 0 & 0 & 0 \\ 0 & 1 & 0 & 0 \\ 0 & 0 & \cos(2\pi) & -\sin(2\pi) \\ 0 & 0 & \sin(2\pi) & \cos(2\pi) \end{pmatrix}$$

$\curvearrowright$ $\cos(2\pi) = 1, \sin(2\pi) = 0$

$$= \begin{pmatrix} 1 & 0 & 0 & 0 \\ 0 & 1 & 0 & 0 \\ 0 & 0 & 1 & 0 \\ 0 & 0 & 0 & 1. \end{pmatrix} \tag{3.45}$$

This is indeed the identity matrix and therefore a vector remains, as expected, completely unchanged by full rotations of the coordinate system.

Next, let's consider the transformation behavior of a spinor under a rotation by $360° = 2\pi$. The transformation of a left-chiral spinor under a rotation around the x-axis is described by Eq. 3.27. For $\theta = 2\pi$, we find:

$$R^{(\chi x)}_{ab}(2\pi) = \begin{pmatrix} \cos(\frac{2\pi}{2}) & i\sin(\frac{2\pi}{2}) \\ i\sin(\frac{2\pi}{2}) & \cos(\frac{2\pi}{2}) \end{pmatrix}$$

$\curvearrowright$ $\cos(\pi) = -1, \sin(\pi) = 0$

$$= \begin{pmatrix} -1 & 0 \\ 0 & -1 \end{pmatrix}. \tag{3.46}$$

This is not the identity matrix! In words, this means that a spinor is not unchanged by a full rotation. Instead, it picks up a minus sign. We therefore only get the identity matrix if we rotate our system by $720° = 4\pi$. This means we need to rotate a spinor twice by 360° to get it back to its initial configuration. This strange behavior under full rotations is one of the most famous properties of spinors and demonstrates clearly that spinors are quite different from ordinary vectors.

One way to think about this curious fact is to imagine that a particle (or field excitation) that is described by a spinor is somehow connected to its surroundings. The connection to its surroundings is flipped after a rotation by 360° and only returns to its original configuration after a rotation by 720°.[38]

[38] There are, of course, no threads that connect particles to their surroundings. Instead, particles that are described by spinors are connected to their surroundings through gauge fields. And, in fact, its only through the interactions with gauge fields that we can detect that a spinor indeed picks up a minus sign after a rotation by 360° (for example, in a neutron interferometer).

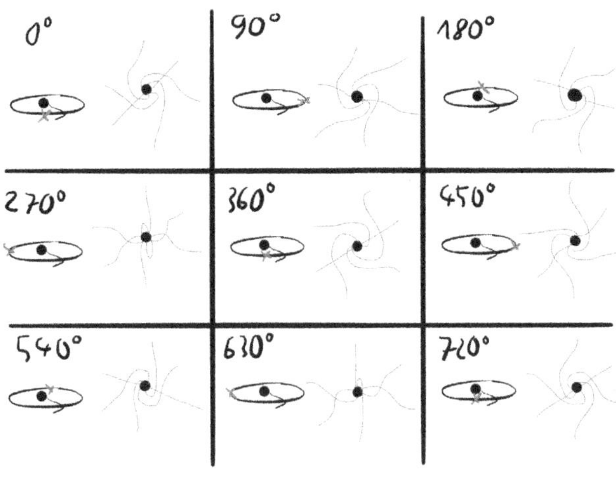

What we've discussed in this section was probably a lot to swallow if you've never heard of spinors before. So maybe you find it comforting that no one finds spinors particularly intuitive. Even Michael Atiyah, winner of the Fields Medal and one of the most influential mathematical physicists of the past century declared that "*no one fully understands spinors. Their algebra is formally understood, but their geometrical significance is mysterious. In some sense they describe the 'square root' of geometry and, just as understanding the concept of $\sqrt{-1}$ took centuries, the same might be true of spinors*".

So let's recap the main lessons before we move on.

The mathematical objects that we use to describe physical systems can be characterized by how they transform if we modify our coordinate system. A scalar always remains completely unchanged, while a vector changes in exactly the same way as the arrows that we use to describe the location of objects in classical mechanics. A third kind of mathematical object that is essential to describing Nature are spinors. A spinor transforms non-trivially if we modify our coordinate system but follows different transformation rules than a vector. Moreover, there are two kinds of fundamental spinors known as left-chiral spinors and right-chiral spinors.[39] Both are two-component objects and transform equally under rotations but slightly differently under boosts. In addition, if we mirror our coordinate axis, a left-chiral spinor becomes a right-chiral spinor and vice versa. This observation motivates us to introduce a new kind of object known as a Dirac spinor which combines one left-chiral and one right-chiral spinor into a single object. Dirac spinors are extremely convenient if we want to make sure that our description remains valid no matter how we mirror our coordinate axis.[40] Since a Dirac spinor consists of two two-component objects, it has four components. Nevertheless, it transforms completely differently than a four-vector.

[39] Reminder: The fundamental two-component spinors are usually called Weyl spinors.

[40] Another reason why Dirac spinors are extremely useful, is that we always need to use a left-chiral spinor and a right-chiral spinor to describe a physical particle like an electron. Even if we manage to prepare a particle such that it can be described solely by a left-chiral spinor, this description only remains valid for a brief moment. All known particles that we describe using spinors constantly jump back and forth between a state that we can only describe using a left-chiral spinor and a state that we can only describe using a right-chiral spinor. This is illustrated in the picture below in which an electron e interacts with the Higgs field, H. As a result, the electron oscillates between a right-chiral and a left-chiral state. We will discuss this in more detail later.

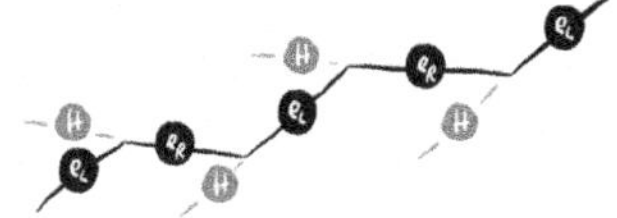

The most important loose ends that we will pick up in a moment are:

- ▷ The meaning of the adjective "chiral" which stems from a physical property of particles known as chirality.
- ▷ The meaning of the word "spinor" which stems from a physical property of particles known as spin.

Once we've discussed these concepts, we can pick up arguably the most interesting loose end: the meaning of spinor components. For a vector, we can easily imagine that, for example, $v_\mu = (0,0,0,1)$ represents an arrow that points in the z-direction. In a physical context, as discussed for the electric field above, this could mean that a test charge gets pushed in the z-direction by the field which is described at the location of the test charge by such a vector.[41] A fundamental spinor, however, has only two components and therefore there is no such direct connection to spacetime directions. Moreover, even though a Dirac spinor has four components, there is no direct connection between its components and spacetime directions.

[41] Recall that a vector field is described by a vector "above" each location. However, only the arrow "above" the location of the test charge is relevant for its description.

These are some of the deepest ideas in modern physics. But before we discuss all of this in detail, let's finish our discussion of fields by talking really quickly about spinor fields.

3.4 Spinor Fields

Completely analogously to how we introduced scalar and vector fields, we can introduce spinor fields. As mentioned already in the introduction:

> A spinor field ψ is a mathematical object that eats a spacetime point x_μ and spits out a spinor, $\psi(x_\mu)$.

Formulated differently, a spinor field assigns a spinor to each spacetime point. Since there are different kinds of spinors, there are also different kinds of spinor fields.

> A left-chiral Weyl spinor field ψ_L is a mathematical object that eats a spacetime point x_μ and spits out a left-chiral Weyl spinor, $\psi_L(x_\mu)$.

Analogously:

> A right-chiral Weyl spinor field ψ_R is a mathematical object that eats a spacetime point x_μ and spits out a right-chiral Weyl spinor, $\psi_R(x_\mu)$.

Moreover:[42]

> A Dirac spinor field Ψ is a mathematical object that eats a spacetime point x_μ and spits out a Dirac spinor, $\Psi(x_\mu)$.

[42] Take note that we use the symbol Ψ for Dirac spinors and ψ for our (two-component) spinor field here.

Let's consider a concrete example:

$$\psi_L(x_\mu) = \chi x_\mu x^\mu , \tag{3.47}$$

where

$$\chi = \begin{pmatrix} 1 \\ 0 \end{pmatrix} \tag{3.48}$$

is a constant, left-chiral spinor. Since $x_\mu x^\mu$ denotes the scalar product, the formula in Eq. 3.47 indeed yields a spinor for each spacetime point. For example, for $x_\mu = (2,1,1,1)^T$ we find

$$\begin{aligned} \psi_L\big((2,1,1,1)^T\big) &= \chi(2^2 - 1^2 - 1^2 - 1^2) && \text{this is Eq. 3.47 for } x_\mu = (2,1,1,1)^T \\ &= \chi && \text{Eq. 3.48} \\ &= \begin{pmatrix} 1 \\ 0 \end{pmatrix} \end{aligned} \tag{3.49}$$

Similarly, we can consider an explicit Dirac spinor field which assigns a Dirac spinor to each spacetime point. For example,

$$\Psi(x_\mu) = \begin{pmatrix} \chi \\ \xi \end{pmatrix} x_\mu x^\mu , \tag{3.50}$$

where

$$\chi = \begin{pmatrix} 1 \\ 0 \end{pmatrix} \tag{3.51}$$

is a left-chiral Weyl spinor and

$$\xi = \begin{pmatrix} 0 \\ 1 \end{pmatrix} \tag{3.52}$$

is a right-chiral Weyl spinor. If we plug in the spacetime point $x_\mu = (2,1,1,1)^T$ into Eq. 3.50, we find

$$\begin{aligned} \Psi(x_\mu) &= \begin{pmatrix} \chi \\ \xi \end{pmatrix} (2^2 - 1^2 - 1^2 - 1^2) \\ &= \begin{pmatrix} \chi \\ \xi \end{pmatrix} && \text{Eq. 3.51 and Eq. 3.52} \\ &= \begin{pmatrix} 1 \\ 0 \\ 0 \\ 1 \end{pmatrix} . \end{aligned} \tag{3.53}$$

One thing that may confuse you if you look at the results in Eq. 3.53 in isolation is that there is no way to tell that this is a Dirac spinor and not a four-vector. Context matters a lot. Of course, in principle you can apply the transformation rules for four-vectors to Dirac spinors. The transformation rules are (4×4) matrices and Dirac spinors look like four-vectors so there is nothing that will look fishy at first glance. But if you do this, you will produce results that no longer match what we observe in experiments. We always need to make sure that every object is transformed using the right transformation rules. Otherwise our description becomes nonsensical.[43]

[43] In the following two sections, we'll discuss several ideas that help us to understand spinors a bit better. If you're already familiar with spinors, spin and chirality, feel free to skip ahead to Section 3.5.

3.4.1 Spinor Formalism

An extremely convenient method to prevent errors is to introduce so-called spinor indices. Just as we denote four-vectors using subscript or superscript Greek indices (e.g. x_μ), we use subscript or superscript Latin indices (that typically start at the beginning of the alphabet) for spinors (e.g. χ_a).[44] This helps to make sure that we always use the correct transformation rules. We say spinor indices transform differently than vector indices. This simply means that the transformation matrix that acts on a spinor needs to have spinor indices, while the transformation matrix that acts on vectors needs to have vector indices:

[44] In contrast, Latin indices like i,j,k etc. are conventionally used for three-component vectors.

$$\begin{aligned} x_\mu &\to \Lambda_{\mu\nu} x^\nu \\ \chi_a &\to \Lambda_{ab} \chi^b , \end{aligned} \tag{3.54}$$

where for a boost in the z-direction, $\Lambda_{\mu\nu}$ is given by Eq. 3.25 and Λ_{ab} by Eq. 3.29.[45] Moreover, since left-chiral spinors and right-chiral spinors transform differently, we introduce dotted indices for right-chiral spinors (e.g. $\xi^{\dot{a}}$).

[45] For your convenience: Eq. 3.25 reads

$$\Lambda^{Bz}_{\mu\nu} = \begin{pmatrix} \cosh(\phi) & 0 & 0 & i\sinh(\phi) \\ 0 & 1 & 0 & 0 \\ 0 & 0 & 1 & 0 \\ i\sinh(\phi) & 0 & 0 & \cosh(\phi) \end{pmatrix}$$

and Eq. 3.29 reads

$$B^{(\chi z)}_{ab} = \begin{pmatrix} e^{\frac{\phi}{2}} & 0 \\ 0 & e^{-\frac{\phi}{2}} \end{pmatrix} .$$

Now you probably wonder why we introduce superscript indices for spinors. The reason is exactly the same as for vectors. It's just a shorthand notation. For vectors a superscript index means that there is an implicit Minkowski metric:[46]

[46] This was discussed in Chapter 2.

$$x^\mu \equiv \eta^{\mu\nu} x_\nu . \tag{3.55}$$

Analogously, for spinors a superscript index means that there is an implicit **spinor metric**:

$$\chi^a = \epsilon^{ab}\chi_b \tag{3.56}$$

where[47]

$$\epsilon^{ab} = \begin{pmatrix} 0 & 1 \\ -1 & 0 \end{pmatrix} . \tag{3.57}$$

[47] The symbol ϵ^{ab} is conventional because the spinor metric is exactly the two-dimensional Levi-Civita symbol.

To understand why the spinor metric shows up quite often in our calculation, recall why we introduced a short-hand notation for the Minkowski metric. The Minkowski metric shows up in the scalar product of vectors. Formulated differently, the Minkowski metric is exactly the tool that we need to combine two vectors and get something that remains unchanged by coordinate transformations (a scalar). We typically want expressions in physics that remain valid no matter which coordinate system we use. Thus it makes sense to introduce a short-hand notation for the Minkowski metric.

The role of the spinor metric is completely analogous. It allows us to combine two spinors in such a way that the result is unchanged by coordinate transformations. This can be shown in general but for now, let's just look at a concrete example. The claim is that

$$\chi_a\chi^a \equiv \chi_a\epsilon^{ab}\chi_b \tag{3.58}$$

remains unchanged by transformations of the coordinate system. In particular, this means that after every coordinate transformation, we can write our expression $\chi_a\epsilon^{ab}\chi_b$ (possibly after some algebraic calculations) again as $\chi_a\epsilon^{ab}\chi_b$.

As a concrete example, we will consider a boost in the z-direction once more. Using the explicit transformation rules for a left-chiral spinor (Eq. 3.29), we find[48]

[48] An important subtlety is that the object on the left of a scalar product always needs to be transposed. This transposition, however, is usually not written explicitly if we use index notation. The scalar product of two (three-component) vectors, for example, should be written

$$\vec{v}\cdot\vec{w} = \vec{v}^T\vec{w} = v_i^T v_j .$$

The transposition turns a column vector into a row vector and therefore, we need it here since only rows multiplied by columns yield a scalar and not a matrix. Analogously, we need to transpose the spinor to the left in a spinor scalar product. For the spinor itself this is not important when we switch to index notation. But if we transform the spinor using a matrix, the transposition has an effect since it means that the matrix needs to be transposed and, in addition, that the spinor and the matrix switch places. (In general, we have $(\vec{v}M)^T = M^T\vec{v}^T$. The same is true for spinors.)

$$\begin{aligned}
\chi_a \epsilon^{ab} \chi_b \rightarrow & \chi'_a \epsilon^{ab} \chi'_b \\
&= \left(\chi_c (B^{(\chi z)}_{ac})^T\right) \epsilon^{ab} \left(B^{(\chi z)}_{bd} \chi_d\right) && \text{Eq. 3.29} \\
&= \chi_c \begin{pmatrix} e^{\frac{\phi}{2}} & 0 \\ 0 & e^{-\frac{\phi}{2}} \end{pmatrix}^T_{ac} \epsilon^{ab} \begin{pmatrix} e^{\frac{\phi}{2}} & 0 \\ 0 & e^{-\frac{\phi}{2}} \end{pmatrix}_{bd} \chi_d && \text{transposition} \\
&= \chi_c \begin{pmatrix} e^{\frac{\phi}{2}} & 0 \\ 0 & e^{-\frac{\phi}{2}} \end{pmatrix}_{ca} \epsilon^{ab} \begin{pmatrix} e^{\frac{\phi}{2}} & 0 \\ 0 & e^{-\frac{\phi}{2}} \end{pmatrix}_{bd} \chi_d && \text{Eq. 3.57} \\
&= \chi_c \begin{pmatrix} e^{\frac{\phi}{2}} & 0 \\ 0 & e^{-\frac{\phi}{2}} \end{pmatrix}_{ca} \begin{pmatrix} 0 & 1 \\ -1 & 0 \end{pmatrix}^{ab} \begin{pmatrix} e^{\frac{\phi}{2}} & 0 \\ 0 & e^{-\frac{\phi}{2}} \end{pmatrix}_{bd} \chi_d && \text{matrix product} \\
&= \chi_c \begin{pmatrix} e^{\frac{\phi}{2}} & 0 \\ 0 & e^{-\frac{\phi}{2}} \end{pmatrix}_{ca} \begin{pmatrix} 0 & e^{\frac{-\phi}{2}} \\ -e^{\frac{\phi}{2}} & 0 \end{pmatrix}_{ad} \chi_d && \text{matrix product} \\
&= \chi_c \begin{pmatrix} 0 & 1 \\ -1 & 0 \end{pmatrix}^{cd} \chi_d && \\
&= \chi_c \epsilon^{cd} \chi_d && \text{renaming indices} \\
&= \chi_a \epsilon^{ab} \chi_b \quad \checkmark
\end{aligned} \tag{3.59}$$

In words this means that thanks to the spinor metric ϵ^{ab}, the two transformation matrices cancel exactly. This happens for every rotation or boost matrix and also for right-chiral spinors. Therefore, as promised above, the spinor metric is the tool that we need to get expressions that remain unchanged.

An important point is that if we multiply a left-chiral spinor by a right-chiral spinor, we only get something Lorentz invariant if we complex conjugate one of the spinors.[49] To understand why, recall that a left-chiral spinor transforms under rotations as (Eq. 3.26)

$$\chi \rightarrow \chi' = \begin{pmatrix} \cos(\frac{\theta}{2}) & i\sin(\frac{\theta}{2}) \\ i\sin(\frac{\theta}{2}) & \cos(\frac{\theta}{2}) \end{pmatrix} \chi\,, \tag{3.60}$$

while a right-chiral spinor transforms as (Eq. 3.31)

$$\xi \rightarrow \xi' = \begin{pmatrix} \cos(\frac{\theta}{2}) & i\sin(\frac{\theta}{2}) \\ i\sin(\frac{\theta}{2}) & \cos(\frac{\theta}{2}) \end{pmatrix} \xi\,. \tag{3.61}$$

[49] We say an object is invariant if it is unchanged by a specific transformation.

Thus, only if we complex conjugate one of the spinors their transformation behaviors cancel exactly:[50]

[50] Try to do the same calculation without complex conjugation if you're not convinced.

$$\begin{aligned}
\xi^\dagger \chi &\to (\xi')^\dagger \chi' \\
&= \left(\begin{pmatrix} \cos(\frac{\theta}{2}) & i\sin(\frac{\theta}{2}) \\ i\sin(\frac{\theta}{2}) & \cos(\frac{\theta}{2}) \end{pmatrix} \xi \right)^\dagger \left(\begin{pmatrix} \cos(\frac{\theta}{2}) & i\sin(\frac{\theta}{2}) \\ i\sin(\frac{\theta}{2}) & \cos(\frac{\theta}{2}) \end{pmatrix} \chi \right) && \text{Eq. 3.60. Eq. 3.61} \\
&= \xi^\dagger \begin{pmatrix} \cos(\frac{\theta}{2}) & i\sin(\frac{\theta}{2}) \\ i\sin(\frac{\theta}{2}) & \cos(\frac{\theta}{2}) \end{pmatrix}^\dagger \begin{pmatrix} \cos(\frac{\theta}{2}) & i\sin(\frac{\theta}{2}) \\ i\sin(\frac{\theta}{2}) & \cos(\frac{\theta}{2}) \end{pmatrix} \chi && (AB)^\dagger = B^\dagger A^\dagger \\
&= \xi^\dagger \begin{pmatrix} \cos(\frac{\theta}{2}) & -i\sin(\frac{\theta}{2}) \\ -i\sin(\frac{\theta}{2}) & \cos(\frac{\theta}{2}) \end{pmatrix} \begin{pmatrix} \cos(\frac{\theta}{2}) & i\sin(\frac{\theta}{2}) \\ i\sin(\frac{\theta}{2}) & \cos(\frac{\theta}{2}) \end{pmatrix} \chi && \text{matrix product} \\
&= \xi^\dagger \begin{pmatrix} \cos^2(\frac{\theta}{2}) + \sin^2(\frac{\theta}{2}) & i\cos(\frac{\theta}{2})\sin(\frac{\theta}{2}) - i\cos(\frac{\theta}{2})\sin(\frac{\theta}{2}) \\ -i\sin(\frac{\theta}{2})\cos(\frac{\theta}{2}) + i\cos(\frac{\theta}{2})\sin(\frac{\theta}{2}) & \cos^2(\frac{\theta}{2}) + \sin^2(\frac{\theta}{2}) \end{pmatrix} \chi && \cos^2 x + \sin^2 x = 1 \\
&= \xi^\dagger \begin{pmatrix} 1 & 0 \\ 0 & 1 \end{pmatrix} \chi \\
&= \xi^\dagger \chi \quad \checkmark
\end{aligned}$$

This motivates us to define that complex conjugation turns a dotted index into an undotted index and vice versa[51]

$$\begin{aligned}
(\chi_a)^\dagger &= \chi_{\dot{a}} \\
(\xi^{\dot{a}})^\dagger &= \xi^a \,.
\end{aligned} \tag{3.62}$$

[51] We will see in a moment why this notation makes sense. Moreover, don't worry, you don't have to remember all these rules about spinor indices. At the few instances where we need them, I will always recite them explicitly.

With this notation, we find for the scalar product of a right-chiral spinor with a left-chiral spinor:[52]

[52] As before, we must transpose the left object in a scalar product because only this way we get a product of the form row times column.

$$\begin{aligned}
\text{scalar product of } \xi \text{ and } \chi &= \xi^\dagger \chi && \text{index notation} \\
&= (\xi^{\dot{a}})^\dagger \chi_a && (\xi^{\dot{a}})^\dagger = \xi^a \\
&= \xi^a \chi_a && \xi^a = \xi_b \epsilon^{ba} \text{ Eq. 3.56} \\
&= \xi_b \epsilon^{ba} \chi_a \,.
\end{aligned} \tag{3.63}$$

This is exactly the index structure for which we already checked in Eq. 3.59 that it yields something invariant. Thus the definitions in Eq. 3.62 are exactly what we need to keep our notation consistent.

The distinction between spinors and four-vectors is not only important when we want to switch coordinate systems but also when we want to interpret our results. As mentioned above already, the way we think about the components of spinors is quite different from how we think about the components of four-vectors. This is what we will talk about next.

3.4.2 Spin

So far, we've treated spinors as some abstract mathematical objects that are defined by how they behave under transformations. Now it's time to fill them with physical content.

To understand how we can interpret the components of a spinor, we need to talk about one of the most important internal properties of elementary particles known as **spin**.[53] And before we discuss spin, it may be helpful to recall how we think about other intrinsic properties like the mass and electric charge of a particle.

[53] Spin, mass and electric charge are not only internal properties of particles but of fields too. But it's much easier to discuss these notions as something that is attached to particles and since we will discover later that particles are field excitation, everything said here remains valid for fields.

For example, we call light particles ($m_e = 9.109 \times 10^{-31}$ kg) with electric charge 1.602×10^{-19} C, electrons. These labels *define* what an electron is. In contrast, we call heavier particles ($m_\mu = 1.88 \times 10^{-28}$ kg) with exactly the same electric charge muons. And we call particles that carry 2/3 of the electric charge of an electron plus an additional kind of charge known as color charge, up quarks.

But particles cannot only carry different charges and a certain mass. They can also spin as they move around.

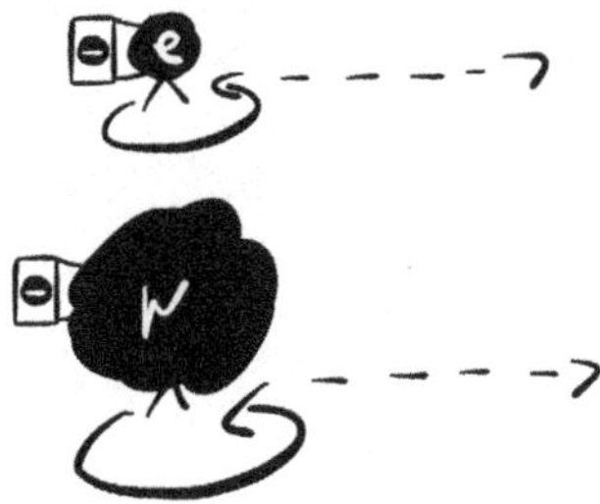

The concept that allows us to describe how objects circle around is angular momentum. While elementary particles can, of course, also revolve around each other, here we are mainly interested in the *internal* angular momentum that also exists in the absence of other objects in the system.[54] The internal angular momentum of elementary particles is simply known as spin.

[54] The quantity that describes the rotation of objects with respect to each other is known as **orbital angular momentum**.

Analogously to how different particles carry different electric charges, they can also carry different spins.

▷ We call a particle without spin, a spin-0 particle. The only known fundamental spin-0 particle is the Higgs particle.

▷ We call a particle that "only spins a little", a spin-1/2 particle. This name is motivated by the fact that the smallest possible, non-zero value of the internal angular momentum of elementary particles is $S = \frac{1}{2}\hbar$, where $\hbar = 1.055 \times 10^{-34}$ J $\cdot$ s denotes the reduced Planck constant. Famous examples of spin-1/2 particles are electrons, quarks, and muons.

▷ We call a particle that "spins a bit more", a spin-1 particle since its internal angular momentum reads $S = 1\hbar$. Famous examples are the photon and gluons.

An important fact about spin is that it cannot be changed. The spin of an elementary particle is a fundamental unchangeable property of it just like its mass or electric charge.

All known elementary particles carry either a spin of 0, 1/2, or 1. Said differently, this means that spin is quantized.[55] This is rather surprising since for the angular momentum of macroscopic objects there is no such restriction. Therefore, it is not surprising that historically, the quantization of spin was only discovered experimentally.

[55] In this context, quantized means that only integer multiples of a certain quantity (here $\frac{1}{2}\hbar$) are possible. Another example of a quantized quantity is electric charge. For electric charge, the fundamental quantum is $\frac{1}{3}e$, where e denotes the electric charge of an electron. All known elementary particles carry an integer multiple of this fundamental quantum of charge.

Spin is one of the most important concepts in modern physics because it's the spin of a particle that determines which role it plays in Nature:

▷ Since there is only one known spin-0 particle, we can't yet derive some general rule. The role of the one spin-0 particle that we know of is quite special. It is responsible for the masses of all elementary particles. Formulated differently, without this spin-0 particle (or formulated more precisely, without the underlying field) all elementary particles would be massless.

▷ Spin-1/2 particles are responsible for matter. In particular, atoms consist of spin-1/2 particles (electrons, quarks).

▷ Spin-1 particles are responsible for the elementary forces. For example, the photon is responsible for all electromagnetic interactions and gluons for all chromodynamic interactions.

Moreover, the spin of a particle also determines which mathematical tool we need to describe it:

▷ We describe spin-0 particles using scalars.

▷ We describe spin-1/2 particles using spinors.

▷ We describe spin-1 particles using vectors.

Before we move on, let's take a brief break and talk about two pressing questions that you may have at this point.

First of all, of course, we do not really believe that elementary particles are little balls that carry backpacks around. As mentioned in the introduction above, according to our modern understanding, elementary particles are excitations of fields. But even in this more mature view of Nature at fundamental scales, there is no good way to understand what it really is that makes a particle more massive than another or why certain particles carry electric charge while others don't. The situation is quite similar for spin. It may be really tempting to think about elementary particles as little spinning balls, but such a picture quickly leads to paradoxical results.[56]

Moreover, you might find that all this talk about internal properties is rather arbitrary. Sure, we can imagine that elementary particles also spin around. But why don't they also, let's say, jump a little and thus possess a label that describes how much they jump around? It turns out that there is a beautiful and systematic way to *derive* which internal properties are relevant for our description of elementary particles.[57]

What happens when we measure the spin of a particle? Let's say we are dealing with a spin-$1/2$ particle. I've already mentioned that the spin of a particle cannot be changed. For a spin-$1/2$ particle, it's always $1/2\hbar$. This may not be too surprising since it simply means that there is nothing that stops or accelerates the spin of elementary particles. But when it comes to actual measurements, there is one additional property of spin that is truly crazy.

[56] Historically, many physicists took the spinning ball idea quite seriously. The idea was attractive because in classical electrodynamics, the field energy of a point particle that carries electric charge would be infinite. Therefore, a group of prominent physicists assumed that, for example, the electron is a little sphere of charge and tried to understand its mass as a result of the electrostatic energy of the concentrated negative charge. (You can find a nice discussion of this picture and its problems in Vol. 2 of the Feynman lectures, `http://www.feynmanlectures.caltech.edu/II_28.html`.) In their calculations, they derived an electron radius of around $r_e \sim e^2/(m_e c^2) \sim 10^{-13}$ cm. If we now imagine that a sphere with radius r_e spins in such a way that its angular momentum is $S = \hbar/2$, we find that points on the surface of the sphere rotate with a velocity of around $v \sim \hbar c/e^2 \sim 137c \gg c$. This violates the fundamental assumptions of special relativity and therefore the naive spinning sphere picture was dismissed.

Nowadays, most physicists simply accept that spin is some magical property that we cannot really understand in intuitive terms from our macroscopic perspectives. There are, however, two noteworthy exceptions which are discussed in [Ohanian, 1986] and [Hestenes, 1990]. In [Ohanian, 1986] a picture is proposed in which spin can be understood as a circulating flow of energy in the underlying field, while in [Hestenes, 1990] spin is discussed as a result of the permanent zigzag movement ("Zitterbewegung") of particles.

[57] To spoil the surprise: each fundamental label like spin, mass, electric charge or color charge is directly related (via Noether's theorem) to a fundamental symmetry of Nature. We discuss Noether's theorem in Chapter 4.3.

When we typically describe rotations, there are two important properties that we need to take into account:

▷ Around which axis the object rotates and

▷ how fast it rotates.

Therefore, if we measure the angular momentum of an object around some arbitrarily chosen axis, we measure only one part of the total angular momentum vector. Only if we choose the object's rotation axis as our measurement axis, we measure the total length of the angular momentum vector.

But for spin the situation is different. The fundamental quantum of spin is $1/2\hbar$ and therefore, there is simply no value closer to zero that we could measure. No matter which axis we choose, there are always only two possible outcomes:

▷ Spin-up, which means $S_{\text{axis}} = 1/2\hbar$, or

▷ spin-down, which means $S_{\text{axis}} = -1/2\hbar$.

In geometrical terms this means that the spin of a spin-1/2 particle is always either aligned to the axis of measurement or anti-aligned. There is nothing in-between.

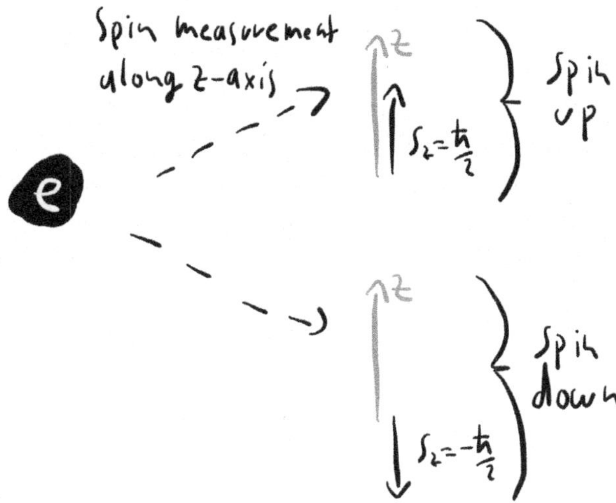

And this experimental fact suggests how we can interpret the components of our fundamental two-component spinors. Since we are always free to choose our coordinate system however we want, it is conventional to choose it in such a way that the measurement axis is directly aligned with the z-axis of the coordinate system.[58] If this choice is made, we can interpret our spinor components as follows:

[58] This is just a choice and any other choice would be equally valid but would require a more complicated description. We will talk about this later in more detail.

▷ A spinor of the form $\begin{pmatrix} 1 \\ 0 \end{pmatrix}$ describes a particle in a spin-up state (with respect to the z-axis). This means, if we prepare a particle such that it is described by the spinor $\begin{pmatrix} 1 \\ 0 \end{pmatrix}$, we will measure the value $1/2\hbar$ for its spin along the z-axis.

▷ A spinor of the form $\begin{pmatrix} 0 \\ 1 \end{pmatrix}$ describes a particle in a spin-down state (with respect to the z-axis). Therefore, if we prepare a particle such that we can describe it by the spinor $\begin{pmatrix} 0 \\ 1 \end{pmatrix}$, we will measure the value $-1/2\hbar$ for its spin along the z-axis.

Moreover, any spinor with a more complicated structure can be rewritten as a linear combination of these basis spinors:

$$\begin{pmatrix} a \\ b \end{pmatrix} = a \begin{pmatrix} 1 \\ 0 \end{pmatrix} + b \begin{pmatrix} 0 \\ 1 \end{pmatrix} . \tag{3.64}$$

In physical terms, the coefficients a and b are directly related to the probabilities to measure a spin-up or spin-down configuration respectively.[59]

[59] You can find a more detailed discussion of spin measurements in

Jakob Schwichtenberg. *No-Nonsense Quantum Mechanics*. No-Nonsense Books, Karlsruhe, Germany, 2018c. ISBN 978-1719838719

Next, let's talk about chirality.[60]

[60] Reminder: spin and chirality are the two loose ends we wanted to talk about in order to understand why we use notions like left-chiral spinor and right-chiral spinor.

3.4.3 Chirality

The defining property of a chiral object is that it looks different from its mirror image. The prototypical example of a chiral object is a human hand. The general structure of your right hand is qualitatively different from the structure of your left hand even if you ignore all details.

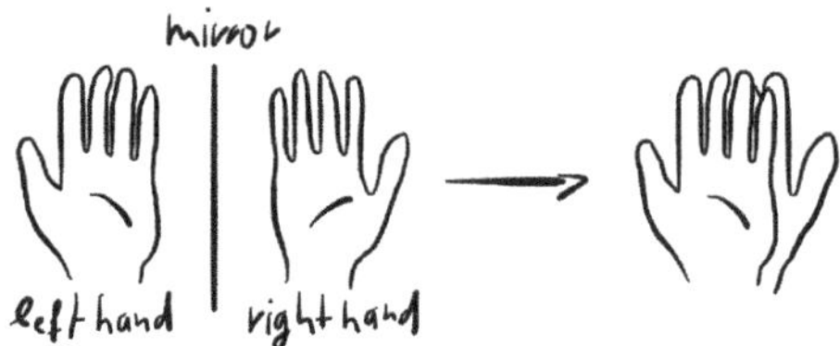

In particular, it's impossible to transform them into each other by a rotation. If you observe your right hand in a mirror, however, it will look exactly like your left hand (again, that is, if we ignore the fine details). In physics we say that the structure of your left hand and your right hand are related by a parity transformation.

A somewhat surprising fact about Nature is that some elementary particles are chiral objects too. We have already discussed in the previous sections that there are two kinds of spinors: left-chiral spinors and right-chiral spinors. Both are mathematical objects with a somewhat unusual transformation behavior under coordinate transformations.[61] Moreover, their names are motivated by the observation that a left-chiral spinor becomes a right-chiral spinor under a parity transformation and vice versa.

[61] Recall that both, left-chiral and right-chiral spinors, pick up a minus sign when we rotate them by 360° and thus only return to the original configuration after a rotation by 720°.

In principle, we can write down all of our equations in such a way that the particles which are described by left-chiral spinors and the particles that are described by right-chiral spinors are indistinguishable. If these equations would describe Nature accurately, we probably wouldn't be talking much about left-chiral spinors vs. right-chiral spinors. Nature, however, clearly distinguishes between left-chiral and right-chiral particles. The experimental discovery of this curious fact of Nature was one of the biggest surprises in modern physics. In technical terms, we say that parity symmetry is broken which is an elaborate way of saying that Nature treats left-chiral particles and right-chiral particles differently.

You are probably wondering in what sense left-chiral particles are different from right-chiral particles. For our hands we can analyze quite easily what makes them chiral objects simply by looking at them. For example, the position of our thumbs plays a crucial role. One property that makes left-chiral particles different from right-chiral particles is that only left-chiral particles carry an additional type of charge known as isospin. Only particles that carry isospin take part in weak interactions, analogous to how only particles that carry electric charge take part in electromagnetic interactions. Thus formulated differently, only left-chiral particles take part in weak interactions.

No one knows why this is the case. The curious connection between chirality and weak interactions is one of the longstanding puzzles in modern physics and it shows that it is important to keep left-chiral and right-chiral spinors separate.

After this quite long detour, let's return to field theory because there is one extremely important aspect that we haven't yet talked about.

3.5 Field Dynamics

So far, we talked about fields as mathematical machines that attach a specific object to each spacetime point. Although it is somewhat against the spirit of special relativity, it is sometimes tremendously useful to split space and time.

In spacetime, nothing moves. Spacetime is frozen since it includes time as one of the axes. As humans, however, we are used to thinking about the behavior of objects in space and time. We typically say that an object moves from some location A at time t_0 to another location B at time t_1. Only by splitting space and time like this can we use the language that we are all familiar with.[62]

[62] We don't split space and time in any mathematical sense, only in our language.

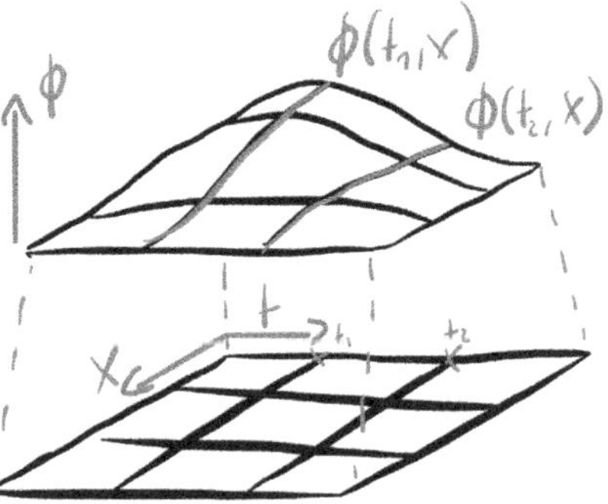

So let's do this and discuss how fields behave as time passes. In general, at one point in time, a field assigns a specific object to a point in space and at some later point it time, it possibly assigns a different object to the same point in space. Formulated differently, fields can change as time passes on.

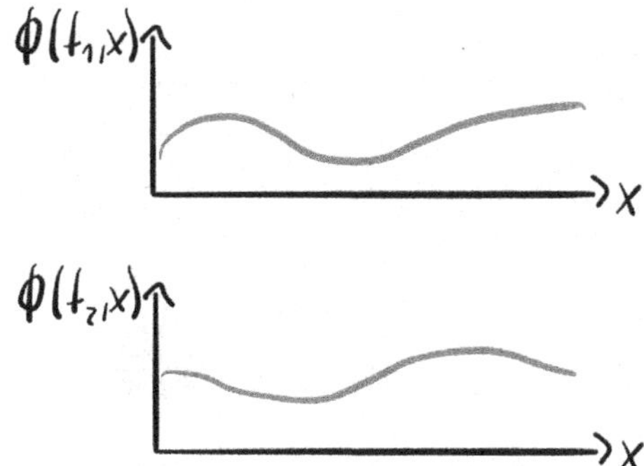

The key question is then of course how and why this happens. We will discuss the equations that allow us to predict the behavior of fields in the next chapter. But already here we can discuss one extremely useful (and surprisingly accurate) model that allows us to think about field dynamics in quite intuitive terms.

The main idea is to think about a scalar field as a spring mattress. For our purposes here, a mattress consists of lots of springs with a mass attached at the end of each spring.

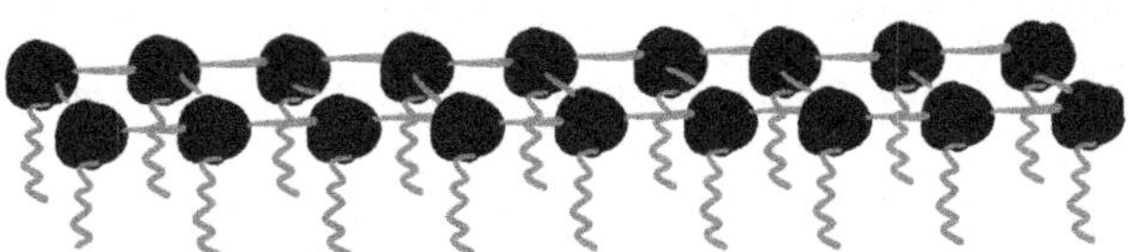

The fundamental building block of a (mathematical) mattress (a spring plus a ball at the end) is known in physics as a harmonic oscillator.

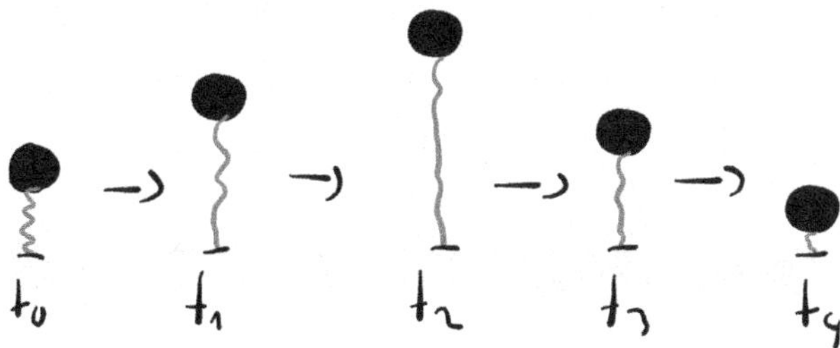

For simplicity, we assume that all of the springs can only bob up and down and never bend or twist. We can describe each such harmonic oscillator using a single number which describes the ball's position with respect to its equilibrium position.

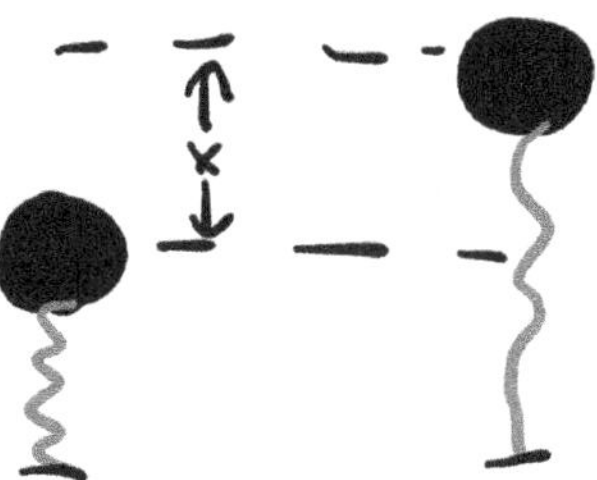

In other words, to describe such a mattress we need exactly one number for each location at each moment in time. This aspect of a mattress is therefore completely analogous to a scalar field. The main difference is that a mattress only assigns a number to certain locations while a scalar field assigns a number to every location.

A mattress therefore represents a discrete version of a scalar field. The transition from discrete to continuous is possible by adding more and more springs to the mattress model.

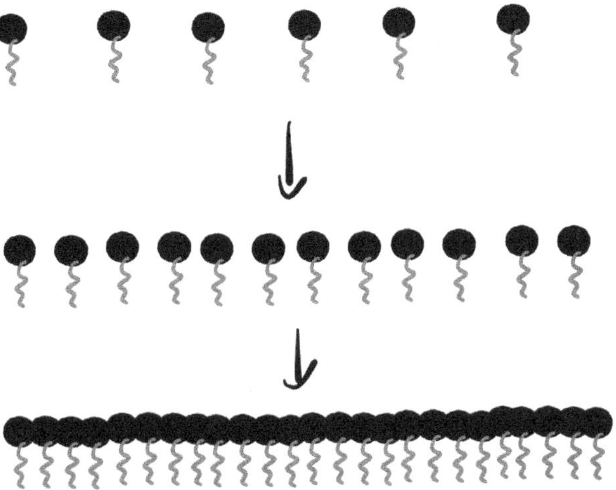

Our mattress model only becomes really interesting once we introduce connections between the individual harmonic oscillators. Without this coupling, each harmonic oscillator can move up and down without any effect on its neighbors and thus, we would be simply dealing with lots of independent harmonic oscillators. So let's imagine that there is a little elastic band between neighboring harmonic oscillators:

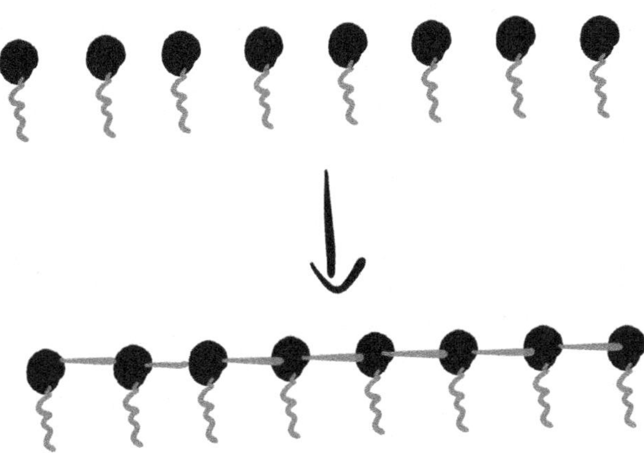

If we now move one of the balls away from its equilibrium position, the situation is far more interesting since this change will affect all neighboring balls too. We can imagine, for example, that the disturbance starts moving through the mattress like a wave that is produced when we throw a stone into a pond. And in fact, this is exactly what happens for a scalar field.

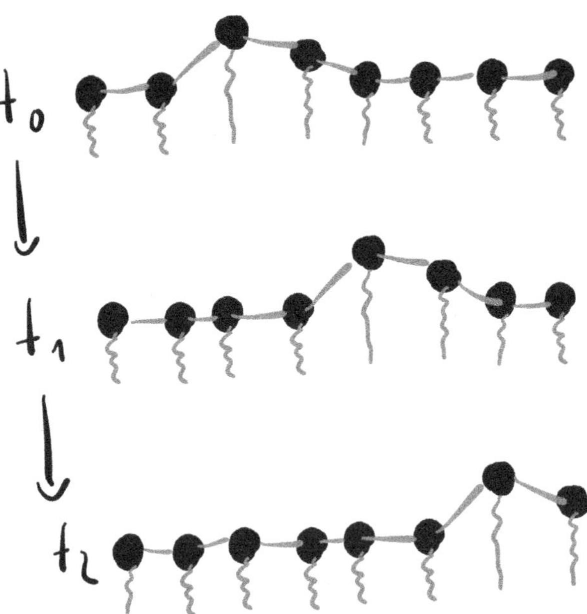

In a physical context, we say that the field is excited if we put energy into it. The excitation will then move through the system in a predictable way. Predicting how a particular excitation moves is one of the main goals in field theory.

3.6 Waves

The structures that emerge when we excite a field (put energy into it) are wave-like. In particular, we will reveal below that the equations of motion that describe the behavior of the various kinds of fields are all wave equations. This is not too surprising if we think about a field as a spring mattress. When we pull one of the springs up, this disturbance will spread out through a mattress somewhat similar to what happens when we throw a stone into a pond. Therefore, it makes sense to talk about waves in somewhat general terms before we discuss the nuances of field theory.

We know that we are dealing with wave phenomena whenever

we encounter an equation of the form

$$(\partial_t^2 - c^2\partial_x^2)\,\varphi = 0\,, \tag{3.65}$$

which is known as the (one-dimensional) **wave equation**. Here, c denotes a constant and we will understand its meaning in a moment.[63]

[63] A constant necessarily appears in an equation that involves spatial derivatives like ∂_x and a time derivative ∂t since $\partial x = \frac{\partial}{\partial x}$ has units $1/m$, while $\partial t = \frac{\partial}{\partial t}$ has units $1/s$. Therefore the constant c has units $\frac{\text{m}}{\text{s}}$ which implies that it's a velocity.

Solutions of the wave equation are typically of the form[64]

$$\varphi(x,t) = e^{i(\omega t - kx)}\,, \tag{3.66}$$

where ω describes the angular frequency, $k = \frac{2\pi}{\lambda}$ the wave number (or spatial frequency), and λ denotes the wavelength.[65] Moreover, functions of the form

[64] We will demonstrate this below.

[65] You can find a detailed discussion of these notions in Appendix C.

$$\varphi(x,t) = \cos(\omega t - kx) \tag{3.67}$$

or

$$\varphi(x,t) = \sin(\omega t - kx) \tag{3.68}$$

work equally well. This follows from Euler's famous formula

$$e^{ix} = \cos(x) + i\sin(x)\,. \tag{3.69}$$

So in some sense, by using $e^{i(\omega t - kx)}$ we can treat the sine and cosine solutions at the same time.[66] Moreover, working with $e^{i(\omega t - kx)}$ is often far more convenient.

[66] In particular, we can carry out all of our calculations with e^{ix} and in the end consider the real and imaginary parts separately to recover what we would have found using the cosine or sine functions respectively.

Solutions of the form given in Eq. 3.66 (and Eq. 3.67, Eq. 3.68) describe plane waves. A plane wave is a structure that spreads out all over space with exactly the same amplitude.

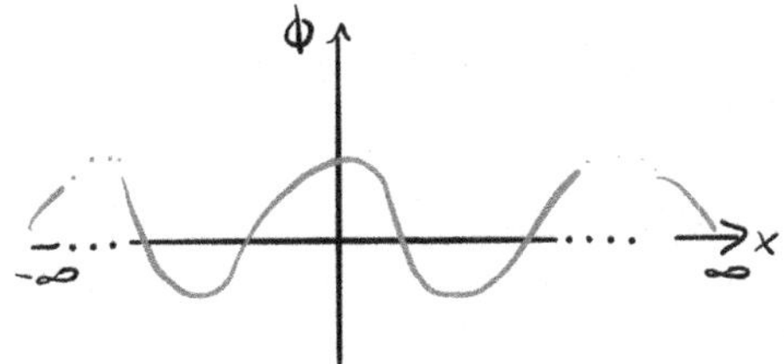

There are infinitely many plane waves that are characterized by different values of ω and k.

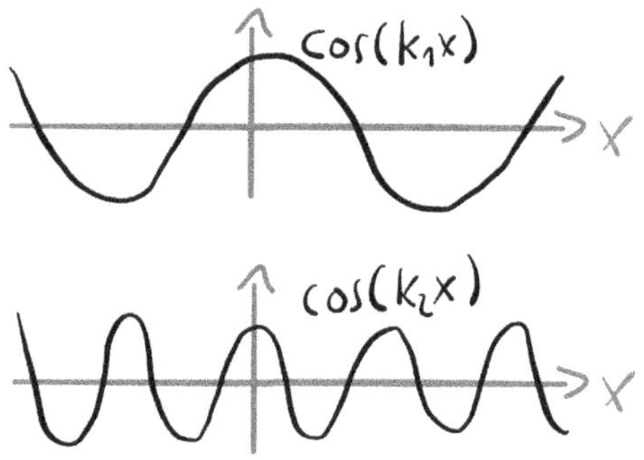

Therefore, it is conventional to label plane waves using ω and k:

$$\begin{aligned} \varphi_{\omega,k}(x,t) &= \cos(\omega t - kx) \\ \text{or: } \varphi(x,t,\omega,k) &= \cos(\omega t - kx)\,. \end{aligned} \tag{3.70}$$

Plane waves are the basic building blocks of all wave structures as we will see below. But first, let's verify that plane waves indeed solve the wave equation.

If we plug Eq. 3.66 into the wave equation (Eq. 3.65), we find

$$\begin{aligned} 0 &= \partial_t^2 \varphi - c^2 \partial_x^2 \varphi && \text{this is Eq. 3.65} \\ &= \partial_t^2 e^{i(\omega t - kx)} - c^2 \partial_x^2 e^{i(\omega t - kx)} && \text{Eq. 3.66} \\ &= i^2 \omega^2 e^{i(\omega t - kx)} - i^2 c^2 k^2 e^{i(\omega t - kx)} && \partial_t e^{i(\omega t - kx)} = i\omega e^{i(\omega t - kx)} \\ &= -\omega^2 + c^2 k^2\,. && \cancel{e^{i(\omega t - kx)}},\ i^2 = -1 \end{aligned} \tag{3.71}$$

Therefore, a function of the form given in Eq. 3.66 indeed solves the wave equation as long as

$$\omega^2 = c^2 k^2\,. \tag{3.72}$$

This formula is known as a **dispersion relation**.[67] In general, a dispersion relation is a formula that describes how the angular frequency ω and the wave number k are related.[68]

[67] We will talk about the meaning of the word "dispersion" in a moment.

[68] There are also different dispersion relations that we will discuss below.

By using the angular and spatial frequency of a wave, we can calculate its (phase) velocity[69]

$$v = \frac{\omega}{k} . \tag{3.73}$$

[69] This is explained in Appendix C.1. See, in particular, Eq. C.10.

If we plug the dispersion relation (Eq. 3.72) into this formula, we find

$$\begin{aligned} v &= \frac{\omega}{k} && \text{Eq. 3.72} \\ &= \frac{ck}{k} && \cancel{k} \\ &= c . \end{aligned} \tag{3.74}$$

This tells us that the constant c that appears in the wave equation (Eq. 3.65) describes the velocity of the waves that are described by it.

There is another kind of wave equation that is extremely important in modern field theory:[70]

$$\left(\partial_t^2 - c^2\partial_x^2 + m^2\right)\varphi = 0 , \tag{3.75}$$

[70] We will discuss fundamental systems that are described by a wave equation with dispersion in Chapter 5.

This equation is commonly called the **wave equation with dispersion**. The only difference to the wave equation that we discussed above is an additional term $m^2\varphi$.

If we plug our general ansatz (Eq. 3.66) into the wave equation with dispersion (Eq. 3.75), we find

$$\begin{aligned} 0 &= \partial_t^2\varphi - c^2\partial_x^2\varphi + m^2\varphi && \text{this is Eq. 3.65} \\ & && \text{Eq. 3.66} \\ &= \partial_t^2 e^{i(\omega t - kx)} - c^2\partial_x^2 e^{i(\omega t - kx)} + m^2 e^{i(\omega t - kx)} \\ & && \partial_t e^{i(\omega t - kx)} = i\omega e^{i(\omega t - kx)} \\ &= i^2\omega^2 e^{i(\omega t - kx)} - i^2c^2k^2 e^{i(\omega t - kx)} + m^2 e^{i(\omega t - kx)} \\ & && \cancel{e^{i(\omega t - kx)}},\ i^2 = -1 \\ &= -\omega^2 + c^2k^2 + m^2 . \end{aligned} \tag{3.76}$$

Thus again, we find that our ansatz indeed solves the equation, but now the dispersion relation reads

$$\omega^2 = c^2k^2 + m^2 . \tag{3.77}$$

This implies that the velocity of waves described by our new wave equation (Eq. 3.75) is no longer simply c. Instead, by using the general formula for the (phase) velocity of a wave (Eq. 3.73), we find

$$\begin{aligned} v &= \frac{\omega}{k} \\ &\quad \text{(Eq. 3.77)} \\ &= \frac{\sqrt{c^2k^2+m^2}}{k} . \end{aligned} \tag{3.78}$$

This little difference has extremely important physical implications. We discovered above that all waves described by the ordinary wave equation (Eq. 3.65) travel at speed c. In contrast, we discovered in Eq. 3.78 that waves which are described by the wave equation with dispersion (Eq. 3.75) travel at different velocities. The velocity of each wave depends on its wave number k.

This is important because functions of the form $\varphi = e^{i(\omega t - kx)}$ (or equivalently $\cos(\omega t - kx)$, $\sin(\omega t - kx)$) do not describe something that we can really observe in Nature. As mentioned above, these functions describe plane waves. However, in the real world we can never create something that oscillates perfectly with equal amplitude everywhere. A much more realistic wave form is a wave packet. The plane waves that we've discussed so far are the basic building blocks that wave packets consist of.[71]

[71] We will discuss this in detail below.

The velocity of plane waves has direct implications for the behavior of wave packets. To cut a long story short:

▷ If we are dealing with a system that is described by the ordinary wave equation, all plane waves travel with exactly the same velocity c. Therefore, a wave packet that consists of these plane waves will keep its form as time passes.

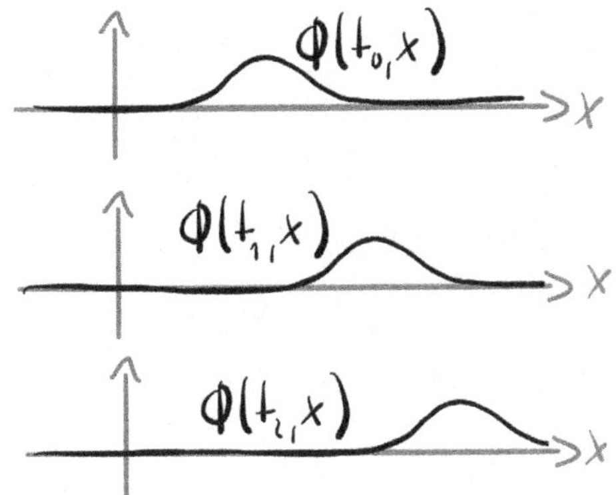

▷ In contrast, if we are dealing with a system that is described by the wave equation with an additional m^2 term, all plane waves travel with different velocities. As a result, the form of a wave packet that consists of these plane waves will change and the wave packet disperses.

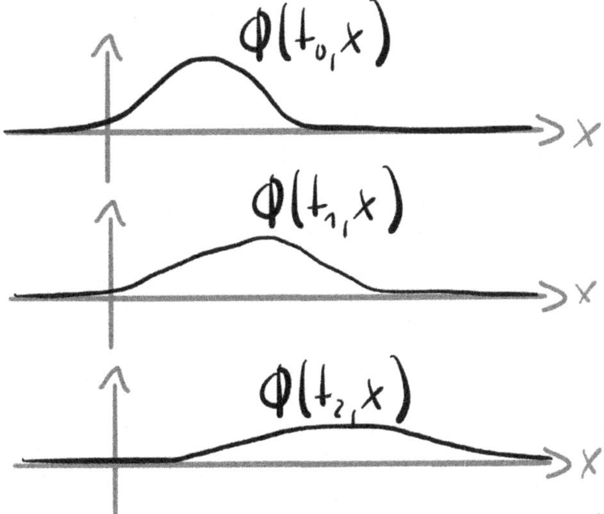

3.6.1 Wave Packets

To understand how wave packets are related to plane waves, take note that we can construct further solutions by using linear combinations of plane wave solutions. To understand why, let's assume we have two solutions of the wave equation with dispersion, $\varphi_1(x_\mu)\varphi_2(x_\mu)$, which implies that

$$(\partial_t^2 - c^2\partial_x^2 + m^2)\varphi_1 = 0$$
$$(\partial_t^2 - c^2\partial_x^2 + m^2)\varphi_2 = 0\,. \tag{3.79}$$

If we now consider a superposition of these two solutions:

$$\varphi_{\text{sup}} = \varphi_1 + \varphi_2\,, \tag{3.80}$$

we find that it also solves the wave equation:

$$\begin{aligned} 0 &\stackrel{!}{=} (\partial_t^2 - c^2\partial_x^2 + m^2)\varphi_{\text{sup}} \\ &\quad \text{Eq. 3.80} \\ &= (\partial_t^2 - c^2\partial_x^2 + m^2)(\varphi_1 + \varphi_2) \\ &\quad \text{rearranging} \\ &= (\partial_t^2 - c^2\partial_x^2 + m^2)\varphi_1 + (\partial_t^2 - c^2\partial_x^2 + m^2)\varphi_2 \\ &\quad \text{Eq. 3.79} \\ &= 0 + 0 \quad \checkmark \end{aligned} \tag{3.81}$$

Mathematically, this works because the wave equation is linear in the field φ which means that no terms of the form φ^2 or φ^3 appear in it.[72]

[72] We can check this by performing the same steps for an equation which includes a φ^2 term.

This observation allows us to understand that plane waves are the fundamental building blocks of all waves. By using a linear combination of plane waves it's possible to construct any waveform you can imagine:

$$\begin{aligned} \varphi^{\text{waveform}} &= \sum_i \varphi_i^{\text{plane wave}} \\ &= \sum_i a_i \cos(k_i^\mu x_\mu) \end{aligned} \tag{3.82}$$

where a_i denotes coefficients that determine how much each individual plane wave contributes to the total wave form and k_i^μ denotes different wave vectors that, however, all fulfill the dispersion relation $k_\mu k^\mu = m^2$.

If we add plane waves, we end up with a **wave packet** because waves with different wavelength (and therefore different wave numbers) only interfere constructively within a finite region. If we consider a superposition of lots of waves, the positive and negative slopes of the different waves average out almost everywhere. As a result, a wave packet is localized within a finite region.

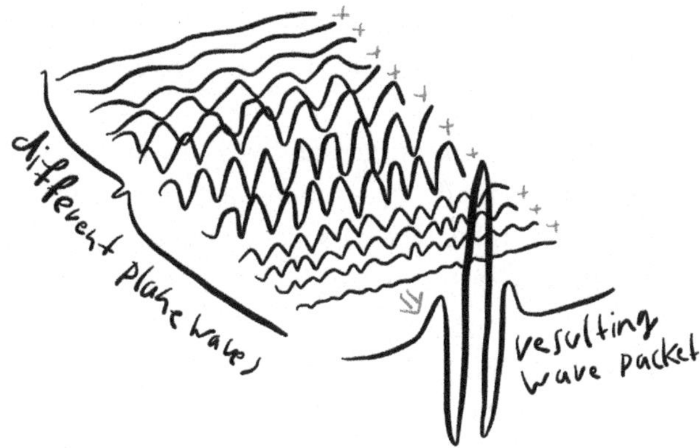

From a slightly different perspective, we can understand this by looking at a given wave packet in wave number space. This representation of a wave packet tells us directly which plane waves contribute how much to the total wave packet:

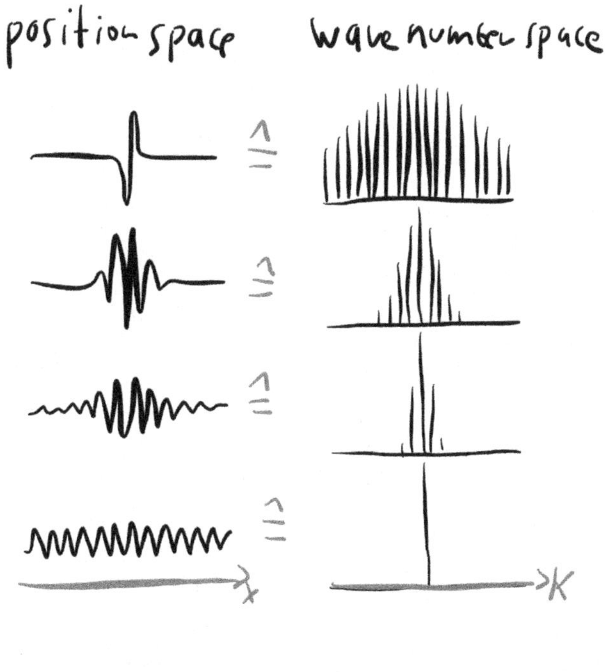

To get a wave packet that is localized within a small region, the plane waves that the packet consists of must be carefully arranged such that they overlap constructively. If we add plane waves randomly, their amplitudes will most likely average out.

With this in mind, we can understand why a wave packet does not change its shape if all of the plane waves it consists of have the same velocity, while a wave packet consisting of plane waves that travel with different velocities will disperse.

If all plane waves travel with the same velocity and we arrange them such that they interfere constructively within a small region, they will continue to do so as time passes on. The only thing that changes is the location at which this constructive interference happens. In contrast, if the plane waves travel with different velocities, the careful arrangement we used to construct the wave packet will necessarily be destroyed. If we wait long enough, the different plane waves will interfere destructively (almost) everywhere. Formulated differently, the various pieces that the wave packet consists of will drift out of phase as time passes and the packet will disperse. This is why wave packets in a system described by a wave equation with a dispersion term will vanish after a while.

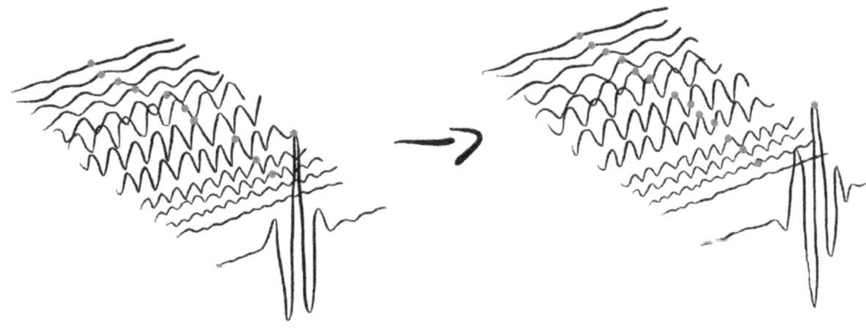

In a modern field theoretical context, a dispersion term is commonly known as a mass term.[73] If we imagine for a moment that a wave packet represents a particle, it follows that if there is no dispersion term the particle can travel, in principle, infinitely far. This is the defining characteristic of a massless particle like, for example, a photon. In contrast, if there is a dispersion term, the particle can usually only travel a finite distance.[74] In a particle context, we say that massive particles decay with time.

[73] Take note that although we will talk about a mass term here, strictly speaking m is not a mass parameter. This follows directly from a dimensional analysis. More carefully, the additional term here reads $\frac{M^2c^4}{\hbar}$, where c is a constant with the units of a velocity and $\hbar$ (another constant with units $\frac{\text{m}^2\cdot\text{kg}}{\text{s}}$). In this case, the parameter M indeed has the correct units to describe a mass. However, to unclutter the notation, we ignore this subtlety in the following discussion.

[74] There are important exceptions to this rule. For example, an electron is stable even though it is massive. This is a result of electric charge conservation. The electron is the lightest particle carrying charge e and thus there is no particle it could decay into without violating electric charge conservation.

In the context of quantum field theory, we say that the mass parameter m of a field determines its **correlation length** $\eta \sim \frac{1}{m}$. Roughly speaking, the correlation length η encodes how far a field can typically spread its influence or similarly, how large ordered structures within the field are. Therefore, this interpretation is completely in line with what we just discussed.

3.7 Field Spaces

There is one final aspects of fields that we need to talk about before we can discuss the framework that allows us to describe how fields evolve in time.

While it is often quite helpful to think about a field as something like a mattress, it is always important to keep in mind that the fields we are talking about in this book do not really oscillate up and down, at least not in a spatial sense. Instead, field oscillations happen in a somewhat abstract field space.

Abstract spaces are one of the most successful ideas in modern physics. For example, the temperature within a room is a scalar field $T(\vec{x})$. Each location within the room $\vec{x}$ is mapped using a thermometer to a real number that we call the temperature. Mathematically, temperatures live on the real line $\mathbb{R}$ which we call, in this context, temperature space. Even though it's mathematically also a real line, temperature space does not correspond to one of the spatial dimension ($\mathbb{R}^x, \mathbb{R}^y, \mathbb{R}^z$). Instead, it's a surplus structure that we introduce to describe our system.

Similarly, we imagine that the numbers a fundamental scalar field spits out for each location live in an abstract field space too. In mathematical terms, a scalar field is a map

$$\mathbb{R}^{1,3} \to \mathbb{R}: \quad x_\mu \to \phi(x_\mu) . \tag{3.83}$$

The space $\mathbb{R}$ in which field values live is not a part of spacetime ($\mathbb{R}^{1,3}$). The field values live in an abstract space "on top" of spacetime. Formulated differently, the field is defined over spacetime, but the value (or amplitude) of the field is along a new axis.

A field is an object that glues this abstract space and spacetime together. An important point is that there is a copy of the basic field space (here $\mathbb{R}$) above *each* spacetime point. The total field space is all these individual basic field spaces taken together.

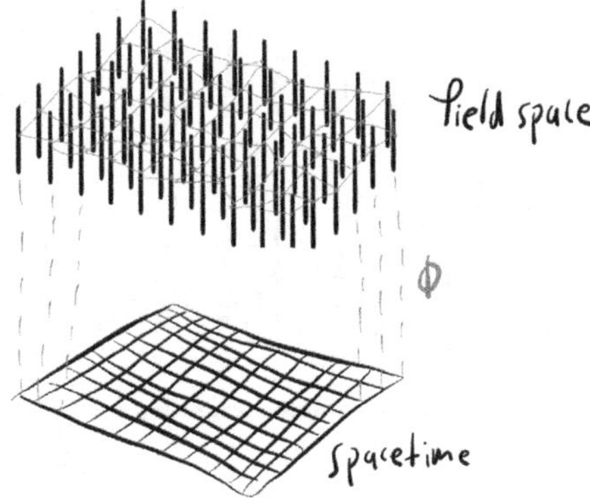

While a field is a map from spacetime to the corresponding field space, we often represent it through its values in field space. In the figure above, these values are indicated by the gray structure that lives in field space.[75] It is often convenient to omit the coordinate systems and we can then draw pictures like the following.

[75] This is analogous to how we can represent a three-vector by using three numbers as soon as we've picked a coordinate system.

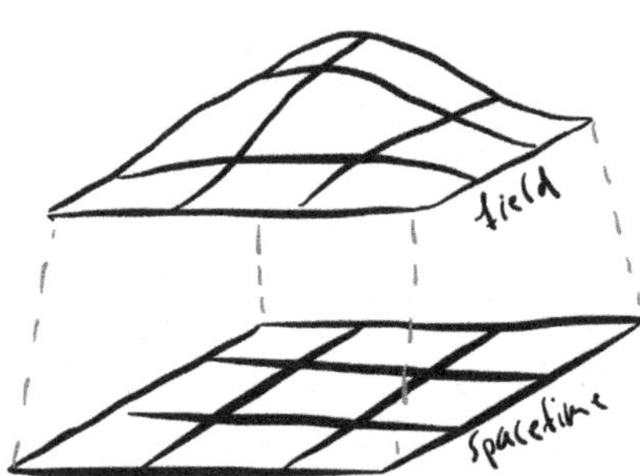

In summary, instead of thinking of a field as an abstract map it is often helpful to treat it as a bed sheet-like structure that lives on top of spacetime.

Another important observation is that there is a different field space for each field. For example, temperatures and the Higgs field occupy different field spaces even though both are mathematical scalar fields.

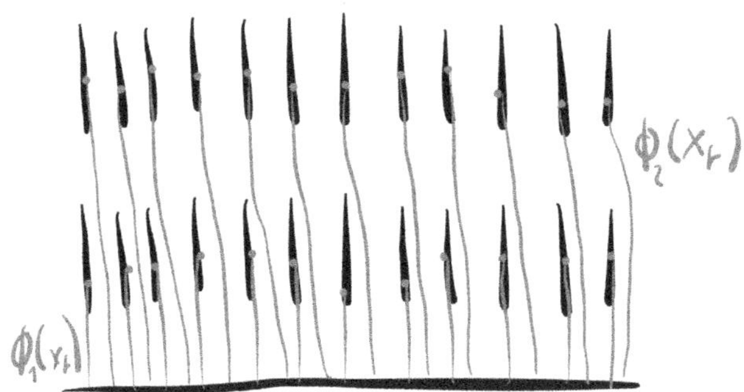

Therefore it is important to keep in mind that the waves we will talk about in the following sections also live in these abstract field spaces and not in physical space. This is in contrast to water waves or the waves that we can observe on a mattress which certainly live in our physical space. For example, the amplitude of a water wave describes its height above the equilibrium sea level, while the amplitude of a fundamental field like the Higgs field, is non-spatial and thus describes its "height" in the corresponding field space.

3.8 Local Coordinate Systems

In the previous section we discussed that we can think of a field as the object that glues the corresponding field space to spacetime. Moreover, we learned that there is a copy of the basic field space (e.g. $\mathbb{R}$) above each spacetime point. The total field space consists of these individual basic field spaces.

The mantra we will focus on in this section is that Nature doesn't care about how we describe her. While this is a truism, we will see in a moment that there is a lot to be learned from it.

For our field space construction, it implies that it doesn't matter which coordinate system we use to describe it. Let's focus on a scalar field. The corresponding basic field space is simply the set of all real numbers which when taken together yield the real line $\mathbb{R}$. Our mantra tells us that nothing should depend on where we put the origin of our coordinate system that we use to describe the field values. If we move the origin of our coordinate system, the field values are shifted. For example, we can imagine that for one choice of coordinate system we find

$$\phi(a_\mu) = 8.19\,, \quad \phi(b_\mu) = 1.21\,, \quad \phi(c_\mu) = 3.56\,, \quad \dots\,. \tag{3.84}$$

We then move the origin of the coordinate system, which implies $\phi \to \phi' = \phi + 5$. After the shift, we find

$$\phi'(a_\mu) = 13.19\,, \quad \phi'(b_\mu) = 6.21\,, \quad \phi'(c_\mu) = 8.56\,, \quad \dots\,. \tag{3.85}$$

It shouldn't make any difference whether we use ϕ or ϕ' to describe a given system since they describe the same field in different coordinate systems.[76]

[76] If this seems strange to you, it may be helpful to think about the most famous scalar field, the electric potential. The only thing that matters in electrodynamics are potential differences. Therefore, we can always shift the electric potential without changing anything.

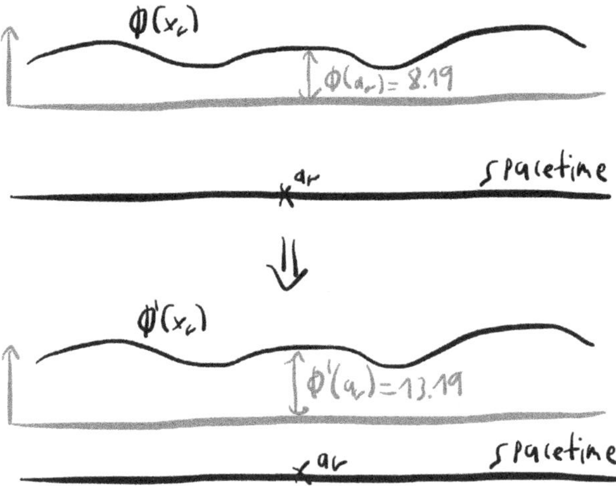

While you may not be impressed by our discussion in this section so far, I promise that things are about to get really interesting.

If it is indeed true that Nature doesn't care about how we describe her, it should also be possible to shift the coordinate system that we use for individual basic field spaces. In the example above, we shifted the origins of the coordinate systems for all copies of the basic field space $\mathbb{R}$ by exactly the same amount. In technical terms, we call this a *global* shift.

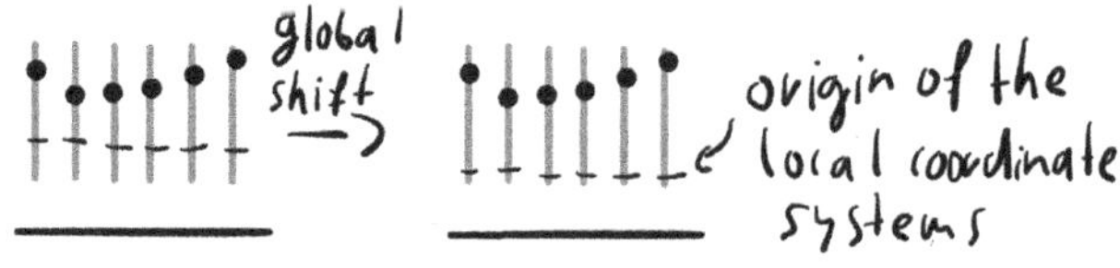

But *local* shifts should be equally allowed.

This is indeed the case. It's just a matter of mathematical ingenuity. In particular, all we need before we can use arbitrarily chosen local coordinate systems is some sort of bookkeeper that keeps track of how the coordinate systems at different locations are related. Among mathematicians, these bookkeepers are known as **connections**.

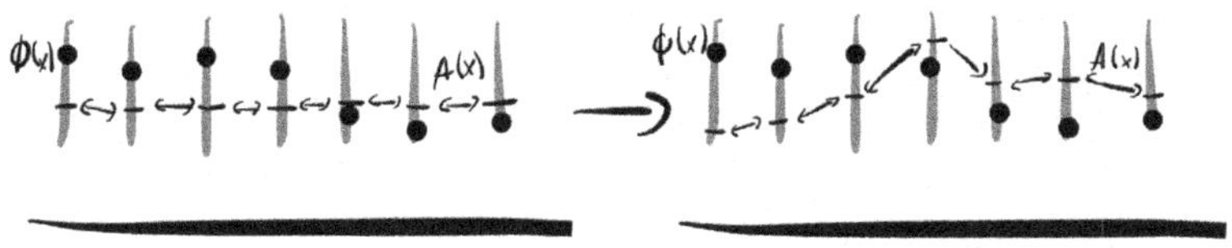

To understand how connections work, we will assume for a moment that spacetime is discrete and two-dimensional. This will make it much easier to visualize what is going on. In this case, we need at each spacetime point $\vec{n}$ two bookkeepers $A_{\vec{n},i}$ ($i \in \{1,2\}$) which tells us how the coordinate system of the field space at this point is related to its neighbors in the two basis directions. We *define* that $A_{\vec{n},1}$ encodes how much the origin of the coordinate system at $\vec{n}$ is shifted relative to the origin of the coordinate system at $\vec{n}+\vec{e}_1$, where $\vec{e}_1$ is a basis vector. Analogously, $A_{\vec{n},2}$ encodes the relative shift between the coordinates systems at $\vec{n}$ and $\vec{n}+\vec{e}_2$.

Let's assume that we have some field value $\phi(\vec{n})$ at one location $\vec{n}$ and want to compare it to the field value $\phi(\vec{n}+\vec{e}_1)$ at the neighboring location $\vec{n}+\vec{e}_1$. The correct way to compare them is:

$$d_1(\vec{n}) = \phi(\vec{n}) - \phi(\vec{n}+\vec{e}_1) - A_{\vec{n},1}\,. \tag{3.86}$$

If we compared the field values $\phi(\vec{n})$ and $\phi(\vec{n}+\vec{e}_1)$ directly without $A_{\vec{n},1}$, we couldn't be sure whether or not the difference we find is simply the result of a differently chosen coordinate system. The additional term $-A_{\vec{n},1}$ subtracts the part of the total difference that only results from a different choice of coordinate system. If we use exactly the same coordinate system at $\vec{n}$ and $\vec{n}+\vec{e}_1$ we have $A_{\vec{n},1} = 0$.

Analogously, we can compare the field value at $\vec{n}$ with the field value at $\vec{n}+\vec{e}_2$:

$$d_2(\vec{n}) = \phi(\vec{n}) - \phi(\vec{n}+\vec{e}_2) - A_{\vec{n},2}\,. \tag{3.87}$$

In summary,

$$d_i(\vec{n}) = \phi(\vec{n}) - \phi(\vec{n}+\vec{e}_i) - A_{\vec{n},i}\,. \tag{3.88}$$

From a slightly different perspective, we can therefore say that a bookkeeper $A_{\vec{n},i}$ allows us to "transport" a given field value to a neighboring location such that we can compare the field values in the same coordinate system. For example, $\phi(\vec{n}) - A_{\vec{n},1}$ yields the field value that we would get if $\phi(\vec{n})$ lived in the same coordinate system as $\phi(\vec{n}+\vec{e}_1)$. This is why $A_{\vec{n},i}$ is usually called a connection.

With this in mind, let's return to our usual continuous spacetime. In mathematical terms, we can switch from a discrete description to a continuous description by taking the continuum limit.

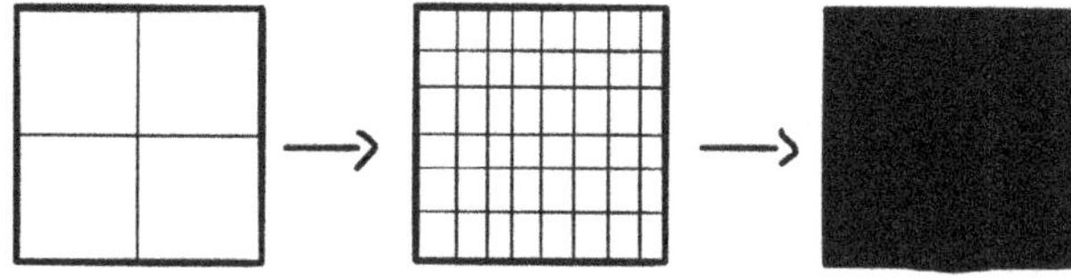

In this limit, Eq. 3.88 becomes[77]

[77] This follows because $\phi(\vec{n}) - \phi(\vec{n} + \vec{e}_i)$ yields the difference quotient in the continuum limit.

$$D_i(\vec{x}) = \partial_i\phi - A_i(\vec{x}), \tag{3.89}$$

where ∂_i denotes the partial derivative in the $\vec{e}_i$ direction. Moreover, if we then switch from two dimensions to four dimensions, we find

$$D_\mu(x_\mu) = \partial_\mu\phi - A_\mu(x_\mu)\,. \tag{3.90}$$

Connections are essential because we need to compare the field values at neighboring points whenever we calculate derivatives.

This follows from the definition of a derivative in terms of a difference quotient:

$$\partial_x f(x) \equiv \lim_{\epsilon \to 0} \frac{(f(x+\epsilon) - f(x))}{\epsilon}. \qquad (3.91)$$

Therefore, what Eq. 3.90 is really telling us is that if we want the freedom to choose arbitrary local coordinate systems, we need to use the **covariant derivative**

$$\boxed{D_\mu(x_\mu) = \partial_\mu - A_\mu(x_\mu)} \qquad (3.92)$$

instead of the usual derivative ∂_μ. This is necessary because the usual derivative ∂_μ compares the field values directly without taking into account that differences can occur as a result of differently chosen local coordinate systems. If we use ∂_μ our formulas only remain valid as long as we use the same conventions for the local coordinate systems everywhere.

In summary, while a field ϕ glues the corresponding field space to spacetime, a connection A_μ glues the individual copies of the basic field space together.

This may not seem like a big deal. Of course, it's nice to write our equations in a way that remains valid no matter how we choose our coordinate system. But is it really worth all the additional complications it brings with it?

In short, yes. In the following section we will discuss why.

3.9 Gauge Fields

A first key idea is that bookkeepers can be "imperfect". To understand what this means, let's go back again to our discrete two-dimensional description.

We start with one specific field value $\phi(\vec{n})$ at a given location $\vec{n}$. We can then use the connection $A_{\vec{n},1}$ to transport the field value into the coordinate system of the field space at the neighboring point $\vec{n}+\vec{e}_1$:

$$\phi^{\vec{n}+\vec{e}_1}(\vec{n}) \equiv \phi(\vec{n}) - A_{\vec{n},1} . \tag{3.93}$$

Moreover, we can use $A_{\vec{n},1}$ to translate a field value at $\vec{n}+\vec{e}_1$ into the coordinate system at $\vec{n}$:

$$\phi^{\vec{n}}(\vec{n}+\vec{e}_1) \equiv \phi(\vec{n}+\vec{e}_1) + A_{\vec{n},1} . \tag{3.94}$$

We can again use $A_{\vec{n},1}$ and only need to use a different sign, because this bookkeeper encodes the difference in the definitions of the two coordinate systems which is, of course, equal irrespective of if we look at it from the "right" or the "left".

This implies that if we move a field value back and forth, we find the value we started with again:

$$\phi(\vec{n}) \to \phi(\vec{n}) - A_{\vec{n},1} \to (\phi(\vec{n}) - A_{\vec{n},1}) + A_{\vec{n},1} = \phi(\vec{n}) \tag{3.95}$$

This is not surprising since there is only one bookkeeper $A_{\vec{n},1}$ involved.

The situation gets more interesting if we transport a field value $\phi(\vec{n})$ in a loop that involves different bookkeepers. For example, let's consider the following loop:

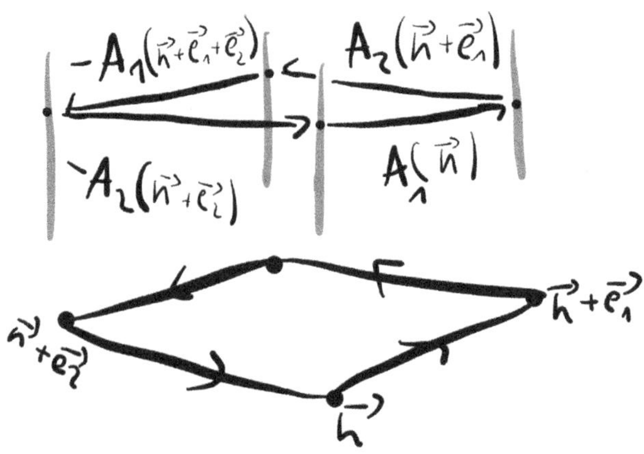

As we move along the loop, the field value $\phi(\vec{n})$ changes as follows:

$$
\begin{aligned}
\phi(\vec{n}) &\to \phi(\vec{n}) - A_{\vec{n},1} \\
&\to (\phi(\vec{n}) - A_{\vec{n},1}) - A_{\vec{n}+\vec{e}_1,2} \\
&\to \Big((\phi(\vec{n}) - A_{\vec{n},1}) - A_{\vec{n}+\vec{e}_1,2}\Big) + A_{\vec{n}+\vec{e}_2,1} \\
&\to \left(\Big((\phi(\vec{n}) - A_{\vec{n},1}) - A_{\vec{n}+\vec{e}_1,2}\Big) + A_{\vec{n}+\vec{e}_2,1}\right) + A_{\vec{n},2} \equiv \tilde{\phi}(\vec{n}) \,.
\end{aligned}
\tag{3.96}
$$

We can rearrange the terms here as follows:

$$
\begin{aligned}
\tilde{\phi}(\vec{n}) &\equiv \phi(\vec{n}) - A_{\vec{n}+\vec{e}_1,2} + A_{\vec{n},2} + A_{\vec{n}+\vec{e}_2,1} - A_{\vec{n},1} \\
&= \tilde{\phi}(\vec{n}) - \Big((A_{\vec{n}+\vec{e}_1,2} - A_{\vec{n},2}) - (A_{\vec{n}+\vec{e}_2,1} - A_{\vec{n},1})\Big) \,.
\end{aligned}
\tag{3.97}
$$

If the exchange rates are perfect, we have

$$
\tilde{\phi}(\vec{n}) = \phi(\vec{n}) \,. \tag{3.98}
$$

By looking at Eq. 3.97, we can conclude that this implies

$$
F_{12}(\vec{n}) \equiv (A_{\vec{n}+\vec{e}_1,2} - A_{\vec{n},2}) - (A_{\vec{n}+\vec{e}_2,1} - A_{\vec{n},1}) = 0 \,. \tag{3.99}
$$

However, if there is some imperfection in the exchange rates, it's possible that we end up with a different field value after the loop ($\tilde{\phi}(\vec{n}) \neq \phi(\vec{n})$). This implies $F_{12}(\vec{n}) \neq 0$.

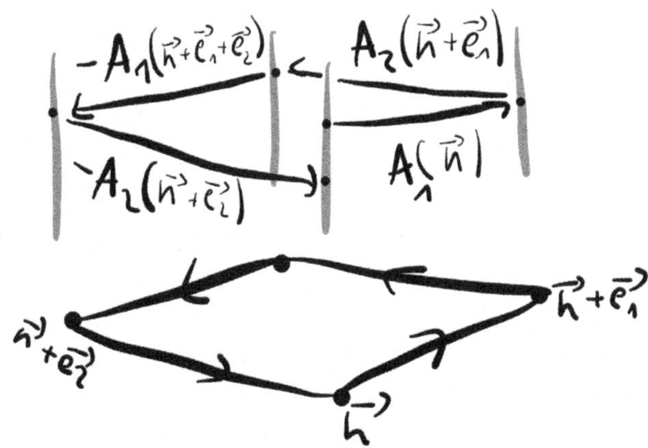

Therefore, the quantity $F_{12}(\vec{n})$ is a measure of the imperfection. Moreover, analogously we can define the quantities $F_{12}(\vec{n}), F_{11}(\vec{n}), F_{21}(\vec{n}), F_{22}(\vec{n})$ which correspond to different loops. Thus we define in more general terms

$$F_{ij}(\vec{n}) \equiv (A_{\vec{n}+\vec{e}_i,j} - A_{\vec{n},j}) - (A_{\vec{n}+\vec{e}_j,i} - A_{\vec{n},i}) . \tag{3.100}$$

But take note that $F_{11}(\vec{n})$ and $F_{22}(\vec{n})$ are necessarily zero since they involve the same exchange rates twice in opposite directions:

$$\begin{aligned} F_{11}(\vec{n}) &\equiv (A_{\vec{n}+\vec{e}_1,1} - A_{\vec{n},1}) - (A_{\vec{n}+\vec{e}_1,1} - A_{\vec{n},1}) \\ &= 0 . \end{aligned} \tag{3.101}$$

Moreover, we have $F_{12}(\vec{n}) = -F_{21}(\vec{n})$. In words, this follows because $F_{21}(\vec{n})$ encodes the difference in the field value if we move around the loop discussed above in the opposite direction. Hence, if we move counterclockwise ($F_{12}(\vec{n}) > 0$) and end up with a larger field value, we will get a smaller field value if we move in the same loop clockwise. Since the involved exchange rates are the same, the total change in the field value is equal and only the sign is different.

If we switch again to a continuous spacetime, the corresponding quantities read[78]

$$F_{ij}(\vec{x}) \equiv \partial_i A_j(\vec{x}) - \partial_j A_i(\vec{x}) . \tag{3.102}$$

Moreover, in a four-dimensional continuous spacetime, we have

$$\boxed{F_{\mu\nu}(x_\mu) \equiv \partial_\mu A_\nu(x_\mu) - \partial_\nu A_\mu(x_\mu) .} \tag{3.103}$$

[78] This follows because $A_{\vec{n}+\vec{e}_i,j} - A_{\vec{n},j}$ becomes the partial derivative of the j-component in the $\vec{e}_i$ direction in the continuum limit. Analogously, $A_{\vec{n}+\vec{e}_j,i} - A_{\vec{n},i}$ becomes the partial derivative of the i-component in the $\vec{e}_j$ direction.

You might rightfully wonder how in the world there can be an imperfection in the bookkeepers. Doesn't this simply mean that there is something wrong with our description?

There is a mathematical and a physical answer to this question. In both cases the conclusion is that it's perfectly reasonable to consider scenarios in which $F_{\mu\nu}(x_\mu) \neq 0$.

Let's start with a mathematical answer. Geometrically, the quantities $F_{\mu\nu}(x_\mu)$ are a measure of the **curvature** of the space under consideration. The canonical example is a vector that is transported along a loop on a sphere. We can imagine that we walk along such a loop while holding the vector in our hands. At each step we make sure that the vector's orientation relative to us stays as it is.[79] But if we compare the orientation of the vector at the end of the loop with its orientation at the beginning, we find that it's different. This is how we can find out if we are moving around on a curved surface.

[79] In mathematical terms, this means that we parallel transport the vector.

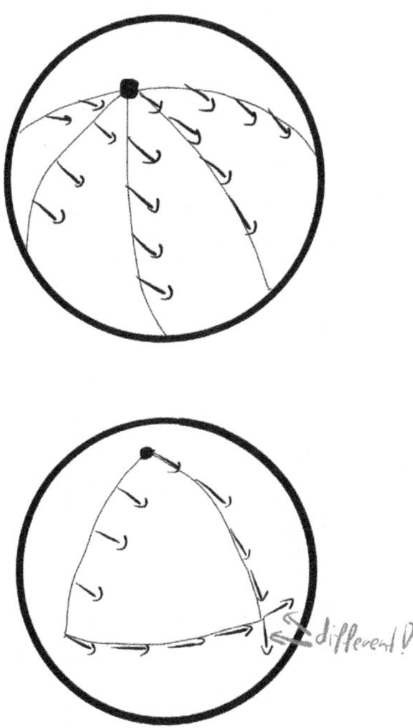

In field theory, we are talking, for example, about the curvature of the field space of a scalar field. Instead of the orientation of a vector, it's the field value itself that is different after the loop. From a slightly different perspective, we can say that $F_{\mu\nu}(x_\mu) \neq 0$ describes the fact that the individual basic field spaces are non-trivially glued together.

So mathematically it can make sense to consider scenarios in which $F_{\mu\nu}(x_\mu) \neq 0$. However, as usual, mathematics alone cannot tell us whether or not Nature makes use of this possibility.

Thus, let's talk about a physical reason to consider curved field spaces.

In modern physics, the connections A_μ are not just mathematical bookkeepers but physical actors that we call gauge fields.

To understand how this comes about recall how we started. In the previous section, we treated the connections A_μ as purely mathematical tools that allow us to use arbitrary local coordinate systems. In this case, they have no influence on anything.

Then we considered the possibility that $F_{\mu\nu}(x_\mu) \neq 0$. If this is the case, the behavior of the scalar field ϕ is directly affected. We can imagine that the connections provide a background structure in front of which all the action happens. If $F_{\mu\nu}(x_\mu) \neq 0$ this background is non-trivial and thus the dynamics of the system in question are affected.

Thirdly, we can promote a connection A_μ to a fully-fledged physical actor by allowing that it evolves dynamically. In practical terms this means that we write down an equation of motion that describes how the connections A_μ evolve in time. At this stage we can study connections A_μ as completely independent objects. For example, we can start with some given configuration, i.e. values of A_μ at all locations x_μ, and then study how it involves in time.

This three-step promotion is summarized in the following diagram:

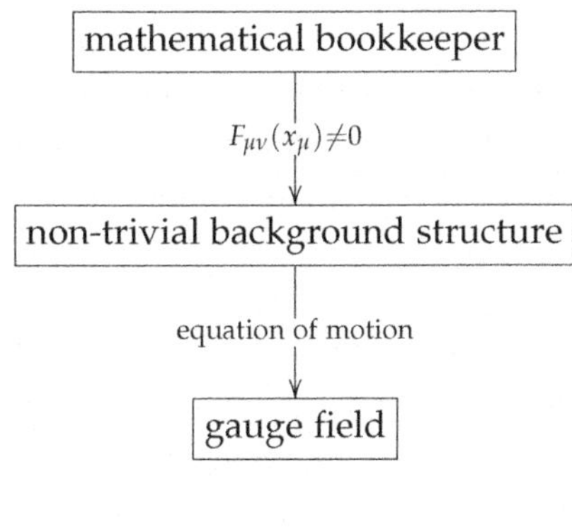

Let's make this a bit more concrete. It turns out that field spaces are automatically curved through the presence of non-zero field values.[80] Moreover, the behavior of a scalar field is directly influenced by the structure of the corresponding field space.[81]

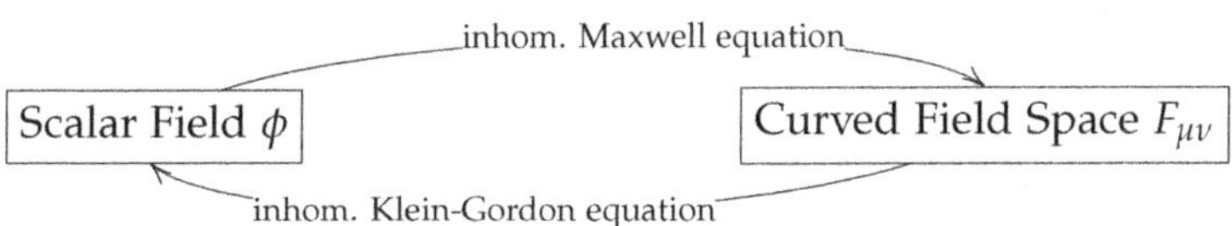

Completely analogously, we have for a spinor field[82]

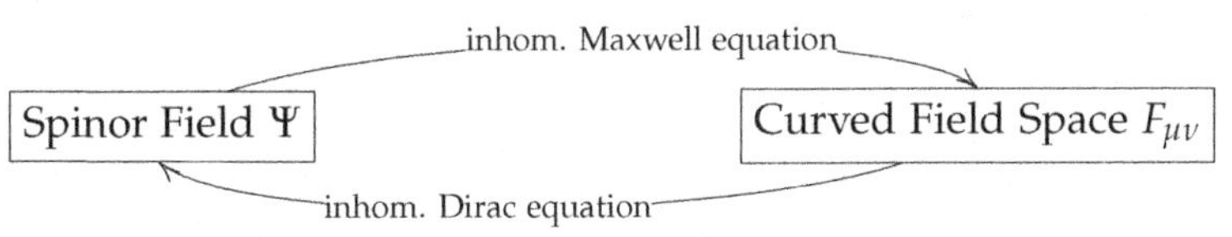

This interplay is the key idea at the heart of modern physics.

Lastly, take note that gauge fields are vector fields. We can see this, for example, because the connection A_μ carries a spacetime

[80] This is described by the famous inhomogeneous Maxwell equation

$$\partial^\mu F_{\mu\nu} = J_\nu(\phi)\,,$$

where $J_\nu(\phi)$ depends on the field strength of the scalar field ϕ. We will discuss the inhomogeneous Maxwel equation, the current $J_\nu(\phi)$ and its implications in detail in Section 6.4.

[81] This is described by the inhomogeneous Klein-Gordon equation

$$(D_\mu D^\mu + m^2)\phi = 0\,,$$

where D_μ is the covariant derivative

$$D_\mu = \partial_\mu - ieA_\mu\,.$$

We will discuss this further in Section 6.4.

[82] Take note that in this case the inhomogeneous Maxwell equation reads

$$\partial^\mu F_{\mu\nu} = J_\nu(\Psi)\,,$$

where the inhomogeneity on the right-hand side now depends on the spinor field Ψ.

index μ. A connection keeps track of how the coordinate systems in a field space change if we move around in spacetime. For example, $A_3(x_\mu)$ encodes information about how the coordinate system in field space changes if we move from x_μ in the z-direction. Hence, A_μ necessarily contains information about directions in spacetime and is thus a vector field.

However, as should be clear from the discussion in the previous two sections, gauge fields are a very special kind of vector field. We will discuss the differences between a general vector field and a gauge field in Section 5.2.4 in more detail.

So far, we've only talked about the main actors in quantum field theory. Next, we will make them dance.

4

The Lagrangian Formalism

In the next chapter, we will talk about the equations that describe how the various kinds of fields behave. We will start with those equations that describe the behavior of free fields when left alone. Afterwards, we will discuss how we can take the fact that different fields often influence each other into account.

But before we talk about equations, we will talk about one mathematical object, called the action, that is even more fundamental.[1] We will discuss the main ideas in the context of particle theory since this makes it easier to build some intuition. Afterwards, we will talk about the things that we need to modify if we want to use the same ideas in field theory.

[1] At this point, you might want to have a second look at the roadmap on page 35 to understand how the concepts discussed in this chapter fit into the bigger picture.

Three key ideas at the heart of modern physics are[2]

[2] You can find a much more detailed discussion of the Lagrangian formalism and all related notions in my book:

Jakob Schwichtenberg. *No-Nonsense Classical Mechanics : a student-friendly introduction.* No-Nonsense Books, Karlsruhe, Germany, 2019b. ISBN 9781096195382

1. The dynamics within a physical system can be described by using a mathematical object called the action functional. (For different systems there are different action functionals.)
2. We can derive the action functional for a given system using

a small number of general principles.

3. The correct path (in configuration space) that describes how a system evolves between two points in time is an extremum of the action. By using this idea, we can derive the correct equations of motion.

Let's unpack these statements.

The action functional is, as the name suggests, not a function. A function eats a number x and spits out another number $f(x)$:

In contrast, a functional eats a *function* $f(x)$ and spits out a number $F[f(x)]$:

A functional is the appropriate tool here because we want a mathematical object that tells us how a physical system evolves in time. In somewhat abstract terms, we can imagine that each possible configuration our system can be in represents a point in a mathematical space that we call configuration space.[3] A path in configuration space corresponds to a specific sequence of configurations.

Our task is to figure out the correct path in configuration space that accurately describes how our system evolves in time. Since a path in configuration space is necessarily a function of t, the mathematical tool we are looking for is a functional.

The key idea then is that there is a specific functional that singles out the correct path because it assigns either a minimum or maximum value to it.[4]

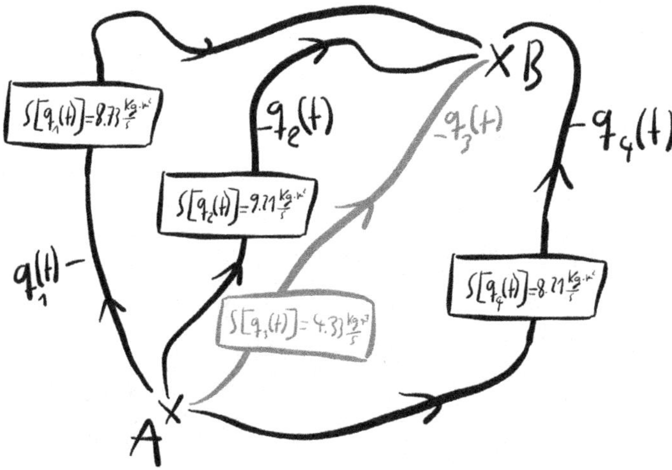

In other words, just as a function can have a minimum, a functional can have a minimum too. The only difference is that a function has a minimum at a particular location x, while a functional spits out its minimum value for a specific function $f(x)$ (or path in this context).

Therefore, if we are successful in writing down such a functional, our only task left is to use a few tricks to find the path that yields the minimum (or maximum) value when put into the functional. Formulated differently, we then only need to per-

[3] In a particle theory, a point in configuration space corresponds to a specific location for each particle. The object that we use to describe a point in configuration space consists of all the location vectors stacked together: $\vec{q} = (\vec{a}, \vec{b}, \vec{c}, \ldots)^T$, where $\vec{a}$ points to the location of the first object, $\vec{b}$ points to the location of the second object and so on. In particular, this implies that for N objects moving freely in our system, configuration space is $3N$-dimensional. However, to unclutter the notation we will usually denote a path in configuration space simply by $q(t)$. We will discuss below how this construction needs to be modified for a field theory.

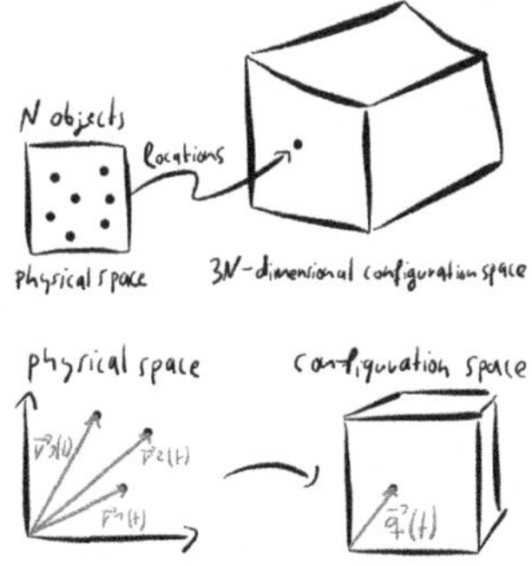

[4] In some situations, saddle points of the action also play an important role. This is analogous to how, if we search for the extrema of a function by searching for points for which the first derivative vanishes, we sometimes also find a saddle point.

form the mathematical steps required to find the extremum of the functional.

Now, how can we write down the correct functional for a given system?

The functional we are looking for is the integral over a function L, called the Lagrangian:

$$S[q(t)] = \int dt \, L(q(t), \dot{q}(t), t) \,. \tag{4.1}$$

The action functional $S[q(t)]$ assigns a number to each path $q(t)$:

In contrast, the Lagrangian $L(q(t), \dot{q}(t), t)$ is a function and therefore yields a number at any moment in time. Since an integral is basically just a finely-grained sum, Eq. 4.1 means that we collect all the numbers the Lagrangian yields between two given moments in time and this yields the total action of the path in question:

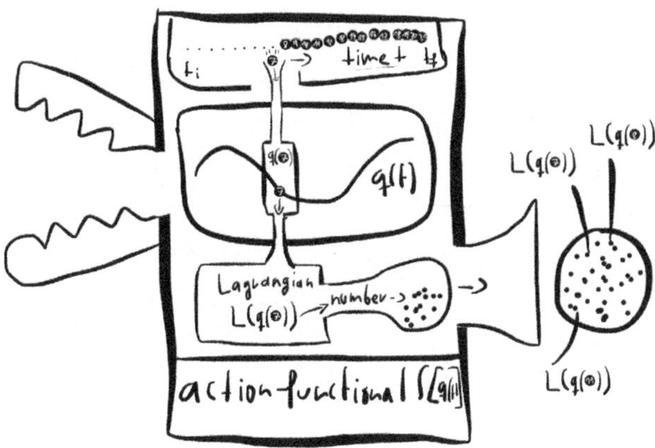

So our real task is to write down the correct Lagrangian for a given system since the action is simply the integral over the Lagrangian.

The idea that allows us to write down the correct Lagrangian for a given system is that the dynamics of the system is governed by symmetry principles. A symmetry, in general, is a transformation that leaves a system unchanged. For example, if a system is unchanged by rotations, we say it's rotationally symmetric. We will discuss this in more detail in Chapter 17.2. In this first part of the book we will simply assume that someone hands us the correct Lagrangians. This will allow us to become somewhat familiar with the main ideas before we dive into more detailed matters like the origin of Lagrangians.[5]

[5] If we consider a concrete system, we can certainly guess the correct Lagrangian by brute force if we compare the corresponding predictions with what we observe in experiments. But a certainly much more beautiful approach is to derive Lagrangians using symmetries and similar guiding principles.

The final puzzle piece we need to talk about is how a Lagrangian is connected to the equation that describes a given system.

4.1 The Euler-Lagrange Equation

As soon as someone hands you a Lagrangian, you can immediately calculate the corresponding equation of motion by plugging the Lagrangian into the **Euler-Lagrange equation**:

$$\boxed{\frac{\partial L}{\partial q} - \frac{d}{dt}\left(\frac{\partial L}{\partial \dot{q}}\right) = 0} \tag{4.2}$$

We can derive the Euler-Lagrange equation by using the idea that the correct path is a minimum of the action.[6] Before we can understand this derivation, we need to take a step back and talk about a smart idea that allows us to calculate the minima of a functional.[7]

[6] For convenience, here and in the following discussion, we will restrict ourselves to minima although exactly the same arguments apply for maxima and saddle points.

[7] The following two sections are an excerpt from my book No-Nonsense Classical Mechanics. So if you've already read this book (or any other book that explains the main ideas behind the derivation of the Euler-Lagrange equation), feel free to jump directly to Section 4.2.

4.1.1 Intermezzo: Variational Calculus

For an ordinary function $f(x)$, we can find the minimum by calculating the zeroes of its derivative:

$$\frac{df(x)}{dx} \stackrel{!}{=} 0\,. \tag{4.3}$$

For example, for $f(x) = 3x^2 + x$, we calculate $\frac{df(x)}{dx} = 6x + 1$ and then find

$$\begin{aligned} 6x + 1 &\stackrel{!}{=} 0 && \text{(condition in Eq. 4.3)} \\ \therefore \quad x &= \frac{-1}{6}\,. \end{aligned} \tag{4.4}$$

And indeed, a minimum of our function $f(x)$ is located at $x = \frac{-1}{6}$.

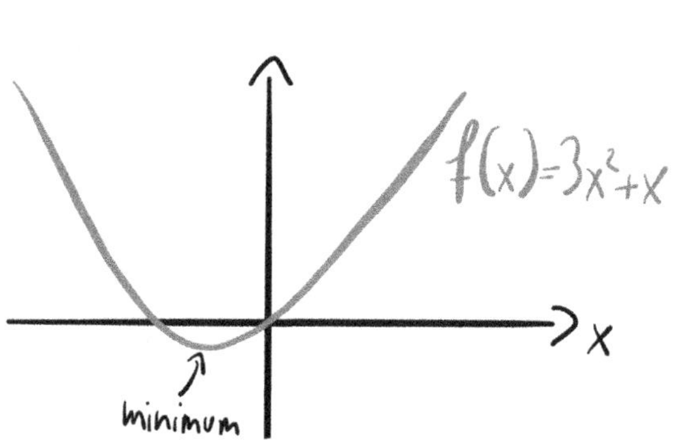

This method works because the derivative tells us something about the slope of $f(x)$ and the slope at a minimum is necessarily zero.

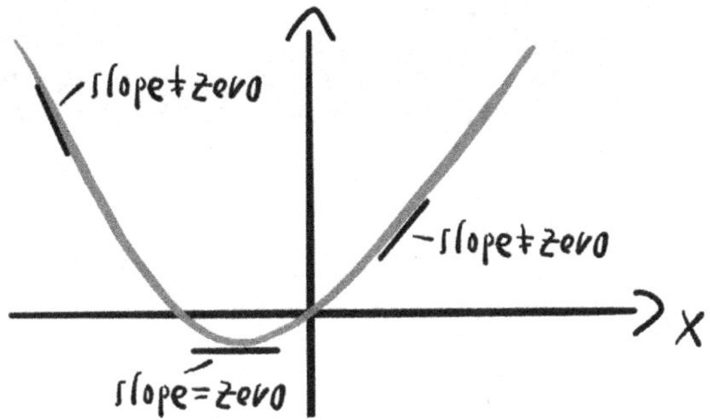

Now the bad news is that this simple method does not work for functionals like the action $S[q(t)]$. Instead, we need a new method to calculate the minimum of a functional.

To understand this alternative method, we need to take a step back and answer the question: what exactly characterizes a minimum?

Let's imagine that we have a function which describes the height of some terrain and want to find out where exactly the terrain height is a minimum.

The key observation is that if we stand at the minimum and look around, we will notice that it's going upward in all directions. This is necessarily the case because otherwise the point we are standing at wouldn't be a minimum otherwise.

This means that a minimum is characterized by its neighborhood. If all neighboring points lie higher, the point in question is a minimum.[8]

[8] Take note that this criterion only tells us that we are dealing with a *local* minimum. There can be much deeper minima in some other region.

Let's use this idea to once more find the minimum of the function $f(x) = 3x^2 + x$ that we have already considered above.[9]

[9] We do this to demonstrate how the method works. In the following section, we will use it to derive the minimum of the action functional.

We now pick one specific location $x = a$ and start investigating its neighborhood $a \to a + \epsilon$, where ϵ is an infinitesimally small (positive or negative) number. In general, we call ϵ a **variation**.

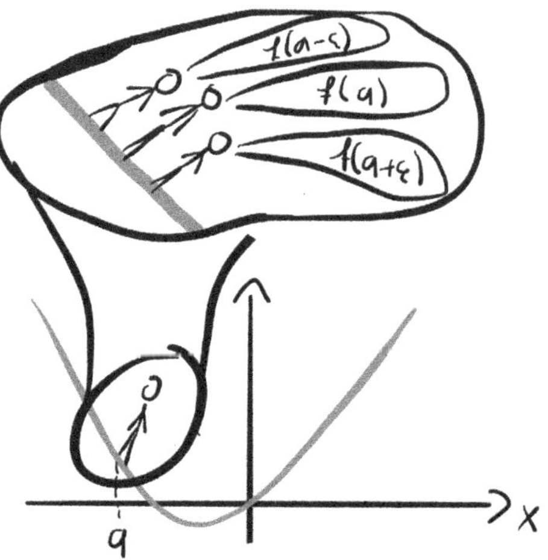

Putting this into the function yields

$$\begin{aligned} f(a+\epsilon) &= 3(a+\epsilon)^2 + (a+\epsilon) \\ &= 3(a^2 + 2a\epsilon + \epsilon^2) + a + \epsilon. \end{aligned} \tag{4.5}$$

If the location a is a minimum, we can't get lower by going in any direction ϵ. Mathematically, this implies:[10]

> All terms first order in ϵ must vanish.

Otherwise, for a negative ϵ the function value $f(a+\epsilon)$ would be smaller than $f(a)$ and therefore, a wouldn't be a minimum. To understand this, take note that if ϵ is an infinitesimally small number, we have $|\epsilon^2| \ll |\epsilon|$. This is true for any small number, e.g., $0.1^2 = 0.01 \ll 0.1$. Therefore, the negative shift due to a negative ϵ cannot be compensated by quadratic or even higher order terms in ϵ.

If we collect all terms linear in ϵ and demand that they vanish,

$$3 \cdot 2a\epsilon + \epsilon \stackrel{!}{=} 0$$

$$\curvearrowright \quad \text{cancel } \epsilon$$

$$6a + 1 \stackrel{!}{=} 0,$$

we find that

$$a = \frac{-1}{6}. \tag{4.6}$$

This specific location has exactly the property we are looking for (in its neighborhood all first order variations in its neighborhood vanish and, therefore, it goes upwards in all directions) and we can conclude that we've found a minimum.

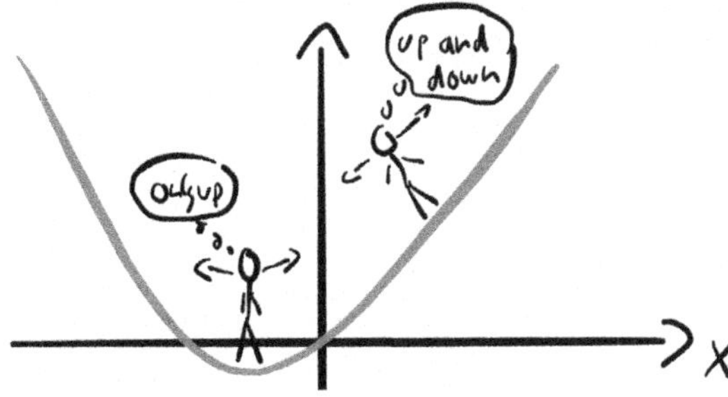

Of course, the result here is exactly equal to what we calculated using the standard method (Eq. 4.4). Thus, what we've discovered for ordinary functions is just another way of reaching the

[10] First order terms are all terms containing ϵ but not ϵ^2, ϵ^3, etc.

same conclusion. However, the variational method of finding minima can also be applied to functionals like the action $S[q(t)]$, not just functions. Take note that for functionals, our goal isn't to find a *location* like a which is the minimum of a function but is instead to find a *function* $q(t)$ which is the minimum of a functional. And this is what we will talk about in the next section.

But first, let's summarize the main lessons learned in this section.

▷ Minima are characterized by their neighborhood. If we are dealing with a minimum, it has to go upward everywhere in its neighborhood.

▷ Mathematically, this means that we can find minima by making a specific choice $x = a$ and then varying it $a \to a + \epsilon$. If a is a minimum, all first order variations ϵ must vanish.

▷ Through this condition, we can find locations a which are minima.

4.1.2 Deriving the Euler-Lagrange Equation

We learned above that the main idea of the Lagrangian formalism is that the path of least action in configuration space correctly describes how a given system evolves. Moreover, the **action functional**[11]

$$S[q(t)] \equiv \int_{t_i}^{t_f} dt L\Big(q(t), \dot{q}(t)\Big) \tag{4.7}$$

is a mathematical object which assigns a number to each possible path $q(t)$ between two fixed configurations $(q_i(t_i), q_f(t_f))$.[12]

Therefore, our task is to find a method which allows us to calculate the path $q_{\mathrm{m}}(t)$ for which the action functional is a minimum. This path $q_{\mathrm{m}}(t)$ correctly describes the evolution of our system. Luckily, we can derive a method which allows us to

[11] The Lagrangian is in general a function of the path $q(t)$ and its velocity $\dot{q}$ but not of higher derivatives like $\ddot{q}$, i.e., it does not depend on the acceleration.

[12] As before, we write $q(t)$ instead of $q^A(t)$, etc., to unclutter the notation. In other words, we use $q(t)$ and $\dot{q}(t)$ as a convenient notation for a path and the velocity in the possibly high-dimensional configuration space.

find $q_{\rm m}(t)$ for any system by repeating everything that we did in the previous section.

Again, we start with a concrete choice $q(t)$ and consider small variations around this specific path

$$q(t) \to q(t) + \epsilon(t)\,, \tag{4.8}$$

where ϵ is again an infinitesimally small variation.

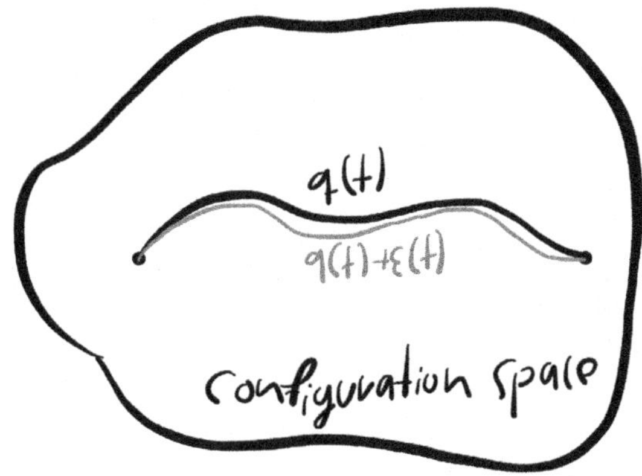

Moreover, since the Lagrangian not only depends on $q(t)$ but also on the velocity $\dot{q}(t)$, we need to consider velocity variations, too:

$$\dot{q}(t) \to \dot{q}(t) + \dot{\epsilon}(t)\,. \tag{4.9}$$

We consider variations between two *fixed* configurations $(q_i(t_i),$ $q_f(t_f))$. Therefore, the variation ϵ has to vanish at t_i and t_f:

$$0 = \epsilon(t_i) = \epsilon(t_f)\,. \tag{4.10}$$

Analogously to what we did in the previous section, we use these variations explicitly

$$S = \int_{t_i}^{t_f} dt L\Big(q(t) + \epsilon(t), \dot{q}(t) + \dot{\epsilon}(t)\Big)\,. \tag{4.11}$$

The key idea is again that our specific path $q(t)$ is a minimum of the action if all terms that are first order in ϵ vanish. This yields a condition which allows us to identify the correct path

$q(t)$ that is a minimum of the action analogously to how in the previous section we were able to find the location for which a given function is a minimum.

We could do this for each possible Lagrangian L individually. But since this is quite cumbersome, it makes sense to try to move forward with a general Lagrangian. We can do this by using the Taylor expansion[13]

$$L(q+\epsilon,\dot{q}+\dot{\epsilon}) = L(q,\dot{q}) + \epsilon\frac{\partial L}{\partial q} + \dot{\epsilon}\frac{\partial L}{\partial \dot{q}} + \ldots\,, \tag{4.12}$$

where the dots indicate higher order terms in the expansion. Putting this Taylor expansion of the Lagrangian into the action (Eq. 4.11) yields

$$\begin{aligned} S &= \int_{t_i}^{t_f} dt L\Big(q(t)+\epsilon(t), \dot{q}(t)+\dot{\epsilon}(t)\Big) \\ &\quad \text{Taylor expansion} \\ &= \int_{t_i}^{t_f} dt \Big(L(q,\dot{q}) + \epsilon\frac{\partial L}{\partial q} + \dot{\epsilon}\frac{\partial L}{\partial \dot{q}} + \ldots\Big)\,. \end{aligned}$$

All additional terms in the Taylor expansion are proportional to ϵ^2, $\dot{\epsilon}^2$ or even higher powers. Therefore, we already have everything we need to use our idea that minima are characterized by vanishing *first order* variations.

So again, we collect all terms first order in the variations and demand that they vanish:

$$\int_{t_i}^{t_f} dt \left[\epsilon\frac{\partial L}{\partial q} + \dot{\epsilon}\frac{\partial L}{\partial \dot{q}}\right] \stackrel{!}{=} 0. \tag{4.13}$$

The path $q(t)$ for which this is true is a minimum of the action.

The key idea is that we can rewrite this condition by using a few mathematical tricks and derive a specific condition for the function $q(t)$ this way.[14] This condition is the equation of motion which allows us to predict how systems evolve in general.

So, first of all, we integrate the second term on the right-hand

[13] The Taylor expansion tells us that the value of a function at a neighboring point is given approximately by the value of the function at the original point plus the rate of change times the distance we are going. For a function which only depends on one variable $f = f(x)$, this means that its value at the point $x+\epsilon$ is approximately

$$f(x+\epsilon) \approx f(x) + \epsilon\frac{\partial f}{\partial x}\,.$$

If we are dealing with a function which depends on multiple variables $g = g(x,y)$, we need to take the rate of change in all directions into account as we move from our original point to the new point

$$g(x+\epsilon, y+\tilde{\epsilon}) \approx g(x,y) + \epsilon\frac{\partial g}{\partial x} + \tilde{\epsilon}\frac{\partial g}{\partial y}\,.$$

Moreover, take note that to unclutter the notation, we do not write the arguments of $x = x(t)$, $\epsilon = \epsilon(t)$, etc., explicitly.

[14] In particular, we can get rid of the nasty integral.

side by parts

$$\int_{t_i}^{t_f} dt\, \dot{\epsilon}\frac{\partial L}{\partial \dot{q}} = \int_{t_i}^{t_f} dt \left(\frac{d}{dt}\epsilon\right)\frac{\partial L}{\partial \dot{q}}$$
$$= \epsilon\frac{\partial L}{\partial \dot{q}}\bigg|_{t_i}^{t_f} - \int_{t_i}^{t_f} dt\, \epsilon\frac{d}{dt}\left(\frac{\partial L}{\partial \dot{q}}\right). \quad (4.14)$$

Since the variation $\epsilon(t)$ vanishes for $t = t_i$ and $t = t_f$ (Eq. 4.10), the first term on the right-hand side in Eq. 4.14 vanishes:

$$\epsilon\frac{\partial L}{\partial \dot{q}}\bigg|_{t_i}^{t_f} = 0. \quad (4.15)$$

Therefore, we can write Eq. 4.13 as

$$\int_{t_i}^{t_f} dt \left[\epsilon\frac{\partial L}{\partial q} + \dot{\epsilon}\frac{\partial L}{\partial \dot{q}}\right] \stackrel{!}{=} 0$$

↷ Eq. 4.14 and Eq. 4.15

$$\int_{t_i}^{t_f} dt \left[\epsilon\frac{\partial L}{\partial q} - \epsilon\frac{d}{dt}\left(\frac{\partial L}{\partial \dot{q}}\right)\right] \stackrel{!}{=} 0$$

↷ factoring out ϵ

$$\int_{t_i}^{t_f} dt\, \epsilon\left[\frac{\partial L}{\partial q} - \frac{d}{dt}\left(\frac{\partial L}{\partial \dot{q}}\right)\right] \stackrel{!}{=} 0. \quad (4.16)$$

Now we're almost finished. We only need to recall that, if $q(t)$ is indeed the path of least action that we are looking for, the condition must be correct for *any* possible variation $\epsilon = \epsilon(t)$. But this can only be correct if, in the last line of Eq. 4.16, the expression between the two big square brackets vanishes:

$$\frac{\partial L}{\partial q} - \frac{d}{dt}\left(\frac{\partial L}{\partial \dot{q}}\right) \stackrel{!}{=} 0 \quad (4.17)$$

This is the famous Euler-Lagrange equation that I have already mentioned at the beginning of this section. We can use it for any given Lagrangian L to derive the corresponding equation of motion.[15] Solutions of this equation of motion correctly describe how a system evolves.

[15] We will discuss below how this works concretely.

Before we discuss how we can use all of the ideas that we've just discussed in field theory, it makes sense to pause for a moment and think about the meaning of the Euler-Lagrange equation within the more intuitive framework of classical mechanics.

4.1.3 The Meaning of the Euler-Lagrange Equation

In classical mechanics, the Lagrangian is always of the form

$$L = T - V\,, \tag{4.18}$$

where T denotes the kinetic energy and V the potential energy.

As soon as someone hands us this Lagrangian, we can calculate the corresponding equation of motion using the Euler-Lagrange equation. Let's consider a concrete example.

The easiest example is, of course, a system which consists of just one object with no external potential $V = 0$. For such a free object, the Lagrangian reads

$$L = T - V = T = \frac{1}{2}m\dot{q}^2. \tag{4.19}$$

The Euler-Lagrange equation (Eq. 4.2) then tells us

$$\frac{\partial L}{\partial q} - \frac{d}{dt}\left(\frac{\partial L}{\partial \dot{q}}\right) = 0$$

$$\rhd \quad L = \frac{1}{2}m\dot{q}^2$$

$$\frac{\partial(\frac{1}{2}m\dot{q}^2)}{\partial q} - \frac{d}{dt}\left(\frac{\partial(\frac{1}{2}m\dot{q}^2)}{\partial \dot{q}}\right) = 0$$

$$\rhd \quad \frac{\partial(\frac{1}{2}m\dot{q}^2)}{\partial q} = 0$$

$$-\frac{d}{dt}\left(\frac{\partial(\frac{1}{2}m\dot{q}^2)}{\partial \dot{q}}\right) = 0$$

$$\rhd \quad \left(\frac{\partial(\frac{1}{2}m\dot{q}^2)}{\partial \dot{q}}\right) = m\dot{q}$$

$$-\frac{d}{dt}(m\dot{q}) = 0$$

$\rhd$ $\frac{d}{dt}\dot{q} = \ddot{q}$ and assuming $m = \text{const.}$

$$m\ddot{q} = 0\,.$$

This is exactly the equation of motion for a free object that we also get by using Newton's second law

$$\frac{d}{dt}p = F$$

↷ $F = 0$ for a free object

$$\frac{d}{dt}p = 0$$

↷ $p = m\dot{q}$ is the momentum for a single object

$$\frac{d}{dt}(m\dot{q}) = 0$$

↷ $\frac{d}{dt}\dot{q} = \ddot{q}$ and assuming $m =$ const.

$$m\ddot{q} = 0\,.$$

This little calculation is not only an important consistency check. It also allows us to understand the Euler-Lagrange equation a little better. In particular, we've seen that the first term $\frac{\partial L}{\partial q}$ yields zero if there is no potential because the kinetic energy only depends on $\dot{q}$ and not on q. Therefore, this term describes the forces F in the system because it is only non-zero if there are forces. In particular, for a general potential $V = V(q)$, this first term yields

$$\frac{\partial L}{\partial q} = \frac{\partial\Big(T(\dot{q}) - V(q)\Big)}{\partial q} = -\frac{\partial V(q)}{\partial q} \equiv F\,. \tag{4.20}$$

Moreover, we've seen that the second term $\frac{d}{dt}\left(\frac{\partial L}{\partial \dot{q}}\right)$ yields the time derivative of the momentum $\frac{d}{dt}p \equiv \frac{d}{dt}m\dot{q}$ for a single object. This motivates us to propose that the term between the brackets describes, in general, the **momentum**:[16]

[16] Take note that this quantity is not always the usual momentum. We will talk about this subtlety below.

$$p \equiv \frac{\partial L}{\partial \dot{q}}\,. \tag{4.21}$$

With this in mind, we can rewrite the Euler-Lagrange equation as follows:

$$\frac{\partial L}{\partial q} - \frac{d}{dt}\left(\frac{\partial L}{\partial \dot{q}}\right) = 0$$

↷ rearranging

$$\therefore \quad \frac{d}{dt}\left(\frac{\partial L}{\partial \dot{q}}\right) = \frac{\partial L}{\partial q}$$

↷ Eq. 4.20 and Eq. 4.21

$$\therefore \quad \frac{d}{dt}p = F. \tag{4.22}$$

This is exactly Newton's second law! We can therefore conclude that the whole Lagrangian machinery indeed yields the correct equation of motion.

Now that we have some rough understanding of how the Lagrangian formalism works, let's move on to field theory.

4.2 The Lagrangian Formalism in Field Theory

In a "particle" theory like classical mechanics, we describe the dynamics within a system by using the locations of the various particles or objects. In a field theory, however, the main actors are fields which exist everywhere in space at the same time.[17] This implies that we are interested in field configurations instead of locations. A field configuration is a snapshot of the field at a specific moment in time. At some locations, the field strength will be zero, while at others it will be non-zero. As time passes, the field strength at other locations becomes non-zero and thus we are dealing with a different configuration. Similarly, for a vector field the direction and length of the vectors possibly change as time passes on.

[17] Recall that a field assigns a number, vector, spinor, or other mathematical object to *every* point in spacetime. Hence, even if the field strength is zero in most regions, we technically still say that a field permeates all of space. In other words, a field is not a localized thing like a ball but spreads out everywhere. Field excitations, however, can be localized.

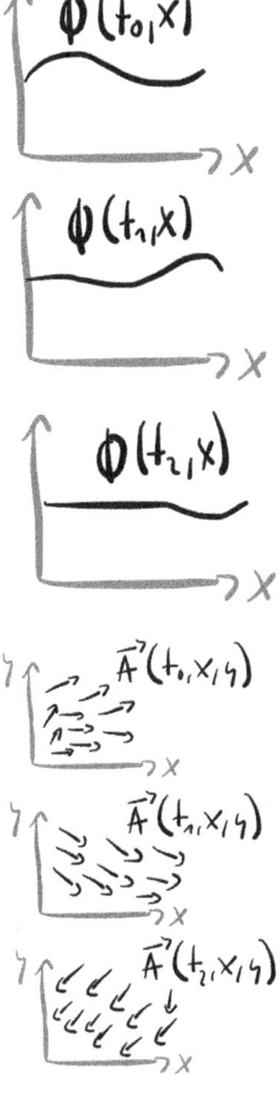

Therefore, in field theory, a point in configuration space represents a specific configuration for all fields that are present in the system.[18] Moreover, as time passes on, the field configurations change and we can again describe this evolution using a path in configuration space.

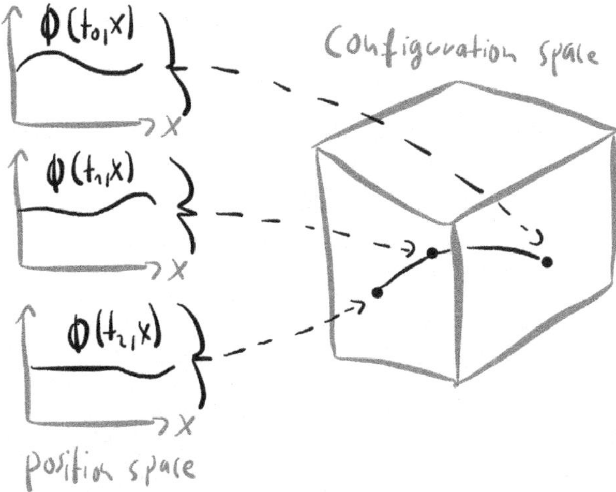

These observations imply that in field theory, the Lagrangian is

[18] Technically, all fields are always present everywhere. However, in experiments we can shield tiny parts of the universe sufficiently such that we can focus just on one or a few fields.

no longer a function of the locations and velocities of all the objects, but a function of the field configurations and their derivatives, $L = L(\phi, \partial_\mu \phi)$.[19] An important difference is that in a particle theory we describe the locations at different moments in time $\vec{q} = \vec{q}(t)$. But in field theory, we describe field configurations at spacetime points $\phi = \phi(x_\mu)$. In other words, in field theory we can put time and space on an equal footing because we no longer care about locations at specific moments in time. Since we can do this, we should do it.[20] That's why the Lagrangian not only depends on the time derivative of the field configuration $\partial_0\phi = \partial_t\phi = \frac{\partial\phi}{\partial t}$ but also on the spatial derivatives $\partial_1\phi \equiv \frac{\partial\phi}{\partial x}$, $\partial_2\phi \equiv \frac{\partial\phi}{\partial y}$, $\partial_3\phi \equiv \frac{\partial\phi}{\partial z}$. It is conventional to denote the Lagrangian's dependence on the time derivatives and spatial derivatives simply by $\partial_\mu\phi$.

[19] We use a short-hand notation ϕ for all of the field configurations. If there are multiple fields that are relevant for our system, we have $\phi = (\phi_1, \phi_2, A^1_\mu \ldots)$, where ϕ_1 denotes the configuration of the first scalar field, ϕ_2 denotes the configuration of the second scalar field, A^1_μ denotes the configuration of the first vector field, and so on. Moreover, take note that ∂_μ is a short-hand notation for $\frac{\partial}{\partial x^\mu}$.

[20] On the one hand, this seems reasonable if we recall what we learned about special relativity. (Space and time are mixed for different observers etc.) On the other hand, the success of this approach should be sufficient motivation. You can, of course, try to only include time derivatives but won't get very far if you want to compare your equations with experimental results.

It is also conventional to introduce the **Lagrangian density**

$$L = \int d^3x \, \mathcal{L}(\phi, \partial_\mu\phi) \tag{4.23}$$

because this helps us, in the spirit of special relativity, to put time and space on an equal footing:

$$S = \int dt L = \int d^4x \mathcal{L}(\phi, \partial_\mu\phi) \tag{4.24}$$

In this formula, time is no longer treated differently and this makes it particularly easy to find expressions that follow the rules of special relativity.

If we then follow exactly the same steps that we discussed in the previous sections for a particle theory, we can derive the Euler-Lagrange equation for field theories:

$$\boxed{\frac{\partial\mathcal{L}}{\partial\phi} - \partial_\mu\left(\frac{\partial\mathcal{L}}{\partial(\partial_\mu\phi)}\right) = 0\,.} \tag{4.25}$$

Once we have this equation, we can proceed exactly as in a particle theory. First, we derive a Lagrangian or take it from someone else and then plug it into the Euler-Lagrange equation to find the correct equations of motion for the system. In the following chapter, we will discuss several examples.

But first, we have to discuss one of the deepest results in modern physics that can be derived by using the Lagrangian formalism.

4.3 Noether's Theorem

In short, Noether's theorem tells us:[21]

> The existence of a (continuous) symmetry implies that there is a conserved quantity.

[21] You can find a detailed discussion, for example, in:

Jakob Schwichtenberg. *No-Nonsense Classical Mechanics : a student-friendly introduction*. No-Nonsense Books, Karlsruhe, Germany, 2019b. ISBN 9781096195382

The most famous examples are:

- ▷ If the system does not change under rotations, we know immediately that angular momentum is conserved. In other words, if we can rotate our system without changing anything, then angular momentum is conserved.
- ▷ If the system does not change under spatial translations $x \to x + \epsilon$, we know immediately that momentum is conserved. This means that if we change the position of the whole system and nothing changes, then momentum is conserved.
- ▷ If the system does not change under temporal translations $t \to t + \epsilon$, we know immediately that energy is conserved. Formulated differently, if the system behaved yesterday exactly as it does today, energy is conserved.

Broadly, there are two kinds of transformation: spacetime transformations and internal transformations. A spacetime transformation is, for example, a rotation or a translation to a different spacetime point. An internal transformation is a modification of the field itself which is unrelated to any spacetime transformation. If the system is invariant under a spacetime transformation, we say it has a spacetime symmetry. If it is unchanged by an internal transformation, we say it has an internal symmetry. Noether's theorem allows us to derive conserved quantities for both kinds of symmetries.

For spacetime symmetries, the corresponding conserved quantities are:

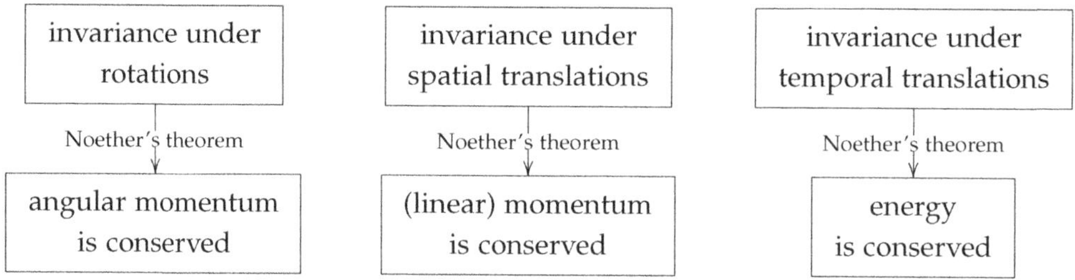

For internal transformations, we find:

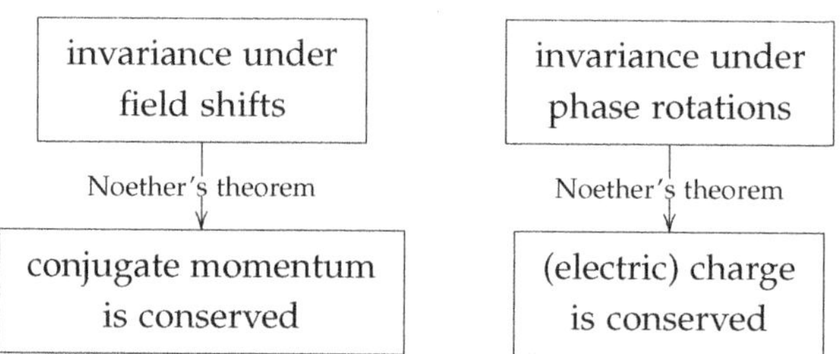

Let's start by discussing the consequences of the more familiar spacetime transformations.

4.3.1 Spacetime Symmetries

We are dealing with a spacetime symmetry if the Lagrangian density $\mathcal{L}\Big((\phi(x_\mu), \partial_\mu\phi(x_\mu), x_\mu\Big)$ remains unchanged by a transformation:

$$x_\mu \to x'_\mu \,. \tag{4.26}$$

Mathematically, this means

$$\delta\mathcal{L} = \mathcal{L}\Big((\phi(x_\mu), \partial_\mu\phi(x_\mu), x_\mu\Big) - \mathcal{L}\Big((\phi'(x'_\mu), \partial_\mu\phi'(x'_\mu), x'_\mu\Big) = 0. \tag{4.27}$$

Take note that we take into account here that, in general, a field ϕ can also be directly affected by a spacetime transformation:[22]

[22] We will discuss this in more explicit terms below.

$$\phi(x_\mu) \to \phi'(x'_\mu) \,. \tag{4.28}$$

If we want to explore the consequences of our symmetry condition (Eq. 4.27), we need to recall how we can rewrite the total change of a function that depends on other functions. If we assume that our transformation is infinitesimal:

$$\begin{aligned} x_\mu &\to x'_\mu = x_\mu + \delta x_\mu \\ \phi &\to \phi' = \phi + \delta\phi \\ (\partial_\mu\phi) &\to (\partial_\mu\phi)' = (\partial_\mu\phi) + \delta(\partial_\mu\phi) \end{aligned} \tag{4.29}$$

we can use a Taylor expansion to rewrite the transformed Lagrangian:[23]

[23] This is analogous to the usual formula for the total derivative of a function

$$df(g(x), h(x), \ldots, x) = \frac{\partial f}{\partial g}\delta g + \frac{\partial f}{\partial h}\delta h + \ldots + \frac{\partial f}{\partial x}\delta x.$$

The total change of f is given by the change rates (derivatives) times the change in the corresponding quantities itself. Maybe it helps to compare this to the total change of a function $f(x,y,z)$ if we modify x,y, and z, which is given by $\frac{\partial f}{\partial x}\delta x + \frac{\partial f}{\partial y}\delta y + \frac{\partial f}{\partial z}\delta z$. Since we are considering an infinitesimal transformation this "first order approximation" is exact.

$$\begin{aligned} \mathcal{L}\Big((\phi'(x'_\mu), \partial_\mu\phi'(x'_\mu), x'_\mu\Big) &= \mathcal{L}\Big((\phi(x_\mu), \partial_\mu\phi(x_\mu), x_\mu\Big) \\ &\quad + \frac{\partial\mathcal{L}}{\partial\phi}\delta\phi + \frac{\partial\mathcal{L}}{\partial(\partial_\mu\phi)}\delta(\partial_\mu\phi) + \frac{\partial\mathcal{L}}{\partial x_\mu}\delta x_\mu \,. \end{aligned} \tag{4.30}$$

If we plug this into Eq. 4.27, we find

$$\begin{aligned}
\delta\mathcal{L} &= \mathcal{L}\Big((\phi(x_\mu), \partial_\mu\phi(x_\mu), x_\mu\Big) - \mathcal{L}\Big((\phi'(x'_\mu), \partial_\mu\phi'(x'_\mu), x'_\mu\Big) \\
&\quad \text{Eq. 4.30} \\
&= \mathcal{L}\Big((\phi(x_\mu), \partial_\mu\phi(x_\mu), x_\mu\Big) - \Bigg(\mathcal{L}\Big((\phi(x_\mu), \partial_\mu\phi(x_\mu), x_\mu\Big) \\
&\quad + \frac{\partial\mathcal{L}}{\partial\phi}\delta\phi + \frac{\partial\mathcal{L}}{\partial(\partial_\mu\phi)}\delta(\partial_\mu\phi) + \frac{\partial\mathcal{L}}{\partial x_\mu}\delta x_\mu\Bigg) \\
&\quad \not{\mathcal{L}} \\
&= -\frac{\partial\mathcal{L}}{\partial\phi}\delta\phi - \frac{\partial\mathcal{L}}{\partial(\partial_\mu\phi)}\delta(\partial_\mu\phi) - \frac{\partial\mathcal{L}}{\partial x_\mu}\delta x_\mu \,.
\end{aligned} \tag{4.31}$$

In words, this formula tells us that the total change of $\mathcal{L}$ is given by the rates of change if we vary one of the functions $(\phi, \partial_\mu\phi)$ or x_μ itself multiplied by the total distance we move in the corresponding "directions".

We can simplify this formula by using the Euler-Lagrange equation and the product rule:[24]

[24] Reminder: the Euler-Lagrange equation for a field ϕ reads (Eq. 4.25)

$$\frac{\partial\mathcal{L}}{\partial\phi} = \partial_\mu\left(\frac{\partial\mathcal{L}}{\partial(\partial_\mu\phi)}\right).$$

$$\begin{aligned}
\delta\mathcal{L} &= -\frac{\partial\mathcal{L}}{\partial\phi}\delta\phi - \frac{\partial\mathcal{L}}{\partial(\partial_\mu\phi)}\delta(\partial_\mu\phi) - \frac{\partial\mathcal{L}}{\partial x_\mu}\delta x_\mu \\
&\quad \text{EL equation, Eq. 4.25} \\
&= -\left(\partial_\mu\left(\frac{\partial\mathcal{L}}{\partial(\partial_\mu\phi)}\right)\right)\delta\phi - \frac{\partial\mathcal{L}}{\partial(\partial_\mu\phi)}\delta(\partial_\mu\phi) - \frac{\partial\mathcal{L}}{\partial x_\mu}\delta x_\mu \\
&\quad \delta(\partial_\mu\phi) = (\partial_\mu\delta\phi) \\
&= -\left(\partial_\mu\left(\frac{\partial\mathcal{L}}{\partial(\partial_\mu\phi)}\right)\right)\delta\phi - \frac{\partial\mathcal{L}}{\partial(\partial_\mu\phi)}(\partial_\mu\delta\phi) - \frac{\partial\mathcal{L}}{\partial x_\mu}\delta x_\mu \\
&\quad \text{product rule} \\
&= -\partial_\mu\left(\frac{\partial\mathcal{L}}{\partial(\partial_\mu\phi)}\delta\phi\right) - \frac{\partial\mathcal{L}}{\partial x_\mu}\delta x_\mu \,.
\end{aligned} \tag{4.32}$$

If we now assume that the transformation we are dealing with (Eq. 4.29) is a symmetry, we have $\delta\mathcal{L} = 0$. We will see below that this allows us to conclude that there must be a corresponding conserved quantity.

Let's start with the simplest possible spacetime transformation: a translation

$$\begin{aligned} x_\mu &\to x'_\mu = x_\mu + a_\mu \\ \phi &\to \phi' = \phi + \delta\phi = \phi - \frac{\partial \phi}{\partial x_\nu} a_\nu \,, \end{aligned} \tag{4.33}$$

where a_μ is a constant four-vector and we used that we need to take the rate of change of our scalar field $\frac{\partial \phi}{\partial x_\nu}$ if we move the system. If we plug this into Eq. 4.32 and assume that the system in question is unchanged by translations, we find

$$\begin{aligned} \delta\mathcal{L} &= -\partial_\mu \left(\frac{\partial \mathcal{L}}{\partial(\partial_\mu \phi)} \delta\phi \right) - \frac{\partial \mathcal{L}}{\partial x_\mu} \delta x_\mu \\ &\quad \text{↷ } \delta\mathcal{L} = 0 \text{ (symmetry), Eq. 4.33} \\ 0 &= \partial_\mu \left(\frac{\partial \mathcal{L}}{\partial(\partial_\mu \phi)} \frac{\partial \phi}{\partial x_\nu} a_\nu \right) - \frac{\partial \mathcal{L}}{\partial x_\mu} a_\mu \\ &\quad \text{↷ } \frac{\partial \mathcal{L}}{\partial x_\mu} \equiv \partial^\mu \mathcal{L},\ \frac{\partial \phi}{\partial x_\nu} \equiv \partial^\nu \phi \\ &= \partial_\mu \left(\frac{\partial \mathcal{L}}{\partial(\partial_\mu \phi)} \partial^\nu \phi \, a_\nu \right) - \partial^\mu \mathcal{L} \, a_\mu \\ &\quad \text{↷ } \delta^\mu_\nu \partial_\mu = \partial_\nu,\ \partial^\mu \mathcal{L} a_\mu \equiv \partial_\nu \mathcal{L} a^\nu,\ \partial^\nu \phi a_\nu \equiv \partial_\nu \phi a^\nu \\ &= \partial_\mu \left(\frac{\partial \mathcal{L}}{\partial(\partial_\mu \phi)} \partial_\nu \phi - \delta^\mu_\nu \mathcal{L} \right) a^\nu \,. \end{aligned} \tag{4.34}$$

We can therefore conclude that the quantity

$$T^\mu_\nu \equiv \frac{\partial \mathcal{L}}{\partial(\partial_\mu \phi)} \partial_\nu \phi - \delta^\mu_\nu \mathcal{L} \tag{4.35}$$

fulfills a continuity equation

$$\partial_\mu T^\mu_\nu = 0 \,. \tag{4.36}$$

The newly defined quantity T^μ_ν is called the **energy-momentum tensor**. Take note that here we have four continuity equations, one for each component $\nu = 0, 1, 2, 3$. We find four continuity equations because we can consider translations in four independent spacetime directions.

What we've discovered here is interesting because a continuity equation (without a source term) always implies that something is conserved. For example, for $\nu = 0$ we find [25]

[25] We integrated over an arbitrary but large volume V. Then we use the divergence theorem

$$\int_V d^3x \, \nabla \vec{v} = \int_{\delta V} d^2\vec{x} \, \vec{v}$$

which allows us to turn a volume integral into a surface integral. Here, δV denotes the surface of the volume V. (A very illuminating proof of the divergence theorem can be found at `http://www.feynmanlectures.caltech.edu/II_03.html`.) This is useful because it allows us to use that field values die off if we move sufficiently far away. (A surface integral is like a sum over the quantities' values on the surface.)

$$
\begin{aligned}
0 &= \partial_\mu T^\mu_0 \\
&\quad \text{(sum convention)} \\
&= \partial_0 T^0_0 - \partial_i T^i_0 \\
&\quad \text{(rearranging)} \\
\partial_0 T^0_0 &= \partial_i T^i_0 \\
&\quad \text{(vector notation and } \partial_0 = \partial_t\text{)} \\
\partial_t T^0_0 &= \nabla \vec{J} \\
&\quad \left(\int_V d^3x\right) \\
\int_V d^3x \, \partial_t T^0_0 &= \int_V d^3x \, \nabla \vec{J} \\
&\quad \text{(divergence theorem)} \\
\int_V d^3x \, \partial_t T^0_0 &= \int_{\delta V} d^2\vec{x} \, \vec{J} \\
&\quad \text{(field vanish at infinity)} \\
\int_V d^3x \, \partial_t T^0_0 &= 0 \\
&\quad (V \text{ is constant}) \\
\partial_t \int_V d^3x \, T^0_0 &= 0 \,. \qquad (4.37)
\end{aligned}
$$

We can therefore conclude that the quantity[26]

$$E \equiv \int_V d^3x \, T^0_0 \qquad (4.38)$$

[26] A quantity is conserved if it doesn't change in time. In mathematical terms this means $\partial_t Q = 0$.

is conserved. The conserved quantity we found here is called the **energy** of the field. Analogously, we can derive for $\nu = i \in \{1,2,3\}$ that the components of the momentum vector

$$P_i \equiv \int_V d^3x \, T^0_i \qquad (4.39)$$

are conserved.

By looking at the explicit transformation law we started with (Eq. 4.33)[27], we can see that for $\nu = 0$ we consider a temporal translation

[27] For your convenience: Eq. 4.33 reads

$$x_\nu \to x'_\nu = x_\nu + a_\nu$$

$$x_0 \to x'_0 = x_0 + a_0 \,, \qquad (4.40)$$

while for $\nu = i$ we consider a spatial translation.

$$x_i \to x'_i = x_i + a_i \,. \qquad (4.41)$$

Therefore, we can conclude that if the system in question is unchanged by temporal translations, energy is conserved. Similarly, if the system is unchanged by spatial translations, momentum is conserved. Analogously, we can derive that if the system is unchanged by rotations, angular momentum is conserved.

In summary:[28]

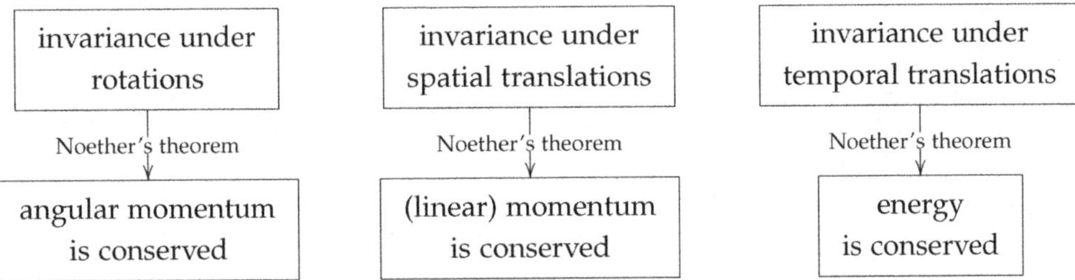

Next, let's talk about *internal* transformations.

[28] This overview diagram appeared already on page 156, but is shown here again for convenience.

4.3.2 Internal Symmetries

The possibility of internal symmetries is a novel feature of field theories. For example, we discussed already in Section 3.9 that a shift

$$\phi \to \phi' = \phi - \Delta\phi \tag{4.42}$$

makes no difference to what we can observe in experiments and is therefore indeed a symmetry. To investigate the consequences of this symmetry, we again introduce the quantity

$$\delta\mathcal{L} = \mathcal{L}(\phi, \partial_\mu\phi) - \mathcal{L}\Big(\phi + \Delta\phi, \partial_\mu(\phi + \Delta\phi)\Big)\,. \tag{4.43}$$

If the transformation in Eq. 4.42 is indeed a symmetry, we have $\delta\mathcal{L} = 0$. For simplicity, we assume that $\Delta\phi$ in Eq. 4.42 is infinitesimal, which implies $(\Delta\phi)^2 = (\Delta\phi)^3 = \ldots = 0$. We can then rewrite Eq. 4.43 by using the Taylor expansion of the second term on the right-hand side:

$$\begin{aligned}
\delta\mathcal{L} &= \mathcal{L}(\phi, \partial_\mu\phi) - \mathcal{L}\Big(\phi + \Delta\phi, \partial_\mu(\phi + \Delta\phi)\Big) \\
0 &= \mathcal{L}(\phi, \partial_\mu\phi) - \mathcal{L}\Big(\phi + \Delta\phi, \partial_\mu(\phi + \Delta\phi)\Big) \\
&= \mathcal{L}(\phi, \partial_\mu\phi) - \left(\mathcal{L}(\phi, \partial_\mu\phi) + \frac{\partial\mathcal{L}(\phi, \partial_\mu\phi)}{\partial\phi}\Delta\phi + \frac{\partial\mathcal{L}(\phi, \partial_\mu\phi)}{\partial(\partial_\mu\phi)}\partial_\mu\Delta\phi + \ldots\right) \\
&= \mathcal{L}(\phi, \partial_\mu\phi) - \left(\mathcal{L}(\phi, \partial_\mu\phi) + \frac{\partial\mathcal{L}(\phi, \partial_\mu\phi)}{\partial\phi}\Delta\phi + \frac{\partial\mathcal{L}(\phi, \partial_\mu\phi)}{\partial(\partial_\mu\phi)}\partial_\mu\Delta\phi\right) \\
&= -\frac{\partial\mathcal{L}(\phi, \partial_\mu\phi)}{\partial\phi}\Delta\phi - \frac{\partial\mathcal{L}(\phi, \partial_\mu\phi)}{\partial(\partial_\mu\phi)}\partial_\mu\Delta\phi\,.
\end{aligned} \tag{4.44}$$

↷ symmetry: $\delta\mathcal{L} = 0$

↷ Taylor expansion

↷ $\Delta\phi^2 = 0, \Delta\phi^3 = 0, \ldots$

↷ $\cancel{\mathcal{L}(\phi, \partial_\mu\phi)}$

[29] Reminder: the Euler-Lagrange equation for a field ϕ reads (Eq. 4.25)

$$\frac{\partial \mathcal{L}}{\partial \phi} = \partial_\mu \left(\frac{\partial \mathcal{L}}{\partial(\partial_\mu \phi)} \right).$$

We can simplify this formula by using the Euler-Lagrange equation and the product rule:[29]

$$\begin{aligned} 0 &= -\frac{\partial \mathcal{L}}{\partial \phi}\Delta\phi - \frac{\partial \mathcal{L}}{\partial(\partial_\mu \phi)}\partial_\mu \Delta\phi \\ &\quad \text{(EL equation (Eq. 4.25))} \\ &= -\partial_\mu \left(\frac{\partial \mathcal{L}}{\partial(\partial_\mu \phi)} \right)\Delta\phi - \frac{\partial \mathcal{L}}{\partial(\partial_\mu \phi)}\partial_\mu \Delta\phi \\ &\quad \text{(product rule } (\partial_x f)g + f(\partial_x g) = (\partial_x fg)\text{)} \\ &= \partial_\mu \left(\frac{\partial \mathcal{L}}{\partial(\partial_\mu \phi)}\Delta\phi \right) \\ &\quad \text{(definition)} \\ &= \partial_\mu J^\mu \end{aligned} \tag{4.45}$$

We have discovered here that if a Lagrangian density $\mathcal{L}$ is invariant under a transformation of the form given in Eq. 4.42, we know immediately that the Noether current

$$J^\mu \equiv \frac{\partial \mathcal{L}}{\partial(\partial_\mu \phi)}\Delta\phi\,, \tag{4.46}$$

fulfills the continuity equation

$$\partial_\mu J^\mu = 0\,. \tag{4.47}$$

This is Noether's theorem for internal symmetries in field theories.

Moreover, by following exactly the same steps as in Eq. 4.37, we can derive that the quantity

$$Q \equiv \int_V d^3x\, J^0 \tag{4.48}$$

is conserved.

An important example is the global shift of a scalar field by a small complex number $i\epsilon$:[30]

[30] Global means that we shift the field value everywhere by the same number. We talked about the global and local transformations in Section 3.9. The imaginary unit i is included here only because it simplifies the further discussion and has no deeper meaning. We could easily get rid of it by defining $\epsilon' \equiv i\epsilon$. Moreover, take note that for vector fields and spinor fields there are also more complicated transformations. For example, we can consider transformations that mix components.

$$\phi \rightarrow \phi' = \phi - i\epsilon \,. \tag{4.49}$$

By using Eq. 4.46 and Eq. 4.48, we can immediately conclude that the corresponding conserved quantity reads:

$$\begin{aligned} Q &\equiv \int_V d^3x \, J^0 && \text{this is Eq. 4.48,} \\ & && \text{Eq. 4.46 with } \mu = 0 \text{ and } \Delta\Phi = i\epsilon \\ &= \int_V d^3x \, \frac{\partial \mathcal{L}}{\partial(\partial_0 \phi)} (i\epsilon) \,. \end{aligned} \tag{4.50}$$

Since in this case $i\epsilon$ is an arbitrary infinitesimal constant, we can define the conserved quantity without it:

$$\begin{aligned} \tilde{Q} &\equiv \frac{Q}{i\epsilon} && \partial_t \\ \partial_t \tilde{Q} &= \partial_t \frac{Q}{i\epsilon} && \partial_t Q = 0 \\ &= 0 \,. \end{aligned} \tag{4.51}$$

The integrand appearing in this simplified conserved quantity[31]

$$\boxed{\pi = \frac{\partial \mathcal{L}}{\partial(\partial_0 \phi)}} \tag{4.52}$$

is known as the **conjugate momentum density**. Even though this quantity is somewhat abstract, we will see in later chapters that it is essential for our understanding of quantum field theory.[32]

[31] We have $\tilde{Q} \equiv \frac{Q}{i\epsilon} = \int_V d^3x \, \frac{\partial \mathcal{L}}{\partial(\partial_0 \phi)} \equiv \int_V d^3x \pi$.

[32] Take note that this is not the usual momentum density associated with a field, which is given by

$$p = \frac{\partial \mathcal{L}}{\partial(\partial_0 \phi)} \frac{\partial \phi}{\partial x_i}$$

and is the Noether charge associated with spatial translations $\phi(x) \rightarrow \phi(x') = \phi(x + \epsilon)$. In contrast, we considered here a shift of the field. Moreover, an important example is the electric field $\vec{E}$ which is the conjugate momentum density associated with the electromagnetic field.

There is a second incredibly important internal symmetry. Nothing changes if we multiply a spinor field ψ by a phase factor[33]

$$\begin{aligned} \psi &\rightarrow \psi' = e^{-i\varphi} \psi \\ \psi^\dagger &\rightarrow \psi'^\dagger = e^{i\varphi} \psi^\dagger \,. \end{aligned} \tag{4.53}$$

[33] Roughly this follows because everything we can measure in experiments is real and thus there is necessarily some freedom if we describe things by using complex objects. This follows if we look at the Lagrangian that we use to describe spinor fields, which we will discuss in the next chapter. Since the Lagrangian is unchanged by this transformation, it is indeed a symmetry.

Similarly, the multiplication of a complex scalar field ϕ by a phase factor is a symmetry too:

$$\phi \to \phi' = e^{-i\varphi}\phi$$
$$\phi^\dagger \to \phi'^\dagger = e^{i\varphi}\phi^\dagger . \tag{4.54}$$

If we restrict ourselves to infinitesimal phase shifts, we can write this as[34]

$$\begin{aligned}\phi \to \phi' &= e^{-i\epsilon}\phi \\ &= \Big(1 - i\epsilon + \ldots\Big)\phi && \text{(}e^x = 1 + x + \tfrac{x^2}{2} + \ldots\text{)} \\ &= \phi - i\epsilon\phi && \text{(}\epsilon^2 = 0,\ \epsilon^3 = 0\text{ etc.)} \\ \phi^\dagger \to \phi'^\dagger &= \phi^\dagger + i\epsilon\phi^\dagger && \epsilon\text{ is real}.\end{aligned} \tag{4.55}$$

[34] The defining property of an infinitesimal quantity is that it's so tiny that $\epsilon^2 = 0$ and therefore $\epsilon^3 = 0$ etc.

Take note that this is a different transformation compared to what we considered before.[35] If we compare this transformation law to the general formula (Eq. 4.42) we can conclude:[36]

$$\Delta\phi = -i\epsilon\phi, \quad \Delta\phi^\dagger = +i\epsilon\phi^\dagger . \tag{4.57}$$

[35] Reminder: we previously considered shifts of the form (Eq. 4.49)

$$\phi \to \phi' = \phi - i\epsilon .$$

[36] For your convenience: Eq. 4.42 reads

$$\phi \to \phi' = \phi - \Delta\phi \tag{4.56}$$

We can plug this into our general formula for the Noether current (Eq. 4.46)

$$\begin{aligned}J_1^\mu &\equiv \frac{\partial\mathcal{L}}{\partial(\partial_\mu\phi)}\Delta\phi \\ &= -\frac{\partial\mathcal{L}}{\partial(\partial_\mu\phi)}i\epsilon\phi && \text{(Eq. 4.57)} \\ J_2^\mu &\equiv \frac{\partial\mathcal{L}}{\partial(\partial_\mu\phi^\dagger)}\Delta\phi^\dagger \\ &= \frac{\partial\mathcal{L}}{\partial(\partial_\mu\phi^\dagger)}i\epsilon\phi^\dagger && \text{(Eq. 4.57)} \\ J^\mu &\equiv J_1^\mu + J_2^\mu ,\end{aligned} \tag{4.58}$$

where the total Noether current J^μ is the sum of the contributions from ϕ and $\phi^\dagger$. The fact that the total Noether current is given by this sum follows if we repeat the steps that we performed in Eq. 4.44 and Eq. 4.45 for a Lagrangian that depends on a complex field. This is demonstrated explicitly in Appendix A.2.

If we now use Eq. 4.48, we can conclude that the corresponding conserved quantity reads

$$
\begin{aligned}
Q &\equiv \int_V d^3x \, J^0 && \text{this is Eq. 4.48} \\
& && \text{Eq. 4.58} \\
&= \int_V d^3x \, (J_1^0 + J_2^0) \\
& && \text{Eq. 4.58} \\
&= \int_V d^3x \left(-\frac{\partial \mathcal{L}}{\partial(\partial_0 \phi)} i\epsilon\phi + \frac{\partial \mathcal{L}}{\partial(\partial_0 \phi^\dagger)} i\epsilon\phi^\dagger \right) . \qquad (4.59)
\end{aligned}
$$

By redefining Q in order to get rid of the factor ϵ, we find

$$\tilde{Q} = i \int_V d^3x \left(\frac{\partial \mathcal{L}}{\partial(\partial_0 \phi^\dagger)} \phi^\dagger - \frac{\partial \mathcal{L}}{\partial(\partial_0 \phi)} \phi \right) . \qquad (4.60)$$

This quantity is important, for instance, because if we multiply it by the charge q each particle associated with the field carries,

$$\tilde{Q}_q = iq \int_V d^3x \left(\frac{\partial \mathcal{L}}{\partial(\partial_0 \phi^\dagger)} \phi^\dagger - \frac{\partial \mathcal{L}}{\partial(\partial_0 \phi)} \phi \right) , \qquad (4.61)$$

we get the total electric charge carried by the field.[37] In other words, the conservation of electric charge follows from the fact that multiplying our fields by a phase factor (Eq. 4.53, Eq. 4.54) is a symmetry of Nature.

[37] The conserved quantity in Eq. 4.60 is usually called the "particle number" where we count particles as $+1$ and antiparticles as -1. We will discuss antiparticles in detail in Section 8.6.

In summary:[38]

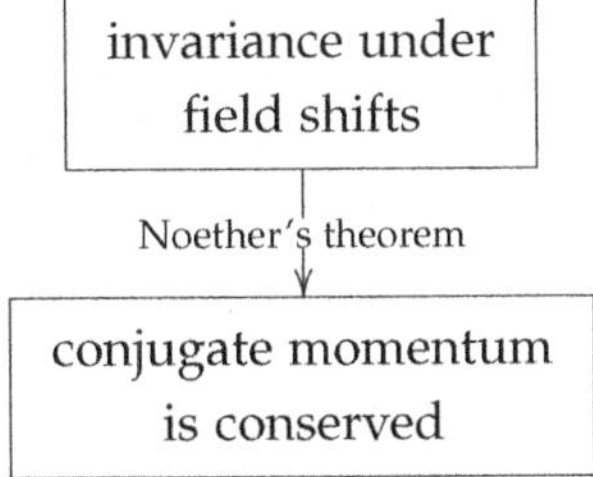

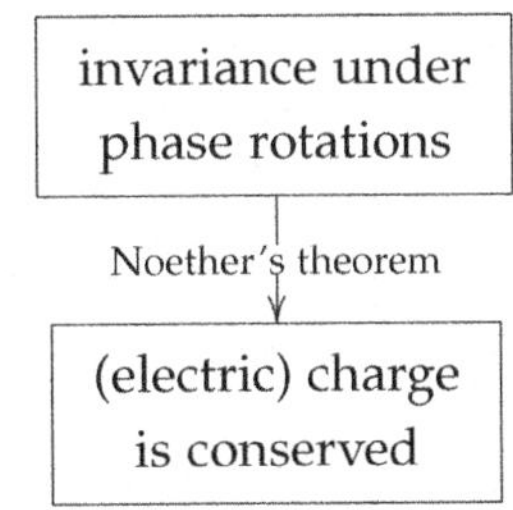

[38] This overview diagram appeared already on page 156, but is shown here again for convenience.

5

The Behavior of Free Fields

To unclutter the notation, from here on we will only work with natural units. This means that we set $\hbar = 1$, $c = 1$.

In this chapter, we will discuss four of the most important equations of motion in modern physics:[1]

[1] It once more probably makes sense to revisit the roadmap on page 35 to understand how this chapter fits into the bigger picture. Moreover, note that we can use all of them either in a field theoretic or in a particle theoretic context. Formulated differently, we can use each of them to describe particles or to describe fields. Although this is a book on quantum field theory, we will sometimes use a particle perspective to discuss certain aspects. In quantum field theory this is a perfectly valid approach since we can always replace the word particle with particle-like field excitation.

▷ The Klein-Gordon equation which describes how free scalar fields evolve in time,

▷ the Dirac equation which describes how free spinor fields evolve in time,

▷ the Proca equation which describes how free *massive* gauge fields evolve in time, and

▷ the Maxwell equation which describes how free *massless* gauge fields evolve in time.

The following diagram summarizes the role of the four equations that we will discuss in this chapter:

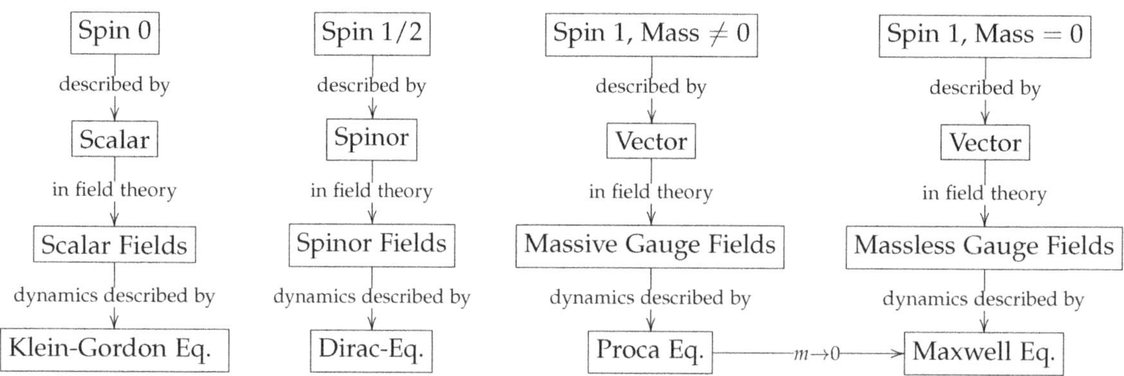

We will assume that someone hands us these equations (or the corresponding Lagrangian) and then discuss their meaning and solutions.

There are, of course, lots of other equations we could write down and discuss. But we will focus on the four equations listed above because they are essential for our description of Nature at fundamental scales. This aspect is especially important when it comes to vector fields. The two equations for vector fields (Proca, Maxwell) that we will discuss are certainly not the easiest or most general equations for vector fields that we can write down.[2] However, the Proca equation and Maxwell equation are what we need to describe a certain type of vector field known as gauge field. This is important for us because all known fundamental vector fields are gauge fields.

[2] In fact, the equation of motion of a general vector field is simply the Klein-Gordon equation for each component of the vector field.

For all equations we will make an ansatz of the form[3]

$$\text{internal structure} \quad \times \quad \text{spacetime structure}\,. \tag{5.1}$$

In words this means that we assume that internal and spacetime degrees of freedom decouple. While there can be solutions that we cannot describe with this ansatz, for our purposes in this book it is completely sufficient.[4]

[3] Reminder: For gauge fields, the internal structure is typically described in terms of polarizations. In contrast, the internal structure of scalar fields is trivial. In other words, a scalar field has no internal structure and is solely characterized by a field strength at each spacetime point.

[4] As an aside: a famous example of a solution in which internal and spacetime degrees of freedom are coupled is the famous "hedgehog" solution that describes magnetic 't Hooft-Polyakov monopoles.

Interestingly, the spacetime part is governed by an ordinary wave equation for every type of field discussed in this book. This implies that all we need to describe the spacetime structure of scalar fields, spinor fields and gauge fields are plane waves. Thus the only true novel information contained in the Dirac, Proca and Maxwell equations compared to the Klein-Gordon equation is what they tell us about the behavior of the internal degrees of freedom.

In short:

▷ The Dirac equation tells us that left-chiral and right-chiral configurations constantly oscillate into each other.

▷ The Proca equation tells us that a massive gauge field has only three linearly-independent polarizations.

▷ The Maxwell equation tells us that a massless gauge field has only two linearly-independent polarizations.

With these ideas in mind, let's discuss the four equations one-by-one.

5.1 Free Scalar fields and the Klein Gordon Equation

Let's assume that we want to describe a single scalar field ϕ and that someone hands us the Lagrangian density

$$\boxed{\mathcal{L} = \frac{1}{2}(\partial_\mu\phi\partial^\mu\phi - m^2\phi^2)\,.} \tag{5.2}$$

It is conventional to call the first term here the **kinetic term** and the second term the **mass term**.

Using the Euler-Lagrange equation (Eq. 4.25), we can immediately derive the corresponding equation of motion

$$\begin{aligned} 0 &= \frac{\partial\mathcal{L}}{\partial\phi} - \partial_\mu\left(\frac{\partial\mathcal{L}}{\partial(\partial_\mu\phi)}\right) \\ &\quad \text{Eq. 5.2} \\ &= \frac{\partial}{\partial\phi}\left(\frac{1}{2}(\partial_\mu\phi\partial^\mu\phi - m^2\phi^2)\right) - \partial_\mu\left(\frac{\partial}{\partial(\partial_\mu\phi)}\left(\frac{1}{2}(\partial_\mu\phi\partial^\mu\phi - m^2\phi^2)\right)\right) \\ &\quad \partial_x x^2 = 2x \\ &= -m^2\phi - \partial_\mu\left(\partial^\mu\phi\right)\,. \end{aligned} \tag{5.3}$$

The resulting equation

$$\boxed{(\partial_\mu\partial^\mu + m^2)\phi = 0} \tag{5.4}$$

is the famous **Klein-Gordon equation** that encodes the behavior of a free scalar field.

Simply looking at the Klein-Gordon equation (Eq. 5.4) and the Klein-Gordon Lagrangian (Eq. 5.2) is probably not very enlightening.[5] So let's try to understand what they're telling us.

[5] Take note that the Klein-Gordon equation is a four-dimensional version of the wave equation that we discussed in Section 3.6.

5.1.1 The Meaning of the Klein-Gordon Equation

I've already mentioned in Section 3.5 that we can understand a scalar field as being like a mattress. In this section, we will make this idea a bit more concrete and develop a better understanding of the Klein-Gordon equation this way.

In our context, a mattress consists of lots of coupled harmonic oscillators. Each oscillator only bounces up and down. We describe an isolated harmonic oscillator in classical mechanics using the Lagrangian

$$L_{\text{HO}} = T - V = \frac{1}{2}M\dot{q}^2 - \frac{1}{2}kq^2 , \tag{5.5}$$

where $q = q(t)$ denotes the position of the end of the spring above or below the equilibrium position, M is the mass of the object attached to the spring, k is a constant that characterizes the spring and $\dot{q} = \frac{dq}{dt}$. The first term $T = \frac{1}{2}M\dot{q}^2$ describes the kinetic energy of the oscillator, while $V = \frac{1}{2}kq^2$ describes the amount of energy stored in the form of potential energy.

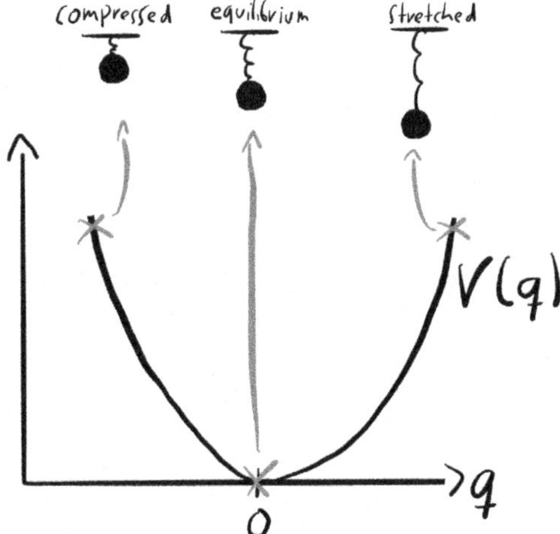

If there are two uncoupled equal harmonic oscillators, we can use the Lagrangian

$$\begin{aligned} L_{2HO} = T - V &= \frac{1}{2}M\dot{q}_1^2 + \frac{1}{2}M\dot{q}_2^2 - \frac{1}{2}kq_1^2 - \frac{1}{2}kq_2^2 \\ &= \frac{1}{2}M\sum_{i=1}^{2}\dot{q}_i^2 - \frac{1}{2}k\sum_{i=1}^{2}q_i^2 , \end{aligned} \tag{5.6}$$

where q_1 describes the location of the first oscillator and q_2 describes the location of the second oscillator. We assume for simplicity that both oscillators have the same mass M and consist of a spring with equal spring constant k.

Analogously, for three uncoupled equal harmonic oscillators, we can use

$$\begin{aligned} L_{3HO} = T - V &= \frac{1}{2}M\dot{q}_1^2 + \frac{1}{2}M\dot{q}_2^2 + \frac{1}{2}M\dot{q}_3^2 - \frac{1}{2}kq_1^2 - \frac{1}{2}kq_2^2 - \frac{1}{2}kq_3^2 \\ &= \frac{1}{2}M\sum_{i=1}^{3}\dot{q}_i^2 - \frac{1}{2}k\sum_{i=1}^{3}q_i^2 . \end{aligned} \tag{5.7}$$

We can see here that if there are lots of oscillators, the sum notation becomes extremely convenient.

The situation becomes more interesting once we consider coupled oscillators:

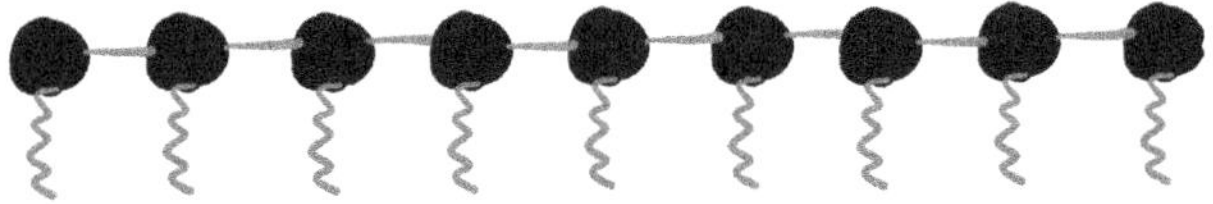

In this case, the individual oscillators influence each other when they bounce up and down and therefore, more complex phenomena can emerge. In mathematical terms, we take the coupling into account by writing down an additional potential energy term.

The potential energy stored in the rubber band between neighboring oscillators depends on its total length. If both oscillators are in their equilibrium position, the length of the band is l and the potential energy stored in it is zero.[6]

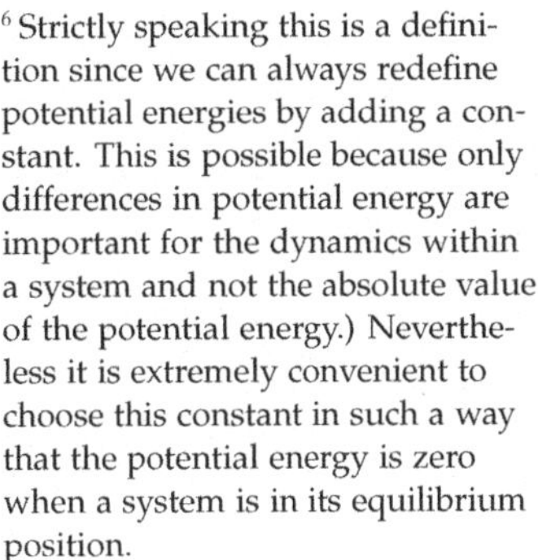

[6] Strictly speaking this is a definition since we can always redefine potential energies by adding a constant. This is possible because only differences in potential energy are important for the dynamics within a system and not the absolute value of the potential energy.) Nevertheless it is extremely convenient to choose this constant in such a way that the potential energy is zero when a system is in its equilibrium position.

If one of the oscillators leaves its equilibrium position, the band between them gets longer.

To calculate the potential energy stored in the spring, we need to determine by how much it has extended.[7] We can determine the total length of the band in this configuration of the system by looking at the following figure.

[7] This is easier for the two springs because the oscillators only move up and down and, therefore, the potential energy is directly given by $V_1(q_1) = -\frac{1}{2}kq_1^2$ and $V_1(q_2) = -\frac{1}{2}kq_2^2$.

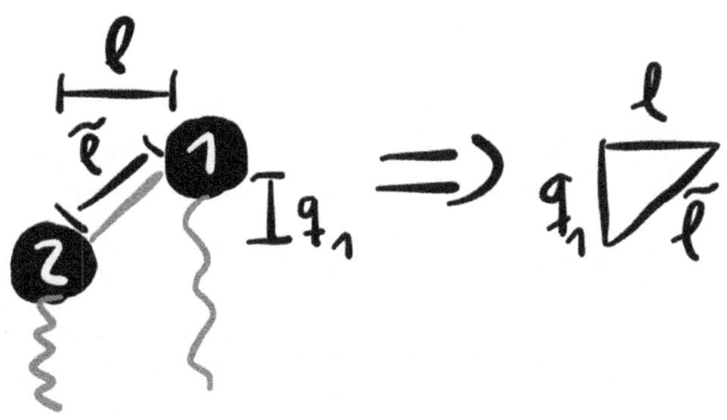

The Pythagorean theorem yields

$$\begin{aligned}\tilde{l}^2 &= l^2 + q_1^2 \\ &\quad \rhd \sqrt{} \\ \tilde{l} &= \sqrt{l^2 + q_1^2} \\ &= \sqrt{l^2\left(1 + \frac{q_1^2}{l^2}\right)} \\ &= l\sqrt{1 + \frac{q_1^2}{l^2}}\,. \end{aligned} \tag{5.8}$$

If we assume that the excitation q_1 is much smaller than the distance between the oscillators, l, we can approximate the expression on the right-hand side using the Taylor series[8]

[8] For $q_1 \ll l$, we have $\frac{q_1}{l} \ll 1$.

$$\begin{aligned}\tilde{l} &= l\sqrt{1 + \frac{q_1^2}{l^2}} \\ &\quad \rhd \sqrt{1+x^2} \approx 1 + \frac{x^2}{2} \text{ for } x << 1 \\ &\approx l\left(1 + \frac{q_1^2}{2l^2}\right) \\ &= l + \frac{q_1^2}{2l}\,. \end{aligned} \tag{5.9}$$

If we compare this length of the rubber band to its length in the equilibrium configuration, l, we find that it became longer. We can calculate its total change in length as follows:

$$\begin{aligned}\Delta l &= \tilde{l} - l \\ &\quad \rhd \text{Eq. 5.9} \\ &\approx l + \frac{q_1^2}{2l} - l \\ &\quad \rhd l \\ &= \frac{q_1^2}{2l}\,. \end{aligned} \tag{5.10}$$

For the sake of argument, let's assume that we can describe the energy stored in the rubber band by using the formula[9]

[9] We could consider different mechanical models consisting of oscillators and rubber bands. However, we focus here on a specific model that is described by the Klein-Gordon equation in the continuum limit.

$$\begin{aligned}V_{12}(q_1, q_2) &= \frac{1}{2}K\Delta l \\ &\quad \rhd \text{Eq. 5.10} \\ &\approx \frac{1}{2}K\frac{q_1^2}{2l}\,, \end{aligned} \tag{5.11}$$

where K is a constant that characterizes the rubber band.

Analogously, we can analyze a configuration in which both oscillators are not in their equilibrium position.

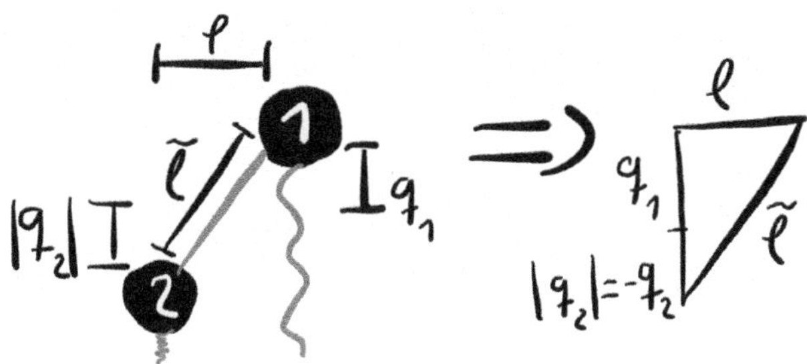

For this configuration, the Pythagorean theorem yields

$$\tilde{l}^2 = l^2 + (q_1 - q_2)^2 . \tag{5.12}$$

If we then follow exactly the same steps as before and assume again that the excitation of both oscillators is much smaller than the distance between the springs $(q_1 - q_2)^2 \ll l^2$, we find

$$\begin{aligned} V_{12}(q_1, q_2) &\approx \frac{1}{2} K \frac{(q_1 - q_2)^2}{2l} \\ &= \frac{1}{2} \frac{K}{2l} (q_1 - q_2)^2 . \end{aligned} \tag{5.13}$$

With this formula at hand, we want to write down the Lagrangian that describes this system.

The kinetic energy of the oscillators and the potential energy stored in the two springs is unaffected by the fact that they're now coupled. Therefore, we can write the Lagrangian for our system consisting of two coupled equal harmonic oscillators by adding these terms together

$$\begin{aligned} L_{2CHO} &= T_1 + T_2 - V_1 - V_2 - V_{12} \\ &\quad \text{Eq. 5.13, Eq. 5.6} \\ &= \frac{1}{2} M \sum_{i=1}^{2} \dot{q}_i^2 - \frac{1}{2} k \sum_{i=1}^{2} q_i^2 - \frac{1}{2} \frac{K}{2l} (q_1 - q_2)^2 . \end{aligned} \tag{5.14}$$

As before, we can generalize this formula for 3 or, to be more general, N oscillators. For N oscillators it is conventional to use the notation

$$L_{\text{NCHO}} = \frac{1}{2}M\sum_{i=1}^{N}\dot{q}_i^2 - \frac{1}{2}k\sum_{i=1}^{N}q_i^2 - \frac{1}{2}\frac{K}{2l}\sum_{ij}(q_i - q_j)^2 . \qquad (5.15)$$

where the sum $\sum_{ij}$ only goes over neighboring oscillators like $i = 1, j = 2$ or $i = 2, j = 3$.

The key idea that allows us to make the transition from a bunch of coupled oscillators to a scalar field is that we imagine that we add more and more oscillators in between every two oscillators. In mathematical terms, this means that we shrink the distance between each pair of oscillators l further and further and ultimately, take the **continuum limit** $l \to 0$.

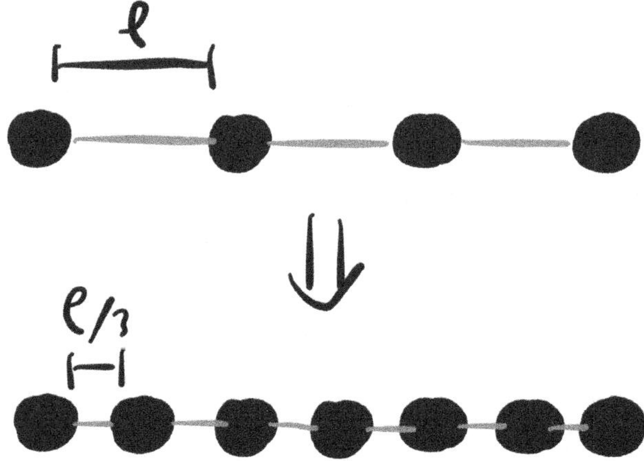

In the continuum limit we have an oscillator at every point in space. Therefore, we no longer need additional labels (i, j) for our oscillators but can simply use a continuous position variable x to identify each oscillator. Moreover, it is conventional to use the Greek letter φ to denote the excitation of each oscillator in the continuum case:[10]

[10] Here we consider only a one-dimensional chain of coupled oscillators and therefore only need a variable x. In the two-dimensional case, we would use $\vec{x} = (x, y)^T$) to label the oscillators in our oscillator lattice. Moreover, take note that in the following we are glossing over several somewhat subtle aspects of the continuum limit. For example, a sum becomes not just an integral but $\int \frac{dx}{l}$, since otherwise the dimensions wouldn't be equal and l is the only fundamental length scale we have in the description. We absorb this factor l into the definition of the continuum variable φ.

$$q_i(t) \to \varphi(x,t)\,. \tag{5.16}$$

What happens to the various terms in the Lagrangian in the continuum limit?

The kinetic energy term in Eq. 5.15 becomes

$$\frac{1}{2}M\sum_{i=1}^{N}\dot{q}_i^2(t) \to \frac{1}{2}M\int dx\;\dot{\varphi}^2(x,t) \tag{5.17}$$

because in the continuum limit, we need to replace the sum over the discrete label i by an integral over the continuous variable x. Analogously, the second term in Eq. 5.15 that describes the potential energy stored in the springs at each location, becomes

$$\frac{1}{2}k\sum_{i=1}^{N}q_i^2 \to \frac{1}{2}k\int dx\;\varphi^2(x,t) \tag{5.18}$$

The continuum limit of the third term in Eq. 5.15 is a bit more subtle and it is clever to rewrite it as follows before we consider the limit[11]

$$\frac{1}{2}\frac{K}{2l}\sum_{ij}(q_i-q_j)^2 = \frac{1}{2}\frac{Kl}{2}\sum_{ij}\frac{(q_i-q_j)^2}{l^2}\,. \tag{5.19}$$

If we now take the continuum limit, we find:

$$\lim_{l\to 0}\frac{1}{2}\frac{Kl}{2}\sum_{ij}\frac{(q_i-q_j)^2}{l^2} = \frac{1}{2}\rho\int dx\,\left(\frac{\partial\varphi(x,t)}{\partial x}\right)^2 \tag{5.20}$$

because $\lim\limits_{l\to 0}\frac{(q_i-q_j)}{l}$ is exactly the definition of the difference quotient and therefore equal to $\frac{\partial\varphi(x,t)}{\partial x}$. In addition, the sum over the discrete indices once more needs to be replaced by an integral over the continuous variable x. Moreover, ρ is a new constant that characterizes the interaction between our oscillators in the continuum limit. Take note that as we consider smaller and smaller distances between the oscillators ($l \to 0$), we need to make our spring constant K larger and larger in order to get any noticeable effects from the coupling. Therefore, we take the continuum limit ($l \to 0$) in such a way that $\frac{Kl}{2}$ does not go to zero but becomes equal to a constant.[12] Putting the

[11] We will see in a moment why this is clever.

[12] We could, of course, also consider a system with a fixed value of the spring constant K. But for such a system, there simply wouldn't be any interactions between the oscillations left in the continuum limit.

three puzzle pieces (Eq. 5.17, Eq. 5.18, Eq. 5.20) together, we find that the Lagrangian for our system of coupled oscillators in the continuum limit reads

$$L_{\text{NCHO}} = \int dx \left(\frac{1}{2} M \dot{\varphi}^2(x,t) - \frac{1}{2} k \varphi^2(x,t) - \frac{1}{2} \rho \left(\frac{\partial \varphi(x,t)}{\partial x} \right)^2 \right) \tag{5.21}$$

Now compare this to the Klein-Gordon Lagrangian density given at the beginning of this section (Eq. 5.2).[13] An obvious difference is that the Lagrangian density we derived here is not written in Minkowski notation. In particular, in Eq. 5.2 the derivatives only appear in the expression $\partial_\mu \varphi \partial^\mu \varphi$ which reads in more explicit terms (Eq. 2.39):

[13] For your convenience: Eq. 5.2 reads

$$\mathcal{L} = \frac{1}{2}(\partial_\mu \phi \partial^\mu \phi - M^2 \phi^2) .$$

$$\partial_\mu \varphi \partial^\mu \varphi = \left(\frac{\partial \varphi}{c \partial t} \right)^2 - \left(\frac{\partial \varphi}{\partial x} \right)^2 - \left(\frac{\partial \varphi}{\partial y} \right)^2 - \left(\frac{\partial \varphi}{\partial z} \right)^2 . \tag{5.22}$$

Motivated by this observation, we introduce an additional factor c^2 in Eq. 5.21:

$$L_{\text{NCHO}} = \int dx \left(\frac{1}{2} M c^2 \left(\frac{\partial \varphi}{c \partial t} \right)^2 - \frac{1}{2} k \varphi^2 - \frac{1}{2} \rho \left(\frac{\partial \varphi}{\partial x} \right)^2 \right) . \tag{5.23}$$

The constant factors Mc^2 and ρ have exactly the same units. Moreover, we have not specified the actual value of ρ. I have only mentioned that it must be some constant that $\frac{Kl}{2}$ approaches in the limit $l \to 0$. In the spirit of special relativity, time and space should be put on an equal footing and therefore, we will now simply *assume* that we are dealing with a system for which $\rho = Mc^2$.[14] Our Lagrangian density then reads:

[14] As always, you're free to consider different systems. But the scalar fields that we typically investigate in field theory are not just some arbitrary set of harmonic oscillators coupled together, but a very special kind. We have already seen this above because we needed to assume a very special potential energy for the rubber band between the oscillators. If we assume a different kind of coupling between the springs, we will end up with a different kind of system in the continuum which will not be equal to a scalar field as we usually encounter it in field theory

$$\begin{aligned}
L_{\text{NCHO}} &= \int dx \left(\frac{1}{2} M c^2 \left(\frac{\partial \varphi}{c \partial t} \right)^2 - \frac{1}{2} k \varphi^2 - \frac{1}{2} \rho \left(\frac{\partial \varphi}{\partial x} \right)^2 \right) \\
& \qquad \rho \to Mc^2 \\
&= \int dx \left(\frac{1}{2} M c^2 \left(\frac{\partial \varphi}{c \partial t} \right)^2 - \frac{1}{2} k \varphi^2 - \frac{1}{2} M c^2 \left(\frac{\partial \varphi}{\partial x} \right)^2 \right) \\
& \qquad \text{Eq. 5.22} \\
&= \int dx \left(\frac{1}{2} M c^2 \partial_\mu \varphi \partial^\mu \varphi - \frac{1}{2} k \varphi^2 \right) .
\end{aligned} \tag{5.24}$$

In this case, the index μ in ∂_μ only runs from 0 to 1. But if we consider a two-dimensional lattice of coupled oscillators, we find exactly the same formulas with μ running from 0 to 2. Moreover, if we consider a three-dimensional oscillator network, μ runs from 0 to 3.

As a final step to bring Eq. 5.24 in the form given at the beginning of this section (Eq. 5.2), we rescale the field variable

$$\varphi \to \phi = \sqrt{Mc^2}\varphi\,. \tag{5.25}$$

This transformation has no deeper meaning, but is simply a clever trick to clean up the Lagrangian a little bit:

$$\begin{aligned}
L_{\text{NCHO}} &= \int dx \left(\frac{1}{2}Mc^2\partial_\mu\varphi\partial^\mu\varphi - \frac{1}{2}k\varphi^2\right) && \text{this is Eq. 5.24} \\
&\quad\text{Eq. 5.25} \\
&= \int dx \left(\frac{1}{2}Mc^2\partial_\mu\frac{\phi}{\sqrt{Mc^2}}\partial^\mu\frac{\phi}{\sqrt{Mc^2}} - \frac{1}{2}k\left(\frac{\phi}{\sqrt{Mc^2}}\right)^2\right) \\
&= \int dx \left(\frac{1}{2}\partial_\mu\phi\partial^\mu\phi - \frac{1}{2}\frac{k}{Mc^2}\phi^2\right) && m^2 \equiv \frac{k}{Mc^2} \text{ (definition)} \\
&= \int dx \left(\frac{1}{2}\partial_\mu\phi\partial^\mu\phi - \frac{1}{2}m^2\phi^2\right).
\end{aligned} \tag{5.26}$$

This is exactly the Klein-Gordon Lagrangian (Eq. 5.2).

Let's recap what we've discovered in this section. We started by discussing a chain of coupled harmonic oscillators. Neighboring oscillators influence each other through a rubber band although each of the oscillators is only allowed to bounce up and down. We then investigated what happens if we add more and more oscillators to the chain and therefore shrink the distance l between neighboring oscillators. In the continuum limit ($l \to 0$), we have an oscillator at each point in space. Taking this limit is non-trivial because as the distance between the oscillators gets smaller it's not immediately clear what happens to the rubber band between them. But we discovered that if we make certain assumptions about the behavior of our chain in the continuum limit, we end up with a Lagrangian that is directly analogous to the Klein-Gordon Lagrangian.

We've therefore discovered that thinking about a scalar field as some kind of mattress is not just a nice picture, but also mathematically not too wrong. As long as we make certain assumptions about the coupling between the oscillators, we indeed end up with the correct Lagrangian for a scalar field in the continuum limit.

This implies that if we want to understand the dynamics of a scalar field, it may be a good idea to start by thinking about the dynamics of a chain of coupled oscillators. For example, we can imagine that if we move one of the oscillators up and then release it, some kind of wave will move through our chain.

We will discover in the following section that the Klein-Gordon Lagrangian indeed has wave-like solutions.

Many physicists will tell you that you shouldn't think of a scalar field as a network of coupled harmonic oscillators. However, as far as I know, there is no better way to visualize a scalar field. The alternative that is commonly proposed is to discard the need for a picture and use scalar fields as abstract bookkeeping devices. This is, of course, a perfectly valid approach. If you don't draw a picture, you certainly draw nothing wrong.

But we will see later that in the context of quantum field theory, the oscillator picture will prove to be quite helpful again. Thus, I'm convinced that as long as we don't imagine that there are really point masses that oscillate in physical space and instead, imagine that the oscillation happens in an abstract field space, the oscillator picture is more useful than confusing.[15]

[15] We discuss the field space idea in Section 3.7.

5.1.2 The Meaning of the Klein-Gordon Lagrangian

With our coupled-oscillator-picture in mind, it makes sense to take a second look at the Klein-Gordon Lagrangian (Eq. 5.2):

$$L = \int d^3x\, \mathcal{L} = \int d^3x\, \frac{1}{2}(\partial_\mu\phi\partial^\mu\phi - m^2\phi^2)$$

↷ summation convention

$$= \int d^3x\, \frac{1}{2}(\partial_0\phi\partial_0\phi - \partial_i\phi\partial_i\phi - m^2\phi^2)\,. \tag{5.27}$$

Using the oscillator picture, we can interpret the three terms in this Lagrangian as follows:

▷ The first term $T \equiv \partial_0\phi\partial_0\phi$ describes the kinetic energies of the oscillators (Eq. 5.17):

$$\frac{1}{2}M\sum_{i=1}^{N}\dot{q}_i^2(t) \rightarrow \frac{1}{2}M\int dx\, \dot{\varphi}^2(x,t) \equiv \frac{1}{2}M\int dx\, \partial_0\varphi(x,t)\partial_0\varphi(x,t) \tag{5.28}$$

▷ The second term $V_r \equiv \partial_i\phi\partial_i\phi$ describes the potential energy stored in the rubber bands that connect neighboring springs (Eq. 5.20):

$$\lim_{l\to 0}\frac{1}{2}\frac{Kl}{2}\sum_{ij}\frac{(q_i - q_j)^2}{l^2} = \frac{1}{2}\rho\int dx\, \left(\frac{\partial\varphi(x,t)}{\partial x}\right)^2$$

$$\equiv \frac{1}{2}\rho\int dx\, \partial_x\varphi(x,t)\partial_x\varphi(x,t)\,. \tag{5.29}$$

▷ The third term $V_s \equiv m^2\phi^2$ describes the potential energy stored in the spring at each location (Eq. 5.18):

$$\frac{1}{2}k\sum_{i=1}^{N}q_i^2 \rightarrow \frac{1}{2}k\int dx\, \varphi^2(x,t)\,. \tag{5.30}$$

Therefore, even though the Klein-Gordon Lagrangian looks completely different from what we are used to from classical mechanics, we can now understand that it in fact has the usual form:

$$L = \int d^3x\, \frac{1}{2}(\partial_0\phi\partial_0\phi - \partial_i\phi\partial_i\phi - m^2\phi^2)$$

↷

$$\equiv T - V = T - (V_r + V_s) = T - V_r - V_s\,. \tag{5.31}$$

A second aspect of the Klein-Gordon Lagrangian that we can now discuss is the meaning of the parameter m. In our oscillator picture, the parameter m is directly related to the harmonic restoring force of the spring at each point. Therefore, if we set $m = 0$ we assume that there is no such restoring force and thus no spring at each point. In other words, if we plug $m = 0$ into our Lagrangian, we are dealing with a system of mass points that are connected to their neighbors, while for $m \neq 0$ we describe a system of connected mass points that are pulled back to their equilibrium position through a harmonic force.

In the continuum limit our (one-dimensional) system of coupled mass points becomes a string. For $m = 0$ this string can wiggle freely, while for $m \neq 0$ there is a restoring force at each point. But take note that for $m = 0$ the mass points at each location are eventually also pulled down as a result of their connection to their neighbors (string tension).

In intuitive terms, we can imagine that a field with a large mass parameter m is analogous to a hard mattress, while a field with a small mass parameter m is analogous to a soft mattress. This follows because from the oscillator chain perspective, the parameter m is proportional to the stiffness k of the spring at each location. Moreover, we will learn later that in quantum field theory, the parameter m encodes, in some sense, a lower energy threshold. If too little energy is available, there will be no noticeable excitation in the field. In other words, for fields with a large mass parameter m it's much harder to cause any noticeable field excitation, while a field with small m can be excited quite easily. If there is not enough energy available to excite a field with large m, the energy will go into fields with a small mass parameter. Using our mattress picture once again, we can imagine that we need much more energy to cause any noticeable disturbance of a hard mattress, while it is easy to disturb a soft mattress.

In addition, recall that I mentioned already in Section 3.6 that for $m = 0$ all plane waves have the same phase velocity. This implies that wave packets keep their shapes as time passes on.

But for $m \neq 0$, the phase velocity depends on the wavelength and thus wave packets eventually dissolve. By using our rope vs. rope attached to springs picture, we can understand how this comes about.

Let's start by considering an ordinary rope without springs. We can imagine that this rope consists of individual mass points which are connected to their neighbors by small strings. A key observation is that for short wavelengths, the small strings between neighboring mass points will be strongly distorted. This implies that a given mass point moves quickly up and down.

In contrast, for a wave with long wavelength, the small strings between neighbors are almost not distorted. Hence, in this case the individual mass points will move quite slowly up and down. At the same time, for small wavelengths the wave repeats faster in space. This is the definition of a small wavelength.

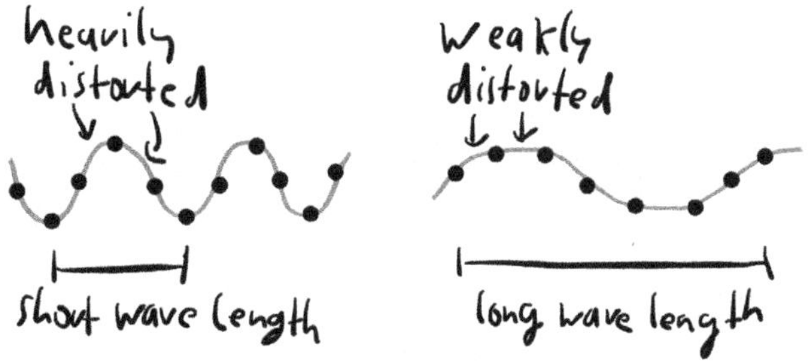

To understand the implications for the phase velocity, let's focus on one specific point on the wave, say a maximum. The phase velocity tells us how far this point travels Δx during a time interval Δt. While the mass points oscillate much quicker if the wavelength is small, they don't get very far during each oscillation. In contrast, the mass points in a wave with long wavelength oscillate slowly up and down but travel extremely far during each full up-down-up cycle.

This implies that even though each individual mass point moves only slowly up and down if the wavelength is large, the total distance Δx that our maximum travels during the time interval Δt will be exactly the same as for a wave with small wavelength. Hence, the phase velocity will be exactly the same.

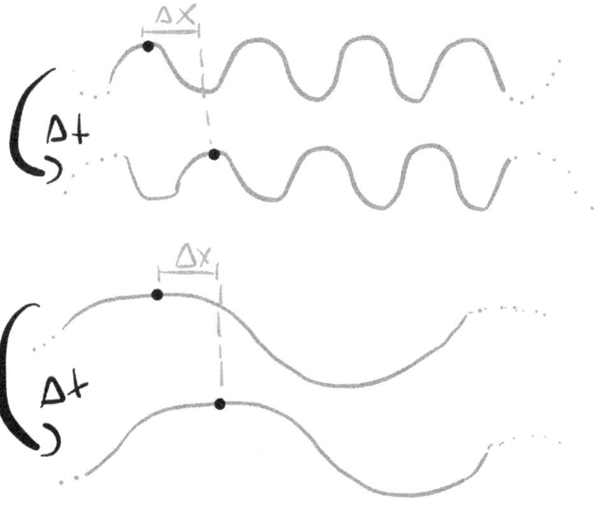

In summary:

▷ small $\lambda \to$ small period $\tau \to$ phase velocity $v = \frac{\lambda}{\tau}$,

▷ large $\lambda' \to$ large period $\tau' \to$ phase velocity $v = \frac{\lambda'}{\tau'}$.

Next, let's try to understand how the situation changes if we consider a string that is attached to springs. This system is different because the speed at which each mass point oscillates up and down is now determined by the springs and the small strings that connect it to its neighbors. Which of the two influences will dominate depends on the wave length. Therefore, the phase velocity depends on the wavelength.

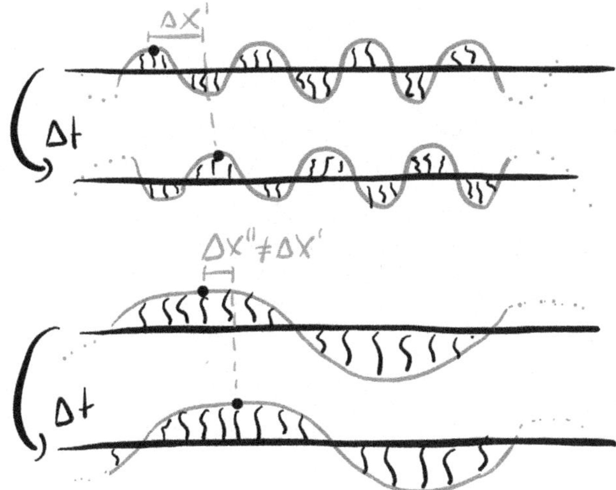

To understand this in more explicit terms, take note that for small wavelengths, $\lambda_1 \ll \frac{1}{m}$, the oscillation is primarily driven by the strings between neighboring mass points since they are strongly distorted.[16] Mathematically this follows if we calculate the $\frac{(2\pi)^2}{\lambda_1^2} \equiv k_1^2 \gg m^2$ limit of the dispersion relation (Eq. 3.77):

$$\begin{aligned} \omega_1 &= \sqrt{k_1^2 + m^2} \\ & \qquad\qquad\qquad\qquad \curvearrowright \quad k_1^2 \gg m^2 \\ &\approx k_1 \,. \end{aligned} \tag{5.32}$$

[16] As usual, notions like large and small have no absolute meaning. If we talk about small wavelengths we must say in relation to what it is small. Here, we can imagine that a characteristic wavelength of our system consisting of a string attached to springs is encoded by $\frac{1}{m}$. This follows if we look at the dispersion relation in which the wave number $k = \frac{2\pi}{\lambda}$ "competes" with m.

The relation $\omega_1 = k_1$ is exactly what we have for a rope without springs (Eq. 3.72).

For large wavelengths, $\lambda_2 \gg \frac{1}{m}$, each of the small strings between neighbors is only a little bit distorted. Hence, the oscillation is primarily driven by the springs. Since the spring stiffness is proportional to m, we can see this mathematically by noting that for $\frac{(2\pi)^2}{\lambda_2^2} \equiv k_2^2 \ll m^2$ we have

$$\begin{aligned} \omega &= \sqrt{k_2^2 + m^2} \\ & \qquad\qquad\qquad \curvearrowright \quad \omega = \sqrt{k_2^2 + m^2} \approx m \\ &\approx m \,. \end{aligned} \tag{5.33}$$

By using the definition of the phase velocity (Eq. C.10), we can therefore conclude [17]

[17] Take note that the phase velocity for short wavelength is 1 here because we work in natural units where $c = 1$. In other units, we find $v_1 = c$.

$$\begin{aligned} v_1 &= \frac{\omega_1}{k_1} \approx \frac{k_1}{k_1} = 1 \\ v_2 &= \frac{\omega_2}{k_2} \approx \frac{m}{k_2} \\ \Rightarrow v_1 &\neq v_2 \,. \end{aligned} \tag{5.34}$$

We can conclude that the phase velocity indeed depends on the wavelength for a rope attached to springs.

The subtle difference in the behavior of a system with and without a dispersion parameter m, has many important implications for modern physics. In particular, we will see in Chapter 6 that the parameter m determines how far a field can spread its influence. For example, for large values of m, the influence of a field disturbance dies off quickly. In some sense this follows from the fact that for large values of m a wave packet will dissolve quickly, while for $m = 0$ it doesn't dissolve at all. Moreover, as mentioned already in Section 3.6, in quantum field theory this implies that heavy particles (=excitations in a field with large m-parameter) usually decay more quickly than lighter ones (=excitations in a field with smaller m-parameter).

A third aspect that is worth discussing are possible modifications of the Klein-Gordon Lagrangian. A Lagrangian represents mathematically a model for a specific system. Therefore, we need different Lagrangians for different systems. We encountered one interesting modification of the Klein-Gordon Lagrangian above already. If there is no restoring force that pulls the field at each location back to its equilibrium position, we use a Lagrangian without a mass term ($m = 0$). As discussed above, it makes a big difference whether or not a mass term is necessary.

But, of course, we can not only remove terms from a Lagrangian but also add new terms.

For example, we can imagine that the restoring force that pulls our mass points back to the equilibrium originates in a more complicated potential than simply $V = kx^2$. As a concrete example, we can consider the potential $V = kx^2 - \frac{\lambda}{4!}x^4$, where $4! = 4 \cdot 3 \cdot 2 \cdot 1 = 24$. In physical terms, we can imagine that this means that we are dealing with a chain of coupled pendulums instead of coupled oscillators.

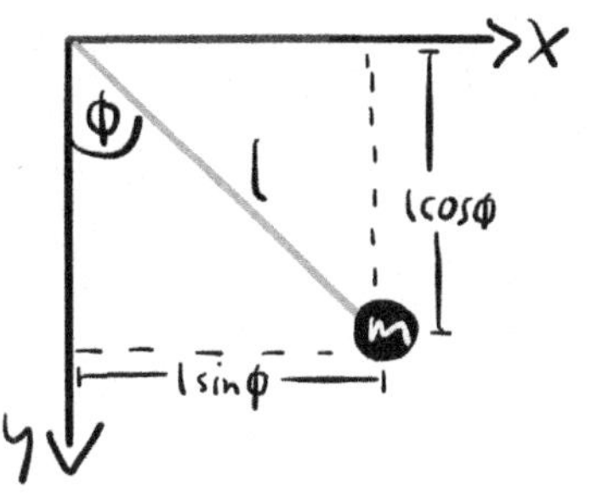

The pendulum potential reads

$$V(\theta) = mgl(1 - \cos(\phi)) \tag{5.35}$$

If we then assume that the pendulum only swings a little, we can Taylor expand this formula:

$$\begin{aligned} V(\theta) &= mgl(1 - \cos(\phi)) \\ & \qquad \qquad \curvearrowright \cos(x) = 1 - \frac{x^2}{2} + \frac{x^4}{4!} + \ldots \\ &\approx mgl\left(1 - \left(1 - \frac{\phi^2}{2} + \frac{\phi^4}{4!}\right)\right) \\ & \qquad \qquad \curvearrowright \not{1} \\ &= mgl\frac{\phi^2}{2} - mgl\frac{\phi^4}{4!} . \end{aligned} \tag{5.36}$$

In words, this means that our original formula ($V = kx^2$) is only a first order approximation for a pendulum. To describe a pendulum more accurately, we need to take higher order terms like $\frac{x^4}{4!}$ into account.

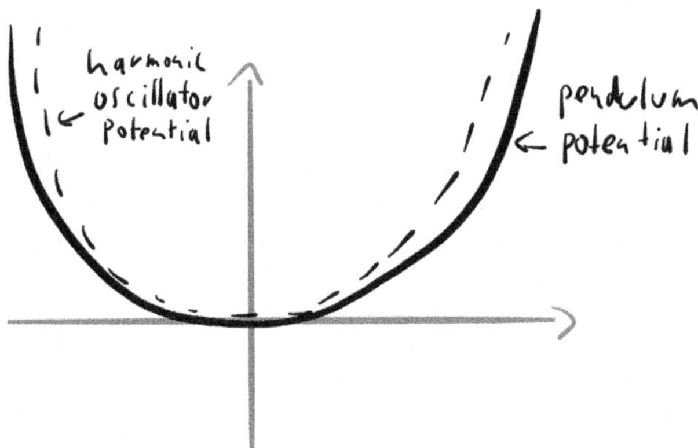

If we assume that our potential reads $V = kx^2 - \frac{\lambda}{4!}x^4$ and then carry out the same analysis as in the previous section, we find in the continuum limit[18]

$$L_{\rm NP} = \int dx \, \left(\frac{1}{2}\partial_\mu \phi \partial^\mu \phi - \frac{1}{2}\mu\phi^2 + \frac{\lambda}{4!}\phi^4 \right) . \tag{5.37}$$

[18] This is Eq. 5.26 with an additional ϕ^4 term.

There are two extremely important lessons to be learned here.

Firstly, take note that, as usual in a sensible Taylor expansion, higher order terms are less important than the first term. If we ignore all higher order terms and only work with $V = kx^2$, we are already getting quite accurate results for most situations. If we care a bit more about details, we can include the next term in the expansion $V = kx^2 - \frac{\lambda}{4!}x^4$ and so on. In particular, as long as the system only oscillates a little bit, the approximation $V \approx kx^2$ yields great results. At higher energies, higher order terms like $\frac{\lambda}{4!}\phi^4$ become increasingly important.

The situation in modern field theory is quite analogous. To start with, we work with the simplest nontrivial Lagrangians for our fields (Eq. 5.2). However, it is now commonly believed that this is just a first approximation and that there are infinitely many higher-order terms ($\phi^4, \phi^6, \ldots$) that play a role. The reason why our simple Lagrangians work so well is that these higher-order terms yield contributions that are too small to be measurable with present day technologies. We say that the best models we currently have are only effective models that need to be modified at higher energies.[19]

[19] We will discuss this idea in more mathematical terms in Chapter 17

You might wonder why we don't use the full potential $V(\theta) = mgl(1 - \cos(\theta))$. One reason is that the formulas we find with this full potential are far too difficult to tell us anything meaningful. A second and more important reason is that when it comes to fundamental physics, we might not know the correct formula for the potential. No one knows if a scalar field is really analogous to a network of coupled pendulums or if something far more complicated is going on. Therefore, the best we can do is to start with some power series $V = a + bx + cx^2 + dx^3 + ex^4 + \ldots$ and then use experimental input to determine the parameters $a, b, c, d, e, \ldots$. Since lots of potentials can be described quite accurately in a first approximation using the harmonic oscillator potential $V = kx^2$, it's not too surprising that fundamental scalar fields behave, in a first approximation, like a bunch of coupled oscillators.[20]

[20] You might wonder why the constant term a or the linear term bx do not play a dominant role. The reason is that a constant term a and a linear term bx have no influence on the dynamics and can therefore be neglected. This follows if we plug the Lagrangian $L = T - V = \frac{1}{2}m\dot{x}^2 - a - bx - x^2$ into the Euler-Lagrange equation (Eq. 4.2):

$$\frac{\partial L}{\partial q} = \frac{d}{dt}\left(\frac{\partial L}{\partial \dot{q}}\right)$$
$$-b - cx = m\ddot{x}\,.$$

We can simply shift our coordinate system $x \to \tilde{x} = x + \frac{b}{c}$. The acceleration remains unaffected by this shift: $\ddot{x} = \frac{d^2x}{dt^2} = \frac{d^2(\tilde{x}-\frac{b}{c})}{dt^2} = \frac{d^2\tilde{x}}{dt^2}$ Therefore, the equation of motion in the shifted coordinate system reads

$$\begin{aligned} -b - cx &= m\ddot{x} \\ \to -b - c(\tilde{x} - \frac{b}{c}) &= m\ddot{\tilde{x}} \\ -b - c\tilde{x} + b &= m\ddot{\tilde{x}} \\ -c\tilde{x} &= m\ddot{\tilde{x}}\,. \end{aligned}$$

This is exactly the equation of motion that we find without the constant term a and linear term bx. In physical terms, the constant term bx represents a constant force that shifts the equilibrium position of our oscillator. As we've seen above, a shift of the equilibrium position has no effect on the dynamics of the system since it can be compensated by a shift of the coordinate system.

Another thing worth mentioning is that the Lagrangian in Eq. 5.37 plays an incredibly important role in modern physics. As we will discuss later in Chapter 14, we can use it to implement the spontaneous mass creation mechanism which is responsible for the masses of all known elementary particles.

Next, to understand in mathematical terms how a scalar field evolves in time, let's talk about solutions of the Klein-Gordon equation.

5.1.3 Solutions of the Klein-Gordon Equation

The Klein-Gordon equation is the three-dimensional version of the wave equation with dispersion term that we discussed in Section 3.6. Nevertheless, it makes sense to discuss its solutions here since there are a few new aspects.

Let's start by looking at the Klein-Gordon equation (Eq. 5.4), which I recite here for convenience

$$(\partial_\mu \partial^\mu + m^2)\phi = 0\,. \qquad (5.38)$$

In words, the equation tells us that we need a function $\phi = \phi(x_\mu)$ that yields the constant m^2 times the same function and a minus sign when differentiated twice. The most famous functions that yield minus itself when differentiated twice are $\sin(x)$, $\cos(x)$ and e^{ix}.[21] By recalling what we discussed in Section 3.6, we can immediately write down solutions of the Klein-Gordon equation. For example,

[21] Take note that e^x doesn't work since we don't get a minus sign here. Moreover, $\partial_x^2 \cos(ax) = \partial_x(-a\sin(ax)) = -a^2\cos(ax)$ since $\partial_x \cos(ax) = -a\sin(ax)$ and $\partial_x \sin(ax) = a\cos(ax)$

$$\phi(x_\mu) = \cos(k_\mu x^\mu) \qquad (5.39)$$

solves the Klein-Gordon equation, as long as the wave-vector k_μ fulfills the dispersion relation

$$k_\mu k^\mu = m^2 . \tag{5.40}$$

The wave four-vector k_μ combines the frequency ω and the usual wave vector $\vec{k}$ into a single object[22]

$$k_\mu = \begin{pmatrix} \omega \\ \vec{k} \end{pmatrix} . \tag{5.41}$$

[22] Take note that we work here in natural units. In SI-units, the wave vector reads

$$k_\mu = \begin{pmatrix} \frac{\omega}{c} \\ \vec{k} \end{pmatrix} .$$

Introducing this object makes sense in a relativistic object because ω denotes the angular frequency and $\vec{k}$ the spatial fequencies. Therefore, analogously to how space and time get combined in a single four-vector x_μ, we combine here the angular frequency (angle per second) and the spatial frequencies (angle per meter) into a single four-vector k_μ.

We can check explicitly that the function in Eq. 3.67 solves the Klein-Gordon equation:

$$\begin{aligned}
0 &= (\partial_\mu \partial^\mu + m^2)\phi && \text{this is the KG equation (Eq. 5.4)} \\
&&& \text{Eq. 3.67} \\
&= (\partial_\mu \partial^\mu + m^2)\cos(k_\mu x^\mu) \\
&&& \partial_x^2 \cos(ax) = -a^2 \cos(ax) \\
&= (-k_\mu k^\mu + m^2)\cos(k_\mu x^\mu) \\
&&& k_\mu k^\mu = m^2 \text{ (Eq. 5.40)} \\
&= (-m^2 + m^2)\cos(k_\mu x^\mu) \\
&= 0 \quad \checkmark
\end{aligned} \tag{5.42}$$

As discussed in Section 3.6, solutions of the form given in Eq. 3.67 are known as **plane wave solutions** since they spread out all over space with exactly the same amplitude.

Completely analogously, we can check that functions of the form $\phi(x_\mu) = \sin(k_\mu x^\mu)$ are also solutions of the Klein-Gordon equation. Moreover, since only the length m of the wave vector k_μ is important in the calculation above, we can conclude that there are lots of different solutions which involve different wave vectors k^i_μ. We can put any four-vector k_μ that fulfills the dispersion relation $k_\mu k^\mu = m^2$ into a cosine or sine function and get a solution of the Klein-Gordon equation.

In addition, as for the wave equation, we can construct wave packets by using linear combinations of plane waves.

Next, let's talk about the third function e^{ix} which possibly plays a role as a solution of the Klein-Gordon equation. Using Euler's famous formula

$$e^{ix} = \cos(x) + i\sin(x) \tag{5.43}$$

we can understand that the general structure of a solution which involves e^{ix} is not too different from what we have just discussed.

Moreover, we can check explicitly that

$$\phi(x) = \mathrm{e}^{-i(k_\mu x^\mu)} \tag{5.44}$$

is a solution of the Klein-Gordon equation:

$$\begin{aligned}
0 &= (\partial_\mu \partial^\mu + m^2)\phi && \text{this is the KG equation (Eq. 5.4)} \\
& && \text{Eq. 5.44} \\
&= (\partial_\mu \partial^\mu + m^2)\mathrm{e}^{-i(k_\mu x^\mu)} \\
&= (-k_\mu k^\mu + m^2)\mathrm{e}^{-i(k_\mu x^\mu)} \\
& && k_\mu k^\mu = m^2 \text{ (Eq. 5.40)} \\
&= (-m^2 + m^2)\mathrm{e}^{-i(k_\mu x^\mu)} \\
&= 0 \quad \checkmark
\end{aligned} \tag{5.45}$$

Analogously, we can check that $\phi(x) = \mathrm{e}^{i(k_\mu x^\mu)}$ also solves the Klein-Gordon equation.

A new aspect of these solutions compared to the solutions discussed previously (Eq. 3.67) is that here we are dealing with a complex function.

In words, this means that the Klein-Gordon equation is not only solved by real scalar fields but also by complex scalar fields. As usual, mathematics alone cannot tell us what kind of solution we should use. We always need experiments to tell us whether we need real solutions or complex solutions to describe a given system.

Since it is often much easier to work with complex functions and to stay as general as possible, we will turn our focus to such complex solutions.[23] Mathematically, a real scalar field is a map

[23] The only known fundamental scalar field, the Higgs field, is indeed complex.

$$\mathbb{R}^{1,3} \to \mathbb{R} \tag{5.46}$$

while a complex scalar field is a map

$$\mathbb{R}^{1,3} \to \mathbb{C}\,. \tag{5.47}$$

Formulated differently, while a real scalar field eats a spacetime point and spits out a real number, a complex scalar field eats a spacetime point and spits out a complex number.

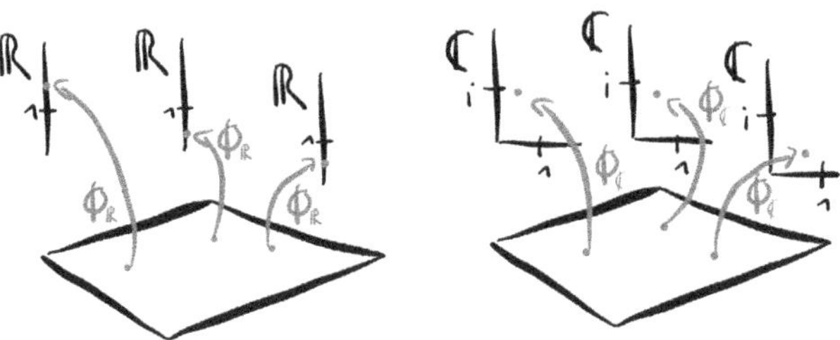

5.1.4 General Solution of the Klein-Gordon Equation

We can construct new solutions by using linear combinations of known solutions. The most general solution of the Klein-Gordon equation reads[24]

[24] This is a continuous version of Eq. 3.82. In Eq. 3.82, we sum over a few specific wave vectors k_i^μ, while here we sum over *all* wave vectors.

$$\phi(x) = \int \frac{\mathrm{d}k^4}{(2\pi)^4} \left(a(k_\mu) \mathrm{e}^{-i(k_\mu x^\mu)} + b(k_\mu) \mathrm{e}^{i(k_\mu x^\mu)} \right), \tag{5.48}$$

where $(2\pi)^4$ is a conventional normalization factor and $a(k_\mu)$, $b(k_\mu)$ are coefficients that describe how much each individual plane wave contributes to the total wave form. Since we sum over all possible wave vectors k_μ, we are dealing with functions of k_μ instead of a discrete set of coefficients.

Take note that for a real scalar field only a small modification is necessary. The defining condition of a real scalar field is $\phi^\dagger = \phi$.[25] This implies that the corresponding expansion reads

$$\phi(x) = \int \frac{dk^4}{(2\pi)^4}\left(a(k_\mu)e^{-i(k_\mu x^\mu)} + a^\dagger(k_\mu)e^{i(k_\mu x^\mu)}\right) \tag{5.49}$$

since it now automatically fulfills the condition $\phi^\dagger = \phi$:

$$\begin{aligned}\phi^\dagger(x) &= \left(\int \frac{dk^4}{(2\pi)^4}\left(a(k_\mu)e^{-i(k_\mu x^\mu)} + a^\dagger(k_\mu)e^{i(k_\mu x^\mu)}\right)\right)^\dagger \\ &\quad \text{↓ } (e^{-i(k_\mu x^\mu)})^\dagger = e^{i(k_\mu x^\mu)},\ (a^\dagger)^\dagger = a \\ &= \int \frac{dk^4}{(2\pi)^4}\left(a^\dagger(k_\mu)e^{i(k_\mu x^\mu)} + a(k_\mu)e^{-i(k_\mu x^\mu)}\right) \\ &= \phi(x) \quad \checkmark\end{aligned} \tag{5.50}$$

The notation in Eq. 5.49 is quite sloppy because we do not really sum over all possible plane wave solutions. Instead, we only include those that fulfill the dispersion relation $k_\mu k^\mu = m^2$ (Eq. 5.40).[26] If we only want to include positive frequency solutions and use the short-hand notation $kx \equiv k_\mu x^\mu$, we can write the general solution of the Klein-Gordon equation as

$$\boxed{\phi(x) = \int dk^3 \frac{1}{(2\pi)^3\sqrt{2\omega_k}}\left(a(\vec{k})e^{-ikx} + a^\dagger(\vec{k})e^{ikx}\right).} \tag{5.51}$$

This is demonstrated explicitly in Appendix A.3.[27] Take note that in Eq. 5.51 new rescaled coefficients $a(\vec{k})$, $a^\dagger(\vec{k})$ instead of $a(k)$, $a^\dagger(k)$ appear in the expansion wich are defined as

$$\begin{aligned} a(\vec{k}) &\equiv \frac{a(k)}{\sqrt{2\omega_k}} \\ a^\dagger(\vec{k}) &\equiv \frac{a^\dagger(k)}{\sqrt{2\omega_k}}. \end{aligned} \tag{5.52}$$

It is conventional to work with the rescaled coefficients $a(\vec{k})$, $a^\dagger(\vec{k})$ since this simplifies many calculations in later chapters. The notation here is rather subtle and it probably would be better to use, for example, $\tilde{a}(k)$ instead of $a(\vec{k})$. But the notation in Eq. 5.52 is the standard one thus we will also use it in the following.[28]

[25] Reminder: † denotes Hermitian conjugation: $A^\dagger = A^{T\star}$. For a scalar field, transposition makes no difference and therefore we have $\phi^\dagger = \phi^\star$. Nevertheless, we use † here to get a uniform notation for all kinds of fields.

[26] We will derive later that in quantum field theory the zeroth component of the wave vector k_μ is directly related to the energy, $k_0 \sim E$.

[27] The discussion in Appendix A.3 is quite technical and you can skip it on a first reading.

[28] It's often very tempting to introduce an improved notation. However, any change in notation makes it much harder for readers to compare statements made in different books and are therefore often more harmful than helpful.

Similarly, we can write the expansion for a complex scalar field as

$$\boxed{\phi(x) = \int \mathrm{d}k^3 \frac{1}{(2\pi)^3\sqrt{2\omega_k}} \left(a(\vec{k})\mathrm{e}^{-ikx} + b(\vec{k})\mathrm{e}^{ikx}\right) .} \tag{5.53}$$

5.2 Free Spinor Fields and the Dirac Equation

As we did in the previous section, let's assume that someone hands us the Lagrangian density

$$\boxed{\mathcal{L}_{\text{Dirac}} = \bar{\Psi}(i\gamma^\mu \partial_\mu - m)\Psi\,,} \tag{5.54}$$

where Ψ is a Dirac spinor (Eq. 3.35), $\bar{\Psi}$ is a "conjugated" Dirac spinor:[29]

$$\bar{\Psi} \equiv (\Psi)^\dagger \gamma^0 = (\Psi^\star)^T \gamma^0 \tag{5.55}$$

[29] The "dagger" † denotes Hermitian conjugation which means complex conjugation ($\star$) plus transposition (T).

and[30]

$$\gamma^0 = \begin{pmatrix} 0 & 0 & 1 & 0 \\ 0 & 0 & 0 & 1 \\ 1 & 0 & 0 & 0 \\ 0 & 1 & 0 & 0 \end{pmatrix} \qquad \gamma^1 = \begin{pmatrix} 0 & 0 & 0 & 1 \\ 0 & 0 & 1 & 0 \\ 0 & -1 & 0 & 0 \\ -1 & 0 & 0 & 0 \end{pmatrix}$$

$$\gamma^2 = \begin{pmatrix} 0 & 0 & 0 & -i \\ 0 & 0 & i & 0 \\ 0 & i & 0 & 0 \\ -i & 0 & 0 & 0 \end{pmatrix} \qquad \gamma^3 = \begin{pmatrix} 0 & 0 & 1 & 0 \\ 0 & 0 & 0 & -1 \\ -1 & 0 & 0 & 0 \\ 0 & 1 & 0 & 0 \end{pmatrix}. \tag{5.56}$$

[30] Strictly speaking, this is only one possible representation of the gamma matrices known as the chiral basis. We will discuss an alternative representation and how it is related to the chiral basis in Section 5.2.3.

Again it is conventional to call the first term in Eq. 5.54 the kinetic term and the second term the mass term.

The conjugated Dirac spinor $\bar{\Psi}$ appears in the Lagrangian because the proper Dirac spinor scalar product reads $\bar{\Psi}\Psi$.[31] To see this, we note that the matrix γ_0 contains two (2×2) unit matrices:

[31] We need a scalar product in the Lagrangian because the Lagrangian itself is a scalar and is thus only allowed to contain scalar terms.

$$\gamma^0 = \begin{pmatrix} 0 & 1_{2\times 2} \\ 1_{2\times 2} & 0 \end{pmatrix}. \tag{5.57}$$

In addition, we recall that a Dirac spinor consists of two Weyl spinors (Eq. 3.35) and we can therefore rewrite the product $\bar{\Psi}\Psi$ as follows[32]

[32] Reminder: Eq. 3.35 reads

$$\Psi = \begin{pmatrix} \chi \\ \xi \end{pmatrix}.$$

$$\begin{aligned}
\bar{\Psi}\Psi &= \Psi^\dagger \gamma^0 \Psi \\
&\quad \text{(Eq. 3.35, Eq. 5.57)} \\
&= \begin{pmatrix} \chi \\ \xi \end{pmatrix}^\dagger \begin{pmatrix} 0 & 1_{2\times 2} \\ 1_{2\times 2} & 0 \end{pmatrix} \begin{pmatrix} \chi \\ \xi \end{pmatrix} \\
&\quad \text{(matrix product)} \\
&= \begin{pmatrix} \chi^\dagger & \xi^\dagger \end{pmatrix} \begin{pmatrix} \xi \\ \chi \end{pmatrix} \\
&= \chi^\dagger \xi + \xi^\dagger \chi \,.
\end{aligned} \tag{5.58}$$

Both terms here are proper scalar products of a right-chiral Weyl spinor and a left-chiral Weyl spinor (Eq. 3.63). We can therefore conclude that the proper scalar product of a Dirac spinor with itself can indeed be written as $\bar{\Psi}\Psi$.

The gamma matrices γ^μ show up everywhere when we do calculations with spinor fields since they provide an essential link between spinors and vectors. Such a link is essential because a spacetime derivative ∂_μ carries a vector index μ, while spinors carry spinor indices.[33] The "four vector" with gamma matrices as its entries

$$\gamma_\mu \equiv \begin{pmatrix} \gamma_0 \\ \gamma_1 \\ \gamma_2 \\ \gamma_3 \end{pmatrix} \tag{5.59}$$

carries a vector index μ and spinor indices. This follows since each gamma matrix acts on spinors and thus carries (like any matrix) two spinor indices.[34] As shown in the Dirac Lagrangian (Eq. 5.54), the gamma matrices allow us to write down a term in the Lagrangian that involves a spacetime derivative ∂_μ and spinors.[35]

There are important relations between gamma matrices that are useful in many calculations.[36] The most famous relation

$$\boxed{\{\gamma^\mu, \gamma^\nu\} \equiv \gamma^\mu\gamma^\nu + \gamma^\nu\gamma^\mu = 2\eta^{\mu\nu} 1_{4\times 4}} \tag{5.60}$$

is known as the **Clifford algebra**. The object on the left-hand side is known as the anticommutator of two gamma matrices,

[33] We discussed spinor indices in Section 3.4.1.

[34] The index μ labels different gamma matrices. Moreover, there are two spinor indices because the result, if we act with a gamma matrix on a spinor, η^i, is another spinor: $\gamma_1^{ij}\eta_j = \eta^i$.

[35] The gamma matrices allow us to construct a term that is invariant under Poincaré transformations. In physical terms this implies that the term respects the laws of special relativity. This line of thought is spelled out in more detail in Chapter 17.

[36] The gamma matrices are also sometimes called Dirac matrices.

$\eta^{\mu\nu}$ on the right-hand side is the Minkowski metric (Eq. 2.30) and $1_{4\times 4}$ is the (4×4) identity matrix. We can check the validity of this formula by using the explicit form of the gamma matrices (Eq. 5.56). For example, for $\mu = \nu = 0$, we find

$$\gamma^0\gamma^0 + \gamma^0\gamma^0 = 2\eta^{00} 1_{4\times 4}$$

↷ $\eta^{00} = 1$, see Eq. 2.30

$$2\gamma^0\gamma^0 = 2\, 1_{4\times 4}$$

↷ $\not{2}$

$$\gamma^0\gamma^0 = 1_{4\times 4}$$

↷ Eq. 5.56

$$\begin{pmatrix} 0 & 0 & 1 & 0 \\ 0 & 0 & 0 & 1 \\ 1 & 0 & 0 & 0 \\ 0 & 1 & 0 & 0 \end{pmatrix} \begin{pmatrix} 0 & 0 & 1 & 0 \\ 0 & 0 & 0 & 1 \\ 1 & 0 & 0 & 0 \\ 0 & 1 & 0 & 0 \end{pmatrix} = 1_{4\times 4}$$

↷ matrix product

$$\begin{pmatrix} 1 & 0 & 0 & 0 \\ 0 & 1 & 0 & 0 \\ 0 & 0 & 1 & 0 \\ 0 & 0 & 0 & 1 \end{pmatrix} = 1_{4\times 4} \quad \checkmark \tag{5.61}$$

Before we can derive the equation of motion that follows from the Dirac Lagrangian, we need to talk about an important subtlety. We discovered in the previous section that there can be complex scalar fields. Similarly, there can be complex spinor fields and that's why a "conjugated" Dirac spinor $\bar{\Psi}$ appears in the Lagrangian. All spinor fields that have been discovered so far are complex fields and thus we will assume here from the start that our spinor field Ψ is complex.

For a complex field, it is conventional to treat $\bar{\Psi}$ and Ψ as independent variables. This is motivated by the observation that we can split a complex field, analogous to a complex number, into a real and an imaginary part:[37]

$$\Psi = \Psi_r + i\Psi_i , \tag{5.62}$$

where Ψ_r and Ψ_i are real spinor fields. Therefore, by using a complex spinor field we effectively consider two spinor fields at

[37] A complex number z, can always be written as

$$z = a + ib,$$

where a is called the real part and b the imaginary part. Both a and b are real numbers.

once. But instead of plugging Eq. 5.62 into the Lagrangian and considering Ψ_r and Ψ_i as independent fields, it is conventional to work with Ψ and $\bar{\Psi}$.

If we plug the Lagrangian density given in Eq. 5.54 into the Euler-Lagrange equation for $\bar{\Psi}$ (Eq. 4.25), we find[38]

$$
\begin{aligned}
0 &= \frac{\partial \mathcal{L}}{\partial \bar{\Psi}} - \partial_\mu \left(\frac{\partial \mathcal{L}}{\partial(\partial_\mu \bar{\Psi})} \right) && \text{this is Eq. 4.25} \\
& && \text{Eq. 5.54} \\
&= \frac{\partial\Big(\bar{\Psi}(i\gamma^\mu \partial_\mu - m)\Psi\Big)}{\partial \bar{\Psi}} - \partial_\mu \left(\frac{\partial\Big(\bar{\Psi}(i\gamma^\mu \partial_\mu - m)\Psi\Big)}{\partial(\partial_\mu \bar{\Psi})} \right) \\
& && \frac{\partial \bar{\Psi}}{\partial \bar{\Psi}} = 1 \\
&= i\partial_\mu \gamma^\mu \Psi - m\Psi
\end{aligned}
\tag{5.63}
$$

The resulting equation

$$
\boxed{i\partial_\mu \gamma^\mu \Psi - m\Psi = 0} \tag{5.64}
$$

is the famous **Dirac equation**.

[38] It is equally possible to consider the Euler-Lagrange equation

$$
\frac{\partial \mathcal{L}}{\partial \Psi} - \partial_\mu \left(\frac{\partial \mathcal{L}}{\partial(\partial_\mu \Psi)} \right) = 0 .
$$

This yields the equation of motion for the field $\bar{\Psi}$. But since the derivation and interpretation of the resulting equation is a bit more subtle, we consider here only the equation of motion for Ψ.

5.2.1 The Meaning of the Dirac Equation

One aspect of the dynamics of a spinor field is not too dissimilar from the dynamics of a scalar field. As for a scalar field, we have a field strength at each location that oscillates in a harmonic oscillator-like manner. We will see below that there can again be wave-like structures in the values of the field strength that move through space.

Additionally, however, a spinor field has a rich internal structure. Lacking any deeper understanding, we describe this internal structure somewhat abstractly using the concepts of spin and chirality. We will see that the Dirac equation not only tells us how field strength values vary in time, but also which spinor structures are permitted in Nature.

We discussed in Section 3.2.1 that it is often helpful to separate the internal structure and the spacetime structure of a vector field. Exactly the same idea can be applied to spinor fields. Analogous to what we did for vector fields (Eq. 3.8), we will write spinor fields as

$$\Psi(x_\mu) = \underbrace{\psi}_{\text{internal structure}} \times \underbrace{f(x_\mu)}_{\text{spacetime structure}} . \tag{5.65}$$

This is useful because the spacetime structure is completely analogous to what we've already discovered for scalar fields. In the following section, we will derive that the spacetime structure of solutions of the Dirac equation are again plane waves:

$$f(x_\mu) = e^{-ik_\mu x^\mu} = e^{-i(k_0 x_0 - k_i x_i)} = e^{-i(\omega t - \vec{k}\cdot\vec{k})} . \tag{5.66}$$

Therefore, the only new thing about the Dirac equation is what it tells us about permitted spinor structures.

In Section 3.4.2, we already started to talk about how we can interpret spinor components. Now that we have the Dirac equation, we can continue this discussion. But first, let's recall the main ideas:

▷ A Dirac spinor Ψ consists of two Weyl spinors χ, ξ:

$$\Psi = \begin{pmatrix} \chi \\ \xi \end{pmatrix} . \tag{5.67}$$

▷ We call χ a left-chiral spinor and ξ a right-chiral spinor.

▷ Each Weyl spinor is a two-component object:

$$\chi = \begin{pmatrix} \chi_1 \\ \chi_2 \end{pmatrix} , \quad \xi = \begin{pmatrix} \xi_1 \\ \xi_2 \end{pmatrix} . \tag{5.68}$$

▷ The structure of a Weyl spinor determines the spin structure of the corresponding field or particle:[39]

$$\text{spin up:} \quad \begin{pmatrix} 1 \\ 0 \end{pmatrix} , \quad \text{spin down:} \quad \begin{pmatrix} 0 \\ 1 \end{pmatrix} \tag{5.69}$$

[39] Spin up and spin down refers here and in the following to spin orientations in the z-direction.

In summary, there are four different basis field configurations:

$$\begin{aligned} &\text{left-chiral, spin up:} \begin{pmatrix} \chi_1 \\ 0 \\ 0 \\ 0 \end{pmatrix} , \quad \text{left-chiral, spin down:} \begin{pmatrix} 0 \\ \chi_2 \\ 0 \\ 0 \end{pmatrix} , \\ &\text{right-chiral, spin up:} \begin{pmatrix} 0 \\ 0 \\ \xi_1 \\ 0 \end{pmatrix} , \quad \text{right-chiral, spin down:} \begin{pmatrix} 0 \\ 0 \\ 0 \\ \xi_2 \end{pmatrix} . \end{aligned} \tag{5.70}$$

Moreover, there are superpositions which are described by linear combinations of these basis spinors.

In the following section, we will derive that solutions of the

Dirac equation are of the form

$$\psi_i = \begin{pmatrix} \mathrm{u}_i \\ \mathrm{u}_i \end{pmatrix} \tag{5.71}$$

where[40] $\mathrm{u}_1 = \begin{pmatrix} 1 \\ 0 \end{pmatrix} \mathrm{e}^{-imt}$ and $\mathrm{u}_2 = \begin{pmatrix} 0 \\ 1 \end{pmatrix} \mathrm{e}^{-imt}$. Moreover, another kind of solution is of the form

[40] This is really a basis choice. The only requirement is that the two u_i are linearly independent.

$$\tilde{\psi}_i = \begin{pmatrix} -\mathrm{v}_i \\ \mathrm{v}_i \end{pmatrix}, \tag{5.72}$$

where $\mathrm{v}_1 = \begin{pmatrix} 1 \\ 0 \end{pmatrix} \mathrm{e}^{+imt}$ and $\mathrm{v}_2 = \begin{pmatrix} 0 \\ 1 \end{pmatrix} \mathrm{e}^{+imt}$.

To understand what these solutions and therefore the Dirac equation are telling us, let's assume that our field starts in a purely left-chiral configuration at one specific location with spin up:

$$e_L^{\uparrow} = \begin{pmatrix} 1 \\ 0 \\ 0 \\ 0 \end{pmatrix}. \tag{5.73}$$

Since this is not a solution of the Dirac equation, we need to rewrite it in terms of solutions to determine its time evolution:

$$\begin{aligned} e_L^{\uparrow} &= \begin{pmatrix} 1 \\ 0 \\ 0 \\ 0 \end{pmatrix} \\ &= \frac{1}{2}\left(\begin{pmatrix} 1 \\ 0 \\ 1 \\ 0 \end{pmatrix} - \begin{pmatrix} -1 \\ 0 \\ 1 \\ 0 \end{pmatrix} \right) && \text{Eq. 5.71, Eq. 5.72} \\ &= \Psi_1(t=0) - \tilde{\Psi}_1(t=0) \end{aligned} \tag{5.74}$$

Writing $e_L^{\uparrow}$ like this is useful, because we know exactly how Ψ_1

and $\tilde{\Psi}_1$ evolve in time:

$$\Psi(t) = \Psi_1(t) - \tilde{\Psi}_1(t)$$

↷ Eq. 5.71, Eq. 5.72

$$= \frac{1}{2}\left(\begin{pmatrix}1\\0\\1\\0\end{pmatrix} e^{-imt} - \begin{pmatrix}-1\\0\\1\\0\end{pmatrix} e^{imt}\right) \tag{5.75}$$

For $t = 0$ this yields exactly the purely left-chiral spin up field $e\Psi(0) = e_L^{\uparrow}$ (see Eq. 5.74). With this formula at hand, we find, for example, that at $t = \frac{\pi}{2m}$:

$$\Psi\left(\frac{\pi}{2m}\right) = \frac{1}{2}\left(\begin{pmatrix}1\\0\\1\\0\end{pmatrix} e^{-i\frac{\pi}{2}} - \begin{pmatrix}-1\\0\\1\\0\end{pmatrix} e^{i\frac{\pi}{2}}\right)$$

↷ $e^{-i\frac{\pi}{2}} = -i$, $e^{i\frac{\pi}{2}} = i$

$$= \frac{i}{2}\left(\begin{pmatrix}-1\\0\\-1\\0\end{pmatrix} - \begin{pmatrix}-1\\0\\1\\0\end{pmatrix}\right)$$

↷

$$= -i\begin{pmatrix}0\\0\\1\\0\end{pmatrix} . \tag{5.76}$$

The spinor that we find here

$$e_R^{\uparrow} = \begin{pmatrix}0\\0\\1\\0\end{pmatrix} \tag{5.77}$$

describes a right-chiral field with spin up.

Therefore, as promised above, the Dirac equation describes how left-chiral and right-chiral configurations oscillate into each other.

It may be helpful to rephrase everything we just learned into a more familiar language.

For clarity, let's assume that the field strength is only non-zero at one specific location $\vec{x}_S$. We can imagine that there is a lump of energy localized at this location. At $t = 0$, the field assigns the spinor $e_L^{\uparrow}$ (Eq. 5.73) to this location. For reasons that we will discuss later in more detail, we call this lump of energy a left-chiral electron with spin up.

The question we investigated above was: what happens to such a specific field configuration as time passes on? Using the Dirac equation, we discovered that after a while the field configuration at $\vec{x}_S$ is described by the spinor $e_R^{\uparrow}$ (Eq. 5.77). When we considered the problem in the rest frame, the lump of energy doesn't move and hence the field strength everywhere else remains zero. Nevertheless, the internal structure of our lump of energy changes. It starts in a purely left-chiral configuration and ends up in a purely right-chiral configuration. Moreover, at different points in time, we will find a configuration that we can describe as a mixture of left-chiral and right-chiral.

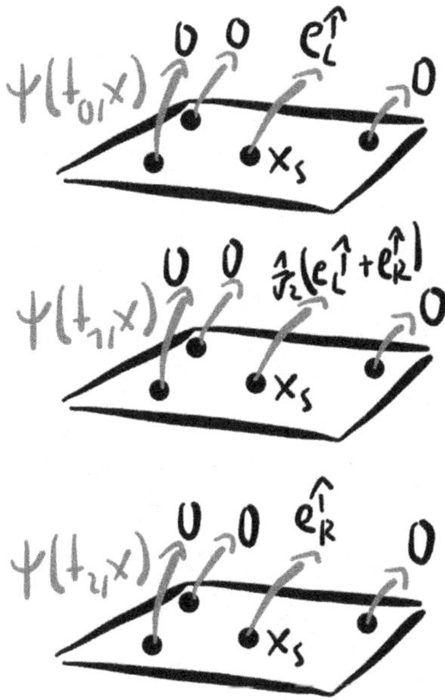

The rate at which a left-chiral configuration oscillates into a right-chiral configuration and vice versa is determined by the parameter m. In physical terms, we interpret the parameter m as the masses of the lumps of energies (particles) associated with the given field. If we only know the Dirac equation, this may seem quite mysterious. But luckily, there is a beautiful modern perspective that allows us to understand what is going on here on a much deeper level. We'll learn in Chapter 14 that we can understand the mass parameter m as a result of the interaction between a scalar field and spinor fields.[41] Moreover, we will reinterpret the mass parameter m associated with a spinor field as the coupling strength y between the scalar field and the spinor field times a constant parameter v that describes an important property of the scalar field: $m = yv$.[42] With this in mind, we can imagine that a given spinor field constantly interacts with the scalar field. Each time an interaction takes place, the chirality of our spinor field configuration flips.

[41] We call this a spontaneous mass creation mechanism, which is closely connected to the phenomenon known as spontaneous symmetry breaking.

[42] Technically, y is a Yukawa coupling and v the vacuum expectation value of the scalar field.

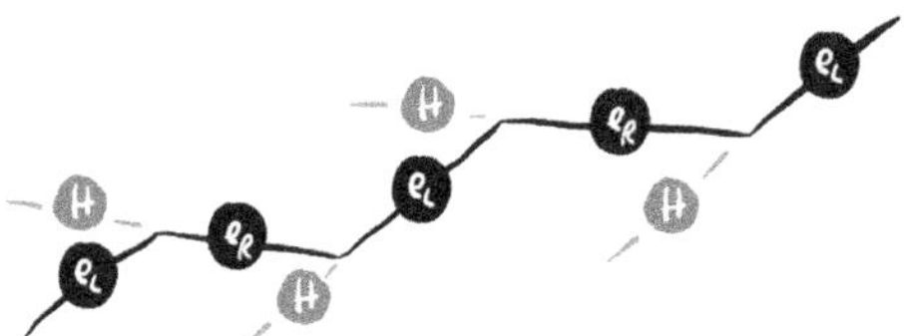

The coupling strength y of a given spinor field determines how often an interaction takes place. For fields with a larger mass parameter m, we also have a bigger coupling strength y. This implies that for fields with a larger m, a change from purely left-chiral to purely right-chiral happens much more quickly.

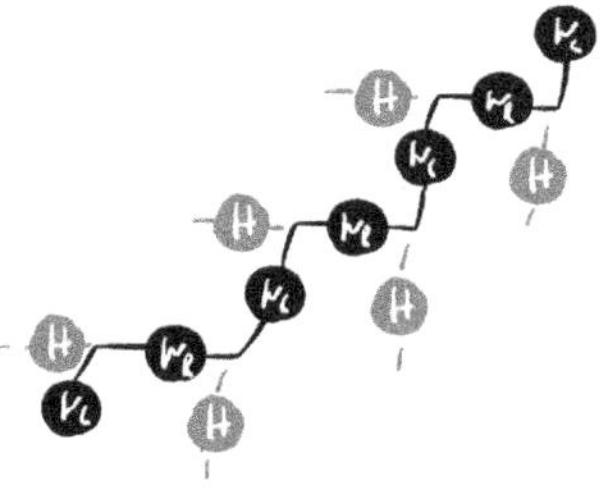

Therefore, from this perspective it's no longer completely mysterious why the mass parameter m determines how quickly left-chiral and right-chiral configurations oscillate into each other.

From a slightly more technical perspective, we can say that chirality flips all the time because states with fixed chirality (Eq. 5.70) are not solutions of the Dirac equation. Solutions of the Dirac equation describe how spinor fields evolve in time. Therefore, when we observe a spinor field in Nature we see a configuration that corresponds to a solution of the Dirac equation. We call configurations that can be described by solutions of the Dirac equation *physical* configurations. For example, a physical electron field is neither purely left-chiral nor purely right-chiral but a mixture that can be described by a linear combination like the one in Eq. 5.75.

Next, let's discuss how we can derive these solutions of the Dirac equation.

5.2.2 Solutions of the Dirac Equation

I mentioned already above that the basic building blocks that describe the spacetime structure of solutions of the Dirac equation are plane waves. To show this, we start by noting that in the Dirac equation (Eq. 5.64) the **Dirac operator** $\hat{D} \equiv i\partial_\mu\gamma^\mu - m$ acts on the spinor Ψ and the result has to be zero:

$$
\begin{aligned}
0 &= i\partial_\mu\gamma^\mu\Psi - m\Psi && \text{this is Eq. 5.64} \\
&&& \hookleftarrow \quad \hat{D} \equiv i\partial_\mu\gamma^\mu - m \\
&= \hat{D}\Psi\,. && (5.78)
\end{aligned}
$$

This is just a fancy way to think about the Dirac equation. This way of thinking is useful for our purposes because we can now consider what happens when we apply the complex conjugated Dirac operator $\hat{D}^\star \equiv -i\partial_\mu\gamma^\mu - m$ to $\hat{D}\Psi$.[43]

[43] We will see in a moment why this is interesting.

On the left-hand side of the Dirac equation, we will still have a zero and therefore find

$$\begin{aligned}
0 &= \hat{D}\Psi && \text{this is Eq. 5.78} \\
&&& \quad \times \hat{D}^\star \\
\hat{D}^\star 0 &= \hat{D}^\star \hat{D}\Psi \\
&&& \quad \hat{D}0 = 0 \\
0 &= \hat{D}^\star \hat{D}\Psi\,. && (5.79)
\end{aligned}$$

If we now calculate $\hat{D}^\star \hat{D}$ explicitly, we discover something remarkable:

$$\begin{aligned}
\hat{D}^\star \hat{D} &= (-i\partial_\mu \gamma^\mu - m)(i\partial_\nu \gamma^\nu - m) \\
&= -i^2 \partial_\mu \gamma^\mu \partial_\nu \gamma^\nu - im\partial_\nu \gamma^\nu + i\partial_\mu \gamma^\mu m + m^2 && \quad -im\partial_\nu\gamma^\nu + i\partial_\mu\gamma^\mu m = 0 \\
&= \partial_\mu \gamma^\mu \partial_\nu \gamma^\nu + m^2 && \quad \frac{1}{2} + \frac{1}{2} = 1 \\
&= \frac{1}{2}\left(\partial_\mu \partial_\nu \gamma^\mu \gamma^\nu + \partial_\mu \partial_\nu \gamma^\mu \gamma^\nu\right) + m^2 && \quad \gamma^\nu\gamma^\mu - \gamma^\nu\gamma^\mu = 0 \\
&= \frac{1}{2}\left(\partial_\mu \partial_\nu \gamma^\mu \gamma^\nu + \partial_\mu \partial_\nu \gamma^\mu \gamma^\nu\right) + m^2 \\
&\quad + \frac{1}{2}\left(\partial_\mu \partial_\nu \gamma^\nu \gamma^\mu - \partial_\mu \partial_\nu \gamma^\nu \gamma^\mu\right) && \quad \text{rearranging} \\
&= \frac{1}{2}\left(\partial_\mu \partial_\nu \gamma^\mu \gamma^\nu + \partial_\mu \partial_\nu \gamma^\nu \gamma^\mu\right) + m^2 \\
&\quad + \frac{1}{2}\left(\partial_\mu \partial_\nu \gamma^\mu \gamma^\nu - \partial_\mu \partial_\nu \gamma^\nu \gamma^\mu\right) && \quad \{\gamma^\mu, \gamma^\nu\} \equiv \gamma^\mu\gamma^\nu + \gamma^\nu\gamma^\mu \\
&= \frac{1}{2}\partial_\mu \partial_\nu \{\gamma^\mu, \gamma^\nu\} + m^2 \\
&\quad + \frac{1}{2}\left(\partial_\mu \partial_\nu \gamma^\mu \gamma^\nu - \partial_\mu \partial_\nu \gamma^\nu \gamma^\mu\right) && \quad [\gamma^\mu, \gamma^\nu] \equiv \gamma^\mu\gamma^\nu - \gamma^\nu\gamma^\mu \\
&= \frac{1}{2}\partial_\mu \partial_\nu \{\gamma^\mu, \gamma^\nu\} + m^2 + \frac{1}{2}\partial_\mu \partial_\nu [\gamma^\mu, \gamma^\nu] && \quad \partial_\mu\partial_\nu[\gamma^\mu, \gamma^\nu] = 0, \text{ see below} \\
&= \frac{1}{2}\partial_\mu \partial_\nu \{\gamma^\mu, \gamma^\nu\} + m^2 && \quad \{\gamma^\mu, \gamma^\nu\} = 2\eta^{\mu\nu}, \text{ Eq. 5.60} \\
&= \partial_\mu \eta^{\mu\nu} \partial_\nu + m^2 && \quad \text{Eq. 2.36} \\
&= \partial_\mu \partial^\mu + m^2\,, && (5.80)
\end{aligned}$$

where we used that $\partial_\mu \partial_\nu [\gamma^\mu, \gamma^\nu] = 0$ which follows because $\partial_\mu \partial_\nu$ is symmetric under the exchange of the indices $\mu \leftrightarrow \nu$, while the commutator $[\gamma^\mu, \gamma^\nu]$ is antisymmetric.[44] We can check this explicitly as follows;

$$\begin{aligned}
\partial_\mu \partial_\nu [\gamma^\mu, \gamma^\nu] &\equiv \partial_\mu \partial_\nu \left(\gamma^\mu \gamma^\nu - \gamma^\nu \gamma^\mu\right) \\
&= \partial_\mu \partial_\nu \gamma^\mu \gamma^\nu - \partial_\mu \partial_\nu \gamma^\nu \gamma^\mu && \text{renaming indices} \\
&= \partial_\mu \partial_\nu \gamma^\mu \gamma^\nu - \partial_\nu \partial_\mu \gamma^\mu \gamma^\nu && \partial_\nu \partial_\mu = \partial_\mu \partial_\nu \\
&= \partial_\mu \partial_\nu \gamma^\mu \gamma^\nu - \partial_\mu \partial_\nu \gamma^\mu \gamma^\nu && \cancel{\partial_\mu \partial_\nu \gamma^\mu \gamma^\nu} \\
&= 0 \quad \checkmark
\end{aligned} \tag{5.81}$$

[44] This is an important general result. Every time we have a sum over something symmetric in its indices multiplied by something antisymmetric in the same indices, the result is zero:

$$\sum_{ij} a_{ij} b_{ij} = 0$$

if $a_{ij} = -a_{ji}$ and $b_{ij} = b_{ji}$ holds for all i, j. We can see this by writing

$$\sum_{ij} a_{ij} b_{ij} = \frac{1}{2}\Big(\sum_{ij} a_{ij} b_{ij} + \sum_{ij} a_{ij} b_{ij}\Big)$$

We are free to rename our indices $i \to j$ and $j \to i$, which we use in the second term

$$\to \sum_{ij} a_{ij} b_{ij} = \frac{1}{2}\Big(\sum_{ij} a_{ij} b_{ij} + \sum_{ij} a_{ji} b_{ji}\Big)$$

Then we use the symmetry of b_{ij} and antisymmetry of a_{ij}, to switch the indices in the second term, which yields

$$\begin{aligned}
\to \sum_{ij} a_{ij} b_{ij} &= \frac{1}{2}\Big(\sum_{ij} a_{ij} b_{ij} + \sum_{ij} \underbrace{a_{ji}}_{=-a_{ij}} \underbrace{b_{ji}}_{=b_{ij}}\Big) \\
&= \frac{1}{2}\Big(\sum_{ij} a_{ij} b_{ij} - \sum_{ij} a_{ij} b_{ij}\Big) = 0
\end{aligned}$$

If we plug Eq. 5.80 into Eq. 5.79, we can conclude that any solution of the Dirac equation *must* fulfill the Klein-Gordon equation.[45]

[45] To be more precise: each component of the Dirac spinor Ψ must fulfill the Klein-Gordon equation. The converse statement is not true. Solutions of the Klein-Gordon equation are not automatically solutions of the Dirac equation since the Klein-Gordon equation is not a spinor equation.

Therefore, the basic building blocks of the spacetime part of our solution will again be plane wave solutions (Eq. 5.44):

$$f(x_\mu) = e^{-ik_\mu x^\mu}, \tag{5.82}$$

where the wave vector k_μ fulfills the dispersion relation (see Eq. 5.40)

$$k_\mu k_\mu = m^2 . \tag{5.83}$$

Motivated by this fact, we make the ansatz

$$\Psi = \psi e^{-ik_\mu x^\mu} \tag{5.84}$$

and plug it into the Dirac equation (Eq. 5.64)

$$\begin{aligned}
0 &= i\partial_\mu \gamma^\mu \Psi - m\Psi && \text{this is Eq. 5.64} \\
&= i\partial_\mu \gamma^\mu \psi e^{-ik_\mu x^\mu} - m\psi e^{-ik_\mu x^\mu} && \text{Eq. 5.84} \\
&= -i^2 k_\mu \gamma^\mu \psi e^{-ik_\mu x^\mu} - m\psi e^{-ik_\mu x^\mu} && \partial_\mu e^{-ik_\mu x^\mu} = -ik_\mu e^{-ik_\mu x^\mu} \\
&= k_\mu \gamma^\mu \psi - m\psi . && \cancel{e^{-ik_\mu x^\mu}},\ i^2 = -1
\end{aligned} \tag{5.85}$$

While the spacetime part of the Dirac equation doesn't tell us anything new, this remaining equation is something truly novel. It tells us which spinor structures are permitted. As usual, we are always free to write down any spinors we like. But the Dirac equation tells us which spinor structures we can really observe in Nature. So by using the ansatz in Eq. 5.84, we have successfully isolated the information the Dirac equation contains about spinor structures that we can observe in Nature.

So next, let's try to understand what the Dirac equation tells us about permitted spinor structures. Since the physical content is the same in all frames of reference, we choose a frame in which our description becomes especially simple. In the rest frame ($\vec{k} = 0$), the wave four-vector is given by (Eq. 2.44)

$$k_\mu = \begin{pmatrix} \omega \\ \vec{k} \end{pmatrix} = \begin{pmatrix} \omega \\ \vec{0} \end{pmatrix} . \tag{5.86}$$

Moreover, we can use the dispersion relation (Eq. 5.83) to determine ω:

$$\begin{aligned} m^2 &= k_\mu k^\mu \\ &= k_0^2 - k_1^2 - k_2^2 - k_3^2 \qquad \text{rest frame: } k_\mu = (\omega, \vec{0})^T \\ &= \omega^2 . \end{aligned} \tag{5.87}$$

Therefore, in the rest frame Eq. 5.85 becomes

$$\begin{aligned} 0 &= k_\mu \gamma^\mu \psi - m\psi \qquad \text{Eq. 5.86} \\ &= \omega\gamma^0 \psi - m\psi \qquad \text{Eq. 5.87} \\ &= m\gamma^0 \psi - m\psi \qquad \not{m} \\ &= \gamma^0 \psi - \psi . \end{aligned} \tag{5.88}$$

Moreover, the spacetime structure part of the solution (Eq. 5.82) also simplifies to

$$\begin{aligned} f(x_\mu) &= e^{ik_\mu x^\mu} \qquad \text{Eq. 5.86, Eq. 5.87} \\ &= e^{imt} . \end{aligned} \tag{5.89}$$

To analyze the spinor structure further, we make the ansatz

$$\psi = \begin{pmatrix} \chi \\ \xi \end{pmatrix}, \tag{5.90}$$

plug it into Eq. 5.88 and use the explicit form of γ^0 (Eq. 5.56)[46]

$$\begin{aligned}
0 &= \gamma^0 \psi - \psi && \text{this is Eq. 5.88} \\
&&& \text{↷ Eq. 5.56, Eq. 5.90} \\
&= \begin{pmatrix} 0_{2\times2} & 1_{2\times2} \\ 1_{2\times2} & 0_{2\times2} \end{pmatrix} \begin{pmatrix} \chi \\ \xi \end{pmatrix} - \begin{pmatrix} \chi \\ \xi \end{pmatrix} \\
&&& \text{↷ matrix product} \\
&= \begin{pmatrix} \xi \\ \chi \end{pmatrix} - \begin{pmatrix} \chi \\ \xi \end{pmatrix}.
\end{aligned} \tag{5.91}$$

[46] $1_{2\times2}$ denotes the (2×2) unit matrix and $0_{2\times2}$ the (2×2) zero matrix.

We learn here that a constant spinor of the form given in Eq. 5.90 fulfills the condition in Eq. 5.88 as long as $\xi = \chi$.

Therefore, if we now recall that the two-component spinors inside a Dirac spinor describe the spin structure, we can immediately write down two linearly-independent solutions of the Dirac equation:

$$\begin{aligned}
\Psi_1 &= \begin{pmatrix} 1 \\ 0 \\ 1 \\ 0 \end{pmatrix} e^{-imt} && \text{Eq. 5.84, Eq. 5.91 with } \xi = \chi = \begin{pmatrix} 1 \\ 0 \end{pmatrix} \\
\Psi_2 &= \begin{pmatrix} 0 \\ 1 \\ 0 \\ 1 \end{pmatrix} e^{-imt} && \text{Eq. 5.84, Eq. 5.91 with } \xi = \chi = \begin{pmatrix} 0 \\ 1 \end{pmatrix}
\end{aligned} \tag{5.92}$$

Completely analogously, we can start with the ansatz[47]

[47] The only difference is a different sign in the exponent.

$$\Psi(x_\mu) = \psi e^{imt}, \tag{5.93}$$

and then find

$$0 = \begin{pmatrix} -\xi \\ -\chi \end{pmatrix} - \begin{pmatrix} \chi \\ \xi \end{pmatrix}. \tag{5.94}$$

This implies that there are two further solutions of the Dirac equation:

$$\Psi_3 = \begin{pmatrix} 1 \\ 0 \\ -1 \\ 0 \end{pmatrix} e^{imt} \qquad \text{Eq. 5.93, Eq. 5.94 with } \xi = -\chi = \begin{pmatrix} 1 \\ 0 \end{pmatrix}$$

$$\Psi_4 = \begin{pmatrix} 0 \\ 1 \\ 0 \\ -1 \end{pmatrix} e^{imt} \qquad \text{Eq. 5.93, Eq. 5.94 with } \xi = -\chi = \begin{pmatrix} 0 \\ 1 \end{pmatrix} . \tag{5.95}$$

Solutions of the Dirac equation are important because they describe how physical particles and fields behave as time passes on. Before we discuss, as we did for the Klein-Gordon equation, a general solution of the Dirac equation, we will talk about a smart trick that allows us to simplify the spinor structure associated with physical particles.

5.2.3 The Mass Basis

First of all, take note that the gamma matrices, γ_μ, only appear in combination with the Dirac spinor Ψ in the Lagrangian. This makes it possible that we introduce terms of the form $1 = N^{-1}N$ between them and then absorb the invertible matrix N that appears here into new definitions of Ψ and γ_μ:

$$\begin{aligned}\partial_\mu \bar{\psi}\gamma_\mu\psi &= \partial_\mu\bar{\psi}\underbrace{N^{-1}N}_{=1}\gamma_\mu\underbrace{N^{-1}N}_{=1}\psi \\ &= \partial_\mu\underbrace{\bar{\psi}N^{-1}}_{\equiv\bar{\psi}'}\underbrace{N\gamma_\mu N^{-1}}_{\equiv\gamma'_\mu}\underbrace{N\psi}_{\equiv\psi'} = \partial_\mu\bar{\psi}'\gamma'_\mu\psi'.\end{aligned} \tag{5.96}$$

This is a change of basis. The basis we used so far is called the **chiral basis** or **Weyl basis**. Depending on which matrix N we use, we can switch to quite different bases in which the gamma matrices look completely different and in which the components of a Dirac spinor have a quite different meaning.[48] A particularly useful basis is the **mass basis** or **Dirac basis**. The change from the chiral basis to the mass basis is described by the matrix:

$$N = \frac{1}{2}\begin{pmatrix}1 & 0 & 1 & 0\\ 0 & 1 & 0 & 1\\ 1 & 0 & -1 & 0\\ 0 & 1 & 0 & -1\end{pmatrix}. \tag{5.97}$$

The primary motivation behind a switch to the mass basis is to diagonalize the matrix γ_0 that appears in the mass term of the Lagrangian:

$$\bar{\Psi}m\Psi = \Psi^\star\gamma_0 m\Psi. \tag{5.98}$$

If we use that $NN = \frac{1}{2}1_{4\times4}$ and therefore $N^{-1} = 2N$, we can check that N indeed diagonalizes γ_0:

[48] Reminder: in the chiral basis the gamma matrices read (Eq. 5.56):

$$\gamma^0 = \begin{pmatrix}0&0&1&0\\0&0&0&1\\1&0&0&0\\0&1&0&0\end{pmatrix}$$

$$\gamma^1 = \begin{pmatrix}0&0&0&1\\0&0&1&0\\0&-1&0&0\\-1&0&0&0\end{pmatrix}$$

$$\gamma^2 = \begin{pmatrix}0&0&0&-i\\0&0&i&0\\0&i&0&0\\-i&0&0&0\end{pmatrix}$$

$$\gamma^3 = \begin{pmatrix}0&0&1&0\\0&0&0&-1\\-1&0&0&0\\0&1&0&0\end{pmatrix}.$$

$$
\begin{aligned}
\gamma_0^{\text{mass}} &\overset{\text{Eq. 5.96}}{=} N\gamma_0^{\text{chiral}}N^{-1} \\
&= \frac{2}{2}\begin{pmatrix} 1 & 0 & 1 & 0 \\ 0 & 1 & 0 & 1 \\ 1 & 0 & -1 & 0 \\ 0 & 1 & 0 & -1 \end{pmatrix}\begin{pmatrix} 0 & 0 & 1 & 0 \\ 0 & 0 & 0 & 1 \\ 1 & 0 & 0 & 0 \\ 0 & 1 & 0 & 0 \end{pmatrix}\begin{pmatrix} 1 & 0 & 1 & 0 \\ 0 & 1 & 0 & 1 \\ 1 & 0 & -1 & 0 \\ 0 & 1 & 0 & -1 \end{pmatrix} \\
&= \begin{pmatrix} 1 & 0 & 0 & 0 \\ 0 & 1 & 0 & 0 \\ 0 & 0 & -1 & 0 \\ 0 & 0 & 0 & -1 \end{pmatrix}.
\end{aligned}
\tag{5.99}
$$

↷ Eq. 5.97, Eq. 5.56

↷ matrix product

For this reason we say that the mass term $\bar{\Psi}m\Psi$ is diagonal in the mass basis, which explains its name. This is really just a useful mathematical trick that allows us to simplify some calculations. For some purposes the chiral basis is more useful, while for others the mass basis is better suited. This is analogous to how we sometimes use Cartesian coordinates and sometimes use spherical coordinates.

Using the explicit form of the matrix N (Eq. 5.97), we can calculate what the remaining γ-matrices look like in the mass basis:

$$
\gamma_1^{\text{mass}} = \begin{pmatrix} 0 & 0 & 0 & 1 \\ 0 & 0 & 1 & 0 \\ 0 & -1 & 0 & 0 \\ -1 & 0 & 0 & 0 \end{pmatrix}, \quad \gamma_2^{\text{mass}} = \begin{pmatrix} 0 & 0 & 0 & -i \\ 0 & 0 & i & 0 \\ 0 & i & 0 & 0 \\ -i & 0 & 0 & 0 \end{pmatrix}
$$
$$
\gamma_3^{\text{mass}} = \begin{pmatrix} 0 & 0 & 1 & 0 \\ 0 & 0 & 0 & -1 \\ -1 & 0 & 0 & 0 \\ 0 & 1 & 0 & 0 \end{pmatrix}. \tag{5.100}
$$

In addition, we must remember that all Dirac spinors are affected by such a basis change too (see Eq. 5.96):

$$
\Psi^{\text{mass}} = N\Psi^{\text{chiral}}. \tag{5.101}
$$

For example, the solution Ψ_1 that we derived in the previous section reads in the mass basis:

$$\Psi_1^{\text{mass}} \equiv N\Psi_1^{\text{chiral}}$$

$$= \frac{1}{2}\begin{pmatrix} 1 & 0 & 1 & 0 \\ 0 & 1 & 0 & 1 \\ 1 & 0 & -1 & 0 \\ 0 & 1 & 0 & -1 \end{pmatrix}\begin{pmatrix} 1 \\ 0 \\ 1 \\ 0 \end{pmatrix} e^{-imt}$$

$$= \begin{pmatrix} 1 \\ 0 \\ 0 \\ 0 \end{pmatrix} e^{-imt}. \tag{5.102}$$

▷ Eq. 5.97, Eq. 5.92

▷

Analogously, we can calculate that the remaining three solutions (Ψ_2, Ψ_3, Ψ_4) read in the mass basis:

$$\Psi_2^{\text{mass}} = \begin{pmatrix} 0 \\ 1 \\ 0 \\ 0 \end{pmatrix} e^{-imt} \quad \Psi_3^{\text{mass}} = \begin{pmatrix} 0 \\ 0 \\ 1 \\ 0 \end{pmatrix} e^{imt} \quad \Psi_4^{\text{mass}} = \begin{pmatrix} 0 \\ 0 \\ 0 \\ 1 \end{pmatrix} e^{imt}. \tag{5.103}$$

Take note that, as in the previous section, these solutions are only valid in the rest frame. However, we can derive the slightly more complicated solutions in a general frame which I list here only for completeness:[49]

$$\Psi_1^{\text{mass}} = u_1 e^{-ik_\mu x^\mu}, \quad \Psi_2^{\text{mass}} = u_2 e^{-ik_\mu x^\mu}$$
$$\Psi_3^{\text{mass}} = v_1 e^{ik_\mu x^\mu}, \quad \Psi_4^{\text{mass}} = v_2 e^{ik_\mu x^\mu}, \tag{5.104}$$

where u_1, u_2, v_1, v_2 are basis spinors

$$u_1 = n\begin{pmatrix} 1 \\ 0 \\ \frac{k_3}{\omega+m} \\ \frac{k_1+ik_2}{\omega+m} \end{pmatrix}, \quad u_2 = n\begin{pmatrix} 0 \\ 1 \\ \frac{k_1-ik_2}{\omega+m} \\ \frac{-k_3}{\omega+m} \end{pmatrix}$$

$$v_1 = n\begin{pmatrix} \frac{k_3}{\omega+m} \\ \frac{k_1+ik_2}{\omega+m} \\ 1 \\ 0 \end{pmatrix}, \quad v_2 = n\begin{pmatrix} \frac{k_1-ik_2}{\omega+m} \\ \frac{-k_3}{\omega+m} \\ 0 \\ 1 \end{pmatrix} \tag{5.105}$$

and $n \equiv \sqrt{\frac{\omega+m}{2m}}$ is a normalization factor.

[49] These solutions can be derived by boosting the rest frame solutions.

5.2.4 General Solution of the Dirac Equation

Finally, let's talk about the general solution of the Dirac equation. Since the Dirac equation is a linear equation, we can construct new solutions by using linear combinations of known solutions. Therefore, analogous to what we did for the Klein-Gordon equation in Section 5.1.4, we can write the general solution of the Dirac equation as:

$$\begin{aligned}\Psi &= \sum_{r=1}^{2}\int \frac{d^3k}{(2\pi)^3\sqrt{2\omega_k}}\left(c_r(\vec{k})u_r(k)\mathrm{e}^{-ik_\mu x^\mu} + d_r(\vec{k})v_r(k)\mathrm{e}^{+ik_\mu x^\mu}\right)\\ &\equiv \Psi^+ + \Psi^- \,. \end{aligned} \tag{5.106}$$

The main difference to the general solution of the Klein-Gordon equation is that here we not only integrate over all possible momenta, but also sum over all possible spin configurations.

5.3 Free Gauge Fields and the Proca/Maxwell equations

Analogous to what we did in the previous sections, let's assume that someone hands us the Lagrangian density[50]

[50] The equivalence of the two forms of the Lagrangian density given here is demonstrated in Appendix A.1.

$$\begin{aligned}\mathcal{L}_{\text{Proca}} &= -\frac{1}{2}F_{\mu\nu}F^{\mu\nu} + m^2 A_\mu A^\mu\\ &= -\frac{1}{2}(\partial^\mu A^\nu \partial_\mu A_\nu - \partial^\mu A^\nu \partial_\nu A_\mu) + m^2 A_\mu A^\mu \,, \end{aligned} \tag{5.107}$$

where $F_{\mu\nu} \equiv \partial_\mu A_\nu - \partial_\nu A_\mu$ is the field strength tensor discussed in Section 3.9. The first two terms are typically called kinetic terms, while the third term is known as the mass term. As usual, we can calculate the corresponding equation of motion by putting this Lagrangian density in to the Euler-Lagrange equation (Eq. 4.25):

$$\frac{\partial \mathcal{L}}{\partial A_\rho} = \partial_\sigma \left(\frac{\partial \mathcal{L}}{\partial(\partial_\sigma A_\rho)} \right) . \tag{5.108}$$

However, evaluating the expression on the right-hand side is a subtle business. For example, let's consider the term[51]

[51] Don't worry if not all of the steps here are immediately clear. The formalism of special relativity takes some time getting used to.

$$\begin{aligned}
&\partial_\sigma \left(\frac{\partial}{\partial(\partial_\sigma A_\rho)} (\partial^\mu A^\nu \partial_\mu A_\nu) \right) \\
&\quad \text{(product rule)} \\
&= \partial_\sigma \left((\partial_\mu A_\nu) \frac{\partial(\partial^\mu A^\nu)}{\partial(\partial_\sigma A_\rho)} + (\partial^\mu A^\nu) \frac{\partial(\partial_\mu A_\nu)}{\partial(\partial_\sigma A_\rho)} \right) \\
&\quad \left(A^\nu = \eta^{\nu\lambda} A_\lambda \text{ (Eq. 2.34)}\right) \\
&= \partial_\sigma \left((\partial_\mu A_\nu) \eta^{\mu\kappa} \eta^{\nu\lambda} \frac{\partial(\partial_\kappa A_\lambda)}{\partial(\partial_\sigma A_\rho)} + (\partial^\mu A^\nu) \frac{\partial(\partial_\mu A_\nu)}{\partial(\partial_\sigma A_\rho)} \right) \\
&= \partial_\sigma \left((\partial_\mu A_\nu) \eta^{\mu\kappa} \eta^{\nu\lambda} \delta^\sigma_\kappa \delta^\rho_\lambda + (\partial^\mu A^\nu) \delta^\sigma_\mu \delta^\rho_\nu \right) \\
&= \partial_\sigma \left(\partial^\sigma A^\rho + \partial^\sigma A^\rho \right) \\
&= 2\partial_\sigma \partial^\sigma A^\rho .
\end{aligned} \tag{5.109}$$

Similarly, we find for the second term in the Lagrangian density (Eq. 5.107):

$$\partial_\sigma \left(\frac{\partial}{\partial(\partial_\sigma A_\rho)} (\partial^\mu A^\nu \partial_\nu A_\mu) \right) = 2\partial^\rho (\partial_\sigma A^\sigma) . \tag{5.110}$$

The only term that is relevant for the left-hand side of the Euler-Lagrange equation is the mass term $m^2 A_\mu A^\mu$ and we can calculate[52]

[52] The other terms in the Lagrangian density yield no contribution to the left-hand side of the Euler-Lagrange since $\frac{\partial}{\partial A_\rho} \partial_\sigma A_\rho = 0$, analogous to how $\frac{\partial}{\partial x} \dot{x} = 0$.

$$\frac{\partial \left(m^2 A_\mu A^\mu \right)}{\partial A_\rho} = 2A^\rho m^2 \tag{5.111}$$

since $\frac{\partial}{\partial x} x^2 = 2x$ but $\frac{\partial}{\partial x} y^2 = 0$.[53] If we now combine these puzzle pieces, we find

[53] This implies that $\frac{\partial(A_\mu A^\mu)}{\partial A_\rho}$ yields zero except for $\mu = \rho$. This is why we get A^ρ in Eq. 5.111.

$$\begin{aligned}
\frac{\partial \mathcal{L}}{\partial A_\rho} &= \partial_\sigma \left(\frac{\partial \mathcal{L}}{\partial(\partial_\sigma A_\rho)} \right) \qquad \text{this is Eq. 5.108} \\
&\quad \text{(Eq. 5.111, Eq. 5.109, Eq. 5.110)} \\
2m^2 A^\rho &= -2\partial_\sigma (\partial^\sigma A^\rho - \partial^\rho A^\sigma) .
\end{aligned} \tag{5.112}$$

The resulting equation

$$\boxed{\begin{aligned} m^2 A^\rho &= -\partial_\sigma(\partial^\sigma A^\rho - \partial^\rho A^\sigma) \\ &\equiv -\partial_\sigma F^{\sigma\rho} \end{aligned}} \tag{5.113}$$

is known as the **Proca equation** and is the equation that we need to describe *massive* gauge fields. If we want to describe a *massless* gauge field, like the electromagnetic field, we use the same equation without a mass term:

$$\boxed{\begin{aligned} 0 &= \partial_\sigma(\partial^\sigma A^\rho - \partial^\rho A^\sigma) \\ &\equiv \partial_\sigma F^{\sigma\rho} . \end{aligned}} \tag{5.114}$$

This is the **inhomogeneous Maxwell equation** in the absence of any external sources.

5.3.1 Meaning of the Proca and Maxwell Equations

It is certainly possible to construct some mechanical model consisting of springs and rubber bands for which the corresponding Lagrangian yields the Proca or Maxwell Lagrangian in the continuum limit. However, such a model would necessarily be quite complicated and involve many ad-hoc assumptions that are hard to justify. Another way to approach the Maxwell equations is by looking at their macroscopic manifestations. But there are already many great books that discuss Maxwell's equations in the context of classical electrodynamics.[54]

[54] For example,

Daniel Fleisch. *A student's guide to Maxwell's equations*. Cambridge University Press, Cambridge, UK New York, 2008. ISBN 978-0521701471

For our purposes, the most important observation is that we are not using the much simpler Lagrangian

$$\mathcal{L} = \partial_\mu A_\nu \partial^\mu A^\nu .$$

This Lagrangian describes an ordinary vector field, while the Proca and Maxwell Lagrangians describe gauge fields.[55] An ordinary vector field is like four scalar fields at once, while a gauge field has novel features that we will discuss below.

[55] Reminder: in some sense, gauge fields are the bookkeepers for all other fields. We discussed their role in Section 3.9.

It again makes sense to separate our field into a spacetime and internal part:[56]

$$A_\mu(x_\mu) = \underbrace{\epsilon_\mu}_{\text{internal structure}} \times \underbrace{f(x_\mu)}_{\text{spacetime structure}} . \quad (5.115)$$

[56] Reminder: only the basic building blocks of all possible solutions look like this. By using linear combinations of these building blocks, we can construct any physically permitted gauge field structure. In particular, we can construct configurations that do not have the same vector structure everywhere.

As discussed in Section 3.2.1, ϵ_μ contains all information about the vector structure of the field, while $f(x_\mu)$ describes how the field strength varies in space.

In short, the two key facts encoded in the Proca equation (Eq. 5.113) are:[57]

[57] We will derive this in Section 5.3.2.

- ▷ The spacetime structure of *massive* gauge fields can be described by plane waves $f(x_\mu) = e^{ik_\mu x^\mu}$, where the wave vector k_μ fulfills the dispersion relation $k_\mu k^\mu = m^2$.
- ▷ A *massive* gauge field has only *three* linearly independent polarizations. Two of them are orthogonal to the direction of motion[58], while the third one points in the direction of motion and in the temporal direction[59]. We say that a massive gauge field excitation can either have a transverse polarization or a longitudinal polarization.

[58] For a wave that travels in the z-direction ($\vec{k} = (0,0,1)^T$)), one valid basis choice is

$$\epsilon^1_\mu \equiv \begin{pmatrix} 0 \\ 1 \\ 0 \\ 0 \end{pmatrix}, \quad \epsilon^2_\mu \equiv \begin{pmatrix} 0 \\ 0 \\ 1 \\ 0 \end{pmatrix}.$$

[59]

$$\epsilon^L_\mu = \begin{pmatrix} \frac{p_z}{m} \\ 0 \\ \frac{E}{m} \\ 0 \end{pmatrix}.$$

Similarly, the Maxwell equation (Eq. 5.114) tells us:[60]

[60] We will derive this in Section 5.3.3

- ▷ The spacetime structure of *massless* gauge fields can be described by plane waves $f(x_\mu) = e^{ik_\mu x^\mu}$, where the wave vector k_μ fulfills the dispersion relation $k_\mu k^\mu = 0$.
- ▷ A *massless* gauge field has only *two* linearly independent polarizations. For a specific field excitation that moves in the z-direction, both are orthogonal to the direction of motion.[61] We say that a massless gauge field excitation can only have transverse polarizations.

[61]

$$\epsilon^1_\mu \equiv \begin{pmatrix} 0 \\ 1 \\ 0 \\ 0 \end{pmatrix}, \quad \epsilon^2_\mu \equiv \begin{pmatrix} 0 \\ 0 \\ 1 \\ 0 \end{pmatrix}.$$

Let's discuss how this comes about.

5.3.2 Solutions of the Proca Equation

To develop some understanding of the structure of solutions of the Proca equation (Eq. 5.113), we start by taking the four-divergence on both sides:

$$
\begin{aligned}
m^2 A^\rho &= -\partial_\sigma F^{\sigma\rho} \\
&\quad \text{↷ } \partial_\rho \\
\partial_\rho m^2 A^\rho &= -\partial_\rho \partial_\sigma F^{\sigma\rho} \\
&\quad \text{↷ } m = \text{const.},\ \partial_\rho\partial_\sigma F^{\sigma\rho} = 0 \\
m^2 \partial_\rho A^\rho &= 0 \\
&\quad \text{↷ } \cancel{m^2} \\
\partial_\rho A^\rho &= 0 \\
&\quad \text{↷} \\
\partial_0 A_0 - \partial_i A_i &= 0 \\
&\quad \text{↷} \\
\partial_t A_0 - \nabla \vec{A} &= 0\,.
\end{aligned} \tag{5.116}
$$

This is known as the **Lorenz condition**. We used here that $F^{\sigma\rho}$ is antisymmetric: $F^{\sigma\rho} = -F^{\rho\sigma}$ but $\partial_\rho\partial_\sigma$ is symmetric: $\partial_\rho\partial_\sigma = +\partial_\sigma\partial_\rho$. Since we sum over ρ and σ, we find[62]

[62] The fact that the sum over an antisymmetric times a symmetric object is always zero was already discussed in Section 5.2.2.

$$
\begin{aligned}
\partial_\rho\partial_\sigma F^{\sigma\rho} &= \frac{1}{2}\Big(\partial_\rho\partial_\sigma F^{\sigma\rho} + \partial_\rho\partial_\sigma F^{\sigma\rho}\Big) \\
&\quad \text{↷ } F^{\sigma\rho} = -F^{\rho\sigma} \text{ (see Eq. 3.103)} \\
&= \frac{1}{2}\Big(\partial_\rho\partial_\sigma F^{\sigma\rho} - \partial_\rho\partial_\sigma F^{\rho\sigma}\Big) \\
&\quad \text{↷ renaming indices} \\
&= \frac{1}{2}\Big(\partial_\rho\partial_\sigma F^{\sigma\rho} - \partial_\sigma\partial_\rho F^{\sigma\rho}\Big) \\
&\quad \text{↷ } \partial_\sigma\partial_\rho = \partial_\rho\partial_\sigma \\
&= \frac{1}{2}\Big(\partial_\rho\partial_\sigma F^{\sigma\rho} - \partial_\rho\partial_\sigma F^{\sigma\rho}\Big) \\
&\quad \text{↷} \\
&= 0\,.
\end{aligned} \tag{5.117}
$$

To understand the Lorenz condition, we can imagine that the arrows that the vector field $\vec{A}$ assigns to each location represent the flux of a hypothetical substance. The divergence of a vector field $\nabla\vec{A}$ at a specific point x_μ tells us the total amount of flux entering or leaving the point.

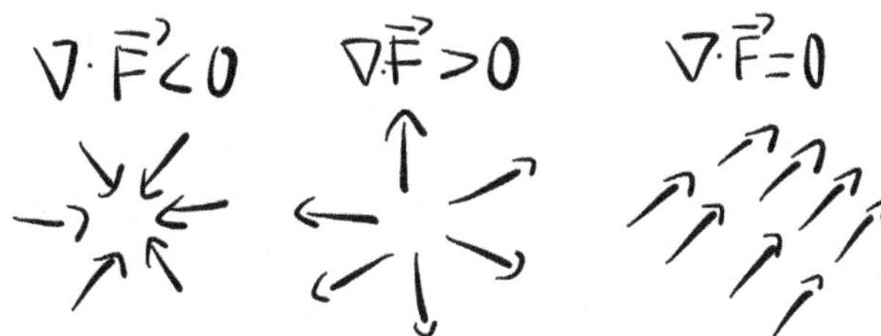

Therefore, the Lorenz condition tells us that the time-evolution of the zeroth component of A_μ is completely determined by this influx or outflux. This implies that A_0 is not an independent dynamical variable. As soon as we know $\vec{A}$, we can use the Lorenz condition to determine A_0.

What we've therefore discovered here is that a massive gauge field has only three independent internal degrees of freedom. Thus once again, we have an equation of motion that tells us which internal structures of a given field are physical. In particular, there is always a close connection between A_0 and the remaining components, which is somewhat analogous to how there is always a close connection between the upper two and lower two components of a physical Dirac spinor.

In addition, we can use the Lorenz condition to simplify the Proca equation (Eq. 5.113):

$$-m^2 A^\rho = \partial_\sigma(\partial^\sigma A^\rho - \partial^\rho A^\sigma) \qquad \text{this is Eq. 5.113}$$

$$\quad \text{↷ } \partial_s igma\partial^\rho = \partial^\rho\partial_\sigma$$

$$= \partial^\sigma\partial_\sigma A^\rho - \partial^\rho\partial_\sigma A^\sigma$$

$$\quad \text{↷ } \partial^\sigma A^\sigma = 0, \text{ Eq. 5.116}$$

$$= \partial^\sigma\partial_\sigma A^\rho\,. \tag{5.118}$$

What this resulting equation tells us is that each component of our four-vector field A_ρ must fulfill the Klein-Gordon equation (Eq. 5.4).[63] For example, for the $\rho = 1$ component, we have

$$-m^2 A^\rho = \partial^\sigma\partial_\sigma A^\rho \qquad \text{this is Eq. 5.118}$$

$$\quad \text{↷ } \rho = 1$$

$$-m^2 A^1 = \partial^\sigma\partial_\sigma A^1$$

$$\quad \text{↷ rearranging}$$

$$0 = (\partial^\sigma\partial_\sigma + m^2)A^1\,. \tag{5.119}$$

[63] For your convenience: the Klein-Gordon equation (Eq. 5.4) reads

$$(\partial_\mu\partial^\mu + m^2)\phi = 0$$

This is completely analogous to what we discovered for Dirac spinors using the Dirac equation. Therefore, we can conclude again that the spacetime structure of gauge fields can be described by plane waves. Let's make this a bit more concrete.

In Section 3.2.1, we already discussed that it makes sense to decompose gauge fields as (Eq. 3.8)

$$A_\mu(x_\mu) = \underbrace{\epsilon_\mu}_{\text{internal structure}} \times \underbrace{f(x_\mu)}_{\text{spacetime structure}} . \tag{5.120}$$

If we put this ansatz into Eq. 5.118, we find

$$\begin{aligned}
-m^2 A_\rho &= \partial^\sigma \partial_\sigma A_\rho && \text{this is Eq. 5.118} \\
& && \text{Eq. 5.120} \\
-m^2\Big(\epsilon_\rho f(x_\mu)\Big) &= \partial^\sigma \partial_\sigma \Big(\epsilon_\rho f(x_\mu)\Big) \\
& && \epsilon_\rho \neq \epsilon_\rho(x_\mu) \\
\epsilon_\rho\Big(-m^2 f(x_\mu)\Big) &= \epsilon_\rho\Big(\partial^\sigma \partial_\sigma f(x_\mu)\Big) .
\end{aligned} \tag{5.121}$$

This equation holds for any four-vector ϵ_ρ and therefore, we can write it without it:

$$-m^2 f(x_\mu) = \partial^\sigma \partial_\sigma f(x_\mu) . \tag{5.122}$$

This is exactly the Klein-Gordon equation (Eq. 5.4) and therefore we can conclude that the basic building blocks of the spacetime part of our solutions are plane waves:

$$f(x_\mu) = e^{ik_\mu x^\mu} . \tag{5.123}$$

If we plug the plane wave ansatz (Eq. 5.123) into Eq. 5.122, we find

$$\begin{aligned}
-m^2 f(x_\mu) &= \partial^\sigma \partial_\sigma f(x_\mu) \\
& && \text{Eq. 5.123} \\
-m^2 e^{ik_\mu x^\mu} &= \partial^\sigma \partial_\sigma e^{ik_\mu x^\mu} \\
& && \partial_\sigma e^{ik_\mu x^\mu} = ik_\sigma e^{ik_\mu x^\mu} \text{ since } \partial_\sigma x^\mu = \delta^\mu_\sigma \\
-m^2 e^{ik_\mu x^\mu} &= i^2 k^\sigma k_\sigma e^{ik_\mu x^\mu} \\
& && \cancel{e^{ik_\mu x^\mu}},\ i^2 = -1 \\
m^2 &= k^\sigma k_\sigma .
\end{aligned} \tag{5.124}$$

This is the dispersion relation for a massive gauge field. Here we learn that plane waves indeed solve Eq. 5.122 as long as the wave four-vector k_μ fulfills the dispersion relation (Eq. 5.124).

In addition, we learn here that the only information the Proca equation contains about the vector structure of our field A_μ (i.e. how different components are related) is contained in the Lorenz condition (Eq. 5.116). We can separate what the Proca equation tells us about the vector structure by putting our ansatz (Eq. 5.120) together with the explicit expression for a plane wave (Eq. 5.123) into the Lorenz condition:

$$0 = \partial_\rho A^\rho \qquad \text{this is Eq. 5.116}$$

$$\downarrow \text{ Eq. 5.120}$$

$$0 = \partial_\rho \left(\epsilon^\rho f(x_\mu) \right)$$

$$\downarrow \text{ Eq. 5.123}$$

$$0 = \partial_\rho \left(\epsilon^\rho e^{ik_\mu x^\mu} \right)$$

$$\downarrow \ \partial_\sigma e^{ik_\mu x^\mu} = ik_\sigma e^{ik_\mu x^\mu} \text{ since } \partial_\sigma x^\mu = \delta^\mu_\sigma$$

$$0 = i\epsilon^\rho k_\rho e^{ik_\mu x^\mu}$$

$$\downarrow \ \cancel{ie^{ik_\mu x^\mu}}$$

$$0 = \epsilon^\rho k_\rho$$

$$\downarrow$$

$$0 = \epsilon_0 k_0 - \epsilon_1 k_1 - \epsilon_2 k_2 - \epsilon_3 k_3 \,, \tag{5.125}$$

where ϵ_μ denotes the component of a four-vector that describes the vector structure of our basis solution and k_μ denotes the wave vector components. For concreteness, let's assume that we are dealing with a field excitation that travels in the z-direction. This means in mathematical terms that the wave three-vector reads $\vec{k} = (0, 0, k_z)^T$. Using the dispersion relation (Eq. 5.124), we can calculate the corresponding wave four-vector:

$$m^2 = k_\mu k^\mu \qquad \text{this is the dispersion relation (Eq. 5.124)}$$

$$\downarrow$$

$$= k_0^2 - \vec{k} \cdot \vec{k}$$

$$\downarrow \ \vec{k} = (0, 0, k_z)^T$$

$$= k_0^2 - k_z^2$$

$$\downarrow \text{ rearranging}$$

$$k_0^2 = m^2 + k_z^2$$

$$\downarrow \ k_0 = \omega \text{ (angular frequency) and therefore } k_0 > 0$$

$$k_0 = \sqrt{m^2 + k_z^2} \,. \tag{5.126}$$

Therefore, the wave four-vector for an excitation of a massive gauge field that moves in the z-direction reads

$$k_\mu = (\sqrt{m^2 + k_z^2}, 0, 0, k_z)^T . \tag{5.127}$$

If we plug this explicit wave four-vector into the Lorenz condition (Eq. 5.125), we find

$$\begin{aligned} 0 &= \epsilon_0 k_0 - \epsilon_1 k_1 - \epsilon_2 k_2 - \epsilon_3 k_3 && \text{this is Eq. 5.125} \\ & && \text{Eq. 5.127} \\ &= \epsilon_0 \sqrt{m^2 + k_z^2} - \epsilon_1 0 - \epsilon_2 0 - \epsilon_3 k_z \\ &= \epsilon_0 \sqrt{m^2 + k_z^2} - \epsilon_3 k_z . \end{aligned} \tag{5.128}$$

This implies that for a field excitation that travels in the z-direction, the x-component and y-component of our four-vector ϵ_μ are not restricted, while there is necessarily a close connection between the zeroth component, k_0, and the third component, k_3. In physical terms, this means that there are in total three linearly independent polarization structures of a massive vector field.[64] It is convenient to choose specific basic building blocks to describe all possible polarizations. Since there are no restrictions on polarizations in the x-direction and in the y-direction, we can work with

[64] We discussed polarization in Section 3.2.1.

$$\epsilon_\mu^1 \equiv \begin{pmatrix} 0 \\ 1 \\ 0 \\ 0 \end{pmatrix} , \quad \epsilon_\mu^2 \equiv \begin{pmatrix} 0 \\ 0 \\ 1 \\ 0 \end{pmatrix} . \tag{5.129}$$

The remaining two naive building blocks[65], however, are not suitable for a massive, physical vector field since they do not fulfill the condition in Eq. 5.128. Instead, a suitable third linearly independent polarization basis vector is

[65]
$$\epsilon_\mu^0 \equiv \begin{pmatrix} i \\ 0 \\ 0 \\ 0 \end{pmatrix} , \quad \epsilon_\mu^3 \equiv \begin{pmatrix} 0 \\ 0 \\ 0 \\ 1 \end{pmatrix}$$

$$\epsilon_\mu^L = \begin{pmatrix} \frac{k_z}{m} \\ 0 \\ 0 \\ \frac{\sqrt{m^2 + k_z^2}}{m} \end{pmatrix} , \tag{5.130}$$

where $\frac{1}{m}$ is a normalization factor, which we can see as follows:[66]

[66] Thanks to the Minkowski metric (Eq. 2.30), the other two polarization basis vectors also fulfill the normalization condition $\epsilon_\mu \epsilon^\mu = -1$.

$$
\begin{aligned}
\epsilon^L_\mu \epsilon^{L\mu} &= \frac{k_z^2}{m^2} - \frac{(\sqrt{m^2+k_z^2})^2}{m^2} \\
&= \frac{k_z^2}{m^2} - \frac{(m^2+k_z^2)}{m^2} \\
&= \frac{-m^2}{m^2} = -1 \quad \checkmark
\end{aligned}
\tag{5.131}
$$

Let's check explicitly that the vector given in Eq. 5.130 indeed fulfills the Lorenz condition (Eq. 5.128):

$$
\begin{aligned}
0 &= \epsilon_0 \sqrt{m^2+k_z^2} - \epsilon_3 k_z && \text{this is Eq. 5.128} \\
& && \text{Eq. 5.130} \\
&= \frac{k_z}{m}\sqrt{m^2+k_z^2} - \frac{\sqrt{m^2+k_z^2}}{m} k_z \\
& && \cancel{\frac{k_z}{m}\sqrt{m^2+k_z^2}} \\
&= 0 \quad \checkmark
\end{aligned}
\tag{5.132}
$$

If the vector structure of a field A_μ can be described by ϵ^L_μ, we say that the field is longitudinally polarized. The two remaining polarization vectors (Eq. 5.129) describe transverse polarizations.

Take note that for a massive gauge field at rest, we have $\vec{k} = (0,0,0)^T$. If we repeat the calculation in Eq. 5.126 for this wave three-vector, we find

$$
\begin{aligned}
m^2 &= k_\mu k^\mu && \text{this is the dispersion relation (Eq. 5.124)} \\
&= k_0^2 - \vec{k}\cdot\vec{k} \\
& && \vec{k} = (0,0,0)^T \\
&= k_0^2 .
\end{aligned}
\tag{5.133}
$$

This implies that the wave four-vector reads $k_\mu = (m,0,0,0)^T$. If we plug this into the Lorenz condition (Eq. 5.125), we find

$$
\begin{aligned}
0 &= \epsilon_0 k_0 - \epsilon_1 k_1 - \epsilon_2 k_2 - \epsilon_3 k_3 && \text{this is Eq. 5.125} \\
& && k_\mu = (m,0,0,0)^T \\
&= \epsilon_0 m - \epsilon_1 0 - \epsilon_2 0 - \epsilon_3 0 \\
&= \epsilon_0 m .
\end{aligned}
\tag{5.134}
$$

Therefore in this case $\epsilon_0 = 0$ and we can use

$$\epsilon^3_\mu \equiv \begin{pmatrix} 0 \\ 0 \\ 0 \\ 1 \end{pmatrix} \qquad (5.135)$$

as our third polarization vector.[67]

[67] The other two polarization vectors (Eq. 5.129) can still be used since there is still no restriction on them.

To summarize, we have learned that the Proca equation contains two crucial pieces of information. Firstly, the spacetime structure of vector fields is described by plane waves. Secondly, there are only three physical polarizations of a massive vector field.

In the next section, we will see that the analysis of the Maxwell equation (Eq. 5.114), which describes *massless* gauge fields, works quite similarly but is slightly more complicated.

5.3.3 Solutions of the Maxwell Equation

First of all, take note that if we try to follow the same steps that allowed us to understand the meaning of the Proca equation, we will not get very far. If we calculate the four-divergence of the Maxwell equation, we find

$$
\begin{aligned}
0 &= -\partial_\sigma F^{\sigma\rho} \\
& \qquad \curvearrowright \ \partial_\rho \\
0 &= -\partial_\rho \partial_\sigma F^{\sigma\rho} \\
& \qquad \curvearrowright \ \partial_\rho \partial_\sigma F^{\sigma\rho} = 0 \text{ (Eq. 5.117)} \\
0 &= 0 \, .
\end{aligned}
\tag{5.136}
$$

While this is a true statement, it doesn't tell us anything new. In contrast, when we calculated the four-divergence of the Proca equation, we discovered the Lorenz condition $\partial_\mu A^\mu = 0$ (Eq. 5.116).

Therefore, the discussion of the physical content of the Maxwell equation is a bit more subtle. The key observation is that all transformations of a massless gauge field A_μ that is described by the Maxwell equation:

$$
A_\mu(x_\mu) \to A'_\mu(x_\mu) = A_\mu(x_\mu) + \partial_\mu \eta(x_\mu) \, , \tag{5.137}
$$

where $\eta(x_\mu)$ is an ordinary function, leave everything we can observe unchanged. This is known as **gauge symmetry**.[68] In words, it means that we can always add the gradient of any (well-behaved) function $\partial_\mu \eta(x_\mu)$ to our field A_μ without changing anything.

[68] Gauge symmetry is commonly discussed in the context of classical electrodynamics. You can find a short summary in Appendix D.

We can see that the dynamics of a gauge field A_μ is invariant under gauge transformations (Eq. 5.137) because the corresponding Lagrangian remains unchanged:

$$
\begin{aligned}
\mathcal{L}_{\text{Maxwell}} &= -\frac{1}{2}\Big(\partial^\mu A^\nu \partial_\mu A_\nu - \partial^\mu A^\nu \partial_\nu A_\mu\Big) && \text{Eq. 5.107 with } m=0 \\
\rightarrow \mathcal{L}'_{\text{Maxwell}} &= -\frac{1}{2}\Big(\partial^\mu A'^\nu \partial_\mu A'_\nu - \partial^\mu A'^\nu \partial_\nu A'_\mu\Big) \\
& && \text{Eq. 5.137} \\
&= -\frac{1}{2}\Big(\partial^\mu (A^\nu + \partial^\nu \eta) \partial_\mu (A_\nu + \partial_\nu \eta) - \partial^\mu (A^\nu + \partial^\nu \eta) \partial_\nu (A_\mu + \partial_\mu \eta)\Big) \\
&= -\frac{1}{2}\Big(\partial^\mu A^\nu \partial_\mu A_\nu + \partial^\mu \partial^\nu \eta \partial_\mu A_\nu + \partial^\mu A^\nu \partial_\mu \partial_\nu \eta + \partial^\mu \partial^\nu \eta \partial_\mu \partial_\nu \eta \\
&\quad - \partial^\mu A^\nu \partial_\nu A_\mu - \partial^\mu \partial^\nu \eta \partial_\nu A_\mu - \partial^\mu A^\nu \partial_\nu \partial_\mu \eta - \partial^\mu \partial^\nu \eta \partial_\nu \partial_\mu \eta\Big) \\
& && \partial^\mu \partial^\nu = \partial^\nu \partial^\mu \\
&= -\frac{1}{2}\Big(\partial^\mu A^\nu \partial_\mu A_\nu + \partial^\mu \partial^\nu \eta \partial_\mu A_\nu + \partial^\mu A^\nu \partial_\mu \partial_\nu \eta + \partial^\mu \partial^\nu \eta \partial_\mu \partial_\nu \eta \\
&\quad - \partial^\mu A^\nu \partial_\nu A_\mu - \partial^\mu \partial^\nu \eta \partial_\nu A_\mu - \partial^\mu A^\nu \partial_\mu \partial_\nu \eta - \partial^\mu \partial^\nu \eta \partial_\mu \partial_\nu \eta\Big) \\
& && \partial^\mu \partial^\nu \eta \partial_\mu \partial_\nu \eta \text{ (cancelled)} \\
&= -\frac{1}{2}\Big(\partial^\mu A^\nu \partial_\mu A_\nu - \partial^\mu A^\nu \partial_\nu A_\mu\Big) = \mathcal{L}_{\text{Maxwell}} \quad \checkmark
\end{aligned}
\tag{5.138}
$$

Take note that this only works if there is no mass term. To see this, we calculate how a mass term changes under a gauge transformation:

$$
\begin{aligned}
m^2 A_\mu A^\mu \rightarrow & m^2 A'_\mu A'^\mu \\
& && \text{Eq. 5.137} \\
&= m^2\Big((A_\mu + \partial_\mu \eta)(A^\mu + \partial^\mu \eta)\Big) \\
&= m^2\Big(A_\mu A^\mu + \partial_\mu \eta A^\mu + A_\mu \partial^\mu \eta + \partial_\mu \eta \partial^\mu \eta\Big) \\
&\neq m^2 A_\mu A^\mu .
\end{aligned}
\tag{5.139}
$$

Therefore, gauge symmetry is a special feature of *massless* gauge fields.

In summary, the defining feature of a massless gauge field is that there are lots of different configurations that describe exactly the same physical situation. If we've found (by solving Maxwell's equation (Eq. 5.114)) some field configuration $A_\mu(x_\mu)$

that describes the situation at hand perfectly, we can immediately write down further configurations

$$A'_\mu(x_\mu) = A_\mu(x_\mu) + \partial_\mu \eta(x_\mu) \tag{5.140}$$

that describe the situation equally well. For any function $\eta(x_\mu)$ we get a different configuration A'_μ. Since the Lagrangian is completely unaffected by gauge transformations (Eq. 5.137), each configuration that differs from the original one by the gradient of a function $\eta(x_\mu)$ describes the same situation. In the rest of this section, we will discuss the physical implications of this curious fact.[69]

[69] As mentioned above, we will talk about the origin and meaning of gauge symmetry in the next chapter because this discussion requires some understanding of how different fields interact with each other. In this section, we only explore the immediate implications.

In the previous section, we discovered the Lorenz condition $\partial_\mu A^\mu = 0$ (Eq. 5.125) and used it to simplify the Proca equation. Moreover, we've learned above that for a massless gauge field the Lorenz condition is no longer mandatory (Eq. 5.136).

However, we can use the freedom to transform our gauge field A_μ to make sure that we're only working with configurations for which $\partial_\mu A^\mu = 0$. Formulated differently, we can use the gauge symmetry to impose the Lorenz condition.

Here's how and why this works. As discussed above, all gauge field configurations that are related by a gauge transformation describe the same situation. Thus we can imagine that there are equivalence classes related to each physical situation. The members within an equivalence class are connected by a gauge transformation. Each A_μ from a given equivalence class describes the situation perfectly well. But to describe the situation one member from each equivalence class is already sufficient. Thus, we can always pick the member for which our description becomes particularly simple.

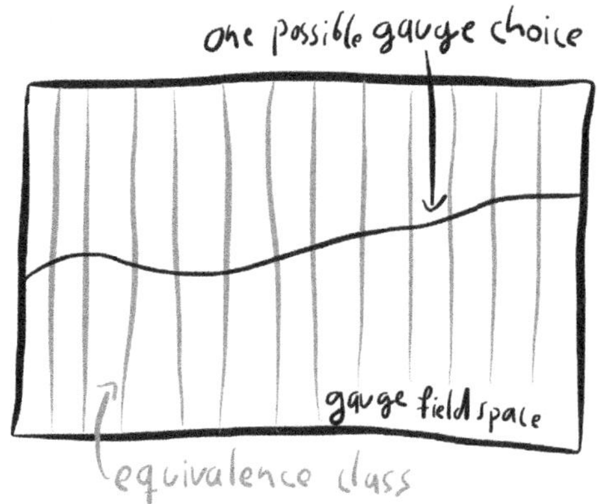

This is analogous to how we can always choose a coordinate system such that our description becomes simpler. For example, for a rotationally symmetric system it usually makes sense to use spherical coordinates instead of Cartesian coordinates.

Motivated by our discussion in the previous section, we can thus try to pick a member from each equivalence class that fulfills the Lorenz condition. The configuration A_μ we start with will, in general, not fulfill the Lorenz condition ($\partial_\mu A^\mu \neq 0$). However, we can then use a gauge transformation (Eq. 5.137) to find another member from the same equivalence class

$$A'_\mu = A_\mu(x_\mu) + \partial_\mu \eta(x_\mu) \tag{5.141}$$

that fulfills it:

$$\begin{aligned} 0 &\stackrel{!}{=} \partial_\mu A'^\mu \\ &= \partial_\mu (A^\mu + \partial^\mu \eta) \qquad \text{Eq. 5.141} \\ &= \partial_\mu A^\mu + \partial_\mu \partial^\mu \eta \\ -\partial_\mu A^\mu &= \partial_\mu \partial^\mu \eta \,. \end{aligned} \tag{5.142}$$

Since A_μ is a known configuration that we start with, this is an equation that we need to solve for $\eta(x_\mu)$. If we find a solution $\eta_s(x_\mu)$, we can immediately write down a gauge field configuration:

$$\tilde{A}_\mu(x_\mu) = A_\mu(x_\mu) + \partial_\mu \eta_s(x_\mu) \tag{5.143}$$

that describes the situation at hand perfectly and, additionally, fulfills the Lorenz condition $\partial_\mu \tilde{A}^\mu = 0$.

Now here's the cool thing. In practice, we don't have to actually solve Eq. 5.142. All we need to know is that it is mathematically possible to find a gauge function $\eta_s(x_\mu)$ that allows us to calculate gauge field configurations that fulfill the Lorenz condition. Using this knowledge, we can simply *choose* to work only with configurations that fulfill the Lorenz condition:[70]

$$\partial_\mu A^\mu = 0 \,. \tag{5.144}$$

While for a massive gauge field this was a mandatory requirement, for a massless gauge field the Lorenz condition is merely a convenient **gauge choice**. We say that by choosing to only work with configurations that fulfill the Lorenz condition, we choose to work in the **Lorenz gauge**. Analogously, we can also make different gauge choices. For example, it is also possible to only work with configurations that fulfill the condition $A_0 = 0$ or $A_3 = 0$. These choices are known as the temporal gauge and axial gauge respectively. But for now, let's stick to the Lorenz gauge.[71]

If we choose to work in the Lorenz gauge, the Maxwell equation simplifies to

$$\begin{aligned} 0 &= \partial_\sigma(\partial^\sigma A^\rho - \partial^\rho A^\sigma) && \text{this is Eq. 5.114} \\ & && \curvearrowright\ \partial_\sigma\partial_\rho = \partial_\rho\partial_\sigma \\ &= \partial_\sigma\partial^\sigma A^\rho - \partial^\rho\partial_\sigma A^\sigma \\ & && \curvearrowright\ \partial_\mu A^\mu = 0 \text{ (Eq. 5.144)} \\ &= \partial_\sigma\partial^\sigma A^\rho \,. \end{aligned} \tag{5.145}$$

We learn here that each component A^ρ has to fulfill the Klein-Gordon equation without a mass term. This implies that we can describe the spatial part of solutions of the Maxwell equation using plane waves for which the wave vectors k_μ fulfill the dispersion relation:[72]

$$k_\mu k^\mu = 0 \,. \tag{5.146}$$

Let's show this in more explicit terms by using once more the

[70] This is really analogous to how we can choose one specific coordinate system for the system we want to describe. However, here we choose a coordinate system that allows us to label gauge field configurations instead of a coordinate system that allows us to label spacetime points. Take note, however, that there is still some gauge freedom even after we choose to work with configurations that fulfill the Lorenz condition. This is discussed in Appendix D.1.

[71] Just as it doesn't matter for the actual physics that we want to describe which coordinate system we pick, it doesn't matter which gauge we choose. Thus, we will discuss the physical implications of the Maxwell equation by using one specific gauge choice. The physical conclusions we derive this way are valid for all gauge choices.

[72] For the Proca equation we found that each component A^ρ has to fulfill the Klein-Gordon equation *with* mass term. Therefore, the corresponding solutions were plane waves with dispersion relation $k_\mu k^\mu = m^2$ (Eq. 5.40).

ansatz

$$A_\mu(x_\mu) = \underbrace{\epsilon_\mu}_{\text{internal structure}} \times \underbrace{f(x_\mu)}_{\text{spacetime structure}} . \tag{5.147}$$

that decouples the internal degrees of freedom from the spacetime degrees of freedom. Moreover, since Eq. 5.145 tells us that each component of a massless gauge field has to fulfill the Klein-Gordon equation, we know that the spacetime part of our solutions can be described by plane waves

$$f(x_\mu) = e^{ik_\mu x^\mu} . \tag{5.148}$$

Plugging the ansatz with a plane wave spacetime structure into the Maxwell equation in the Lorenz gauge (Eq. 5.145) yields

$$\begin{aligned} 0 &= \partial_\sigma \partial^\sigma A^\rho && \text{this is Eq. 5.145} \\ & && \text{ansatz Eq. 5.147, Eq. 5.148} \\ &= \partial_\sigma \partial^\sigma \left(\epsilon^\rho e^{ik_\mu x^\mu} \right) \\ & && \epsilon^\rho \neq \epsilon^\rho(x_\mu),\ \partial_\sigma e^{ik_\mu x^\mu} = ik_\sigma e^{ik_\mu x^\mu} \\ &= i^2 k_\sigma k^\sigma \epsilon^\rho e^{ik_\mu x^\mu} . \end{aligned} \tag{5.149}$$

Therefore, our ansatz indeed solves the Maxwell equation as long as the dispersion relation (Eq. 5.146) is fulfilled.

Next, let's talk about the internal degrees of freedom of a massless gauge field.

For concreteness, we assume that we are dealing with a field excitation that moves in the z-direction. In mathematical terms, this implies that the wave three-vector $\vec{k} = (0, 0, k_z)^T$. Using the dispersion relation, we can calculate the corresponding wave four-vector:

$$
\begin{aligned}
0 &= k_\mu k^\mu && \text{this is the dispersion relation (Eq. 5.146)} \\
&= k_0^2 - \vec{k} \cdot \vec{k} && \vec{k} = (0,0,k_z)^T \\
&= k_0^2 - k_z^2 && \text{rearranging} \\
k_0^2 &= k_z^2 && k_0 = \omega \text{ (angular frequency) and therefore } k_0 > 0 \\
k_0 &= k_z && (5.150)
\end{aligned}
$$

Therefore, the wave four-vector for an excitation of a massless gauge field that moves in the z-direction reads $k_\mu = (k_z, 0, 0, k_z)^T$. Let's plug this explicit wave four-vector into the Lorenz condition:

$$
\begin{aligned}
0 &= \epsilon_0 k_0 - \epsilon_1 k_1 - \epsilon_2 k_2 - \epsilon_3 k_3 && \text{this is the Lorenz condition (Eq. 5.125)} \\
&= \epsilon_0 k_z - \epsilon_1 0 - \epsilon_2 0 - \epsilon_3 k_z && k_\mu = (k_z,0,0,k_z)^T \\
&= \epsilon_0 k_z - \epsilon_3 k_z \,. && (5.151)
\end{aligned}
$$

We can conclude that transverse polarizations (Eq. 5.129) are again permitted since there are no restrictions on ϵ_1 and ϵ_2.[73] Moreover, recall that the relation that we discovered in the previous section for a massive gauge field (Eq. 5.128) told us that longitudinal polarizations (Eq. 5.130) are equally possible.[74] What about longitudinal polarizations of a massless gauge field? The relation in Eq. 5.151 seems to suggest that an analogous construction might be possible.

[73] Reminder: transverse polarizations are described by (Eq. 5.129)

$$\epsilon^1_\mu \equiv \begin{pmatrix} 0 \\ 1 \\ 0 \\ 0 \end{pmatrix}, \quad \epsilon^2_\mu \equiv \begin{pmatrix} 0 \\ 0 \\ 1 \\ 0 \end{pmatrix}.$$

[74] Reminder: a longitudinal polarization of a massive gauge field is described by the four-vector (Eq. 5.130):

$$\epsilon^L_\mu = \begin{pmatrix} \frac{k_z}{m} \\ 0 \\ \frac{\sqrt{m^2+k_z^2}}{m} \\ 0 \end{pmatrix},$$

In particular, the condition in Eq. 5.151 is fulfilled by a third linearly-independent four-vector:

$$\epsilon^L_\mu = \begin{pmatrix} 1 \\ 0 \\ 0 \\ 1 \end{pmatrix} \qquad (5.152)$$

as we can check:

$$
\begin{aligned}
0 &= \epsilon_0 k_z - \epsilon_3 k_z && \text{this is Eq. 5.151} \\
&= 1k_z - 1kz = 0 \quad \checkmark && \epsilon_0 = 1, \epsilon_3 = 1 \text{ (Eq. 5.152)} \qquad (5.153)
\end{aligned}
$$

However, all field configurations that are proportional to ϵ^L_μ live in the same equivalence class as the trivial configuration $A_\mu = 0$.[75] To see this, we start with a field configuration of the form

$$A^L_\mu = \epsilon^L_\mu e^{ik_\mu x^\mu} \tag{5.154}$$

and use a gauge transformation with gauge function $\eta = \frac{i}{k_z} e^{ik_\mu x^\mu}$:

$$\begin{aligned}
A^L_\mu \rightarrow & A^L_\mu + \partial_\mu \eta \\
& \quad \text{Eq. 5.154 and } \eta = \frac{i}{k_z} e^{ik_\mu x^\mu} \\
&= \epsilon^L_\mu e^{ik_\mu x^\mu} + \partial_\mu \frac{i}{k_z} e^{ik_\mu x^\mu} \\
& \quad \partial_\mu e^{ik_\mu x^\mu} = ik_\mu e^{ik_\mu x^\mu} \\
&= \epsilon^L_\mu e^{ik_\mu x^\mu} + \frac{i^2}{k_z} k_\mu e^{ik_\mu x^\mu} \\
& \quad \text{Eq. 5.152, } k_\mu = (k_z, 0, 0, k_z)^T \\
&= \begin{pmatrix} 1 \\ 0 \\ 0 \\ 1 \end{pmatrix} e^{ik_\mu x^\mu} - \frac{1}{k_z} \begin{pmatrix} k_z \\ 0 \\ 0 \\ k_z \end{pmatrix} e^{ik_\mu x^\mu} \\
& \quad \cancel{k_z}, \\
&= \begin{pmatrix} 1 \\ 0 \\ 0 \\ 1 \end{pmatrix} e^{ik_\mu x^\mu} - \begin{pmatrix} 1 \\ 0 \\ 0 \\ 1 \end{pmatrix} e^{ik_\mu x^\mu} = \begin{pmatrix} 0 \\ 0 \\ 0 \\ 0 \end{pmatrix} \quad \checkmark
\end{aligned} \tag{5.155}$$

This works for any configuration that is proportional to ϵ^L_μ and therefore, for a massless gauge field all possible configurations with longitudinal polarization are physically equivalent to the trivial configuration $A_\mu = 0$. This, in turn, implies that all non-trivial excitations are transversally polarized.[76]

We can therefore conclude that a massless gauge field has only two physical polarizations (Eq. 5.129). This is in contrast to a completely general four-vector field which has four possible polarizations. The fact that we can choose to work with configurations that fulfill the Lorenz condition ($\partial_\mu A^\mu = 0$, Eq. 5.144) implies that there are only three linearly-independent configurations. Moreover, we have just learned that only two of them are realizable in physically nontrivial field configurations.

[75] Take note that this follows not just for an excitation that moves in the z-direction but in general. No matter how we choose k_μ, the third linearly-independent polarization vector for a massless gauge field is always proportional to k_μ. And this implies that all configurations that are proportional to it are gauge transformations of $A_\mu = 0$.

[76] Another argument against longitudinally polarized massless gauge fields is that the corresponding polarization vector ϵ^L_μ (Eq. 5.130) is not normalizable since:

$$\epsilon^L_\mu (\epsilon^L)^\mu = 1^2 - 1^2 = 0 \, .$$

Finally, let's write down solutions of the Maxwell and Proca equation in more general terms.

5.3.4 General Solution of the Proca and Maxwell equation

Since the Maxwell equation (Eq. 5.114) and the Proca equation (Eq. 5.113) are both linear in A_μ we can construct new solutions by using linear combinations of known solutions. To be as general as possible we write down a "sum" over all possible plane waves and all possible polarizations. In addition, as discussed in Section 5.1.4, we restrict ourselves to a sum over physically permitted configurations and only consider real gauge fields here:[77]

$$A_\mu(x) = \sum_{r=0}^{N} \int \frac{d^3p}{(2\pi)^3} \frac{1}{\sqrt{2k_0}} \left(\epsilon_\mu^r a^r(\vec{k}) e^{-ik_\mu x^\mu} + \epsilon_\mu^r a^{r\dagger}(\vec{k}) e^{ik_\mu x^\mu} \right) , \tag{5.156}$$

where N denotes the number of polarizations and the index r labels different polarization basis vectors.[78]

[77] Analogous to what we discussed in Section 5.1.4, our restriction to real fields implies that the coefficients $a_k^r, a_k^{r\dagger}$ in front of the $e^{-ik_\mu x^\mu}$ and $e^{ik_\mu x^\mu}$ terms are related by complex conjugation.

[78] Take note that Eq. 5.156 represents the Fourier decomposition of a general wave excitation in terms of plane waves.

Dancing alone gets boring after a while. So let's see how we can pair fields up and make them dance together.

6

Interacting Classical Fields

There are three important types of interactions in fundamental physics:[1]

[1] As in the previous chapters, it might make sense to have another look at the roadmap on page 35 to understand the context of this final chapter of the first part of this book.

- ▷ self-interactions,
- ▷ Yukawa interactions, which describe how scalar fields interact with spinor fields, and
- ▷ gauge interactions, which describe how gauge fields interact with spinor fields and scalar fields.[2]

[2] Reminder: a gauge field is a special type of vector field that is either described by the Maxwell equation or by the Proca equation depending on whether it's massless or massive.

This is summarized by the following diagram:[3]

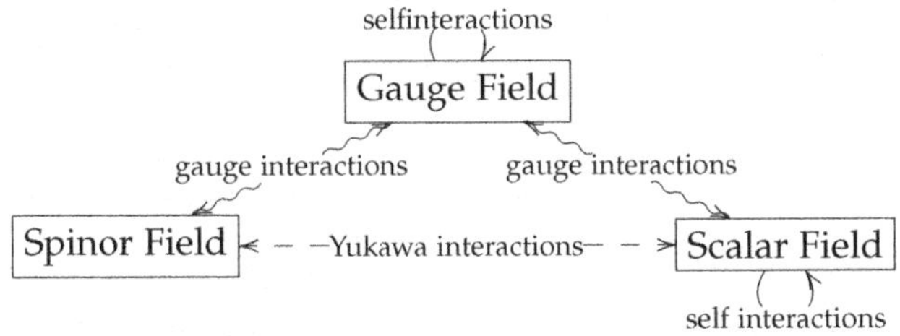

[3] Take note that self interactions only take place for a special type of gauge field known as non-abelian gauge fields. For the most famous gauge field, the electromagnetic field, no self-interactions are possible. The mathematical reason for this is that the corresponding gauge group ($U(1)$) is abelian which implies that there is no self-interaction term in the Lagrangian.

In this chapter, we will discuss these different kinds of interactions in a purely classical context.[4] In the second part of the book, we will discuss them again but in a quantum context.

[4] The discussion in this chapter is inspired by a paper titled "Solving Classical Field Equations" by Robert C. Helling.

6.1 Green's Functions

Before we talk about the various kinds of interactions, I want to tell you about an extremely useful mathematical idea that we need all the time when we want to describe how fields interact with each other.

To illustrate the method, we will restrict ourselves to scalar fields and the Klein-Gordon equation.[5] When the scalar field in question interacts with other fields or with itself, there are additional terms in the Lagrangian, $V(\phi)$, that describe these interactions:

[5] Reminder: the Klein-Gordon equation (Eq. 5.4) reads

$$(\partial_\mu \partial^\mu + m^2)\phi = 0$$

$$\mathcal{L} = \frac{1}{2}(\partial_\mu \phi \partial^\mu \phi - m^2 \phi^2) + V(\phi)\,, \tag{6.1}$$

[6] Here we use that conventional interaction terms only involve the field ϕ but not its derivatives $\partial_\mu \phi$.

If we put this modified Lagrangian into the Euler-Lagrange equation (Eq. 4.25), we find a slightly modified Klein-Gordon equation:[6]

$$\begin{aligned}
0 &= \frac{\partial \mathcal{L}}{\partial \phi} - \partial_\mu \left(\frac{\partial \mathcal{L}}{\partial(\partial_\mu \phi)} \right) \\
&\quad \text{⤷ Eq. 5.2} \\
&= \frac{\partial}{\partial \phi} \left(\frac{1}{2}(\partial_\mu \phi \partial^\mu \phi - m^2 \phi^2) + V(\phi) \right) \\
&\quad - \partial_\mu \left(\frac{\partial}{\partial(\partial_\mu \phi)} \left(\frac{1}{2}(\partial_\mu \phi \partial^\mu \phi - m^2 \phi^2) + V(\phi) \right) \right) \\
&\quad \text{⤷ } \partial_x x^2 = 2x \\
&= -m^2 \phi + \frac{\partial V(\phi)}{\partial \phi} - \partial_\mu (\partial^\mu \phi) \\
&\quad \text{⤷ } V'(\phi) \equiv \frac{\partial V(\phi)}{\partial \phi} \text{ (definition)} \\
V'(\phi) &= \left(\partial_\mu \partial^\mu - m^2 \right) \phi\,.
\end{aligned} \tag{6.2}$$

In general, for different interaction terms $V_1(\phi), V_2(\phi), \ldots$ we will find different solutions $\phi_1, \phi_2, \ldots$. A key observation is that if ϕ_1 is a solution of the equation involving V_1':

$$V_1' = \left(\partial_\mu \partial^\mu + m^2 \right) \phi_1 \tag{6.3}$$

and ϕ_2 is a solution for the equation involving V_2'

$$V_2' = \left(\partial_\mu \partial^\mu + m^2\right) \phi_2 \,, \tag{6.4}$$

we know immediately that $\phi_{12} = \phi_1 + \phi_2$ is a solution for the equation with $V_1' + V_2'$ on the right-hand side:

$$\begin{aligned}
V_1' + V_2' &= \left(\partial_\mu \partial^\mu + m^2\right) \phi_{12} \\
&\quad \text{↷ } \phi_{12} = \phi_1 + \phi_2 \\
V_1' + V_2' &= \left(\partial_\mu \partial^\mu + m^2\right) (\phi_1 + \phi_2) \\
&\quad \text{↷} \\
V_1' + V_2' &= \left(\partial_\mu \partial^\mu + m^2\right) \phi_1 + \left(\partial_\mu \partial^\mu + m^2\right) \phi_2 \\
&\quad \text{↷ Eq. 6.3, Eq. 6.4} \\
V_1' + V_2' &= V_1' + V_2' \quad \checkmark
\end{aligned} \tag{6.5}$$

Therefore, it might be possible to find basic building blocks that all solutions consist of. This is possible if we can somehow decompose all functions that appear on the right-hand side in Eq. 6.2 in terms of "fundamental" functions:

$$V'(\phi) = \sum_i c_i v_i(\phi) \,, \tag{6.6}$$

where c_i are numbers that encode how much each elementary function $v_i(\phi)$ contributes to the sum. If such a decomposition is possible and we can solve the equations with these elementary functions on the left-hand side:

$$v_i = \left(\partial_\mu \partial^\mu + m^2\right) \phi_i \,, \tag{6.7}$$

we can write any solution in the form

$$\phi = \sum_i c_i \phi_i \,. \tag{6.8}$$

6.1.1 Delta Decomposition

One possible decomposition is in terms of Dirac delta distributions:

$$V'\left(\phi(x_\mu)\right) = \int d^4y V'\left(\phi(y_\mu)\right) \delta(x_\mu - y_\mu) \,. \tag{6.9}$$

In this decomposition $\delta(x_\mu - y_\mu)$ represents our "fundamental functions", analogous to v_i in Eq. 6.6. Take note that instead of a discrete index i, here we use a continuous parameter y_μ to label these basic building blocks. We get a different delta distribution for each y_μ. This implies that we need to use an integral instead of a sum and that we get a function $V'\Big(\phi(y_\mu)\Big)$ instead of a discrete set of coefficients c_i.

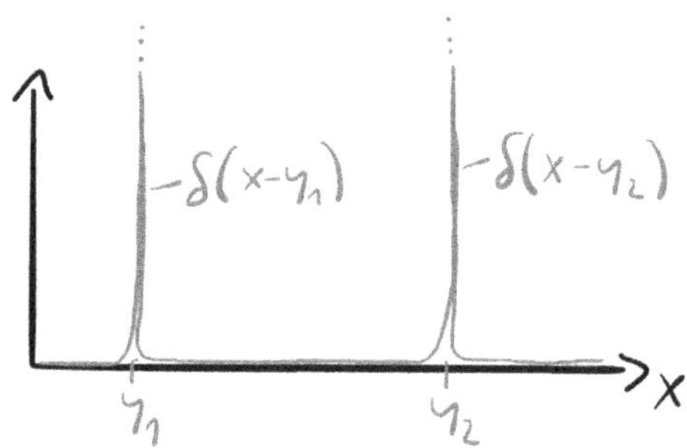

Although any mathematician will frown at the following comment, here's an intuitive way to think about this formula. The delta distribution $\delta(x_\mu - y_\mu)$ represents, in some sense, an infinitely narrow peak that is localized at y_μ. Moreover, we can imagine that any function can be decomposed in terms of sharp peaks.

In mathematical terms this means that we multiply $\delta(x_\mu - y_\mu)$ by the required height of the peak at y_μ, $V'\Big(\phi(y_\mu)\Big)$, and then sum over all possible locations y_μ to get the total function $V'\Big(\phi(x_\mu)\Big)$. In this sense, we can imagine that the delta distributions $\delta(x_\mu - y_\mu)$ at different locations y_μ represent the "atoms" or basic building blocks of all functions.

With this in mind, let's recall why we are interested in a decomposition of $V'\Big(\phi(x_\mu)\Big)$. The main idea discussed above is that if we want to construct general solutions ϕ_g using basis solutions

ϕ_s, we first need to solve the equation in question with the basis building blocks $\delta(x_\mu - y_\mu)$ on the left-hand side:[7]

$$\delta(x_\mu - y_\mu) = \left(\partial_\mu \partial^\mu + m^2\right) \phi_s(x_\mu, y_\mu), \tag{6.10}$$

[7] This is analogous to Eq. 6.7. In particular, take note that these special solutions ϕ_s are labeled by an "index" y_μ analogously to how the special solutions ϕ_i in Eq. 6.7 are labeled by an index i.

As soon as we've found the solutions $\phi_s(x_\mu, y_\mu)$, we know immediately that the solution of the equation

$$V'(\phi_g) = \left(\partial_\mu \partial^\mu + m^2\right) \phi_g, \tag{6.11}$$

where V' can now be any interaction term, is given by[8]

$$\phi_g(x_\mu) = \int d^4y\, V'\left(\phi_g(y_\mu)\right) \phi_s(x_\mu, y_\mu). \tag{6.12}$$

[8] We can compare this to Eq. 6.8, which I recite here for convenience:

$$\phi = \sum_i c_i \phi_i .$$

The argument of the "coefficient function" $V'\left(\phi_g(y_\mu)\right)$ has to be the same as the argument of the interaction term on the left-hand side. This follows from the decomposition in Eq. 6.9 and because the coefficients in Eq. 6.6 and Eq. 6.8 have to be exactly equal. An even better argument, of course, is that this expression is only a solution if $V'\left(\phi_g(y_\mu)\right)$ appears in the integral instead of, say, $V'\left(\phi_s(y_\mu)\right)$. This can be confusing at first because the solution we are looking for, $\phi_g(x_\mu)$, appears on both sides here and thus it is not immediately clear how we can evaluate the right-hand side if we don't know $\phi_g(x_\mu)$ yet.

We can check explicitly that Eq. 6.12 solves Eq. 6.11:

$$\begin{aligned}
V'\left(\phi_g(x_\mu)\right) &= \left(\partial_\mu \partial^\mu + m^2\right) \phi_g(x_\mu) \\
&\quad \text{(Eq. 6.12)} \\
&= \left(\partial_\mu \partial^\mu + m^2\right) \int dy_\mu\, V'\left(\phi_g(y_\mu)\right) \phi_s(x_\mu, y_\mu) \\
&\quad \left(\partial^\mu V'\left(\phi(y_\mu)\right) = V'\left(\phi(y_\mu)\right)\partial^\mu\right) \\
&= \int d^4y\, V'\left(\phi_g(y_\mu)\right) \left(\partial_\mu \partial^\mu + m^2\right) \phi_s(x_\mu, y_\mu) \\
&\quad \text{(Eq. 6.10)} \\
&= \int d^4y\, V'\left(\phi_g(y_\mu)\right) \delta(x_\mu - y_\mu) \\
&\quad \left(\int dy f(y)\delta(x-y) = f(x)\right) \\
&= V'\left(\phi_g(x_\mu)\right) \quad \checkmark
\end{aligned} \tag{6.13}$$

Before we can discuss in the following section using a concrete example why the solution in Eq. 6.12 is useful although $\phi_g(x_\mu)$ appears on the right-hand side too, we need to talk about the special solutions $\phi_s(x_\mu, y_\mu)$ in a bit more detail.

6.1.2 Green's Function of the Klein-Gordon Equation

To determine the special solutions $\phi_s(x_\mu, y_\mu)$ we need to solve Eq. 6.10. As you probably know, solving equations is an art. Therefore, we will not focus on mathematical details and instead imagine that an experienced mathematician hands us the correct solution:

$$\boxed{\phi_s(x_\mu, y_\mu) = \int \frac{d^4k}{(2\pi)^4} \frac{e^{-ik^\mu(x_\mu - y_\mu)}}{-k_\mu k^\mu + m^2}} \tag{6.14}$$

This is known as the Green's function of the Klein-Gordon equation. First of all, let's check if Eq. 6.14 indeed solves Eq. 6.10:

$$\begin{aligned}
\delta(x_\mu - y_\mu) &= \left(\partial_\mu \partial^\mu + m^2\right) \phi_s && \text{this is Eq. 6.10} \\
&\qquad\qquad \rhd \text{ Eq. 6.14} \\
&= \left(\partial_\mu \partial^\mu + m^2\right) \int \frac{d^4k}{(2\pi)^4} \frac{e^{-ik^\mu(x_\mu - y_\mu)}}{-k_\mu k^\mu + m^2} \\
&\qquad\qquad \rhd \ \partial_\mu \equiv \frac{\partial}{\partial x^\mu} \\
&= \int \frac{d^4k}{(2\pi)^4} \left(\partial_\mu \partial^\mu + m^2\right) \frac{e^{-ik^\mu(x_\mu - y_\mu)}}{-k_\mu k^\mu + m^2} \\
&\qquad\qquad \rhd \ \partial_x^2 e^{-ikx} = -k^2 e^{-ikx} \\
&= \int \frac{d^4k}{(2\pi)^4} \left(-k_\mu k^\mu + m^2\right) \frac{e^{-ik^\mu(x_\mu - y_\mu)}}{-k_\mu k^\mu + m^2} \\
&\qquad\qquad \rhd \ \cancel{\left(-k_\mu k^\mu + m^2\right)} \\
&= \int \frac{d^4k}{(2\pi)^4} e^{-ik^\mu(x_\mu - y_\mu)} \\
&\qquad\qquad \rhd \\
&= \delta(x_\mu - y_\mu) \quad \checkmark
\end{aligned} \tag{6.15}$$

In the final step we used that $\int \frac{d^4k}{(2\pi)^4} e^{-ik^\mu(x_\mu - y_\mu)}$ is an integral representation of the delta distribution $\delta(x_\mu - y_\mu)$. This can be understood as follows. The delta distribution $\delta(x_\mu - y_\mu)$ represents an infinitely thin wave packet. We've already learned that wave packets consist of plane waves, $e^{-ik^\mu(x_\mu - y_\mu)}$. Thus, the formula here tells us that to create a delta wave packet, we need contributions from all possible plane waves with equal magnitude. In general, the thinner a wave packet, the more plane waves must contribute. The delta wave packet is an extreme case since it is infinitely thin and thus a superposition of all possible plane waves is necessary to describe it. We can understand this by looking again at wave packets in wave number space:

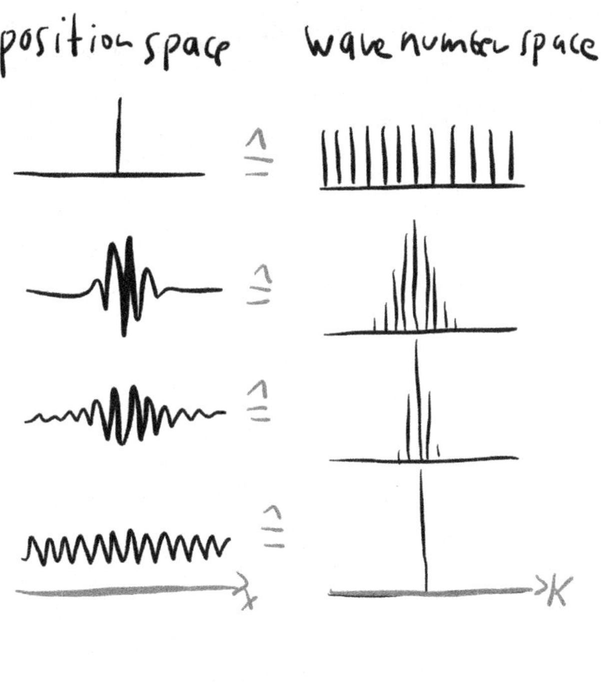

Let's try to understand what our special solutions $\phi_s(x_\mu, y_\mu)$ describe in physical terms.[9] The defining property of the special solutions is that they solve the equation (Eq. 6.10)

[9] Plural, because technically y_μ labels different special solutions.

$$\delta(x_\mu - y_\mu) = \left(\partial_\mu \partial^\mu + m^2\right) \phi_s(x_\mu, y_\mu) . \tag{6.16}$$

This equation describes a scalar field that is almost free. The only thing that disturbs it is a sharp peak at y_μ. This is what the delta distribution $\delta(x_\mu - y_\mu)$ on the left-hand side describes.

The fundamental solution $\phi_s(x_\mu, y_\mu)$ therefore encodes how the field value of a scalar field at x_μ is affected by a disturbance that is sharply localized at y_μ.

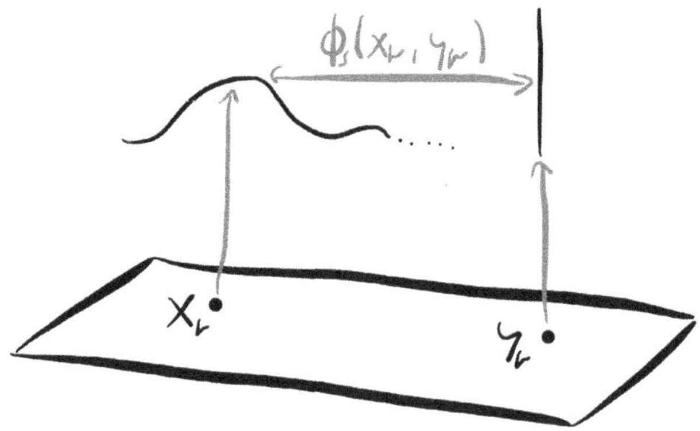

This is extremely useful because we can decompose any disturbance in terms of sharp peaks (Eq. 6.9).[10] Using the special solutions $\phi_s(x_\mu, y_\mu)$ we can then immediately calculate how each isolated disturbance affects the field at x_μ.

[10] Reminder: Eq. 6.9 reads

$$V'\Big(\phi(x_\mu)\Big) = \int d^4y V'\Big(\phi(y_\mu)\Big)\delta(x_\mu - y_\mu) .$$

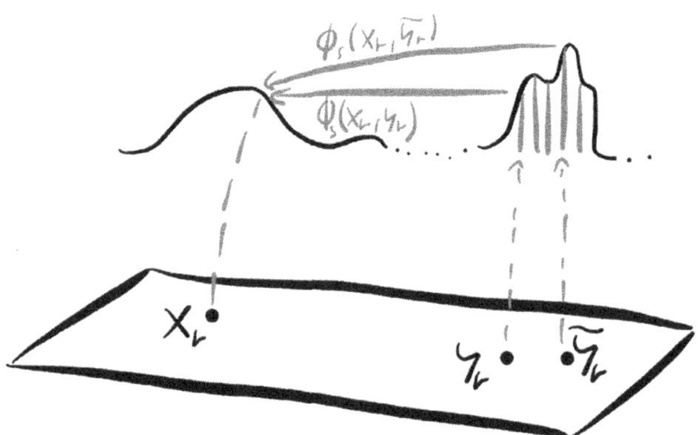

If we then sum over y_μ, we find the contributions from all possible isolated disturbances and this yields the final disturbed field value at x_μ (Eq. 6.12):

$$\phi_g(x_\mu) = \int d^4y \; V'\Big(\phi_g(y_\mu)\Big)\phi_s(x_\mu, y_\mu) , \tag{6.17}$$

where $V'\Big(\phi_g(y_\mu)\Big)$ describes the amplitude of the disturbance at y_μ.

Next, we try to understand the impact of a single completely localized disturbance in more explicit terms. For simplicity, we assume that the disturbance is time-independent and restrict ourselves to one spatial dimension. This means, we are now interested in the solutions to the equation[11]

$$\delta(x - x') = \left(-\partial_x^2 + m^2\right) \phi_s(x, x') . \tag{6.18}$$

The solutions reads[12]

$$\phi_s(x, x') = \int \frac{dk}{2\pi} \frac{e^{-ik(x-x')}}{-k^2 + m^2} . \tag{6.19}$$

To understand the physical content of this solution, we need to solve the integral. This, however, is only possible with lots of mathematical machinery and thus we will simply assume that someone hands us the solution:

$$\phi_s(x, x') = \frac{e^{-mr}}{4\pi r} , \tag{6.20}$$

where $r \equiv |x - x'| = \sqrt{(x - x')^2}$. This function is sometimes called a **Yukawa potential**.

As discussed above, a fundamental solution $\phi_s(x, x')$ encodes the impact of an isolated disturbance localized at x' on the field value at x. We can see here, that the impact is quite large if x is close to the location of the disturbance, x', and small if x is far away from x'.

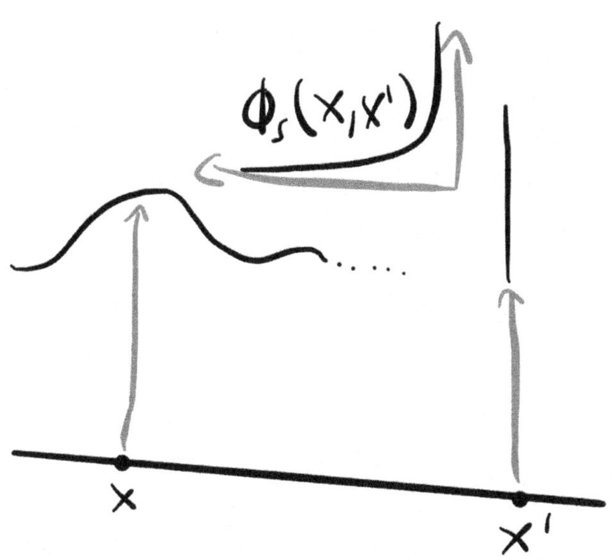

[11] This equation has the same structure as Eq. 6.10 and we use it here to understand the general features of its solutions. We use the notation x' instead of y to make clear that we mean another location on the x axis.

[12] This is completely analogous to the four-dimensional solution in Eq. 6.14. Moreover, you can verify that this is indeed a solution by plugging it into Eq. 6.18.

In addition, we can see that the parameter m determines how quickly the impact of a disturbance dies off. For small values of m, the disturbance affects field values significantly even if they are far away. In the extreme case where $m = 0$, the impact of the disturbance is noticeable across large distances. In contrast, the function in Eq. 6.20 dies off almost immediately for large values of m.

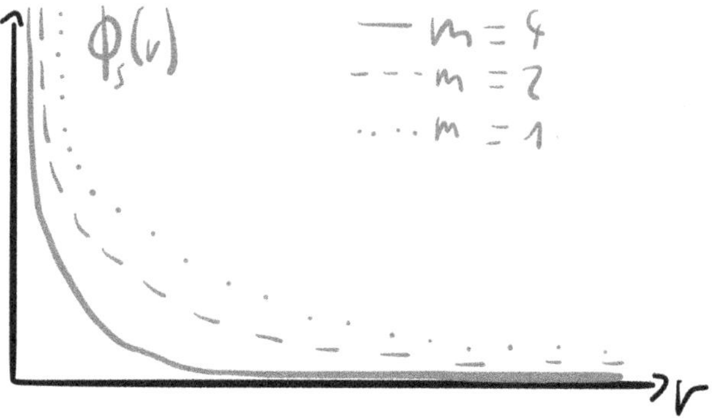

In summary, we learn that m encodes how far the "signal" that there is a disturbance at some location can travel.

With this in mind, we can understand the general solution in Eq. 6.12, which I recite here for convenience,

$$\phi_g(x_\mu) = \int d^4y \; V'\Big(\phi_g(y_\mu)\Big)\phi_s(x_\mu, y_\mu) \,. \tag{6.21}$$

from a slightly different perspective. In words, it tells us that we modulate the disturbance $V'\Big(\phi_g(y_\mu)\Big)$ at a specific location y_μ by a damping factor $\phi_s(x_\mu, y_\mu)$. This damping factor takes into account that the impact of a disturbance gets smaller if it is far away from the location x_μ we evaluate the field at. The total disturbed solution $\phi_g(x_\mu)$ is the "sum" (integral) over these modulated disturbances.

In the following section, we will discuss in more explicit terms how the special solutions $\phi_s(x_\mu, y_\mu)$ help us to describe how fields interact. But first, let's recap what we've learned so far in a bit more general terms.

6.1.3 Summary

A common situation in physics is that we are dealing with a homogeneous equation

$$Df(x) = 0 \tag{6.22}$$

where D is some derivative operator like, for example, $D \equiv \partial_x^2$ or $D \equiv \partial_x^2 + m^2$. In field theory, homogeneous equations describe free fields. Moreover, we often want to calculate the solutions of the corresponding inhomogeneous equation

$$Df_g(x) = h(x) \,. \tag{6.23}$$

In field theory, inhomogeneous equations describe how fields behave when they interact with other fields or with themselves. The idea that we talked about in this section is that we can construct solutions to this inhomogeneous equation, no matter which term appears on the right-hand side, by using the solutions $f_s(x,y)$ to the special inhomogeneous equation

$$Df_s(x,y) = \delta(x-y) \,. \tag{6.24}$$

In general, the solutions to an inhomogeneous equation with a delta distribution on the right-hand side are known as **Green's functions.**[13]

[13] Mathematicians sometimes call Green's functions "**fundamental solutions**".

With the Green's functions for a specific equation at hand, we can immediately write down the solution for the inhomogeneous equation (Eq. 6.23) with any specific inhomogeneity $h(x)$ on the right-hand side:

$$f_g(x) = \int dy \; h(y) f_s(x,y) \,. \tag{6.25}$$

In the following section, we use the ideas discussed above to describe field interactions.

6.2 Self-Interactions

In Section 5.1.2, we discussed the possibility of adding higher-order terms to the Klein-Gordon Lagrangian. We introduced the Lagrangian density (Eq. 5.37):[14]

$$\mathcal{L} = \frac{1}{2}\partial_\mu\phi\partial^\mu\phi - \frac{1}{2}\mu^2\phi^2 + \frac{1}{4!}\lambda\phi^4 \,. \tag{6.26}$$

[14] Reminder: the original Klein-Gordon Lagrangian density (Eq. 5.2) reads:

$$\mathcal{L} = \frac{1}{2}(\partial_\mu\phi\partial^\mu\phi - m^2\phi^2)\,.$$

Note that if we consider self-interactions it is conventional to call the parameter in front of the quadratic term μ^2 instead of m^2.

It is conventional to call the additional ϕ^4 term a **self-interaction term**. In this section, we will understand why.

Before we can use what we've learned in the previous section, we have to compare the Lagrangian density in Eq. 6.26 with the more general density we discussed in the previous section (Eq. 6.1).[15] This comparison tells us that here $V(\phi) = \frac{1}{4!}\lambda\phi^4$. Therefore, the modified Klein-Gordon equation for a system described by the Lagrangian in Eq. 6.26 reads

[15] For your convenience: Eq. 6.1 reads

$$\mathcal{L}_{\text{int}} = \frac{1}{2}(\partial_\mu\phi\partial^\mu\phi - m^2\phi^2) + V(\phi)$$

$$\begin{aligned}
\left(\partial_\mu\partial^\mu + \mu^2\right)\phi &= \frac{\partial V(\phi)}{\partial\phi} && \text{this is Eq. 6.2} \\
&= \frac{\partial(\frac{1}{4!}\lambda\phi^4)}{\partial\phi} && \text{↷ } V(\phi) = \frac{1}{4!}\lambda\phi^4 \\
&= \frac{4}{4!}\lambda\phi^3 && \text{↷ } \frac{\partial}{\partial x}x^4 = 4x^3 \\
&= \frac{1}{3!}\lambda\phi^3 \equiv V'(\phi)\,. && \text{↷ } \frac{4}{4!} = \frac{4}{4\cdot 3\cdot 2\cdot 1} = \frac{1}{3!}
\end{aligned} \tag{6.27}$$

With this result at hand, we can use the formulas that we've discussed in the previous section.

In particular, we can use Eq. 6.12 to immediately write down a

solution to this modified Klein-Gordon equation:

$$\phi(x_\mu) = \int d^4y \, V'\Big(\phi(y_\mu)\Big)\phi_s(x_\mu, y_\mu) \qquad \text{this is Eq. 6.12}$$

$$\quad V'(\phi) \equiv \frac{1}{3!}\lambda\phi^3 \text{ (Eq. 6.27)}$$

$$= \int d^4y \, \frac{1}{3!}\lambda\phi^3(y_\mu)\phi_s(x_\mu, y_\mu) \,, \tag{6.28}$$

where $\phi_s(x_\mu, y_\mu)$ is the Green's function of the Klein-Gordon equation (Eq. 6.14).[16]

[16] Reminder: Eq. 6.14 reads

$$\phi_s(x_\mu, y_\mu) = \int \frac{d^4k}{(2\pi)^4} \frac{e^{-ik^\mu(x_\mu - y_\mu)}}{-k_\mu k^\mu + m^2}$$

A problematic aspect of this solution is that $\phi(x_\mu)$, the function that we want to determine, appears on the right-hand side too. Thus we need another smart idea to make use of it.

Let's try a **perturbation ansatz** for ϕ:

$$\phi(x_\mu) = \sum_n \lambda^n \phi_n(x_\mu) = \lambda^0\phi_0(x_\mu) + \lambda^1\phi_1(x_\mu) + \lambda^2\phi_2(x_\mu) + \dots$$

$$\lambda^0 = 1$$

$$= \phi_0(x_\mu) + \lambda\phi_1(x_\mu) + \lambda^2\phi_2(x_\mu) + \dots \,, \tag{6.29}$$

where λ is the coupling parameter that also appears in the interaction term $V(\phi) = \frac{1}{4!}\lambda\phi^4$. This ansatz is motivated by the observation that the parameter λ encodes the impact of the additional term (the "perturbation") in the equation of motion. In particular, for $\lambda = 0$ there is no additional term. Moreover, the solution of the modified Klein-Gordon equation will certainly depend on λ. What we do in Eq. 6.29 is to expand the quite complicated solution of the modified Klein-Gordon equation around the known free solution ϕ_0. If we can ignore the interaction term, we work with ϕ_0. If we want to include the interaction term but don't care much about details, we additionally include $\lambda\phi_1$. If we care more about details, we additionally include $\lambda\phi_2$.[17]

[17] This, of course, only works if λ is a small parameter ($\lambda < 1$). Otherwise, higher order terms in the contribution are more important than lower order terms and the ansatz becomes useless.

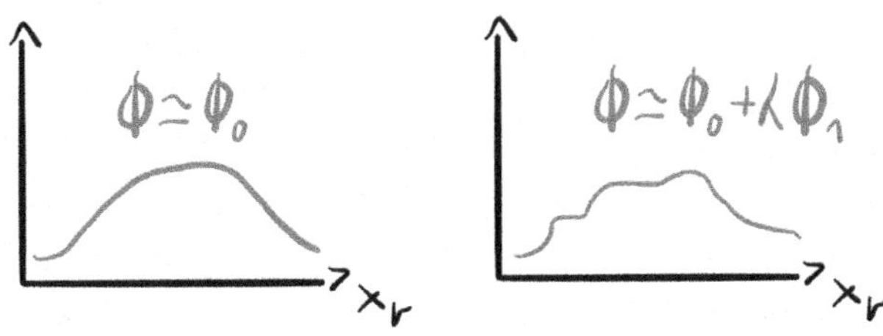

To understand how this works, we plug the perturbation ansatz into the modified Klein-Gordon equation (Eq. 6.27):[18]

[18] We use here that $(a+b)^3 = a^3 + 3a^2b + 3ab^2 + b^3$

$$
\begin{aligned}
\left(\partial_\mu\partial^\mu + \mu^2\right)\phi &= \frac{1}{3!}\lambda\phi^3 \\
&\quad \text{Eq. 6.29} \\
\left(\partial_\mu\partial^\mu + \mu^2\right)\left(\phi_0 + \lambda\phi_1 + \ldots\right) &= \frac{1}{3!}\lambda\left(\phi_0 + \lambda\phi_1 + \ldots\right)^3 \\
\left(\partial_\mu\partial^\mu + \mu^2\right)\left(\phi_0 + \lambda\phi_1 + \ldots\right) &= \frac{1}{3!}\lambda\left(\phi_0^3 + 3\lambda\phi_0^2\phi_1 + 3\lambda^2\phi_0\phi_1^2 + \lambda^3\phi_1^3 + \ldots\right) \\
\left(\partial_\mu\partial^\mu + \mu^2\right)\left(\phi_0 + \lambda\phi_1 + \ldots\right) &= \frac{1}{3!}\lambda\phi_0^3 + \frac{1}{2}\lambda^2\phi_0^2\phi_1 + \frac{1}{2}\lambda^3\phi_0\phi_1^2 + \frac{1}{3!}\lambda^4\phi_1^3 + \ldots\Big) .
\end{aligned}
\tag{6.30}
$$

This is useful because the terms involving different powers of λ must be equal and thus we find

$$
\begin{aligned}
\left(\partial_\mu\partial^\mu + \mu^2\right)\phi_0 &= 0 && \text{all terms without } \lambda \\
\left(\partial_\mu\partial^\mu + \mu^2\right)\phi_1 &= \frac{1}{3!}\phi_0^3 && \text{all terms} \propto \lambda^1 \\
\left(\partial_\mu\partial^\mu + \mu^2\right)\phi_2 &= \frac{1}{2}\phi_0^2\phi_1 && \text{all terms} \propto \lambda^2 \\
&\vdots
\end{aligned}
\tag{6.31}
$$

This suggests that we can determine the terms in the perturbative expansion (Eq. 6.29) iteratively. Once we know ϕ_0, we can determine ϕ_1. Once we know ϕ_1, we can determine ϕ_2 and so on. Moreover, the equation for ϕ_0 is simply the Klein-Gordon equation. Thus ϕ_0 is given by the free solution that we discussed in Section 5.1.3.

To determine the higher order terms iteratively, we plug the ansatz into Eq. 6.28:

$$\phi(x_\mu) = \int d^4y \, \frac{1}{3!} \lambda \phi^3(y_\mu) \phi_s(x_\mu, y_\mu)$$

↷ Eq. 6.29

$$\phi_0 + \lambda\phi_1 + \lambda^2\phi_2 + \ldots = \int d^4y \, \frac{1}{3!} \lambda \Big(\phi_0 + \lambda^1 \phi_1 + \ldots \Big)^3 \phi_s$$

↷

$$= \int d^4y \, \frac{1}{3!} \Big(\lambda\phi_0^3 + 3\lambda^2\phi_0^2\phi_1 + 3\lambda^3\phi_0\phi_1^2 + \lambda^4\phi_1^3 + \ldots \Big) \phi_s \,, \tag{6.32}$$

where we again sorted the terms on the right-hand side by powers in λ. By comparing the left-hand side with the right-hand side we can conclude

$$\begin{aligned} \phi_1 &= \frac{1}{3!} \int d^4y \, \phi_0^3 \phi_s \\ \phi_2 &= \frac{3}{3!} \int d^4y \, \phi_0^2 \phi_1 \phi_s = \frac{1}{2!} \int d^4y \, \phi_0^2 \phi_1 \phi_s \\ &\vdots \end{aligned} \tag{6.33}$$

Thus, as promised, we can determine all terms in the perturbation series (Eq. 6.29) iteratively.

Let's try to understand a bit more systematically what we've discovered here. Our goal is to determine the "shape" of the scalar field ϕ by calculating its field value $\phi(x_\mu)$ at all possible locations x_μ. At lowest order, we use the unperturbed solution, $\phi \approx \phi_0$.

Higher order terms in our expansion (Eq. 6.29) describe that this solution is modified $\phi \approx \phi_0 + \lambda\phi_1 + \lambda^2\phi_2$ as a result of the interaction term.

For example, the first correction term reads (Eq. 6.33)[19]

$$\phi_1(x_\mu) = \frac{1}{3!} \int d^4y \, \phi_0^3(y_\mu) \phi_s(x_\mu, y_\mu) \,. \tag{6.34}$$

One way interpret this first non-trivial modification of the free solution is shown in the following illustration.

[19] For clarity, I've again included the arguments of the various fields.

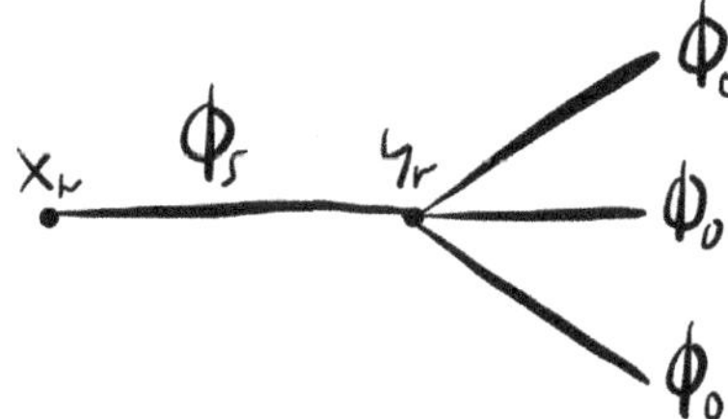

In words, we can describe it as follows. The free field solution ϕ_0 depends on how we prepare the system. For example, we can imagine that we only excite the scalar field within a small region. Mathematically, this means that ϕ_0 is a small wave packet. The factor $\phi_0^3(y_\mu)$ in the integrand then describes the contributions coming from this wave packet interacting with itself at y_μ. The second factor in the integrand, $\phi_s(x_\mu, y_\mu)$, describes how the contributions coming from these points in the wave packet influence the field values at x_μ.

Since a field spreads out all over space, we need to sum over all possible locations y_μ from which a contribution is possible.

The second term reads (Eq. 6.33)

$$\begin{aligned}
\phi_2(x_\mu) &= \frac{1}{2}\int d^4y\ \phi_0^2(y_\mu)\phi_1(y_\mu)\phi_s(x_\mu, y_\mu) \\
&\quad \text{Eq. 6.34} \\
&= \frac{1}{2}\int d^4y\ \phi_0^2(y_\mu)\left(\frac{1}{3!}\int d^4y'\ \phi_0^3(y'_\mu)\phi_s(y_\mu, y'_\mu)\right)\phi_s(x_\mu, y_\mu) \\
&\quad \text{rearranging} \\
&= \frac{1}{12}\int d^4y \int d^4y'\ \phi_0^2(y_\mu)\phi_0^3(y'_\mu)\phi_s(y_\mu, y'_\mu)\phi_s(x_\mu, y_\mu)\,.
\end{aligned} \tag{6.35}$$

We can interpret this term analogously to the first correction term. The factor $\phi_0^3(y'_\mu)$ describes the contributions from the field values of the wave packet interacting three times with itself at y'_μ. Similarly, the factor $\phi_0^2(y_\mu)$ describes the contributions from the wave packet interacting twice with itself at y_μ. In addition, we take into account how the field structure at y_μ is affected by the field interaction at y'_μ. This is described by $\phi_s(y_\mu, y'_\mu)$. As before, since our field spreads out over all of spacetime, we integrate over all possible locations y'_μ for which a contribution is possible.

Lastly, we take into account how the modified field values at y_μ affect the field configuration at x_μ. This is what $\phi_s(x_\mu, y_\mu)$ describes. And again, we need to integrate over y_μ to take contributions from all possible spacetime points into account.

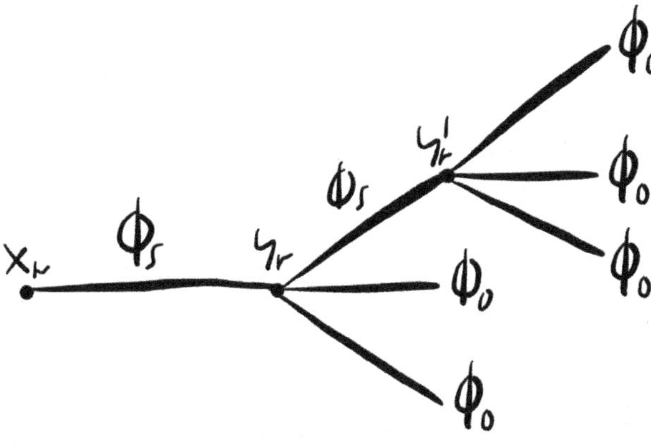

You might not find these interpretations of the different terms in our perturbation series very enlightening. But the message to take away is simply that we can again decompose our now quite complicated field structure in terms of plane waves. The different terms in the perturbation series (Eq. 6.29) take more and more and more ways into account how different plane wave structures can affect each other.

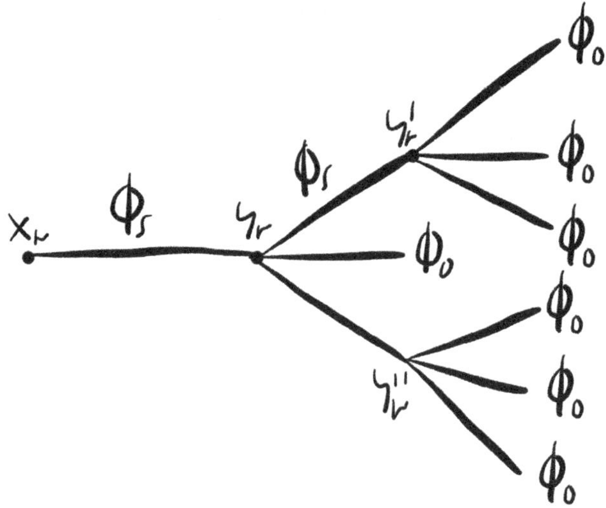

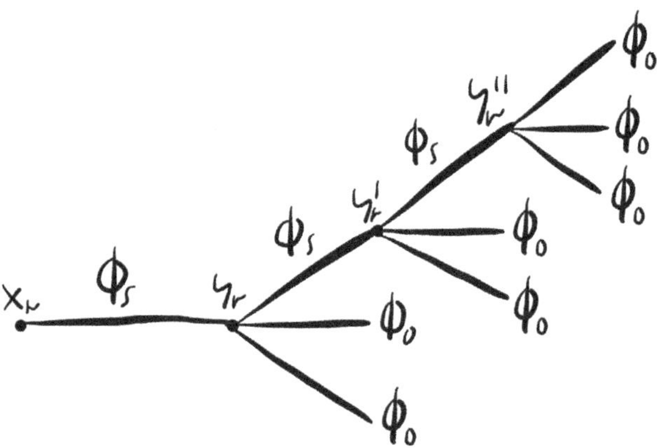

This is why we call a term like $\frac{\lambda}{4!}\phi^4$ in the Lagrangian an interaction term. Or, to be a bit more precise, since there is only one field we call $\frac{\lambda}{4!}\phi^4$ a *self*-interaction term.

Next, let's finally talk about how different fields interact with each other.

6.3 Yukawa Interactions

If we want to take into account fields other than scalar fields, we need to include additional terms in the Lagrangian. For example, if we want to consider one scalar field and one spinor field, we simply add the two corresponding Lagrangian densities:

$$\begin{aligned}\mathcal{L}_{\text{scalar+spinor}} &= \mathcal{L}_{\text{free scalar}} + \mathcal{L}_{\text{free spinor}} \\ &= \frac{1}{2}(\partial\phi)^2 - \frac{m_\phi^2}{2}\phi^2 + i\bar{\psi}\gamma^\mu\partial_\mu\psi - m_\psi^2\bar{\psi}\psi\,, \end{aligned} \tag{6.36}$$

Eq. 5.2, Eq. 5.54

where m_ϕ is the mass parameter associated with the scalar field ϕ and m_ψ is the mass parameter associated with the spinor field ψ. This Lagrangian describes two completely independent free fields and, therefore, we can learn nothing new here. In the real world, however, scalar fields interact with spinor fields, and this is where things become interesting. Mathematically, this implies that we need to include at least one additional term in the Lagrangian which describes this interaction. The simplest term we can come up with that couples a spinor field to a scalar field is $\bar{\psi}\psi\phi$ since a product of the form $\bar{\psi}\psi$ describe the scalar product of two spinors.[20] Therefore, the total Lagrangian density now reads

[20] The Lagrangian is mathematically a scalar. Therefore, all terms we can write down in the Lagrangian must be scalar too. This implies, for example, that a term of the form $\psi\phi$ is not allowed since we need to multiply a spinor ψ by another spinor, $\bar{\psi} \equiv \psi^\dagger\gamma_0$, to get a scalar.

$$\begin{aligned}\mathcal{L}_{\text{scalar+spinor+interaction}} &= \mathcal{L}_{\text{free scalar}} + \mathcal{L}_{\text{free spinor}} + \mathcal{L}_{\text{Yukawa}} \\ &= \frac{1}{2}(\partial\phi)^2 - \frac{m_\phi^2}{2}\phi^2 + i\bar{\psi}\gamma^\mu\partial_\mu\psi - m_\psi^2\bar{\psi}\psi + g\bar{\psi}\psi\phi\,, \end{aligned} \tag{6.37}$$

Eq. 5.2, Eq. 5.54

where the interaction term $\bar{\psi}\psi\phi$ is called a **Yukawa term** and the parameter g encodes how strongly ψ and ϕ are coupled. Moreover, we say $\bar{\psi}\psi\phi$ describes **Yukawa interactions**.

If we now want to explore the implications of this additional term, we can use all the technology introduced in the previous sections. On the one hand, we can use the Green's function of the Klein-Gordon equation (Eq. 6.14) to investigate how the interaction term affects the scalar field ϕ. On the other hand, we can use the Green's function of the Dirac equation to understand how the interaction affects the spinor field ψ.

Since we haven't talked about the Green's function of the Dirac equation yet, let's start by discussing the implications for the scalar field.

6.3.1 Scalar Field in the Presence of Yukawa Interactions

The interaction term we are now interested in reads $V(\phi) = g\bar{\psi}\psi\phi$. Therefore, the modified Klein-Gordon equation now reads:[21]

[21] We find this equation of motion by plugging the Lagrangian in Eq. 6.37 into the Euler-Lagrange equation (Eq. 4.25). However, all the terms that only involve the spinor field ψ, yield no additional terms and thus we can simply plug V into Eq. 6.2.

$$\begin{aligned}
\left(\partial_\mu \partial^\mu + m^2\right)\phi &= \frac{\partial V}{\partial \phi} && \text{this is Eq. 6.2} \\
& && \text{↷ } V(\phi) = g\bar{\psi}\psi\phi \\
&= \frac{\partial(g\bar{\psi}\psi\phi)}{\partial \phi} \\
& && \text{↷} \\
&= g\bar{\psi}\psi\,. && (6.38)
\end{aligned}$$

Moreover, we can again use Eq. 6.12 to (formally) write down the solution to this modified Klein-Gordon equation:

$$\begin{aligned}
\phi(x_\mu) &= \int d^4y\, V'\Big(\phi(y_\mu)\Big)\phi_s(x_\mu, y_\mu) && \text{this is Eq. 6.12} \\
& && \text{↷ } V'(\phi) \equiv \frac{\partial V}{\partial \phi} = g\bar{\psi}\psi \text{ (Eq. 6.38)} \\
&= \int d^4y\, g\bar{\psi}\psi\, \phi_s(x_\mu, y_\mu)\,, && (6.39)
\end{aligned}$$

where $\phi_s(x_\mu, y_\mu)$ is the Green's function of the Klein-Gordon equation (Eq. 6.14).[22]

[22] Reminder: Eq. 6.14 reads

$$\phi_s(x_\mu, y_\mu) = \int \frac{d^4k}{(2\pi)^4} \frac{e^{-ik^\mu(x_\mu - y_\mu)}}{-k_\mu k^\mu + m^2}$$

As in Section 6.2, the next step is to make the ansatz (Eq. 6.29)

$$\begin{aligned}
\phi(x_\mu) &= \phi_0(x_\mu) + g\phi_1(x_\mu) + g^2\phi_2(x_\mu) + \ldots \\
\psi(x_\mu) &= \psi_0(x_\mu) + g\psi_1(x_\mu) + g^2\psi_2(x_\mu) + \ldots\,, && (6.40)
\end{aligned}$$

where $\phi_0(x_\mu)$ is a solution of the free Klein-Gordon equation and the remaining terms $(\phi_1, \phi_2, \ldots)$ describe how it is modified through interactions. Analogously, $\psi_0(x_\mu)$ is a solution to the free Dirac equation and $(\psi_1, \psi_2, \ldots)$ describe corrections that we will discuss in the following sections in more detail. We can determine the correction terms $\phi_1, \phi_2, \ldots$ iteratively

$$
\begin{aligned}
\phi &= \int d^4y \; g\bar{\psi}\psi \; \phi_s & &\text{this is Eq. 6.39} \\
& & &\text{↷ Eq. 6.29} \\
\phi_0 + g\phi_1 + g^2\phi_2 + \ldots &= \int d^4y \; g\Big(\bar{\psi}_0 + g\bar{\psi}_1 + \ldots\Big)\Big(\psi_0 + g\psi_1 + \ldots\Big)\phi_s \\
&= \int d^4y \; g\Big(\bar{\psi}_0\psi_0 + g\bar{\psi}_1\psi_0 + g\bar{\psi}_0\psi_1 + g^2\bar{\psi}_1\psi_1 + \ldots\Big)\phi_s \\
&= \int d^4y \; \Big(g\bar{\psi}_0\psi_0 + g^2\bar{\psi}_1\psi_0 + g^2\bar{\psi}_0\psi_1 + g^3\bar{\psi}_1\psi_1 + \ldots\Big)\phi_s
\end{aligned}
\tag{6.41}
$$

Comparing coefficients, we find

$$
\begin{aligned}
\phi_1(x_\mu) &= \int d^4y \; \bar{\psi}_0(y_\mu)\psi_0(y_\mu)\phi_s(x_\mu, y_\mu) & &\text{all terms} \propto g \\
\phi_2(x_\mu) &= \int d^4y \; \Big(\bar{\psi}_1(y_\mu)\psi_0(y_\mu) + \bar{\psi}_0(y_\mu)\psi_1(y_\mu)\Big)\phi_s(x_\mu, y_\mu) & &\text{all terms} \propto g^2 \\
&\vdots
\end{aligned}
\tag{6.42}
$$

We can now interpret the first correction term ϕ_1 that appears as a result of the Yukawa term analogously to how we interpreted the self-interaction corrections.

The factor $\bar{\psi}_0\psi_0$ describes the product of the free spinor wave packets. We evaluate the value of this product at the location y_μ and the damping factor $\phi_s(x_\mu, y_\mu)$ tells us how it affects the field value of ϕ at the location x_μ.

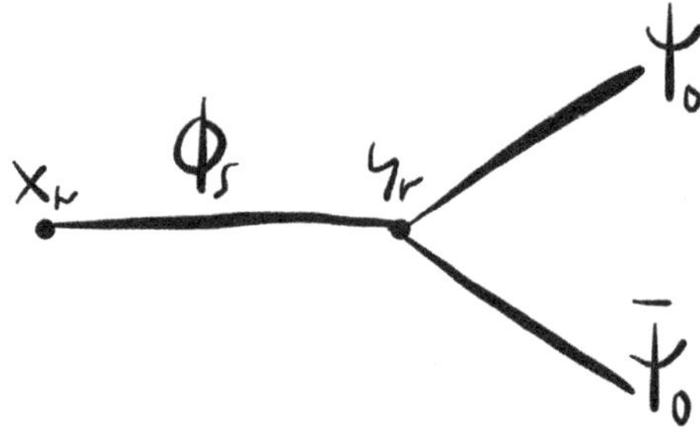

Moreover, we integrate over all possible locations y_μ to take the impact of the field structure of ψ_0 and $\bar{\psi}_0$ everywhere into account.

Before we can interpret the second correction term, we need to talk about the correction ψ_1 to the free spinor field solution ψ_0.

6.3.2 Green's Function of the Dirac Equation

If we want to understand how interaction terms affect spinor fields, we need to solve the modified Dirac equation. We can derive a modified Dirac equation by considering the Dirac Lagrangian density (Eq. 5.54) plus an interaction term:

$$\mathcal{L} = \bar{\psi}(i\gamma^\mu \partial_\mu - m)\psi + V(\psi, \bar{\psi}) \,. \qquad (6.43)$$

We assume here that the interaction term depends on $\psi, \bar{\psi}$ but not on their derivatives. If we plug this Lagrangian density into the Euler-Lagrange equation (Eq. 4.25), we find[23]

[23] The steps here are analogous to what we did in Eq. 5.63. In particular, recall that we treat $\bar{\psi}$ and ψ as independent fields.

$$\frac{\partial \mathcal{L}}{\partial \bar{\psi}} = \partial_\mu \left(\frac{\partial \mathcal{L}}{\partial(\partial_\mu \bar{\psi})} \right)$$

↷ Eq. 6.43

$$\frac{\partial\Big(\bar{\psi}(i\gamma^\mu \partial_\mu - m)\psi + V(\psi, \bar{\psi})\Big)}{\partial \bar{\psi}} = \partial_\mu \left(\frac{\partial\Big(\bar{\psi}(i\gamma^\mu \partial_\mu - m)\psi + V(\psi, \bar{\psi})\Big)}{\partial(\partial_\mu \bar{\psi})} \right)$$

↷

$$(i\gamma^\mu \partial_\mu - m)\psi + \frac{\partial V(\psi, \bar{\psi})}{\partial \bar{\psi}} = 0$$

↷ $\frac{\partial V(\psi, \bar{\psi})}{\partial \bar{\psi}} \equiv V'(\psi, \bar{\psi})$

$$(i\gamma^\mu \partial_\mu - m)\psi = -V'(\psi, \bar{\psi}) \,. \qquad (6.44)$$

This is the modified Dirac equation that we need to solve if we want to take interactions into account.

Analogous to what we did in Section 6.1.2 for the modified Klein-Gordon equation, the key idea is to look for fundamental solutions ψ_s. The defining property of these fundamental solutions is that they solve the modified Dirac equation with a delta distribution on the right-hand side. However, there is a subtlety. The Dirac equation is an equation that determines the behavior of a spinor ψ. Therefore, the interaction term on the right-hand side of the equation, $-V'(\psi,\bar{\psi})$, will be a spinor too. This is necessarily the case because otherwise we would be comparing apples to oranges. In more mathematical terms, we can say that both sides of the modified Dirac equation carry a spinor index α:

$$(i\gamma^\mu \partial_\mu - m)\psi^\alpha = -V'^\alpha(\psi,\bar{\psi}) , \tag{6.45}$$

The index reminds us that we are dealing with four-component objects. Therefore, the decomposition of the interaction $V'^\alpha(\psi,\bar{\psi})$ now reads[24]

[24] This formula is analogous to Eq. 6.12.

$$\psi_g^\alpha(x_\mu) = \int d^4y\, \psi_s^{\alpha\beta}(x_\mu, y_\mu) V'^\beta\Big(\psi(y_\mu), \bar{\psi}(y_\mu)\Big) , \tag{6.46}$$

where $\psi_s^{\alpha\beta}(x_\mu, y_\mu)$ is now a *matrix* that encodes how each component of the spinorial object $V'^\beta\Big(\psi(y_\mu), \bar{\psi}(y_\mu)\Big)$ affects the components of the Dirac spinor $\psi_g^\alpha(x_\mu)$. In other words, instead of a single basis solution we now need a basis solution for each spinor component. The object we are now looking for, $\psi_s^{\alpha\beta}(x_\mu, y_\mu)$, contains the basis solutions for all four components. Thus the defining equation reads

$$(i\gamma^\mu \partial_\mu - m)^{\alpha\sigma} \psi_s^{\sigma\beta} = -\delta(x_\mu - y_\mu)\delta^{\alpha\beta} , \tag{6.47}$$

where $\delta^{\alpha\beta}$ is the (4×4) unit matrix.[25] In words, this means that we perturb each spinor component with a delta peak.

[25] Recall that γ^μ denotes (4×4) matrices (Eq. 5.56). Moreover, there is an implicit unit matrix behind m. This is why $(i\gamma^\mu \partial_\mu - m)$ carries spinor indices. In addition, it has one spinor index in common with ψ_s since we are dealing with a matrix product.

We will again simply assume that someone hands us the correct solution ψ_s to the Dirac equation with the delta distribution on the right-hand side:

$$\boxed{\psi_S^{\alpha\beta}(x_\mu, y_\mu) = \int \frac{d^4k}{(2\pi)^4} e^{-ik^\nu(x_\nu - y_\nu)} \frac{(-k_\rho\gamma^\rho + m)^{\alpha\beta}}{-k_\lambda k^\lambda + m^2}.} \tag{6.48}$$

This is the fundamental solution or **Green's function of the Dirac equation**. In physical terms, this Green's function represents again a damping factor that encodes how the impact of a completely localized perturbation becomes smaller as we move farther away from it.

Let's check that it indeed solves Eq. 6.47:

$$\begin{aligned}
-\delta(x_\mu - y_\mu)\delta^{\alpha\beta} &= (i\gamma^\mu\partial_\mu - m)^{\alpha\sigma}\psi_S^{\sigma\beta} && \text{this is Eq. 6.47} \\
&= (i\gamma^\mu\partial_\mu - m)^{\alpha\sigma} \int \frac{d^4k}{(2\pi)^4} e^{-ik^\nu(x_\nu - y_\nu)} \frac{(-k_\rho\gamma^\rho + m)^{\sigma\beta}}{-k_\lambda k^\lambda + m^2} && \text{Eq. 6.48} \\
&= \int \frac{d^4k}{(2\pi)^4} (i\gamma^\mu\partial_\mu - m)^{\alpha\sigma} e^{-ik^\nu(x_\nu - y_\nu)} \frac{(-k_\rho\gamma^\rho + m)^{\sigma\beta}}{-k_\lambda k^\lambda + m^2} && \partial_\mu \equiv \frac{\partial}{\partial x^\mu} \\
&= \int \frac{d^4k}{(2\pi)^4} (i\gamma^\mu(ik_\mu) - m)^{\alpha\sigma} e^{-ik^\nu(x_\nu - y_\nu)} \frac{(-k_\rho\gamma^\rho + m)^{\sigma\beta}}{-k_\lambda k^\lambda + m^2} && \partial_x e^{ikx} = ike^{ikx} \\
&= \int \frac{d^4k}{(2\pi)^4} e^{-ik^\nu(x_\nu - y_\nu)} \frac{(-\gamma^\mu k_\mu - m)^{\alpha\sigma}(-k_\rho\gamma^\rho + m)^{\sigma\beta}}{-k_\lambda k^\lambda + m^2} && i^2 = -1
\end{aligned} \tag{6.49}$$

The final puzzle piece here is that we need to evaluate the product:[26]

[26] ρ and μ are dummy indices that we can rename freely and $x_\mu y^\mu = x^\mu y_\mu = y_\mu x^\mu$. Therefore, $mk_\rho\gamma^\rho = m\gamma^\mu k_\mu$

$$
\begin{aligned}
&(-\gamma^\mu k_\mu - m)^{\alpha\sigma}(-k_\rho\gamma^\rho + m)^{\sigma\beta} \\
&= (\gamma^\mu)^{\alpha\sigma}k_\mu k_\rho(\gamma^\rho)^{\sigma\beta} + m\delta^{\alpha\sigma}k_\rho(\gamma^\rho)^{\sigma\beta} - (\gamma^\mu)^{\alpha\sigma}k_\mu m\delta^{\sigma\beta} - m\delta^{\alpha\sigma}m\delta^{\sigma\beta} \\
& \qquad \text{↷ } (\gamma^\mu)^{\alpha\sigma}\delta^{\sigma\beta} = (\gamma^\mu)^{\alpha\beta},\ \delta^{\alpha\sigma}\delta^{\sigma\beta} = \delta^{\alpha\beta} \\
&= (\gamma^\mu)^{\alpha\sigma}k_\mu k_\rho(\gamma^\rho)^{\sigma\beta} + mk_\rho(\gamma^\rho)^{\alpha\beta} - (\gamma^\mu)^{\alpha\beta}k_\mu m - m^2\delta^{\alpha\beta} \\
& \qquad \text{↷ } \cancel{(\gamma^\mu)^{\alpha\beta}k_\mu m} \\
&= k_\mu k_\rho(\gamma^\mu)^{\alpha\sigma}(\gamma^\rho)^{\sigma\beta} - m^2\delta^{\alpha\beta} \\
& \qquad \text{↷ } k_\mu k_\rho\gamma^\mu\gamma^\rho = k_\mu k^\mu \text{ (Eq. 5.80)} \\
&= (k_\mu k^\mu - m^2)\delta^{\alpha\beta}\,.
\end{aligned}
\tag{6.50}
$$

If we plug this back into Eq. 6.49, we find

$$
\begin{aligned}
-\delta(x_\mu - y_\mu)\delta^{\alpha\beta} &= \int \frac{d^4k}{(2\pi)^4}\, e^{-ik^\nu(x_\nu - y_\nu)} \frac{(-\gamma^\mu k_\mu - m)^{\alpha\sigma}(-k_\rho\gamma^\rho + m)^{\sigma\beta}}{-k_\sigma k^\sigma + m^2} \qquad \text{this is Eq. 6.49} \\
& \qquad \text{↷ Eq. 6.50} \\
&= \int \frac{d^4k}{(2\pi)^4}\, e^{-ik^\nu(x_\nu - y_\nu)} \frac{(k_\mu k^\mu - m^2)\delta^{\alpha\beta}}{-k_\sigma k^\sigma + m^2} \\
& \qquad \text{↷ } \cancel{k_\mu k^\mu - m^2} \\
&= -\int \frac{d^4k}{(2\pi)^4}\, e^{-ik^\nu(x_\nu - y_\nu)}\delta^{\alpha\beta} \\
& \qquad \text{↷ } \int \frac{d^4k}{(2\pi)^4}\, e^{-ik^\nu(x_\nu - y_\nu)} \equiv \delta(x_\mu - y_\mu) \\
&= -\delta(x_\mu - y_\mu)\delta^{\alpha\beta} \quad \checkmark
\end{aligned}
\tag{6.51}
$$

Now that we have some confidence in the validity of the fundamental solution in Eq. 6.48, we can evaluate the impact of Yukawa interactions on a spinor field.

6.3.3 Spinor Field in the Presence of Yukawa Interactions

To unclutter the notation, we will suppress all spinor indices in this section. Just keep in mind that ψ_s is a matrix.

We start by making a perturbative ansatz (Eq. 6.40)

$$\begin{aligned}\phi(x_\mu) &= \phi_0(x_\mu) + g\phi_1(x_\mu) + g^2\phi_2(x_\mu) + \dots \\ \psi(x_\mu) &= \psi_0(x_\mu) + g\psi_1(x_\mu) + g^2\psi_2(x_\mu) + \dots ,\end{aligned} \tag{6.52}$$

where, as before, $\phi_0(x_\mu)$ is a solution of the free Klein-Gordon equation and $\psi_0(x_\mu)$ is a solution of the free Dirac equation.[27] If we plug this into our general formula (Eq. 6.46) and use that we consider a Yukawa interaction term (Eq. 6.37),

[27] For $\psi_0(x_\mu)$ this follows when we plug the ansatz into the modified Dirac equation (Eq. 6.44). For $\phi_0(x_\mu)$ we saw this explicitly in Eq. 6.30 and Eq. 6.31.

$$\begin{aligned}V &= g\bar{\psi}\psi\phi \\ \frac{\partial V}{\partial \bar{\psi}} &= \frac{\partial(g\bar{\psi}\psi\phi)}{\partial\bar{\psi}} = g\psi\phi \equiv V'(\phi,\bar{\phi}) ,\end{aligned} \tag{6.53}$$

we find

$$\begin{aligned}\psi_g &= \int d^4y\ \psi_s V'\left(\psi,\bar{\psi}\right) \\ &\quad \text{(Eq. 6.53)} \\ \psi_g &= \int d^4y\ \psi_s\ g\psi\phi \\ &\quad \text{(Eq. 6.52)} \\ \psi_0 + g\psi_1 + g^2\psi_2 \dots &= \int d^4y\ \psi_s\ g\Big((\psi_0 + g\psi_1 + \dots)(\phi_0 + g\phi_1 + \dots)\Big) \\ &= \int d^4y\ \psi_s\ g\Big(\psi_0\phi_0 + g\psi_1\phi_0 + \psi_0 g\phi_1 + g^2\psi_1\phi_1 + \dots\Big) \\ &= \int d^4y\ \psi_s\ \Big(g\psi_0\phi_0 + g^2\psi_1\phi_0 + g^2\psi_0\phi_1 + g^3\psi_1\phi_1 + \dots\Big) .\end{aligned} \tag{6.54}$$

Comparing coefficients yields

$$\begin{aligned}\psi_1(x_\mu) &= \int d^4y\ \psi_s(x_\mu, y_\mu)\ \psi_0(y_\mu)\phi_0(y_\mu) && \text{all terms} \propto g \\ \psi_2(x_\mu) &= \int d^4y\ \psi_s(x_\mu, y_\mu)\ \Big(\psi_1(y_\mu)\phi_0(y_\mu) + \psi_0(y_\mu)\phi_1(y_\mu)\Big) && \text{all terms} \propto g^2 \\ &\ \vdots\end{aligned} \tag{6.55}$$

We can interpret these correction terms as being analogous to the correction terms in the previous section. The first correction term $\psi_1(x_\mu)$ takes into account how the scalar wave packet $\phi_0(y_\mu)$ and spinor wave packet $\psi_0(y_\mu)$ overlap. To that end, we calculate the product $\psi_0\phi_0$, evaluate it at y_μ and then use the Green's function $\psi_s(x_\mu, y_\mu)$ to find out how it affects the spinor field at x_μ. As usual, we take contributions from all possible locations into account by integrating over y_μ.

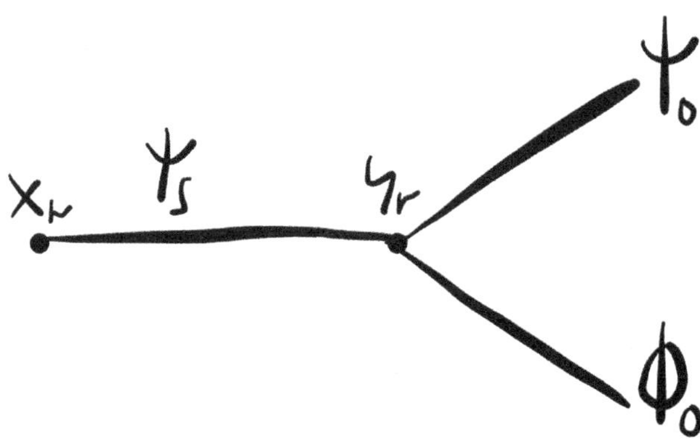

To interpret the second correction term, we rewrite it using the explicit form of ψ_1 and ϕ_1:[28]

[28] We have here three different integrals and therefore three independent integration variables y_μ, y'_μ, y''_μ.

$$
\begin{aligned}
\psi_2(x_\mu) &= \int d^4y\ \psi_s(x_\mu, y_\mu)\ \Big(\psi_1(y_\mu)\phi_0(y_\mu) + \psi_0(y_\mu)\phi_1(y_\mu)\Big) \\
&\qquad \text{Eq. 6.42, Eq. 6.55} \\
&= \int d^4y\ \psi_s(x_\mu, y_\mu)\ \Bigg(\Big(\int d^4y'\ \psi_0(y'_\mu)\phi_0(y'_\mu)\psi_s(y_\mu, y'_\mu)\Big)\phi_0(y_\mu) \\
&\quad + \psi_0(y_\mu)\Big(\int d^4y''\ \bar{\psi}_0(y''_\mu)\psi_0(y''_\mu)\phi_s(y_\mu, y''_\mu)\Big)\Bigg)
\end{aligned}
\tag{6.56}
$$

Instead of using lots of words, let me simply refer you to the following two illustrations.[29]

[29] Analogously, you can now also interpret the second correction term ϕ_2 in Eq. 6.42 using the solution in Eq. 6.55.

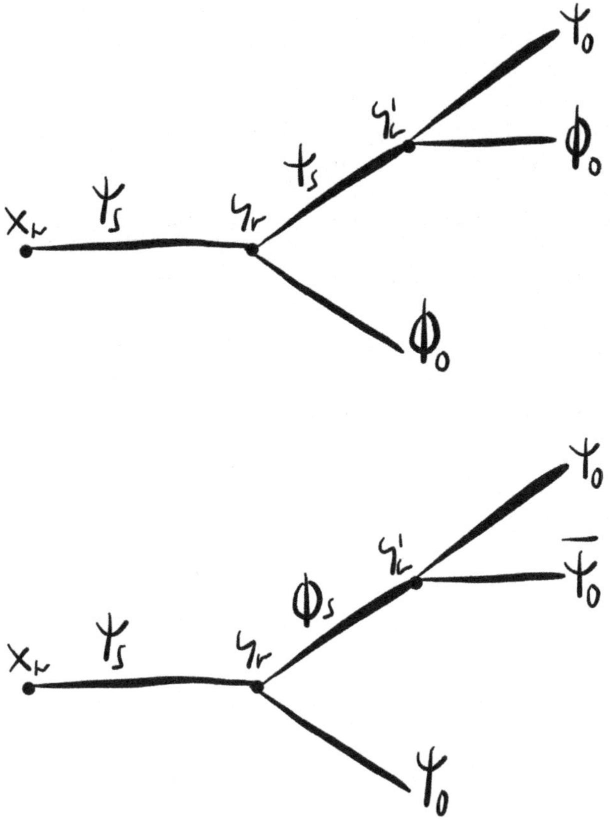

So far, we've discussed how a scalar field interacts with itself and how scalar and spinor fields interact with each other. Next, we will discuss how gauge fields enter the picture.

6.4 Gauge Interactions

For simplicity, we will restrict our discussion in this chapter to massless gauge fields.

For most practical purposes it's completely sufficient to only know the following recipe:[30]

[30] We discussed in Section 3.9 that gauge fields are bookkeepers that keep track of local conventions. Moreover, when we calculate a derivative we necessarily compare a function's values at two different locations. This follows from the definition of a derivative in terms of a difference quotient. Therefore, we need to include the bookkeeper A_μ to make sure the difference in the function's values is not only a result of differently chosen local coordinate systems. In mathematical terms, this implies that we need to replace the derivative ∂_μ by the covariant derivative $\partial_\mu - ieA_\mu$ (Eq. 3.92).

1. Take the Lagrangian that describes a free scalar field (Eq. 5.2) or alternatively, the Lagrangian that describes a free spinor field (Eq. 5.54).
2. Replace the derivative ∂_μ by the covariant derivative[31]

$$D_\mu = \partial_\mu - ieA_\mu \,, \tag{6.57}$$

where e is a parameter that describes the coupling strength.

3. Add the Lagrangian that describes a free gauge field $\mathcal{L}_{\text{Maxwell}}$ (Eq. 5.107 with $m = 0$).

[31] In short, we do this to make sure that our equations remain valid no matter which coordinate system we use for the field space above each spacetime point. The gauge field A_μ is a bookkeeper that makes sure that our description stays consistent. In the third step, we then promote the bookkeeper to an independent physical field. This is the hallmark of a gauge theory.

The resulting Lagrangian describes perfectly how a gauge field interacts with other fields.

As an example, let's consider the interactions between a single spinor field ψ and a gauge field A_μ. Following the recipe outlined above, we start by writing down the free Lagrangian density for the spinor fields (Eq. 5.54):

$$\mathcal{L}_{\text{Dirac}} = \bar{\psi}(i\gamma^\mu\partial_\mu - m)\psi \,. \tag{6.58}$$

We then replace the derivative ∂_μ with the covariant derivative D_μ:

$$\begin{aligned} \mathcal{L}_{\text{Dirac+gauge interaction}} &= \bar{\psi}(i\gamma^\mu D_\mu - m)\psi \\ &\quad \text{(Eq. 6.57)} \\ &= \bar{\psi}\Big(i\gamma^\mu(\partial_\mu - ieA_\mu) - m\Big)\psi \\ &= \bar{\psi}\Big(i\gamma^\mu\partial_\mu + e\gamma^\mu A_\mu - m\Big)\psi \,. \end{aligned} \tag{6.59}$$

Lastly, we add the free gauge field Lagrangian (Eq. 5.107 with $m = 0$):

$$\mathcal{L}_{\text{Dirac+gauge interaction+Maxwell}} = \bar{\psi}\Big(i\gamma^\mu\partial_\mu + e\gamma^\mu A_\mu - m\Big)\psi \\ - \frac{1}{2}(\partial^\mu A^\nu \partial_\mu A_\nu - \partial^\mu A^\nu \partial_\nu A_\mu)\,. \tag{6.60}$$

This is one of the most famous and most successful Lagrangians in all of physics. It describes correctly how the electromagnetic field A_μ interacts with a spinor field ψ like, for example, the electron field.

Completely analogously, we can write down the Lagrangian that describes how a gauge field interacts with a scalar field

$$\mathcal{L}_{\text{Klein-Gordon+gauge interaction+Maxwell}} = \frac{1}{2}(D_\mu\phi D^\mu\phi - m^2\phi^2) \\ - \frac{1}{2}(\partial^\mu A^\nu \partial_\mu A_\nu - \partial^\mu A^\nu \partial_\nu A_\mu)\,. \tag{6.61}$$

Equipped with these Lagrangians, we can proceed exactly as in the previous sections. By plugging the Lagrangian in Eq. 6.60 into the Euler-Lagrange equation for A_μ, we find the modified Maxwell equation:[32]

$$\partial_\mu(\partial^\mu A^\nu - \partial^\nu A^\mu) = e\bar{\psi}\gamma^\nu\psi \equiv J^\nu\,. \tag{6.62}$$

This is the Maxwell equation in the presence of an external source $J^\nu \equiv V'^\nu \equiv \frac{\partial V}{\partial A_\nu}$.[33]

Similarly, if we plug Eq. 6.60 into the Euler-Lagrange equation for $\bar{\psi}$, we find the equation that describes how a spinor field behaves in the presence of a gauge field A_μ:[34]

$$(i\gamma^\mu\partial_\mu - m)\psi = -e\gamma^\mu A_\mu\psi \equiv V'\,. \tag{6.63}$$

The only missing puzzle piece that we need before we can start our perturbative analysis once again is the Green's function of the Maxwell equation.

[32] The steps here are analogous to what we did at the beginning of Section 5.1. The only additional term that contributes to the equation of motion is the interaction term $V(A_\mu) = e\bar{\psi}\gamma^\mu A_\mu\psi$ since $\frac{\partial\psi}{\partial A_\mu} = 0$.

[33] It's conventional in this context to use the symbol J instead of V', which is what we used in the previous section for self-interactions and Yukawa interactions.

[34] The steps here are analogous to what we did in Eq. 6.44. The only difference is that we are now dealing with a different interaction term $e\bar{\psi}\gamma^\mu A_\mu\psi$.

6.4.1 Green's Function of the Maxwell Equation

The Green's function of the Maxwell equation is defined as the solution to the equation

$$\partial_\sigma(\partial^\sigma A_s^{\rho\lambda} - \partial^\rho A_s^{\sigma\lambda}) = \delta(x_\mu - y_\mu)\eta^{\rho\lambda} . \tag{6.64}$$

In words, this means that we need to find a solution to the modified Maxwell equation (Eq. 6.62) in the presence of a "delta"-source. As for the Dirac equation, the Green's function here, $A_s^{\rho\lambda}$, is a matrix. This follows because the Maxwell equation is an equation that encodes the behavior of a four-vector field. Thus, we need a Green's function for each component of this four-vector field. On the right-hand side we have the Minkowski metric $\eta^{\rho\lambda}$ since this is the appropriate "unit matrix" in Minkowski space.

Once we've found the matrix that contains these Green's functions, we can write the general solution of the modified Maxwell equation as

$$A^\nu(x_\mu) = \int d^4y \; A_s^{\nu\zeta}(x_\mu, y_\mu) J_\zeta\Big(\psi(y_\mu), \bar\psi(y_\mu)\Big) . \tag{6.65}$$

We will see below that $A_s^{\nu\zeta}(x_\mu, y_\mu) \propto \eta^{\nu\zeta}$, which is exactly what we need to properly raise the index of J_ζ such that we have the same index on the left-hand and right-hand side of the equation: $\eta^{\nu\zeta}J_\zeta = J^\nu$ (Eq. 2.34). This is another way to understand why we included the Minkowski metric on the right-hand side in Eq. 6.64. If instead we would search for a solution to Eq. 6.64 with $\eta^{\rho\lambda}$ replaced by the unit matrix $\delta^{\rho\lambda}$, we would find $\tilde A_s^{\nu\zeta}(x_\mu, y_\mu) \propto \delta^{\nu\zeta}$. But this object is not what we need in the expansion in Eq. 6.65.

As in the previous sections, we will assume that someone hands us the correct Green's functions

$$\boxed{A_s^{\nu\zeta}(x_\mu, y_\mu) = \int \frac{d^4k}{(2\pi)^4} \frac{e^{-ik^\mu(x_\mu - y_\mu)}}{-k_\mu k^\mu} \eta^{\nu\zeta} .} \tag{6.66}$$

Let's verify that it indeed solves the defining equation (Eq. 6.64). For simplicity, we will restrict ourselves to configurations that fulfill the Lorenz condition (Eq. 5.144) $\partial_\mu A^\mu = 0$. This is possible without loss of generality thanks to the gauge freedom in A_μ.[35]. The modified Maxwell equation (Eq. 6.62) in the Lorenz gauge reads

[35] This was discussed in Section 5.3.3.

$$\begin{aligned} J^\nu &= \partial_\mu(\partial^\mu A^\nu - \partial^\nu A^\mu) \\ & \quad \text{↷ } \partial_\mu A^\mu = 0 \\ &= \partial_\mu \partial^\mu A^\nu \,. \end{aligned} \tag{6.67}$$

Therefore, the defining equation for the matrix $A_s^{\nu\zeta}$ (Eq. 6.64) simplifies to

$$\partial_\sigma(\partial^\sigma A_s^{\rho\lambda}) = \delta(x_\mu - y_\mu)\eta^{\rho\lambda} \,. \tag{6.68}$$

With this simplified formula at hand, let's verify that the proposed matrix in Eq. 6.66 indeed solves it:

$$\begin{aligned} \delta(x_\mu - y_\mu)\eta^{\rho\lambda} &= \partial_\sigma\partial^\sigma A_s^{\rho\lambda} \\ & \quad \text{↷ Eq. 6.66} \\ &= \partial_\sigma\partial^\sigma \int \frac{d^4k}{(2\pi)^4} \frac{e^{-ik^\mu(x_\mu - y_\mu)}}{-k_\mu k^\mu}\eta^{\rho\lambda} \\ & \quad \text{↷ } \partial_\sigma\partial^\sigma \equiv \frac{\partial}{\partial x^\mu}\frac{\partial}{\partial x_\mu} \\ &= \int \frac{d^4k}{(2\pi)^4} \partial_\sigma\partial^\sigma \frac{e^{-ik^\mu(x_\mu - y_\mu)}}{-k_\mu k^\mu}\eta^{\rho\lambda} \\ & \quad \text{↷ } \partial_x^2 e^{ikx} = -k^2 e^{ikx} \\ &= -\int \frac{d^4k}{(2\pi)^4} k_\sigma k^\sigma \frac{e^{-ik^\mu(x_\mu - y_\mu)}}{-k_\mu k^\mu}\eta^{\rho\lambda} \\ & \quad \text{↷ } \cancel{-k_\sigma k^\sigma} \\ &= \int \frac{d^4k}{(2\pi)^4} e^{-ik^\mu(x_\mu - y_\mu)}\eta^{\rho\lambda} \\ & \quad \text{↷ } \int \frac{d^4k}{(2\pi)^4} e^{-ik^\mu(x_\mu - y_\mu)} \equiv \delta(x_\mu - y_\mu) \\ &= \delta(x_\mu - y_\mu)\eta^{\rho\lambda} \quad \checkmark \end{aligned} \tag{6.69}$$

Next, we want to understand the physical meaning of Eq. 6.66. We can use it, for example, to evaluate how a gauge field is affected by a static and completely localized source:[36]

[36] These assumptions are analogous to what we discussed in Section 6.1.2 for the Green's function of the Klein-Gordon equation.

$$J_\mu(x_\mu) = \begin{pmatrix} q\delta(\vec{x} - \vec{a}) \\ 0 \\ 0 \\ 0 \end{pmatrix} . \tag{6.70}$$

The delta distribution $\delta(\vec{x} - \vec{a})$ indicates that our source q is localized at $\vec{x} = \vec{a}$.

If we plug this into the general solution of the modified Maxwell equation (Eq. 6.65), we find

$$\begin{aligned} A^{\nu}(x_\mu) &= \int d^4y \, A_s^{\nu\zeta} J_\zeta(y_\mu) \\ & \qquad \text{↷ } J_1 = J_2 = J_3 = 0 \text{ (Eq. 6.70)} \\ &= \int d^4y \, A_s^{\nu 0} J_0(y_\mu) \\ & \qquad \text{↷ } J_0 = q \text{ (Eq. 6.70)} \\ &= \int d^4y \, A_s^{\nu 0} \, q\delta(\vec{y} - \vec{a}) \, . \end{aligned} \tag{6.71}$$

By looking at the explicit form of A_s (Eq. 6.66), we can see that all components $A_s^{\nu 0}$ vanish except for $\nu = 0$. This follows because $A_s^{\mu\nu} \propto \eta^{\mu\nu}$ and $\eta^{\mu\nu} = 0$ except for $\mu = \eta$.[37] Therefore, we can focus on the 00-component, A_s^{00}, which describes how a source affects the zeroth component of the four-vector field A_μ. Moreover, for simplicity, we will restrict ourselves to one spatial dimension:

[37] Reminder: the Minkowski metric reads (Eq. 2.30):

$$\eta^{\mu\nu} = \begin{pmatrix} 1 & 0 & 0 & 0 \\ 0 & -1 & 0 & 0 \\ 0 & 0 & -1 & 0 \\ 0 & 0 & 0 & -1 \end{pmatrix} .$$

$$\begin{aligned} A_s^{00}(x, x') &= \int \frac{dk}{2\pi} \frac{e^{-ik(x-x')}}{-k^2} \eta^{00} \qquad \text{this is Eq. 6.66 in } 1D \text{ with } \nu\zeta = 00 \\ & \qquad \text{↷ } \eta^{00} = 1 \text{ (Eq. 2.30)} \\ &= \int \frac{dk}{2\pi} \frac{e^{-ik(x-x')}}{-k^2} \, . \end{aligned} \tag{6.72}$$

This is exactly the Green's function of the Klein-Gordon equation (Eq. 6.19) with m set to zero![38]

[38] Reminder: Eq. 6.19 reads

$$\phi_s(x, x') = \int \frac{dk}{2\pi} \frac{e^{-ik(x-x')}}{-k^2 + m^2} .$$

Moreover, take note that if we start with the Proca Lagrangian (Eq. 5.107) instead of with the Maxwell Lagrangian, we find exactly the Green's function of the Klein-Gordon equation here.

Therefore, if we carry out the integration, we analogously find

$$A_s^{00}(x, x') = \frac{1}{4\pi r} \qquad \text{this is Eq. 6.20 with } m = 0 \tag{6.73}$$

where $r \equiv |x - x'| = \sqrt{(x - x')^2}$. This is the **Coulomb potential** of a point charge q which is located at a.[39]

[39] It is instructive to compare the Coulomb potential to the Yukawa potential (Eq. 6.20):

$$\phi_s(x, x') = \frac{e^{-mr}}{4\pi r} .$$

The Yukawa potential becomes the Coulomb potential in the limit $m \to 0$. For non-zero values of m, the damping in the Yukawa potential is much stronger than in the Coulomb potential as a result of the additional exponential factor.

Analogous to what we did in the previous sections, we could now make a perturbative ansatz for the gauge field A_μ and then evaluate in more explicit terms how it interacts with a spinor field or a scalar field. However, there isn't really anything new to be learned here. The main lesson is again that we can understand the structure of a gauge field in the presence of a scalar or spinor field in terms of overlapping free solutions that happen at specific isolated locations. To determine the overall structure of the gauge field we can then integrate over all possible locations. Since we've discussed the main ideas twice already in the context of spinor fields and scalar fields, we will not discuss any further details here.

We've now reached the point beyond which we can no longer ignore that Nature at fundamental scales behaves quite differently from what we are used to from our everyday experiences. Therefore, we move on to the next part of the book in which we discuss the modifications that are necessary if we want to describe fields in a quantum context.

Part I
What Everybody Ought to Know About Quantum Field Theory

"The universe is full of magical things patiently waiting for our wits to grow sharper."

Eden Phillpotts

PS: You can discuss the content of Part I with other readers and give feedback at `www.nononsensebooks.com/qft/bonus`.

7

Quantum Mechanics

Our main goal in this part of the book is to discuss quantum fields. However, we will start by talking about quantum mechanics because it makes sense to discuss the main features of quantum theories in this simpler context first. Of course, a full discussion of quantum mechanics requires more than a few pages. Thus we will focus solely on those aspects that are relevant for quantum field theory.[1] Most paragraphs in the following sections are excerpts from my book "No-Nonsense Quantum Mechanics"[2].

[1] If you're already familiar with quantum mechanics, feel free to skip this chapter. Moreover, if you know nothing about quantum mechanics yet, it probably makes sense if you pick up a dedicated quantum mechanics textbook after finishing this book.

[2] Jakob Schwichtenberg. *No-Nonsense Quantum Mechanics*. No-Nonsense Books, Karlsruhe, Germany, 2018c. ISBN 978-1719838719

7.1 The Quantum Formalism

In the standard formulation of quantum mechanics, we introduce an abstract object $|\Psi\rangle$ that describes the system in question.[3] In addition, we introduced quantum operators that we can use to extract information about the system. For example, if we want to know the momentum of a system, we use the momentum operator $\hat{p}$:

[3] In mathematical terms, $|\Psi\rangle$ is a vector in a Hilbert space.

$$\hat{p}\,|\Psi_1\rangle = p_1\,|\Psi_1\rangle\ . \tag{7.1}$$

However, we often do not get such a simple answer. Instead, if we measure the momentum of equally prepared systems, we could possibly end up with different results. Each possible result occurs with a certain probability. In our quantum framework, we describe such a situation using a linear combination such as

$$|\Psi\rangle = a\,|\Psi_1\rangle + b\,|\Psi_2\rangle + \dots\,, \tag{7.2}$$

where $|\Psi_1\rangle$ is a state with momentum p_1, $|\Psi_2\rangle$ is the state with momentum p_2. The coefficients a and b are directly related to the probability of measuring p_1 and p_2, respectively. For example, $|a|^2$ is the probability of measuring the value p_1.

We can understand Eq. 7.2 as the expansion of a general state $|\Psi\rangle$ in terms of states with definite momenta. These states with definite momenta are commonly called momentum eigenstates.

The expansion is analogous to how we can expand an arbitrary vector in terms of basis vectors,

$$\vec{e}_x = \begin{pmatrix} 1 \\ 0 \\ 0 \end{pmatrix}, \quad \vec{e}_y = \begin{pmatrix} 0 \\ 1 \\ 0 \end{pmatrix}, \quad \vec{e}_z = \begin{pmatrix} 0 \\ 0 \\ 1 \end{pmatrix}. \tag{7.3}$$

For example,

$$\vec{v} = \begin{pmatrix} 1 \\ 3 \\ 5 \end{pmatrix} = 1\vec{e}_x + 3\vec{e}_y + 5\vec{e}_z = 1\begin{pmatrix} 1 \\ 0 \\ 0 \end{pmatrix} + 3\begin{pmatrix} 0 \\ 1 \\ 0 \end{pmatrix} + 5\begin{pmatrix} 0 \\ 0 \\ 1 \end{pmatrix}. \tag{7.4}$$

An important task in quantum mechanics is to calculate the expectation value for a given observable and system.[4] The basic idea is that we "sandwich" the corresponding operator between a ket $|\Psi\rangle$ and a bra $\langle\Psi|$:

$$\langle\Psi| \equiv |\Psi\rangle^\dagger = (|\Psi\rangle^\star)^T\,. \tag{7.5}$$

For example, the momentum expectation value reads

$$\langle\Psi|\,\hat{p}\,|\Psi\rangle\,.$$

[4] If you're unfamiliar with expectation values, you can find a short discussion in Appendix F.1.

A bra together with a ket denotes the scalar product between two abstract vectors. This is analogous to $\langle \vec{v}_1 | \vec{v}_2 \rangle \equiv \vec{v}_1 \cdot \vec{v}_2$. Here we have $\langle \vec{v}_1 | \equiv \vec{v}_1^T$ ("row times column"). But in quantum mechanics we deal with complex vectors and therefore have $\langle \Psi|_1 \equiv |\Psi_1\rangle^\dagger = |\Psi_1\rangle^{*T}$. In addition, we can calculate the probability of measuring one *specific* value. All we have to do is multiply the ket which describes our system by the bra which describes the system in a state with this particular value. For example, the probability of measuring p_1 is $|\langle \Psi_1 | \Psi \rangle|^2$.

This procedure is analogous to how we can determine how much a given vector spreads out, say, in the z-direction. All we have to do is multiply the vector by the z-basis vector $\vec{e}_z$:

$$\vec{e}_z \cdot \vec{v} = \vec{e}_z^T \vec{v} = \begin{pmatrix} 0 & 0 & 1 \end{pmatrix} \begin{pmatrix} 1 \\ 3 \\ 5 \end{pmatrix} = 5 .$$

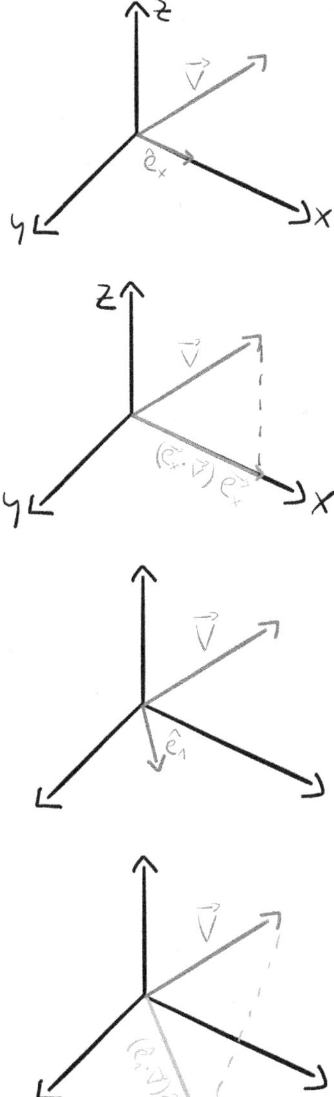

We can make the analogy even more explicit by using the notation from Eq. (7.4):

$$\begin{aligned} \vec{e}_z \cdot \vec{v} &= \vec{e}_z \cdot \left(1\vec{e}_x + 3\vec{e}_y + 5\vec{e}_z\right) \\ &= 1\vec{e}_z \cdot \vec{e}_x + 3\vec{e}_z \cdot \vec{e}_y + 5\vec{e}_z \cdot \vec{e}_z \quad \text{(}\vec{e}_z \cdot \vec{e}_x = 0,\ \vec{e}_z \cdot \vec{e}_z = 1\text{)} \\ &= 1 \times 0 + 3 \times 0 + 5 \times 1 = 5 . \end{aligned} \tag{7.6}$$

Two additional ingredients that we need in our quantum framework is an explicit form of the quantum operators like $\hat{p}$ and an equation that describes how states evolve in time. This is what we will talk about next.

One puzzle piece that allows us to understand quantum operators a little better is Noether's theorem which we discussed already in Section 4.3.[5]

[5] There are, in fact, two famous theorems by Emmy Noether that are relevant in this context. The one I'm talking about is her first one that deals with *global* symmetries. Her second one is about *local* symmetries.

The second piece we need is how symmetries are described mathematically.

You are probably wondering what all this has to do with quantum mechanics. As we will see in the next section, actually, a lot! The mathematical ideas in the next section are exactly what we need to find the explicit form of quantum operators. Most importantly, this explicit form allows us to derive the famous canonical commutation relation, and the Schrödinger equation.

7.1.1 Group Theory

The role and description of symmetries in physics is a huge topic.[6] So there is no way we can cover all the details. However, I will try to emphasize the basic ideas that are necessary to understand quantum mechanics.

[6] In fact, I've written a whole book on exactly this topic:

Jakob Schwichtenberg. *Physics from Symmetry*. Springer, Cham, Switzerland, 2018b. ISBN 978-3319666303

First of all: what is a symmetry?

Imagine a friend stands in front of you and holds an object in her hands. Then you close your eyes and she performs a transformation of the object (e.g. a rotation). Then you open your eyes again. If you can't tell if your friend changed anything at all, the transformation she performed is a symmetry of the object. For example, if she holds a perfectly round, single-colored ball in her hands, any rotation is a symmetry of the ball. In contrast, if she holds a box in her hand, only very specific rotations are symmetries of the box. Doing nothing is always a symmetry.

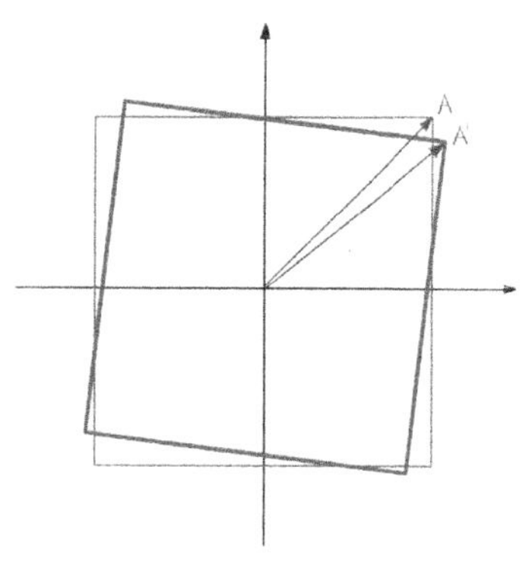

The bottom line is:

> **A symmetry is a transformation that leaves the object in question unchanged.**

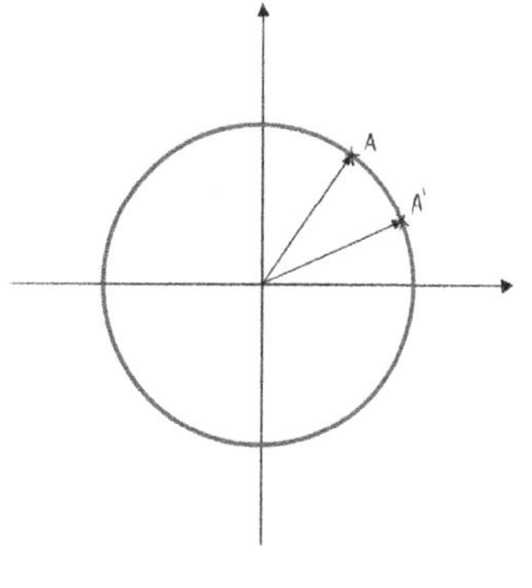

The part of mathematics which deals with symmetries is called **group theory**. A group is a set of transformations which fulfill special rules plus an operation that tells us how to combine the transformations. The rules are known as group axioms and we can motivate them by investigating an intuitive symmetry like rotational symmetry. We will not discuss details like this since we don't need them for what follows.

Also, we only need one special part of group theory, namely the part that deals with *continuous* symmetries. An example of a continuous symmetry is the one I just mentioned: rotations of a ball. Rotations are continuous because we can label them with a continuous parameter: the angle of rotation. In contrast, there are also *discrete* symmetries. The most famous examples are mirror symmetries.

There is one property that makes continuous symmetries especially nice to deal with: they have elements which are arbitrarily close to the identity transformation.[7]

[7] The identity transformation is the transformation that changes nothing at all. For example, for rotations, the identity transformation is a rotation by 0°.

For example, think about the symmetries of a circle. Any rotation about the origin is a symmetry of a circle. Therefore, a rotation extremely close to the identity transformation, say a rotation by 0.000001°, is a symmetry of the circle.

In contrast, an arbitrary group has, in general, no element close to the identity.

For example, think about the symmetries of a square. The set of transformations that leaves a square invariant comprises four rotations: a rotation by 0°, 90°, 180° and 270°, plus some mirror symmetries. But a rotation by 0.000001° is not a symmetry.

Mathematically, we write an element g close to the identity I as:

$$g(\epsilon) = I + \epsilon G \,, \tag{7.7}$$

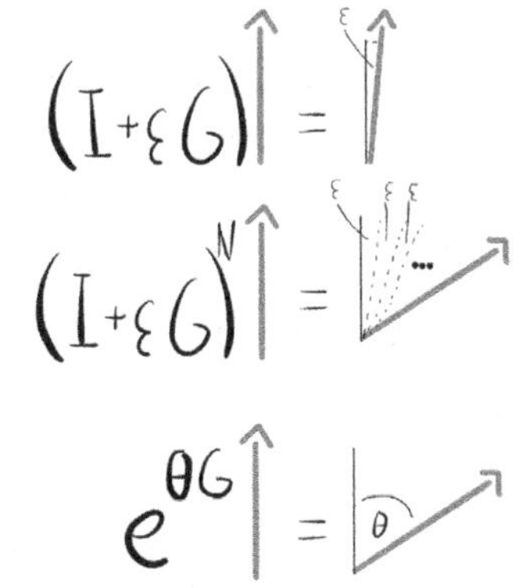

where ϵ is a really, really small number and G is an object, called a **generator**, that we will talk about in a moment. In the smallest possible case, such transformations are called **infinitesimal transformations**.

$$(I+\epsilon G)\uparrow = \uparrow$$

$$(I+\epsilon G)^N\uparrow = \nearrow$$

$$e^{\theta G}\uparrow = \nearrow$$

Such small transformations barely change anything. However, if we repeat an infinitesimal transformation many times, we end up with a finite transformation.

Let's return to our discussion about rotations. Many small rotations in one direction are equivalent to one big rotation in the same direction.

Mathematically, we can write the idea of repeating a small transformation many times as follows

$$h(\theta) = (I + \epsilon G)(I + \epsilon G)(I + \epsilon G)... = (I + \epsilon G)^k, \tag{7.8}$$

where k denotes how often we repeat the small transformation.

If θ denotes some finite transformation parameter, e.q., 50° or so, and N is some huge number that makes sure we are close to the identity, we can write Eq. (7.7) as

$$g(\theta) = I + \frac{\theta}{N} G. \tag{7.9}$$

The transformations we want to consider are the smallest possible, which means N must be the biggest possible number, i.e., $N \to \infty$. To get a finite transformation from such an infinitesimal transformation, one has to repeat the infinitesimal transformation infinitely often. Mathematically we can write this as

$$h(\theta) = \lim_{N \to \infty} \left(I + \frac{\theta}{N} G \right)^N, \tag{7.10}$$

which is in the limit $N \to \infty$ the exponential function

$$h(\theta) = \lim_{N \to \infty} \left(I + \frac{\theta}{N} G \right)^N = e^{\theta G}. \tag{7.11}$$

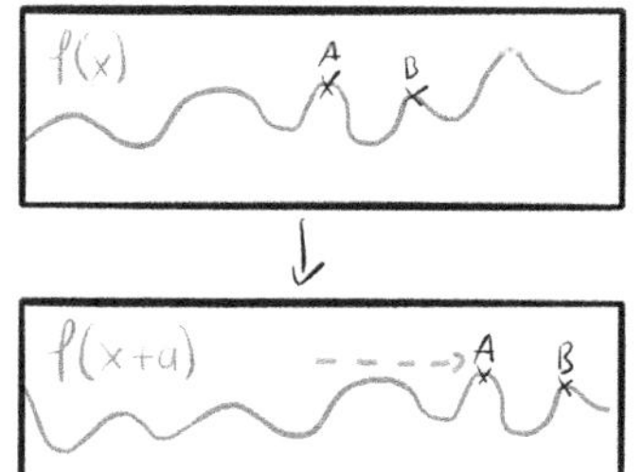

The bottom line is that the object G *generates* the finite transformation h. This is why we call objects like these **generators**.

What do these generators explicitly look like?

Let's consider a function $f(x,t)$ and assume that our goal is to generate a spatial translation such that $Tf(x,t) = f(x+a,t)$. The generator

$$G_{\text{xtrans}} = \partial_x \tag{7.12}$$

does the job:[8]

[8] Here ∂_x is a shorthand notation for the derivative $\frac{\partial}{\partial x}$.

$$e^{aG_{\text{xtrans}}} f(x,t) = (1 + aG_{\text{xtrans}} + \frac{a^2}{2} G_{\text{xtrans}}{}^2 + \ldots) f(x,t)$$

↷ Eq. 7.12

$$= (1 + a\partial_x + \frac{a^2}{2} \partial_x{}^2 + \ldots) f(x,t)$$

↷ Taylor expansion

$$= f(x+a,t) \tag{7.13}$$

Here we used the series expansion of $e^x = \sum_{n=0}^{\infty} \frac{x^n}{n!}$. In the last step, we used that in the second to last line we have exactly the Taylor expansion of $f(x+a,t)$. Alternatively, consider an infinitesimal translation: $a \to \epsilon$ with $\epsilon \ll 1$. We then have

$$e^{\epsilon G_{\text{xtrans}}} f(x,t) = (1 + \epsilon G_{\text{xtrans}} + \frac{\epsilon^2}{2} G_{\text{xtrans}}{}^2 + \ldots) f(x,t)$$

↷ Eq. 7.12, $\epsilon^2 \approx 0$, $\epsilon^3 \approx 0$ etc. for $\epsilon \ll 1$

$$\approx (1 + \epsilon\partial_x) f(x,t)$$

↷

$$= f(x,t) + \epsilon\partial_x f(x,t) = f(x+\epsilon,t)\,. \tag{7.14}$$

Here $\partial_x f(x,t)$ is the **rate of change** of $f(x,t)$ in the x-direction. If we multiply this rate of change by the distance ϵ that we move in the x-direction, we end up with the total change of $f(x,t)$ if we move by ϵ in the x-direction. Thus, $f(x,t) + \epsilon\partial_x f(x,t)$ really *is* the value of f at the location $x + \epsilon$.

The bottom line is: $G_{\text{xtrans}} = \partial_x$ generates *spatial* translations.

Completely analogously, $G_{\text{ttrans}} = \partial_t$ generates *temporal* translations:

$$f(x,t) \to= e^{aG_{\text{ttrans}}} f(x,t) = f(x,t+a)\,.$$

What we have learned here is that generators are the crucial mathematical ingredient that we need to describe continuous symmetries. We can describe *any* continuous symmetry by acting on the function in question with the corresponding generator many, many times.

So we can summarize:

The core of each continuous symmetry is the corresponding generator.

This idea is already everything we need to determine what the most important quantum operators look like.

7.1.2 Quantum Operators

We now put the puzzle pieces together. The pieces we have so far are:

- ▷ We are looking for quantum operators. When we act with, for example, the momentum operator on the ket $|\Psi_1\rangle$ that describes our system, we want to get $\hat{p}\,|\Psi_1\rangle = p_1\,|\Psi_1\rangle$.
- ▷ Noether's theorem tells us that there is a deep connection between symmetries and the most important physical quantities: momentum, energy, etc.
- ▷ Group theory tells us that the essential objects which are responsible for these symmetries are the corresponding generators.

The crucial idea is to take Noether's theorem seriously. Instead of saying that we get a conserved quantity if there is a symmetry, we say the operator responsible for the symmetry (the generator) also describes the conserved quantity (the quantum operator).

In slogan form:

$$\textbf{quantum operator} \leftrightarrow \textbf{generator of symmetry} \tag{7.15}$$

This may seem like quite a stretch, but we will see that this idea works incredibly well in the next section.

Now, let's make the above statement explicit.

Momentum is connected to symmetry under spatial translations. Therefore, we make the identification[9]

[9] Note that there is an additional imaginary unit i. This is just a convention that physicists like to use. The translation of a function then works like this: $e^{i\epsilon G_{\text{trans}}}f(x,t)$. So all we have done is to introduce two additional imaginary units that cancel since $i^2 = -1$. The reason why physicists like to introduce the imaginary unit i is that we want to interpret the eigenvalues of our quantum operators as something that we can measure in experiments. Without the additional i the eigenvalues would be imaginary. Hence, we introduce an additional i to make them real. However, this is really just a convenient way to make the framework easier to use. In addition, we have an additional minus sign for the momentum operator. This is motivated by the Minkowski metric of special relativity. However, it is clear that we could also absorb it into the parameter ϵ.

$$\text{momentum } \hat{p}_i \leftrightarrow \text{ generator of spatial translations } (-i\hbar\partial_i) \tag{7.16}$$

Analogously, energy is connected to symmetry under temporal translations. Therefore

$$\text{energy } \hat{E} \leftrightarrow \text{ generator of temporal translations } (i\hbar\partial_t) \tag{7.17}$$

Take note that we have introduced a new fundamental constant: $\hbar$. This constant is known as the **Planck constant**[10] and encodes the magnitude of quantum effects. We can understand the need for a new constant by observing that momentum has dimensions $[p] = \text{kg} \cdot \text{m/s}$. However, ∂_i has the unit[11] $[\partial_i] = 1/\text{m}$. Similarly, ∂_t has the unit $[\partial_t] = 1/\text{s}$, while energy has the unit $[E] = \text{kg} \cdot \text{m}^2/\text{s}^2$. Therefore, we need something to get the same units on the right-hand and left-hand side of the equations. Using the units of energy, momentum and the differential operators we can conclude that $[\hbar] = \text{kg} \cdot \text{m}^2/\text{s}$ since[12]

$$[p] = \text{kg} \cdot \frac{\text{m}}{\text{s}} \stackrel{!}{=} [-i\hbar\partial_i] = \text{kg} \cdot \frac{\text{m}^2}{\text{s}}\frac{1}{\text{m}} = \text{kg} \cdot \frac{\text{m}}{\text{s}} \quad \checkmark$$

$$[E] = \text{kg} \cdot \frac{\text{m}^2}{\text{s}^2} \stackrel{!}{=} [i\hbar\partial_t] = \text{kg} \cdot \frac{\text{m}^2}{\text{s}}\frac{1}{\text{s}} = \text{kg} \cdot \frac{\text{m}^2}{\text{s}^2} \quad \checkmark$$

The Planck constant is one of the most important fundamental constants and we need to extract its value from experiments: $\hbar \approx 1.055 \cdot 10^{-34}\ \text{kg} \cdot \text{m}^2/\text{s}$. Since there is no symmetry connected to the conservation of position, the position operator stays as is[13] $\hat{x}$. In addition, using the definition of angular momentum ($\vec{L} = \vec{x} \times \vec{p}$), we can, in principle, write down the angular momentum operator by simply replacing $\vec{p}$ with the corresponding quantum operator $\hat{p}$.

Now, equipped with the ideas discussed in this section, we are able to derive one of the most important equations in *all* of physics.

[10] To be precise $\hbar$ is the reduced Planck constant (speak: "h-bar") defined by $\frac{h}{2\pi}$ where h is the real Planck constant.

[11] Recall $\partial_x = \frac{\partial}{\partial x}$. The symbol ∂x, in some sense, simply means a tiny amount of x and therefore has the same unit as x. Therefore, $\partial_x \propto 1/\partial x$ has the unit $1/m$.

[12] Reminder: square brackets around a quantity mean that we are talking about the units of the quantity.

[13] This may seem confusing at first. But all this operator does if we act with it on a function $f(x)$ is to multiply it by x, i.e., $\hat{x}f(x) = xf(x)$ since x really is the location we evaluate $f(x)$ at.

7.1.3 The Canonical Commutation Relation

A crucial new feature of quantum mechanics compared to classical mechanics is an inherent uncertainty. This uncertainty comes about since the momentum changes every time we measure position and the position changes every time we measure momentum. Mathematically, this statement means that it makes a difference whether we first measure the momentum or first measure the location: $\hat{x}\hat{p}\,|\Psi\rangle \neq \hat{p}\hat{x}\,|\Psi\rangle$. We can also write this statement as $\left(\hat{x}\hat{p} - \hat{p}\hat{x}\right)|\Psi\rangle \neq 0$. The shorthand notation for this expression is

$$[\hat{x}, \hat{p}] \equiv \hat{x}\hat{p} - \hat{p}\hat{x}\,. \tag{7.18}$$

We call this the **commutator** of $\hat{x}$ and $\hat{p}$.

To get an intuitive understanding for what it means for operators to have a non-zero commutator, compare the situation where you first put on your socks and then your shoes with the situation where you first put on your shoes and then your socks. The outcome is clearly different — the ordering of the operations "putting shoes on" and "putting socks on" therefore matters. In technical terms, we say these two operations do not commute. In contrast, it makes no difference if you put on your left sock first and then your right sock or your right sock first and then your left sock. These two operations do commute.

Now, using the explicit quantum operator $\hat{p}_i = -i\hbar\partial_i$ (Eq. (7.16)), we can actually *derive* that $[\hat{p}_i, \hat{x}_j] \neq 0$:

$$\begin{aligned}
[\hat{p}_i, \hat{x}_j]\,|\Psi\rangle &= \left(\hat{p}_i\hat{x}_j - \hat{x}_j\hat{p}_i\right)|\Psi\rangle \\
&\quad \text{(Eq. 7.16)} \\
&= \left(-i\hbar\partial_i\hat{x}_j + \hat{x}_j i\hbar\partial_i\right)|\Psi\rangle \\
&\quad \text{(product rule)} \\
&= -\left(i\hbar\partial_i\hat{x}_j\right)|\Psi\rangle - \cancel{\hat{x}_j\left(i\hbar\partial_i|\Psi\rangle\right)} + \cancel{\hat{x}_j i\hbar\partial_i|\Psi\rangle} \\
&= -i\hbar\delta_{ij}\,|\Psi\rangle
\end{aligned} \tag{7.19}$$

In the last step we used that, for example, $\partial_y x = 0$ but $\partial_y y = 1$.[14] We didn't assume anything about $|\Psi\rangle$, so the equation is

[14] The Kronecker delta δ_{ij} is, by definition, zero for $i \neq j$ and one for $i = j$.

valid for any $|\Psi\rangle$. Therefore, we can write the equation without it, which makes the equation a bit shorter. However, we always have to remember that there is an implicit ket in such equations and we are only too lazy to write it all the time. In conclusion:

$$\boxed{[\hat{p}_i, \hat{x}_j] = -i\hbar\delta_{ij}} \tag{7.20}$$

This little equation is known as the **canonical commutation relation**. As the name already indicates this equation is extremely important. In fact, many textbooks and lectures use it as a *starting point* for quantum mechanics.[15]

[15] Formulated differently, many textbooks use this equation as the fundamental postulate of quantum mechanics. For example, using this equation, we can derive what the momentum operator looks like etc.

As mentioned above, a second crucial ingredient that we need in our framework is something that allows us to determine how a given state evolves in time. In the following section, we will discuss an equation that allows us to describe the time-evolution of quantum systems.

7.1.4 The Schrödinger Equation

Mathematically, what we need is an equation of this form:

$$\partial_t |\Psi\rangle = \dots$$

Here, $\partial_t |\Psi\rangle$ is the rate of change of $|\Psi\rangle$ if we move with respect to t. In other words, $\partial_t |\Psi\rangle$ describes how $|\Psi\rangle$ changes as time passes — exactly what we need! On the right-hand side, we need something that contains specific details about the system in question. Thus, the right-hand side will be different for each system. Then, as soon as we have such an equation, we have to solve it to understand how $|\Psi\rangle$ depends on t.

Luckily, we don't have to guess. All we have to do is take a second look at what we derived in the previous section. The main actor here, ∂_t, is almost exactly the quantum energy operator

$i\hbar\partial_t$ (Eq. 7.17), only without the imaginary unit and Planck's constant. Therefore, we know that we have the energy on the right-hand side of the equation:

$$i\hbar\partial_t |\Psi\rangle = E |\Psi\rangle .$$

Is there anything else we know about energy?

In classical mechanics, the total energy is given as the sum of kinetic energy and potential energy:

$$E = T + V \equiv \text{ kinetic energy } + \text{ potential energy.} \tag{7.21}$$

The usual formula for the kinetic energy is

$$T = \frac{1}{2}mv^2 = \frac{p^2}{2m} \tag{7.22}$$

since $p = mv$. We can turn this equation into a quantum equation by replacing the classical momentum, p, with the quantum momentum operator, $\hat{p}_i = -i\hbar\partial_i$, which we derived above.[16]

[16] The index i is necessary because, in general, we are dealing with systems that can change in three spatial dimensions. The index takes on the values $i = \{x, y, z\}$ or equivalently $i = \{1, 2, 3\}$.

The potential energy usually only depends on the position: $V = V(x)$. Therefore, we can turn it into a quantum operator by letting $x \to \hat{x}$.[17]

[17] If there is more than one dimension, we have $\hat{x}_i$.

Returning to our equation,

$$i\hbar\partial_t |\Psi\rangle = E |\Psi\rangle,$$

we can use the usual formula $E = T + V$ and replace the classical variables with the corresponding quantum operators:

$$\begin{aligned}
i\hbar\partial_t |\Psi\rangle &= E |\Psi\rangle \\
&\quad \text{(Eq. 7.21)} \\
&= (T + V) |\Psi\rangle \\
&\quad \text{(Eq. 7.22)} \\
&= \left(\frac{p^2}{2m} + V(x)\right) |\Psi\rangle \\
&\quad \text{(introducing operators)} \\
\Rightarrow \quad i\hbar\partial_t |\Psi\rangle &= \left(\frac{\hat{p}^2}{2m} + V(\hat{x})\right) |\Psi\rangle \\
&\quad \text{(Eq. 7.16)} \\
&= \left(\frac{(-i\hbar\partial_i)^2}{2m} + V(\hat{x})\right) |\Psi\rangle \\
&\quad (i^2 = -1) \\
&= \left(-\frac{\hbar^2\partial_i^2}{2m} + V(\hat{x})\right) |\Psi\rangle . \qquad (7.23)
\end{aligned}$$

The resulting equation,

$$i\hbar\partial_t |\Psi\rangle = -\frac{\hbar^2\partial_i^2}{2m} |\Psi\rangle + V(\hat{x}) |\Psi\rangle , \qquad (7.24)$$

is the famous **Schrödinger equation**. Our main job in quantum mechanics is usually to solve it for a given potential $V(x)$ and specific boundary conditions.

Note that for historical reasons, the energy operator on the right-hand side of the Schrödinger equation is known as the **Hamiltonian operator,**

$$\hat{H} \equiv \left(-\frac{\hbar^2\partial_i^2}{2m} + V(\hat{x})\right) . \qquad (7.25)$$

Therefore, in terms of the Hamiltonian operator, the Schrödinger equation reads

$$i\hbar\partial_t |\Psi\rangle = \hat{H} |\Psi\rangle . \qquad (7.26)$$

This general form of the Schrödinger equation is also valid in quantum field theory. The only difference is that we need to replace $\hat{H}$ appropriately. We will discuss this in detail in the next chapter.

7.1.5 Time Evolution

A convenient alternative way to describe the time-evolution of quantum systems is with the so-called **time evolution operator** $U(t)$. We define this operator through the following formula

$$|\Psi(x,t)\rangle = U(t)\,|\Psi(x,0)\rangle \,. \tag{7.27}$$

In words, this means that if we act with this operator on some ket $|\Psi(x,0)\rangle$, the resulting ket describes the system at time t: $|\Psi(x,t)\rangle$. This operator is not merely an abstract thing. We can write it down explicitly by putting Eq. (7.27) into our Schrödinger equation:

$$\begin{aligned} i\hbar\partial_t|\Psi(x,t)\rangle &= H|\Psi(x,t)\rangle \\ &\quad \text{↷ Eq. 7.27} \\ i\hbar\partial_t U(t)\,|\Psi(x,0)\rangle &= HU(t)\,|\Psi(x,0)\rangle \end{aligned} \tag{7.28}$$

This equation holds for any $|\Psi(x,0)\rangle$ and we can therefore write it without it:

$$\begin{aligned} i\hbar\partial_t U(t) &= HU(t) \\ &\quad \text{↷} \\ i\hbar\frac{\partial_t U(t)}{U(t)} &= H\,. \end{aligned} \tag{7.29}$$

This is a differential equation for $U(t)$ and the general solution is

$$U(t) = \mathrm{e}^{-\frac{i}{\hbar}\int_0^t dt' H(t')} \tag{7.30}$$

since

$$\begin{aligned} i\hbar\frac{\partial_t U(t)}{U(t)} &= H \\ &\quad \text{↷ Eq. 7.30} \\ i\hbar\frac{\partial_t \mathrm{e}^{-\frac{i}{\hbar}\int_0^t dt' H(t')}}{\mathrm{e}^{-\frac{i}{\hbar}\int_0^t dt' H(t')}} &= H \\ &\quad \text{↷ } \partial_x e^{ikx} = ike^{ikx} \\ i\hbar\left(-\frac{i}{\hbar}\partial_t\int_0^t dt' H(t')\right)\frac{\cancel{\mathrm{e}^{-\frac{i}{\hbar}\int_0^t dt' H(t')}}}{\cancel{\mathrm{e}^{-\frac{i}{\hbar}\int_0^t dt' H(t')}}} &= H \\ &\quad \text{↷ } \partial_t\int_0^t dt' H(t') = H \\ H &= H \quad \checkmark \end{aligned} \tag{7.31}$$

So the time-evolution operator is simply a convenient way to write the information encoded in the Schrödinger equation a bit differently. We will see in the next chapter that the time-evolution operator plays an extremely important role in quantum field theory.

7.1.6 Quantum Waves

An important aspect of quantum mechanics is that, in general, different operators have different states with definite measurement values (eigenstates).[18] This means that we can expand a general state vector in terms of different eigenstates:

$$|\Psi\rangle = \sum_i b_i |\tilde{o}_i\rangle = b_1 |\tilde{o}_1\rangle + b_2 |\tilde{o}_2\rangle + \dots , \tag{7.32}$$

where $|\tilde{o}_i\rangle$ are the eigenstates corresponding to a different operator $\hat{\tilde{O}}$.

[18] Take note that for operators which commute

$$\hat{A}\hat{B} - \hat{B}\hat{A} = 0$$

there is a common set of eigenstates.

The key idea is that if we are interested in, for example, the momentum of the system, we expand our general state vector in terms of momentum eigenstates. If we are instead interested in the energy of the system, then we would expand the state vector in terms of energy eigenstates, and so on. The numbers a_i and b_i that we get by expanding a general state vector directly tell us the probability to measure a given result. Formulated differently, expanding a general state vector in this manner yields coefficients (a_i or b_i) which are directly related to the probability of measuring a given value.

The set of possible outcomes is not necessarily discrete. In the case of a continuous set of possible outcomes, we must replace the sum in Eq. 7.32 with an integral:[19]

$$|\Psi\rangle = \int do\, a(o)\, |o\rangle . \tag{7.33}$$

[19] In some sense, an integral is simply a sum over a continuous set of values.

Take note that our discrete coefficients a_i are replaced by a function $a(o)$. However, the basic idea is still the same. For each possible measurement outcome o, we get a specific probability amplitude $a(o)$. The probability of measuring the value o is $|a(o)|^2$.

The function $\psi(x)$ that we get by expanding a state vector in terms of position eigenstates

$$|\Psi\rangle = \int dx\, \psi(x)\, |x\rangle \tag{7.34}$$

is usually called the **wave function.**

Analogously to how we can describe a given vector $\vec{v}$ using the specific coefficients for some given basis, we can use $\psi(x)$ to describe the system.[20]

[20] In principle, a vector is a little arrow sitting somewhere in space. Only by using a specific coordinate system and therefore specific basis vectors like $\vec{e}_x$, $\vec{e}_y$, $\vec{e}_z$ can we describe the vector using concrete numbers $\vec{v} = (3,2,3)^T$. Take note that for a different choice of coordinate system or a different set of basis vectors (e.g., spherical basis vectors), we get different numbers.

The magical tools which help us switch between bases are called **projection operators**. These projection operators aren't unique to quantum mechanics. Projection operators also exist for ordinary vectors. In the previous section, we used the most common basis vectors $\vec{e}_x, \vec{e}_y, \vec{e}_z$ (Eq. (7.3)). However, an equally good (orthogonal and normalized) choice for the basis vectors is:[21]

[21] The factors $\frac{1}{\sqrt{2}}$ are normalization constants that make sure that our vectors have length 1.

$$\vec{e}_1 = \frac{1}{\sqrt{2}} \begin{pmatrix} 1 \\ 1 \\ 0 \end{pmatrix}, \quad \vec{e}_2 = \frac{1}{\sqrt{2}} \begin{pmatrix} 1 \\ -1 \\ 0 \end{pmatrix}, \quad \vec{e}_3 = \begin{pmatrix} 0 \\ 0 \\ 1 \end{pmatrix}. \tag{7.35}$$

How can we calculate what our vector $\vec{v} = (1,3,5)^T$ looks like in this basis?

We already discussed how we can determine how much a given vector spreads out in any given direction. For example, to find out how much $\vec{v}$ spreads out in the z-direction, we multiplied it by $\vec{e}_z$ (Eq. (7.6)). Here, Eq. (7.35) defines new axes relative to the old ones. Therefore, to find out how much $\vec{v}$ spreads out in the direction defined by $\vec{e}_1$, we calculate the scalar product of the two vectors.

$$\tilde{\vec{e}}_1 \cdot \vec{v} = \frac{1}{\sqrt{2}} \begin{pmatrix} 1, 1, 0 \end{pmatrix} \begin{pmatrix} 1 \\ 3 \\ 5 \end{pmatrix} = \frac{4}{\sqrt{2}}.$$

Analogously, we can calculate how much $\vec{v}$ spreads out in the other two new directions:

$$\tilde{\vec{e}}_2 \cdot \vec{v} = \frac{1}{\sqrt{2}} \begin{pmatrix} 1 \\ -1 \\ 0 \end{pmatrix}^T \begin{pmatrix} 1 \\ 3 \\ 5 \end{pmatrix} = \frac{-2}{\sqrt{2}} .$$

$$\tilde{\vec{e}}_3 \cdot \vec{v} = \begin{pmatrix} 0 \\ 0 \\ 1 \end{pmatrix}^T \begin{pmatrix} 1 \\ 3 \\ 5 \end{pmatrix} = 5 .$$

This tells us that, in the new basis (Eq. (7.35)), our vector $\vec{v}$ reads as:

$$\vec{v} = \frac{4}{\sqrt{2}}\vec{e}_1 - \frac{2}{\sqrt{2}}\vec{e}_2 + 5\vec{e}_3 \hat{=} \begin{pmatrix} \frac{4}{\sqrt{2}} \\ \frac{-2}{\sqrt{2}} \\ 5 \end{pmatrix}_{\text{new basis}} .$$

The general method to rewrite a vector in a new basis is therefore:

1. Calculate the scalar product of the vector with each new basis vector.
2. Multiply each result with the corresponding basis vector.
3. The vector in the new basis is the sum of all of terms calculated in the second step.

So mathematically, we have

$$\vec{v}_{\text{new basis}} = \sum_i (\vec{e}_i) \underbrace{(\vec{e}_i \cdot \vec{v})}_{\text{a number}} . \tag{7.36}$$

To convince you that this formula is really correct, let's again consider our example from above:

$$\begin{aligned} \vec{v}_{\text{new basis}} &= \sum_i (\vec{e}_i)(\vec{e}_i \cdot \vec{v}) \\ &= (\vec{e}_1)(\vec{e}_1 \cdot \vec{v}) + (\vec{e}_2)(\vec{e}_2 \cdot \vec{v}) + (\vec{e}_3)(\vec{e}_3 \cdot \vec{v}) \\ &= \vec{e}_1 \frac{4}{\sqrt{2}} + \vec{e}_2 \frac{-2}{\sqrt{2}} + 5\vec{e}_3 \quad \checkmark \end{aligned} \tag{7.37}$$

We use *exactly* the same method in quantum mechanics. We have the ket in the momentum basis,

$$|\Psi\rangle = a\,|\Psi_1\rangle + b\,|\Psi_2\rangle , \tag{7.38}$$

and want to calculate how it looks like in the position basis:

$$|\Psi\rangle = c\,|x_1\rangle + d\,|x_2\rangle \,. \tag{7.39}$$

In other words, we want to calculate the coefficients c and d. For simplicity, we assume that only two locations, x_1 and x_2, are possible. In addition, we use a more suggestive notation: $|x_1\rangle$ is the configuration of the system where we will definitely find our particle at location x_1, similar to how $|\Psi_1\rangle$ corresponds to the configuration with momentum p_1.

Using the algorithm we just discussed, we calculate

$$\begin{aligned} |\Psi\rangle &= \sum_i |x_i\rangle\,\langle x_i|\Psi\rangle \\ &= |x_1\rangle\,\langle x_1|\Psi\rangle + |x_2\rangle\,\langle x_2|\Psi\rangle \\ &\equiv c\,|x_1\rangle + d\,|x_2\rangle \,, \end{aligned}$$

where the **probability amplitudes in the position basis** are

$$\begin{aligned} c &= \langle x_1|\Psi\rangle \\ d &= \langle x_2|\Psi\rangle \,. \end{aligned}$$

In general, there is a continuum of possible locations and not just a discrete set. Luckily, we can take this into account by simply replacing this sum with an integral:[22]:

$$\equiv \int dx \Psi(x)\,|x\rangle \,, \tag{7.40}$$

where $\Psi(x) \equiv \langle x|\Psi\rangle$. This function $\Psi(x)$ is analogous to the coefficients we have discussed previously (i.e., a, b, c, and d). But we now have one coefficient for *each* location x.[23]

Take note that we can read of Eq. 7.40 that

$$\int dx\,|x\rangle\,\langle x| = 1 \,. \tag{7.41}$$

This means that we can insert a unit operator in the form of $\int dx\,|x\rangle\,\langle x|$ anywhere in our formulas and this way get expressions in terms of the position basis. In the jargon of quantum

[22] An integral is, in some sense, the continuum limit of a sum. If we make the steps in a sum smaller and smaller, we end up with an integral.

[23] Take note that $|\Psi\rangle$ and therefore also $\Psi(x)$ both depend on the time t. Here we suppress this dependence to unclutter the notation. We will revisit this time dependence later on. Keep in mind, however, that wavefunctions generally depend not only on position, but also on time.

mechanics, it is conventional to say that we insert a complete basis this way.

Often it will be easier to choose a specific basis before we solve the Schrödinger equation. For example, we can use the position basis and therefore the wave functions that we introduced above. To unclutter the notation, we will restrict ourselves to one spatial dimension. We are then left with

$$i\hbar\partial_t |\Psi\rangle = -\frac{\hbar^2\partial_x^2}{2m} |\Psi\rangle$$

$\curvearrowright$ Eq. 7.40

$$i\hbar\partial_t \int dx\psi(x,t)\,|x\rangle = -\frac{\hbar^2\partial_x^2}{2m} \int dx\psi(x,t)\,|x\rangle$$

$\curvearrowright$

$$i\hbar\partial_t\psi(x,t) = -\frac{\hbar^2\partial_x^2}{2m}\psi(x,t)\,. \tag{7.42}$$

One solution to this equation is

$$\psi(x,t) = \mathrm{e}^{-i(Et-px)/\hbar} \tag{7.43}$$

as we can check

$$i\hbar\partial_t\psi(x,t) = -\frac{\hbar^2\partial_x^2}{2m}\psi(x,t)$$

$\curvearrowright$ Eq. 5.44

$$i\hbar\partial_t \mathrm{e}^{-i(Et-px)/\hbar} = -\frac{\hbar^2\partial_x^2}{2m}\mathrm{e}^{-i(Et-px)/\hbar}$$

$\curvearrowright$

$$E\mathrm{e}^{-i(Et-px)/\hbar} = \frac{p^2}{2m}\mathrm{e}^{-i(Et-px)/\hbar}$$

$\curvearrowright$

$$\frac{p^2}{2m}\mathrm{e}^{-i(Et-px)/\hbar} = \frac{p^2}{2m}\mathrm{e}^{-i(Et-px)/\hbar} \quad \checkmark\,, \tag{7.44}$$

where in the last step we used the fact that E is the numerical value for the total energy of a free particle: $E = \frac{p^2}{2m}$.

7.1.7 de Broglie Relations

By comparing our usual formula for a plane wave (Eq. 5.44)

$$\phi(x) = e^{-i(k_\mu x^\mu)} = e^{-i(k_0 x_0 - \vec{k}\cdot\vec{x})} \tag{7.45}$$

with the solution of the Schrödinger equation introduced in the previous section (Eq. 7.43)

$$\psi(x,t) = e^{-i(Et-\vec{p}\cdot\vec{x})/\hbar} \tag{7.46}$$

we can conclude

$$E = \hbar\omega$$
$$\vec{p} = \hbar\vec{k}\,. \tag{7.47}$$

These are known as the de Broglie relations. In words, they tell us that in a quantum context the angular frequency ω is directly related to the energy E, and the wave vector $\vec{k}$ is directly related to the momentum $\vec{p}$.

7.1.8 The Stationary Schrödinger Equation

For systems in which the potential does not depend on time, we can split the Schrödinger equation into two simpler equations and solve them separately. This trick is known as **separation of the variables** and works as follows.

First, we split our wave function into two parts:

$$\Psi(x,t) \equiv T(t)\psi(x)\,. \tag{7.48}$$

The first part $T(t)$ describes how the wave function changes over time, while the second part $\psi(x)$ describes how the wave function depends on the location. We now put this ansatz into the Schrödinger equation:[24]

$$i\hbar\partial_t\Psi(x,t) = H\Psi(x,t)$$

↓ Eq. 7.48

$$i\hbar\partial_t T(t)\psi(x) = HT(t)\psi(x)$$

↓

$$i\hbar\frac{\partial_t T(t)}{T(t)} = \frac{H\psi(x)}{\psi(x)}\,.$$

[24] Reminder: For a particle in a potential $V(x)$, the Schrödinger equation reads

$$i\hbar\frac{\partial\Psi}{\partial t} = -\frac{\hbar^2}{2m}\frac{\partial^2\Psi}{\partial x^2} + V(x)\Psi.$$

The operator H is the energy operator and it is directly related to the classical energy = kinetic energy plus potential energy.

In the last step we used that H only contains the spatial derivative ∂_x^2 and $T(t)$ only depends on t and not on x. In addition, we used that the left-hand side only contains the derivative ∂_t while $\psi(x)$ only depends on x.

Now what we are left with on the left-hand side is something that only depends on t, and on the right-hand side something that only depends on x. Still, both sides must be equal. This is only possible if both sides are constant. If, for example, the left-hand side is not constant, this would mean that we could change its value by varying t. Since the right-hand side does not depend on t at all, there is then no way that both sides are equal. Both sides of the equation are thus constant and equal to the energy, E. We are then left with two equations as promised:

$$\begin{aligned} i\hbar\frac{\partial_t T(t)}{T(t)} &\equiv E \equiv \frac{H\psi(x)}{\psi(x)} \\ \therefore \quad i\hbar\frac{\partial_t T(t)}{T(t)} &\equiv E \quad \text{and} \quad \frac{H\psi(x)}{\psi(x)} \equiv E\,. \end{aligned}$$

Written a bit differently,

$$i\hbar\partial_t T(t) = ET(t) \tag{7.49}$$

$$H\psi(x) = E\psi(x)\,. \tag{7.50}$$

The first equation is easy to solve and does not depend on the specific problem at all. All information about the features of the system is encoded in H. So the first lesson is that, as long as V (and therefore also H) does not depend on t,[25] the explicit time-dependence of the wave function is given by

$$\boxed{T(t) = \mathrm{e}^{-\frac{iEt}{\hbar}}\,.} \tag{7.51}$$

[25] Remember that this was the crucial restriction that I've mentioned at the beginning. The whole trick we used only works if H does not depend on t. Otherwise, the ansatz $\Psi(x,t) \equiv T(t)\psi(x)$ does not help us.

This equation can be derived as follows:

$$i\hbar\partial_t T(t) = ET(t)$$

this is Eq. 7.49

$\rightarrow$ Eq. 7.51

$$i\hbar\partial_t e^{-\frac{iEt}{\hbar}} = Ee^{-\frac{iEt}{\hbar}}$$

$\rightarrow$

$$i\hbar\left(\frac{-iE}{\hbar}\right)e^{-\frac{iEt}{\hbar}} = Ee^{-\frac{iEt}{\hbar}}$$

$\rightarrow$

$$Ee^{-\frac{iEt}{\hbar}} = Ee^{-\frac{iEt}{\hbar}} \checkmark$$

The second lesson is that all specific information about the system is encoded in the solutions of the second equation which only depends on x:[26]

[26] Take note that this equation is really of the same type as the equations we considered all the time (an eigenvalue equation). The energy operator H acts on Ψ and what we get back is the energy E.

$$\boxed{H\psi = E\psi} \tag{7.52}$$

This equation is known as the **stationary Schrödinger equation** or **time-independent Schrödinger equation**. After we have solved it for a specific problem (i.e., a specific H), all that is left to do is to remember that the full solution reads

$$\Psi(x,t) = \psi(x)T(t) = \psi(x)e^{-\frac{iEt}{\hbar}}. \tag{7.53}$$

A solution of the stationary Schrödinger equation $\psi(x)$ is known as a **stationary solution** or a **stationary state**.

We already discussed that we can understand a field in many aspects analogous to a mattress. The basic building blocks a mattress consists of are harmonic oscillators. Therefore, if we want to promote our classical fields to quantum fields, we need to start by promoting our oscillators to quantum oscillators. This is what we will discuss in the next section.

7.2 The Quantum Harmonic Oscillator

While it is possible to describe the quantum harmonic oscillator in terms of wave functions, there is a much smarter method. Although this method seems quite abstract at first, it turns out to be invaluable. In particular, we will see in the following chapter that we can apply all the lessons we learn here directly to quantum fields.

The potential of the harmonic oscillator reads (Eq. 5.5)

$$V(x) = \frac{1}{2}kx^2 , \tag{7.54}$$

where k is the spring constant which characterizes the stiffness of the spring. Alternatively, we write the potential often as

$$V(x) = \frac{1}{2}m\omega^2 x^2 , \tag{7.55}$$

where $\omega = \sqrt{k/m}$ denotes the classical oscillation frequency and m the mass at the end of the spring.

The stationary Schrödinger equation (Eq. (7.52)) reads

$$H\psi = E\psi = -\frac{\hbar^2}{2m}\frac{\partial^2 \psi}{\partial x^2} + V(x)\psi$$

$\quad$ ↷ Eq. 7.55

$$= -\hbar^2 \frac{\partial_x^2}{2m}\psi + \frac{1}{2}m\omega^2 x^2 \psi \tag{7.56}$$

We define the following two operators and then use them instead of $\hat{x}$ and $\hat{p}$[27]

[27] Take note that $a^\dagger$ is the Hermitian adjoint of a, where $\dagger \equiv *T$, i.e., conjugation plus transposition.

$$a \equiv \sqrt{\frac{m\omega}{2\hbar}}x + i\frac{1}{\sqrt{2m\omega\hbar}}p \tag{7.57}$$

$$a^\dagger \equiv \sqrt{\frac{m\omega}{2\hbar}}x - i\frac{1}{\sqrt{2m\omega\hbar}}p. \tag{7.58}$$

We will understand the physical meaning of these operators in a moment.

We can also invert these equations, which yields

$$\text{Eq. 7.57 + Eq. 7.58} \Rightarrow a + a^\dagger = 2\sqrt{\frac{m\omega}{2\hbar}}x$$

$\quad$ ↷

$$x = \sqrt{\frac{\hbar}{2m\omega}}(a + a^\dagger) \tag{7.59}$$

and

$$\text{Eq. 7.57 - Eq. 7.58} \Rightarrow a - a^\dagger = 2i\frac{1}{\sqrt{2m\omega\hbar}}p$$

$$\curvearrowright \quad \frac{1}{i} = \frac{-i^2}{i}) - i$$

$$p = -i\sqrt{\frac{\hbar m\omega}{2}}(a - a^\dagger). \tag{7.60}$$

In addition, by using the canonical commutation relation $[x, p] = i\hbar$ we can calculate the commutator of a and $a^\dagger$:[28]

[28] It will become clear in a moment why this is useful.

$$\begin{aligned}
[a, a^\dagger] &= aa^\dagger - a^\dagger a \\
&\quad \curvearrowright \text{ Eq. 7.57} \\
&= \left(\sqrt{\frac{m\omega}{2\hbar}}x + i\frac{1}{\sqrt{2m\omega\hbar}}p\right)\left(\sqrt{\frac{m\omega}{2\hbar}}x - i\frac{1}{\sqrt{2m\omega\hbar}}p\right) \\
&\quad \curvearrowright \\
&\quad - \left(\sqrt{\frac{m\omega}{2\hbar}}x - i\frac{1}{\sqrt{2m\omega\hbar}}p\right)\left(\sqrt{\frac{m\omega}{2}}x + i\frac{1}{\sqrt{2m\omega\hbar}}p\right) \\
&\quad \curvearrowright \\
&= \cancel{\frac{m\omega}{2\hbar}x^2} - \frac{i}{2\hbar}xp + \frac{i}{2\hbar}px + \cancel{\frac{1}{2m\omega\hbar}p^2} - \cancel{\frac{m\omega}{2\hbar}x^2} - \frac{i}{2\hbar}xp + \frac{i}{2\hbar}px - \cancel{\frac{1}{2m\omega\hbar}p^2} \\
&\quad \curvearrowright \\
&= \frac{i}{\hbar}(px - xp) = \frac{i}{\hbar}[p, x] = -\frac{i}{\hbar}[x, p] = -\frac{i}{\hbar}i\hbar \\
&= 1
\end{aligned} \tag{7.61}$$

We can use these equations to rewrite the Schrödinger equation for the harmonic oscillator (Eq. (7.56)) in terms of a and $a^\dagger$

$$\begin{aligned}
E\psi &= \frac{p^2}{2m}\psi + \frac{m\omega^2}{2}x^2\psi \\
&\quad \curvearrowright \text{ Eq. 7.59, Eq. 7.60} \\
&= \frac{1}{2m}\left(i\sqrt{\frac{\hbar m\omega}{2}}(a^\dagger - a)\right)^2\psi + \frac{m\omega^2}{2}\left(\sqrt{\frac{\hbar}{2m\omega}}(a + a^\dagger)\right)^2\psi \\
&\quad \curvearrowright \\
&= \frac{\hbar\omega}{4}\left(-\cancel{a^\dagger a^\dagger} + a^\dagger a + aa^\dagger - \cancel{aa}\right)\psi + \frac{\hbar\omega}{4}\left(\cancel{aa} + a^\dagger a + aa^\dagger + \cancel{a^\dagger a^\dagger}\right)\psi \\
&\quad \curvearrowright \\
&= \frac{\hbar\omega}{2}\left(a^\dagger a + aa^\dagger\right)\psi
\end{aligned} \tag{7.62}$$

We can then use the commutator relation in Eq. (7.61) to simplify the expression on the right-hand side as follows:

$$\begin{aligned}
E\psi &= \frac{\hbar\omega}{2}\left(a^\dagger a + aa^\dagger\right)\psi \\
&\quad \text{↷ } -a^\dagger a + a^\dagger a = 0 \\
&= \frac{\hbar\omega}{2}(a^\dagger a + aa^\dagger - a^\dagger a + a^\dagger a)\psi \\
&\quad \text{↷} \\
&= \frac{\hbar\omega}{2}(2a^\dagger a + [a, a^\dagger])\psi \\
&\quad \text{↷ } [a, a^\dagger] = 1, \text{ Eq. 7.61} \\
&= \frac{\hbar\omega}{2}\left(2a^\dagger a + 1\right)\psi \\
&\quad \text{↷} \\
&= \hbar\omega\left(a^\dagger a + \frac{1}{2}\right)\psi .
\end{aligned}$$

What we have on the right-hand side is the quantum energy operator. As already mentioned, we usually call this operator the Hamiltonian and denote it by H:

$$H \equiv \hbar\omega\left(a^\dagger a + \frac{1}{2}\right) . \tag{7.63}$$

Acting with this operator on a state that describes our system tells us the energy of the system[29]:

[29] At least it does when the system is in an energy eigenstate.

$$H\,|E_1\rangle = E_1\,|E_1\rangle . \tag{7.64}$$

Now we want to understand these new operators a and $a^\dagger$. The most important thing for us is what a and $a^\dagger$ *do* when they act on the ket that describes our system. To get a feeling for this, let's calculate the energy of such a new state[30].

[30] Acting with a on our state $|E_1\rangle$ yields a new state. What we do now is to check if the operators change the energy. All this will make a lot more sense in a moment.

Before we can do this, we need one more thing: the commutator $[H, a]$ as we will see in a second. Using Eq. (7.61) and Eq. (7.63),

we find

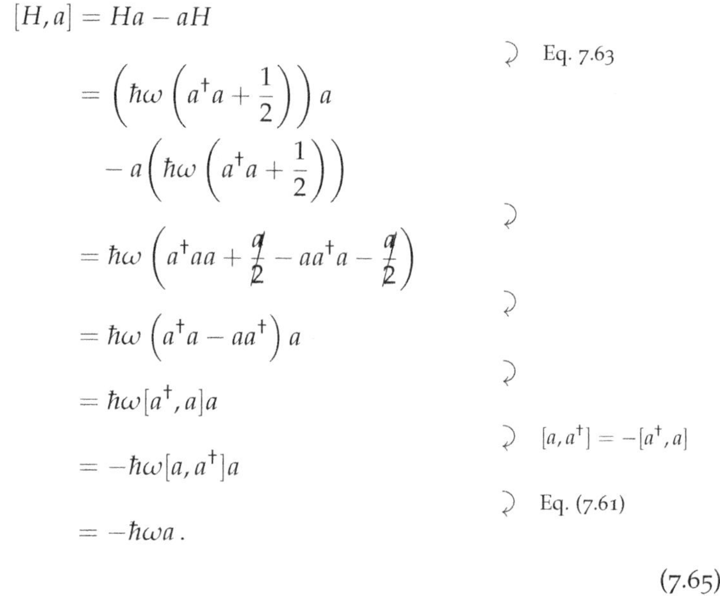

$$
\begin{aligned}
[H,a] &= Ha - aH \\
&\quad \text{(Eq. 7.63)} \\
&= \left(\hbar\omega\left(a^\dagger a + \frac{1}{2}\right)\right)a \\
&\quad - a\left(\hbar\omega\left(a^\dagger a + \frac{1}{2}\right)\right) \\
&= \hbar\omega\left(a^\dagger a a + \frac{a}{2} - a a^\dagger a - \frac{a}{2}\right) \\
&= \hbar\omega\left(a^\dagger a - a a^\dagger\right)a \\
&= \hbar\omega[a^\dagger, a]a \\
&\quad \text{(} [a,a^\dagger] = -[a^\dagger,a] \text{)} \\
&= -\hbar\omega[a,a^\dagger]a \\
&\quad \text{(Eq. (7.61))} \\
&= -\hbar\omega a\,.
\end{aligned}
\tag{7.65}
$$

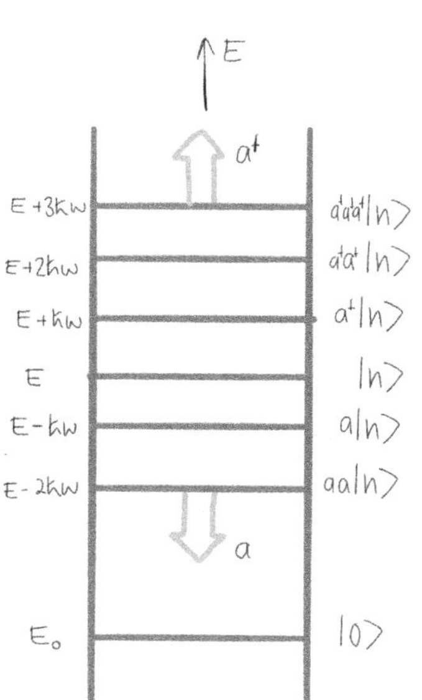

Completely analogously, we can calculate

$$[H, a^\dagger] = \hbar\omega a^\dagger\,. \tag{7.66}$$

With this information at hand, we are finally ready to calculate the energy of our new state $a\,|E_1\rangle$:

$$
\begin{aligned}
\hat{H}\left(a\,|E_1\rangle\right) &= (\hat{H}a - a\hat{H} + a\hat{H})\,|E_1\rangle \\
&\quad \text{(} -a\hat{H} + a\hat{H} = 0,\ \hat{H}a - a\hat{H} \equiv [\hat{H},a] \text{)} \\
&= a\hat{H}\,|E_1\rangle + [\hat{H},a]\,|E_1\rangle \\
&\quad \text{(Eq. 7.64)} \\
&= aE_1\,|E_1\rangle + [\hat{H},a] \\
&\quad \text{(Eq. 7.65)} \\
&= \left(aE_1 - \hbar\omega a\right)|E_1\rangle \\
&= \left(E_1 - \hbar\omega\right)\left(a\,|E_1\rangle\right).
\end{aligned}
\tag{7.67}
$$

Analogously for $a^\dagger$ we find

$$\hat{H}a^\dagger\,|E_1\rangle = (E_1 + \hbar\omega)a^\dagger\,|E_1\rangle\,. \tag{7.68}$$

What do we learn here?

By looking at Eq. (7.67) we see that $a\,|E_1\rangle$ can be interpreted as a new state with energy $E_1 - \hbar\omega_k$!

Let's make this more concrete. We define

$$|E_0\rangle \equiv a\,|E_1\rangle \tag{7.69}$$

with

$$\begin{aligned} \hat{H}|E_0\rangle &= \hat{H}(a\,|E_1\rangle) && \text{using Eq. 7.69} \\ & && \circlearrowright \text{ Eq. 7.67} \\ &= (E_1 - \hbar\omega)\,|E_0\rangle\,. \end{aligned} \tag{7.70}$$

Analogously, by looking at Eq. (7.68) we see that $a^\dagger\,|E_1\rangle$ can be interpreted as a new state with energy $E + \hbar\omega_k$.

We have

$$|E_2\rangle \equiv a^\dagger\,|E_1\rangle$$

with

$$\hat{H}\,|E_2\rangle = (E_1 + \hbar\omega)\,|E_2\rangle \qquad \text{(using Eq. 7.68).}$$

This is why a and $a^\dagger$ are known as **ladder operators**. They allow us to move between the energy eigenstates. Using $a^\dagger$, we can jump to the next eigenstate above. Using a, we can jump to the next eigenstate below it.

The non-trivial part of the Hamiltonian operator (Eq. (7.63)) is

$$N \equiv a^\dagger a\,. \tag{7.71}$$

With this definition, we can rewrite the Hamiltonian in the form:

$$H = \hbar\,\omega\left(N + \frac{1}{2}\right)\,. \tag{7.72}$$

So the operator N tells us in which energy eigenstate we currently are:

$$N\,|n\rangle = n\,|n\rangle\,, \tag{7.73}$$

where we use n to label the n-th energy eigenstate with energy E_n. It is conventional to use the notation $|1\rangle, |2\rangle, \ldots, |n\rangle$ for these states. The operators a and $a^\dagger$ let us move between them in discrete jumps.

Let's summarize what we have learned here:

▷ There is a state with the lowest possible energy $E_0 = \frac{\hbar\omega}{2}$. This is the **ground state energy** of the Harmonic oscillator. Interestingly it is non-zero, so there is always *some* fluctuation.[31]

▷ All other energy eigenstates can be generated by acting with the **raising operator** $a^\dagger$ on this state with the lowest energy multiple times. Each time we use $a^\dagger$, we generate a new state with an energy that is higher than the previous one by $\hbar\omega$.

▷ The energy spectrum is therefore *discrete*. The distance between the energy states is $\hbar\omega$.

With this in mind, we're finally ready to talk about quantum fields.

[31] This leads to a curious result in quantum field theory. As already mentioned above, in some sense, a quantum field is a set of infinitely many harmonic oscillators. Now we just learned that the ground state energy of a single harmonic oscillator is non-zero, $E_0 = \frac{\hbar\omega}{2}$. The ground state energy of a system consisting of two harmonic oscillators is therefore $\hbar\omega$, and the ground state energy of a system consisting of infinitely many harmonic oscillators is infinity. In other words, the ground state energy of a quantum field is infinitely large. However, we can only measure energy differences and since every field has an infinite ground state energy, we usually simply ignore this strange feature of quantum fields.

8

Quantum Fields

In this chapter, we will finally start talking about *quantum* fields. A quantum field is a field with an astonishing additional property which can be described using a so-called canonical commutation relation. The canonical commutation relation for a field tells us that its fundamental excitations have exactly the properties that we typically associate with particles. In this sense, particles are also important players in quantum field theory but they are not fundamental. They merely represent a very specific way in which a quantum field can be excited.

As for classical fields, the easiest thing we can study is how quantum fields behave when left alone. Luckily, the equations that describe free classical fields are useful for quantum fields too.[1] We will therefore discuss in this chapter the meaning of the solutions of these equations of motion in a quantum context and how they allow us to describe particles. One of the most important tools in this context are propagators. In general, a propagator encodes how a given field varies in space and time. Arguably the most important propagator, the Feynman propagator, will play an essential role in our description how

[1] Take note that only the equation (Maxwell's equation) for one particular type of field (massless gauge fields) is really used in a classical context *and* a quantum context. While the remaining equations can, in principle, also be used in classical models, there is nothing in the real world that could be described with them. Thus their usage in the context of classical field theory is merely an academic exercise (although an interesting one). One reason is that the only known fundamental scalar field (the Higgs field) is massive and thus does not operate on macroscopic scales. (Technically, the non-zero mass corresponds to a finite correlation length. More intuitively, we can imagine that the excitations of a massive field decay before they can make a difference on macroscopic scales.) Moreover, the fundamental excitations of all spinor fields can never occupy the same state and thus cannot reinforce one another to produce a macroscopic field. (This is known as the Pauli exclusion principle and we'll discuss it in more detail below.) In addition, all known spinor fields are massive. For all fields except for the lightest ones (electron, up-quark, down-quark) this means again that the corresponding field excitations decay quickly. Finally, all gauge fields except for the electromagnetic field also cannot operate at macroscopic scales. For the gauge field responsible for weak interactions, the reason is again that it's a massive field. For the strong interaction field, the reason is called "confinement" which is a quite subtle concept and still not fully understood. To summarize, there are no classical macroscopic fields except for the electromagnetic field.

quantum fields interact with each other.

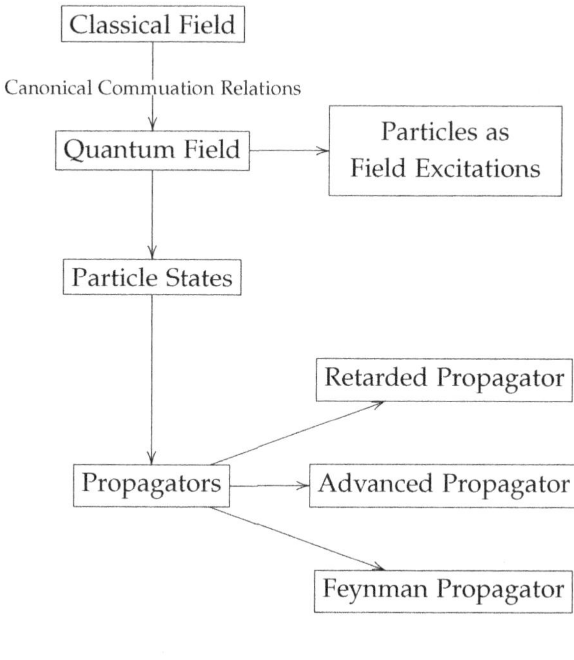

The discussions for different kinds of fields are quite similar but there are important differences that we need to talk about:

▷ For *complex* scalar fields there are two kinds of particles associated with them that are typically interpreted as particles and antiparticles.

▷ For spinor fields, there are fundamental anticommutation relations instead of commutation relations. In physical terms these imply that there can never be two spinor particles in exactly the same state.

▷ For gauge fields, we must be careful since not all four components are independent, physical degrees of freedom. Since a massive gauge field has only three possible physical polarizations, we promote only three of its components to quantum degrees of freedom. Moreover, to take into account that a massless gauge field has only two possible polarizations, we must use "transverse" commutation relations.

This is summarized in the following diagram:

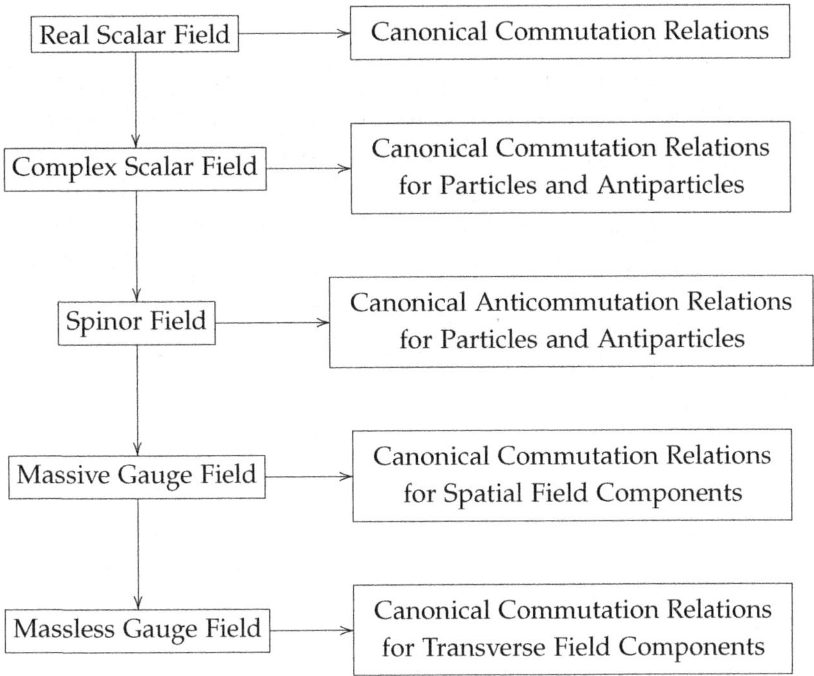

8.1 Quantum Fields vs. Classical Fields

Roughly speaking, while a classical field behaves like a network of coupled harmonic oscillators, a quantum field behaves like a network of coupled quantum oscillators. We discovered in the previous chapter that for a quantum oscillator only a discrete set of oscillation modes is possible. Moreover, the ground state energy is non-zero. One way to interpret this is by saying that a quantum oscillator is never really at rest. We can apply these lessons directly to a network of quantum oscillators.

First of all, there is a minimum amount of energy that we need to put into the network before we can see any excitation above the ground state at all. In other words, we must put in enough energy to push at least one of the oscillators into a higher oscillation mode.

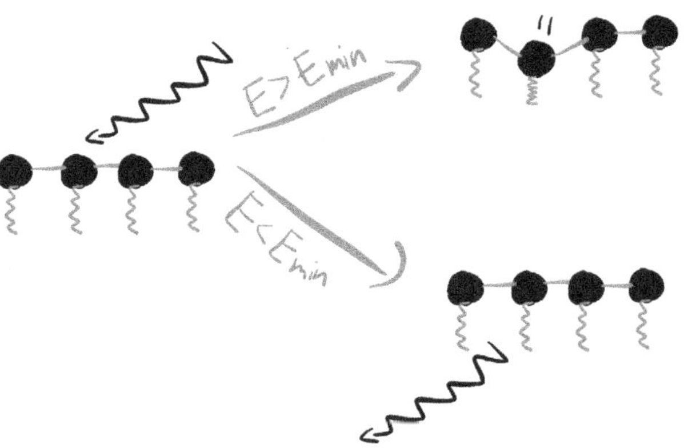

Secondly, the quantized spectrum of a quantum oscillator implies that only a discrete set of excitations is possible for the network. There is not just a discrete jump from the ground state to the first excited state but also from the first to the second excited state, from the second to the third excited state and so on. We have a ladder of allowed energy values for each oscillator in the network.

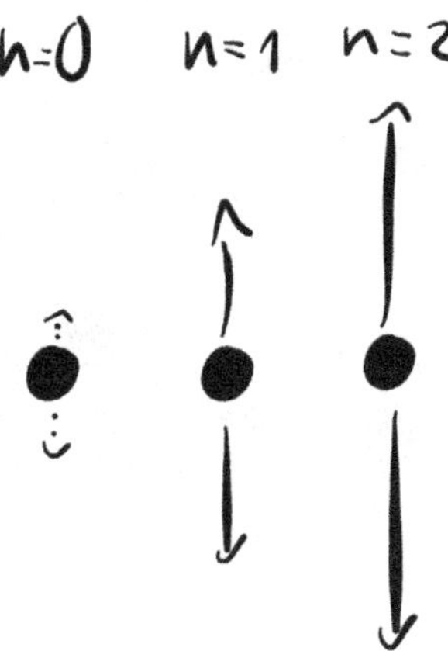

Thirdly, since we consider a network of oscillators, a given *quantized* excitation can move through the network. The adjective "quantized" is important here. For a network of classical oscillators we can imagine that if we excite one of the oscillators, this disturbance will move through the system like ripples in a pond.

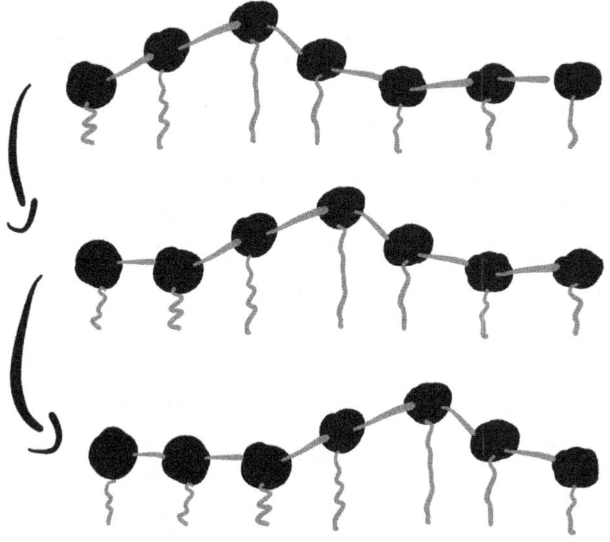

For a network of quantum oscillators, however, only a quantized spectrum of energy values are possible and thus the dynamics will not be so smooth.

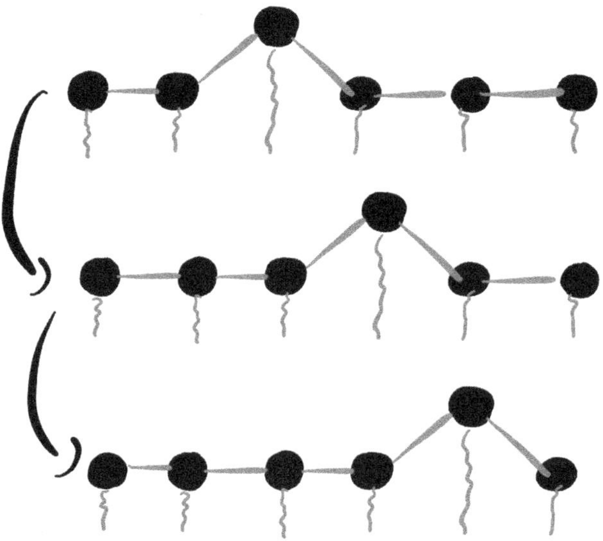

The most important observation here is that the excitations of a network of quantum oscillators have all the properties that we typically associate with particles. When we kick a quantum field at one specific location, we excite one of the oscillators. From a particle perspective, we say that we've created a particle at this location. If we put more energy into the same location, we create more particles of the same type. Depending on how we create these particles, they start to move around afterwards. But since there is an energy gap between the ground state and the first excited state, we will always find discrete chunks even after they've moved to different locations.[2]

[2] Take note that there is still an aspect of field excitations that dissolves. This has to do with our probabilistic interpretation of quantum theories. The function that describes how likely it is to find a given particle at a specific location might diffuse over space as time passes. However, no matter where we find the particle, it will always appear as a discrete undissolved chunk of energy.

Another important aspect is that our quantum oscillators are not only coupled to their neighbors in the network but also to members of different networks (i.e. different fields). Therefore, a given excitation can spread from one network to another. Each network has a characteristic energy gap between allowed states. Therefore, one fundamental excitation in a network with a large energy gap is able to cause many fundamental excitations in other networks with lower energy gaps. From a particle perspective, we interpret this by saying that a heavy particle can decay into lighter particles.

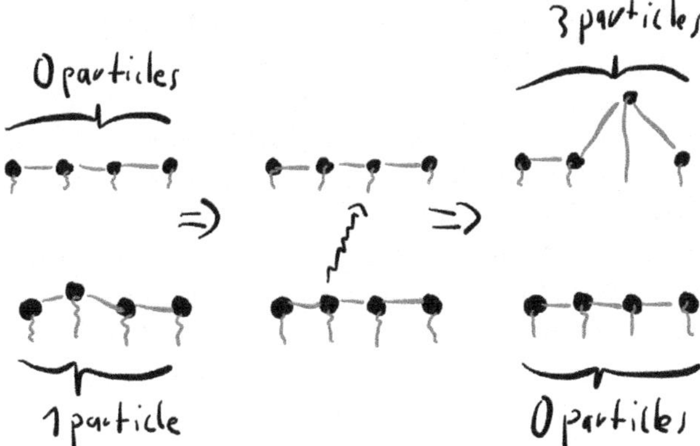

In summary, in quantum field theory particles are localized deviations from the ground state. An interesting aspect of this way of thinking about particles is that it explains why all particles of a given type look exactly the same. For example, all electrons we have ever observed have had exactly the same properties (mass, charge, spin). From a field perspective this is no longer mysterious because each electron simply represents a fundamental excitation of the underlying electron field.

Next, let's discuss how we can describe these ideas mathematically.

8.2 The Canonical Commutation Relations

In the previous chapter I've mentioned that we can motivate the explicit form of quantum operators like $\hat{p}_x = i\hbar\partial_x$ by invoking Noether's theorem. This idea will again be our guiding principle.

In Section 7.1.1, we discussed how we can describe each continuous transformation by using a generator G. A generator G

is the non-trivial part of infinitesimal transformation operators (Eq. 7.7)

$$g(\epsilon) = I + \epsilon G , \tag{8.1}$$

where $g(\epsilon)$ describes an infinitesimal transformation and I the identity transformation that changes nothing. The generator which is responsible for an infinitesimal field shift (Eq. 4.42)

$$\phi \to \phi' = \phi - i\epsilon \tag{8.2}$$

is $G = -i\frac{\partial}{\partial \phi}$, because

$$\begin{aligned}
\phi' &= g(\epsilon)\phi \\
& \quad \text{Eq. 7.7} \\
&= (I + \epsilon G)\phi \\
& \quad G = -i\frac{\partial}{\partial \phi} \\
&= (I - i\epsilon\frac{\partial}{\partial \phi})\phi \\
& \quad \frac{\partial \phi}{\partial \phi} = 1 \\
&= \phi - i\epsilon \quad \checkmark
\end{aligned} \tag{8.3}$$

With this in mind, it's time to recall our mantra (Eq. 7.15)

quantum operator $\leftrightarrow$ generator of symmetry

We discussed in the previous section that the conserved quantity associated with field shifts is called the conjugate momentum density π. Therefore, we now propose

$$\text{conjugate momentum density } \pi \leftrightarrow \text{ generator field shifts } \quad -i\frac{\partial}{\partial \phi} \tag{8.4}$$

This identification allows us to derive the following commutator relation:

$$[\phi(t,\vec{x}),\pi(t,\vec{y})]\,|\psi\rangle$$

$$= \left[\phi(t,\vec{x}), -i\frac{\partial}{\partial\phi(t,\vec{y})}\right]|\psi\rangle$$

▷ Eq. 8.4

$$= \phi(t,\vec{x})\left(-i\frac{\partial}{\partial\phi(t,\vec{y})}\right)|\psi\rangle - \left(-i\frac{\partial}{\partial\phi(t,\vec{y})}\right)\phi(t,\vec{x})\,|\psi\rangle$$

▷ $[A,B] \equiv AB - BA$

$$= \phi(t,\vec{x})\left(-i\frac{\partial}{\partial\phi(t,\vec{y})}\right)|\psi\rangle - \left(-i\frac{\partial}{\partial\phi(t,\vec{y})}\phi(t,\vec{x})\right)|\psi\rangle - \phi(t,\vec{x})\left(-i\frac{\partial}{\partial\phi(t,\vec{y})}|\psi\rangle\right)$$

▷ product rule

$$= -\left(-i\frac{\partial}{\partial\phi(t,\vec{y})}\phi(t,\vec{x})\right)|\psi\rangle$$

▷ $\phi(x_\mu)\left(-i\frac{\partial}{\partial\phi(t,\vec{y})}\right)|\psi\rangle$ (crossed out)

$$= i\delta(\vec{x}-\vec{y})\,|\psi\rangle\,. \tag{8.5}$$

▷ $\frac{\partial f(\vec{x})}{\partial f(\vec{y})} = \delta(\vec{x}-\vec{y})$

This calculation is analogous to what we did in Section 7.1.3. In particular, we included a ket $|\psi\rangle$ to remind us that operators need to act on something. Moreover, we used $\frac{\partial f(\vec{x})}{\partial f(\vec{y})} = \delta(\vec{x}-\vec{y})$ which is analogous to $\frac{\partial x_i}{\partial x_j} = \delta_{ij}$. Since Eq. 8.5 is valid for any ket $|\psi\rangle$, we can write it without it:

$$[\phi(t,\vec{x}),\pi(t,\vec{y})] = i\delta(\vec{x}-\vec{y}) \tag{8.6}$$

Moreover, we can conclude that

$$\begin{aligned}[\phi(t,\vec{x}),\phi(t,\vec{y})] &= 0\\ [\pi(t,\vec{x}),\pi(t,\vec{y})] &= 0\end{aligned} \tag{8.7}$$

since partial derivatives commute $\partial_x\partial_y = \partial_y\partial_x$. These are the **canonical commutation relations** for a scalar field in quantum field theory.

8.3 Field Operators

The most important message encoded in the canonical commutation relation (Eq. 8.6) is that in quantum field theory, fields and the conjugate momentum density are operators. This is analogous to how in quantum mechanics the classical location and momentum become operators.

Let's try to use the canonical commutation relation to understand the meaning of field operators. For simplicity, we focus on a scalar field $\phi(x_\mu)$. We start by recalling some facts about scalar fields that we've already discussed in previous chapters. The Lagrangian density for a free scalar field reads (Eq. 5.2)

$$\mathcal{L} = \frac{1}{2}(\partial_\mu \phi \partial^\mu \phi - m^2\phi^2)\,. \tag{8.8}$$

The corresponding equation of motion is the Klein-Gordon equation (Eq. 5.4)

$$(\partial_\mu \partial^\mu + m^2)\phi = 0\,. \tag{8.9}$$

A general solution of the Klein-Gordon equation reads (Eq. 5.51)

$$\phi(x) = \int \mathrm{d}k^3 \frac{1}{(2\pi)^3\sqrt{2\omega_k}} \left(a(\vec{k})\mathrm{e}^{-i(kx)} + a^\dagger(\vec{k})\mathrm{e}^{i(kx)} \right)\,. \tag{8.10}$$

Moreover, we can use the Lagrangian density (Eq. 5.2) to calculate the corresponding conjugate momentum density (Eq. 4.52):

$$\begin{aligned}
\pi &= \frac{\partial \mathcal{L}}{\partial(\partial_0 \phi)} \\
&\quad \text{(Eq. 5.2)} \\
&= \frac{\partial\Big(\frac{1}{2}(\partial_\mu \phi \partial^\mu \phi - m^2\phi^2)\Big)}{\partial(\partial_0 \phi)} \\
&\quad \text{(sum convention)} \\
&= \frac{\partial\Big(\frac{1}{2}(\partial_0 \phi \partial_0 \phi - \partial_i \phi \partial_i \phi - m^2\phi^2)\Big)}{\partial(\partial_0 \phi)} \\
&\quad \text{(}\partial_x x^2 = 2x\text{)} \\
&= \partial_0 \phi\,.
\end{aligned} \tag{8.11}$$

Using our explicit solution (Eq. 5.51), we therefore find

$$
\begin{aligned}
\pi &= \partial_0 \phi \\
&= \partial_0 \Big(\int dk^3 \frac{1}{(2\pi)^3 \sqrt{2\omega_k}} \Big(a(\vec{k}) e^{-i(kx)} + a^\dagger(\vec{k}) e^{i(kx)} \Big) \Big) \\
&= \int dk^3 \frac{1}{(2\pi)^3 \sqrt{2\omega_k}} \Big(a(\vec{k}) \partial_0 e^{-i(kx)} + a^\dagger(\vec{k}) \partial_0 e^{i(kx)} \Big) \\
&= \int dk^3 \frac{1}{(2\pi)^3 \sqrt{2\omega_k}} \Big(a(\vec{k})(-ik_0) e^{-i(kx)} + a^\dagger(\vec{k})(ik_0) e^{i(kx)} \Big) \\
&= \int dk^3 \frac{(-i)}{(2\pi)^3 \sqrt{2\omega_k}} \Big(a(\vec{k}) \omega_k e^{-i(kx)} - a^\dagger(\vec{k}) \omega_k e^{i(kx)} \Big) \\
&= \int dk^3 \frac{(-i)\sqrt{\omega_k}}{(2\pi)^3 \sqrt{2}} \Big(a(\vec{k}) e^{-i(kx)} - a^\dagger(\vec{k}) e^{i(kx)} \Big) . \qquad (8.12)
\end{aligned}
$$

↩ Eq. 5.51

↩

↩ $kx \equiv k_0 x_0 - k_i x_i$, $\partial_0 e^{ik_0 x_0} = i k_0 e^{ik_0 x_0}$

↩ $k_0 \equiv \omega_k$

↩ $\frac{\omega_k}{\sqrt{\omega_k}} = \sqrt{\omega_k}$

The key question is now: which part of the conjugate momentum density (Eq. 8.12) and the field itself (Eq. 8.10) is responsible for the non-trivial commutation relation (Eq. 8.6)

$$[\phi(t, \vec{x}), \pi(t, \vec{y})] = i\delta(\vec{x} - \vec{y}) \ ? \qquad (8.13)$$

The correct answer is that we can take the non-trivial commutation relation into account by assuming that the coefficients $a(\vec{k})$ and $a^\dagger(\vec{k})$ fulfill the commutation relations[3]

$$
\begin{aligned}
[a(\vec{k}), a^\dagger(\vec{k}')] &= (2\pi)^3 \delta(\vec{k} - \vec{k}') \\
[a(\vec{k}), a(\vec{k}')] &= 0 \, , \quad [a^\dagger(\vec{k}), a^\dagger(\vec{k}')] = 0 \, . \qquad (8.14)
\end{aligned}
$$

[3] You can find a verification of this statement in Appendix A.4.

This implies that the expansion coefficients $a(\vec{k})$ and $a^\dagger(\vec{k})$ in quantum field theory are operators.

The logical next question is therefore: what are the operators $a(\vec{k}), a^\dagger(\vec{k})$ doing when they act on a ket that represents our system? We will see below that $a(\vec{k}), a^\dagger(\vec{k})$ are ladder operators analogous to those that we introduced in our discussion of the quantum harmonic oscillator.[4] By looking at the field ex-

[4] We discussed the quantum harmonic oscillator in Section 7.2.

pansion in Eq. 8.10 we can then conclude, as promised above, that a quantum field can be understood as a network of quantum oscillators. In physical terms, we say that $a^\dagger(\vec{k})$ creates a particle when it acts on a ket, while $a(\vec{k})$ annihilates a particle. Therefore, in the context of quantum field theory $a^\dagger(\vec{k}), a(\vec{k})$ are known as creation and annihilation operators.

Let's see how this comes about.

8.3.1 Creation and Annihilation Operators

To understand the meaning of the operators $a(\vec{k}), a^\dagger(\vec{k})$ it is instructive to focus on an aspect of fields we have at least some intuitive understanding of: their energy. But before we can discuss how thinking about the energy stored in a field allows us to understand the operators $a(\vec{k}), a^\dagger(\vec{k})$, we need to go on a short tangent. This is necessary because there are several somewhat subtle aspects of the formulas that we find for the field energy in a quantum theory.

First of all, the energy of a field is the Noether charge that follows from invariance under temporal translations $t \to t + \epsilon$ and reads (Eq. 4.38):

$$E \equiv \int_V d^3x \, T_0^0 \,. \qquad (8.15)$$

In quantum field theory, this expression also becomes an operator which we call the Hamiltonian:

$$\begin{aligned}
H &\equiv \int d^3x \, T_0^0 \\
&\quad \text{(Eq. 4.35)} \\
&= \int d^3x \, \frac{\partial \mathcal{L}}{\partial(\partial_0\phi)} \partial_0\phi - \mathcal{L} \\
&\quad \left(\mathcal{L} = \frac{1}{2}(\partial_\mu\phi\partial^\mu\phi - m^2\phi^2) \text{ (Eq. 5.2)}\right) \\
&= \int d^3x \left((\partial_0\phi)^2 - \frac{1}{2}(\partial_\mu\phi\partial^\mu\phi - m^2\phi^2) \right) \\
&\quad \left(\partial_\mu\partial^\mu = \partial_0\partial_0 - \partial_i\partial_i\right) \\
&= \frac{1}{2} \int d^3x \left((\partial_0\phi)^2 + (\partial_i\phi)^2 + m^2\phi^2 \right) \\
&\quad \left(\partial_0\phi \equiv \pi \text{ (Eq. 8.11)}\right) \\
&= \frac{1}{2} \int d^3x \left(\pi^2 + (\partial_i\phi)^2 + m^2\phi^2 \right) . \qquad (8.16)
\end{aligned}$$

The integrand $\frac{1}{2}\left(\pi^2 + (\partial_i\phi)^2 + m^2\phi^2\right)$ describes the energy density of a scalar field. By using the explicit formulas for the conjugate momentum density (Eq. 8.12) and the field itself (Eq. 5.51), the energy can be written as[5]

$$H = \frac{1}{2} \int dk^3 \frac{\omega_k}{(2\pi)^3} \left(a^\dagger(\vec{k})a(\vec{k}) + a(\vec{k})a^\dagger(\vec{k}) \right) . \qquad (8.17)$$

[5] Note how similar this formula is to the formula we derived for the energy of a harmonic oscillator (Eq. 7.62):

$$H = \frac{\hbar\omega}{2}\left(a^\dagger a + a a^\dagger\right) .$$

This is demonstrated in Appendix A.5. We can then use the commutator relation (Eq. 8.14),

$$
\begin{aligned}
(2\pi)^3\delta(\vec{k}-\vec{k}') &= [a(k), a^\dagger(k')] \\
&\quad \text{↷ } [A,B] \equiv AB - BA \\
&= a(\vec{k})a^\dagger(\vec{k}') - a^\dagger(\vec{k}')a(\vec{k}) \\
&\quad \text{↷} \\
(2\pi)^3\delta(\vec{k}-\vec{k}') + a^\dagger(\vec{k}')a(\vec{k}) &= a(\vec{k})a^\dagger(\vec{k}'),
\end{aligned}
\tag{8.18}
$$

to simplify Eq. 8.17:

$$
\begin{aligned}
H &= \frac{1}{2}\int dk^3 \frac{\omega_k}{(2\pi)^3}\Big(a^\dagger(\vec{k})a(\vec{k}) + a(\vec{k})a^\dagger(\vec{k})\Big) \\
&\quad \text{↷ Eq. 8.18} \\
&= \frac{1}{2}\int dk^3 \frac{\omega_k}{(2\pi)^3}\Big(a^\dagger(\vec{k})a(\vec{k}) + (2\pi)^3\delta(\vec{k}-\vec{k}) + a^\dagger(\vec{k})a(\vec{k})\Big) \\
&\quad \text{↷} \\
&= \frac{1}{2}\int dk^3 \frac{\omega_k}{(2\pi)^3}\Big(2a^\dagger(\vec{k})a(\vec{k}) + (2\pi)^3\delta(\vec{0})\Big) \\
&\quad \text{↷} \\
&= \int dk^3 \frac{\omega_k}{(2\pi)^3} a^\dagger(\vec{k})a(\vec{k}) + \frac{1}{2}\int_V dk^3 \omega_k \delta(\vec{0}) .
\end{aligned}
\tag{8.19}
$$

This result is problematic. The second term on the right-hand side yields infinity since $\delta(\vec{0})$ describes an infinitely high spike and we integrate over infinitely many such spikes here.

We can understand this strange result by recalling that the ground state energy of a harmonic oscillator in quantum mechanics is non-zero $E_0 = \frac{\hbar\omega}{2}$.[6] Intuitively this means that a quantum oscillator can never be completely at rest and always oscillates a little bit. If we imagine a field as a network of oscillators, we can therefore conclude that the ground state energy of a field is non-zero too. Moreover, since we imagine that there is an oscillator attached to each spacetime point, our field consists of infinitely many oscillators.[7] From this perspective it's not too surprising that we find a field energy that is formally infinitely

[6] We discovered this in Section 7.2.

[7] If we assume that spacetime is continuous, there are infinitely many points between any two given points. Since we attach an oscillator to each point, there are infinitely many oscillators in our network.

large. But this is not a problem as long as we are only interested in excitations above the ground state. In fact, in physics we are usually only interested in energy differences. Each field configuration is characterized by its energy above the formally infinite ground state energy.

For example, we can imagine that one field configuration is characterized by the energy

$$E_1 = e_1 + \frac{1}{2}\int dk^3 \omega_k \delta(\vec{0})\,, \tag{8.20}$$

while a second field configuration is characterized by

$$E_2 = e_2 + \frac{1}{2}\int dk^3 \omega_k \delta(\vec{0})\,. \tag{8.21}$$

Formally, both field energies are infinite. But the information we are usually interested in is how far the field is excited above the ground state. This is described by e_1, e_2.

A pragmatic solution is therefore to simply ignore the infinite contribution from the ground state and focus on the contribution to the total energy that characterizes non-trivial field configurations:

$$H \equiv \int dk^3 \frac{\omega_k}{(2\pi)^3} a^\dagger(\vec{k})a(\vec{k})\,. \tag{8.22}$$

The operator

$$\mathcal{H} \equiv \omega_k a^\dagger(\vec{k})a(\vec{k})\,. \tag{8.23}$$

is commonly called the **Hamiltonian density**.

This approach works quite well for most applications in which we can ignore the non-trivial ground state structure of quantum fields. The ground state of quantum fields is an exciting topic in its own right and we will revisit the issue in Chapter 14.

With this formula at hand, we can finally figure out the meaning of the operators $a^\dagger(\vec{k}), a(\vec{k})$. A key ingredient is the commutator:[8]

[8] We will see in a moment why knowing this commutator is really useful if we want to understand the meaning of $a^\dagger(k)$.

$$
\begin{aligned}
&[H, a^\dagger(\vec{k}')] \\
&= \left[\left(\int dk^3 \frac{1}{(2\pi)^3} \omega_k a^\dagger(\vec{k}) a(\vec{k}) \right), a^\dagger(\vec{k}') \right] && \text{Eq. 8.22} \\
&= \int dk^3 \frac{1}{(2\pi)^3} \omega_k \Big(a^\dagger(\vec{k}) a(k) a^\dagger(\vec{k}') - a^\dagger(\vec{k}') a^\dagger(\vec{k}) a(\vec{k}) \Big) && [A,B] \equiv AB - BA \\
&= \int dk^3 \frac{1}{(2\pi)^3} \omega_k \Big(a^\dagger(\vec{k}) a(\vec{k}) a^\dagger(\vec{k}') - a^\dagger(\vec{k}) a^\dagger(\vec{k}') a(\vec{k}) \Big) && [a^\dagger(\vec{k}), a^\dagger(\vec{k}')] = 0 \text{ (Eq. 8.14)} \\
&= \int dk^3 \frac{1}{(2\pi)^3} \omega_k a^\dagger(k) [a(\vec{k}), a^\dagger(\vec{k}')] && AB - BA \equiv [A,B] \\
&= \int dk^3 \omega_k a^\dagger(\vec{k}) \delta^3(k - k') && \text{Eq. 8.14} \\
&= \omega_{k'} a^\dagger(\vec{k}') \,. && \int dx' f(x') \delta(x - x') = f(x)
\end{aligned} \tag{8.24}
$$

Analogously, we can compute

$$[H, a(\vec{k}')] = -\omega_{\vec{k}'} a(\vec{k}') \tag{8.25}$$

In the quantum framework, we act with operators on abstract objects $|\psi\rangle$ that describe the system in question. For example, if we act with the energy operator H on a system that we prepared in an energy eigenstate, we find

$$H |\psi_E\rangle = E |\psi_E\rangle \,, \tag{8.26}$$

where E denotes the energy of the system. What we want to understand is what happens when we act with a field operator or, equivalently, with $a(k)$, $a^\dagger(\vec{k})$ on a ket $|\psi\rangle$.

To that end, we check if $a(\vec{k})$ changes the energy of a given system:[9]

[9] The steps here are completely analogous to what we did in Eq. 7.67 to understand the meaning of the harmonic oscillator ladder operators.

$$\begin{aligned}
H\left(a(\vec{k}')\,|\psi_E\rangle\right) &= \left(Ha(\vec{k}') - a(\vec{k}')H + a(\vec{k}')H\right)|\psi_E\rangle && \text{$-a(\vec{k}')H + a(\vec{k}')H = 0$} \\
&&& \text{$Ha - aH \equiv [H,a]$} \\
&= a(\vec{k}')H\,|\psi_E\rangle + [H, a(\vec{k}')]\,|\psi_E\rangle \\
&&& \text{Eq. 8.26} \\
&= a(\vec{k}')E\,|\psi_E\rangle + [H, a(\vec{k}')]\,|\psi_E\rangle \\
&&& \text{Eq. 8.25} \\
&= \left(a(\vec{k}')E - \omega_{k'}a(\vec{k}')\right)|\psi_E\rangle \\
&= \left(E - \omega_{k'}\right)\left(a(\vec{k}')\,|\psi_E\rangle\right). && (8.27)
\end{aligned}$$

In words, this means that the operator $a_{\vec{k}'}$ *lowers* the energy of the system by $\omega_{k'}$. Analogously, we can compute

$$H\left(a^\dagger(\vec{k}')\,|\psi_E\rangle\right) = \left(E + \omega_{k'}\right)\left(a(\vec{k}')\,|\psi_E\rangle\right). \tag{8.28}$$

Therefore, we can conclude that $a^\dagger(\vec{k}')$ *raises* the energy of the system by $\omega_{k'}$.

Formulated differently, $\left(a^\dagger(\vec{k}')\,|\psi_E\rangle\right)$ describes a new configuration of the system with energy $E + \omega_{k'}$, while $\left(a(\vec{k}')\,|\psi_E\rangle\right)$ describes a new configuration with energy $E - \omega_{k'}$.

In an analogous way to the case of the harmonic oscillation discussed in Section 7.2, we can act with the operators $a(\vec{k}')$ and $a^\dagger(\vec{k}')$ repeatedly on a given ket and move up and down the energy ladder in this way. To understand all of this a bit better, let's assume that we are dealing with a completely empty system which is described by $|0\rangle$. In field theory, this corresponds to a ground state configuration of the field. If we act on $|0\rangle$ with $a^\dagger(\vec{k})$, we get a configuration with an energy that lies ω_k above the ground state energy:

$$a^\dagger(\vec{k})\,|0\rangle \equiv |1_{\vec{k}}\rangle \quad \text{with} \quad H\,|1_{\vec{k}}\rangle = (E_0 + \omega_k)\,|1_{\vec{k}}\rangle\,, \tag{8.29}$$

where E_0 denotes the ground state energy which, as discussed above, is set to zero. If we now act with $a^\dagger(\vec{k})$ on the ket we created this way, we find a new configuration with an even larger energy:

$$a^\dagger(\vec{k})\,|1_{\vec{k}}\rangle \equiv |2_{\vec{k}}\rangle \quad \text{with} \quad H\,|2_{\vec{k}}\rangle = (E_0 + 2\omega_k)\,|2_{\vec{k}}\rangle\,. \tag{8.30}$$

Moreover, if we act on the configuration we created this way with an operator $a^\dagger(\vec{k}')$ that is labeled by a different wave vector $\vec{k}'$, we find

$$a^\dagger(\vec{k}')\,|2_{\vec{k}}\rangle \equiv |2_{\vec{k}}1_{\vec{k}'}\rangle \quad \text{with} \quad H\,|2_{\vec{k}}1_{\vec{k}'}\rangle = (E_0 + 2\omega_k + \omega_{k'})\,|2_{\vec{k}}1_{\vec{k}'}\rangle\,.$$

We say that $a^\dagger(\vec{k})$ creates a particle with momentum $\vec{k}$.[10] The energy of a particle created this way is $\omega_k = \sqrt{m^2 + \vec{k}^2}$, which is the relativistic energy-momentum relation (Eq. 2.43), $E = \sqrt{m^2 + \vec{p}^2}$, in disguise. Similarly, we say that $a(\vec{k})$ annihilates a particle of momentum $\vec{k}$. We call $a^\dagger(\vec{k})$ a **creation operator** and $a(\vec{k})$ an **annihilation operator**. An important property of the annihilation operator is that if it acts on a completely empty system $|0\rangle$ we find zero because there is nothing left the operator could annihilate

$$a(\vec{k})\,|0\rangle = 0\,. \tag{8.31}$$

[10] Reminder: in quantum mechanics the wave number $\vec{k}$ and the momentum $\vec{p}$ are directly related. We discussed this in Section 7.1.7.

This is the defining property of the ground state $|0\rangle$.

It's entirely normal to be a bit confused at this point. In particular, it's natural to wonder: what about energy and charge conservation? How can we create a particle in an empty system without violating these fundamental conservation laws? Even Richard Feynman was confused about this as he recalled in his Nobel lecture:

> "I remember that when someone had started to teach me about creation and annihilation operators, that this operator creates an electron, I said, "how do you create an electron? It disagrees with the conservation of charge", and in that way, I blocked my mind from learning a very practical scheme of calculation."

We will see later that creation and annihilation operators act in quantum field theory in a way that makes sure that the fundamental conservation laws are respected. The operators $a^\dagger(k)$ and $a(k)$ appear under an integral that represents a physical field configuration. Moreover, they necessarily act on a ket $|\psi\rangle$ which describes the system that we prepared in a particular way. Embedded in this context, there is nothing strange about the way creation and annihilation operators act. It's only if we look at them in isolation that they seem a bit strange.

By using this new interpretation of $a^\dagger(\vec{k})$ and $a(\vec{k})$ it is instructive to take a second look at the Hamiltonian operator (Eq. 8.22):

$$H \equiv \int_V dk^3 \frac{\omega_k}{(2\pi)^3} a^\dagger(\vec{k}) a(\vec{k}) . \tag{8.32}$$

The result if this operator acts on a ket like $|2_{\vec{k}} 1_{\vec{k}'}\rangle$ should be (ignoring a possibly non-zero ground state energy E_0)

$$H\, |2_{\vec{k}} 1_{\vec{k}'}\rangle = (2\omega_k + \omega_{k'})\, |2_{\vec{k}} 1_{\vec{k}'}\rangle . \tag{8.33}$$

This suggests that $N(\vec{k}) \equiv a^\dagger(\vec{k}) a(\vec{k})$ is a number operator that is able to extract the number of particles with momentum k from a given ket.[11] For example

$$N(\vec{k})\, |2_{\vec{k}} 1_{\vec{k}'}\rangle = 2\, |2_{\vec{k}} 1_{\vec{k}'}\rangle \tag{8.34}$$

[11] Similarly, we defined the number operator for the harmonic oscillator in Eq. 7.71.

and

$$N(\vec{k}')\, |2_{\vec{k}} 1_{\vec{k}'}\rangle = 1\, |2_{\vec{k}} 1_{\vec{k}'}\rangle . \tag{8.35}$$

In general

$$N(\vec{k})\, |n_{\vec{k}} n_{\vec{k}'}, \ldots\rangle = n_{\vec{k}}\, |n_{\vec{k}} n_{\vec{k}'} \ldots\rangle . \tag{8.36}$$

The Hamiltonian operator in terms of the number operator reads

$$H = \int_V dk^3 \frac{\omega_k}{(2\pi)^3} N(\vec{k}) . \tag{8.37}$$

We can understand the meaning of this formula as follows. The number operator $N(\vec{k})$ extracts the number of particles with momentum $\vec{k}$ from the ket the Hamiltonian operator acts on. Then we multiply the resulting number with the corresponding energy associated with each such particle ω_k. In addition, we integrate over all possible momenta, which makes sure that we extract all particles from the given ket. This way, we can sum over the energies of all of the individual particles and find the total energy of the system.

We've discovered that when we act with the creation operator $a^\dagger(\vec{k})$ on the ground state ket $|0\rangle$, we get a ket that describes a single particle with energy $\omega_k = \sqrt{m^2 + \vec{k}^2}$:

$$|1_{\vec{k}}\rangle \equiv a^\dagger(\vec{k})\,|0\rangle\,. \tag{8.38}$$

The notation already suggests that $|1_{\vec{k}}\rangle$ describes a particle with momentum $\vec{k}$. As usual in the quantum framework, we can check this by using the momentum operator $\hat{P}_i$. Momentum is the Noether charge associated with invariance under spatial translations $x_i \to x_i + \epsilon_i$ and reads (Eq. 4.39):

$$\begin{aligned}
\hat{P}_i &\equiv \int_V d^3x\, T^0_i \\
&\quad \text{Eq. 4.35} \\
&= \int_V d^3x\, \left(\frac{\partial \mathcal{L}}{\partial(\partial_0\phi)}\partial_i\phi - \delta^i_0\mathcal{L}\right) \\
&\quad \mathcal{L} = \ldots \text{ (Eq. 5.2)}, \delta^i_0 = 0 \\
&= \int_V d^3x\, \frac{\partial\left(\frac{1}{2}(\partial_\mu\phi\partial^\mu\phi - m^2\phi^2)\right)}{\partial(\partial_0\phi)}\partial_i\phi \\
&\quad \partial_x x^2 = 2x \\
&= \int_V d^3x\, \partial_0\phi\partial_i\phi \\
&\quad \text{Eq. 8.11} \\
&= \int_V d^3x\, \pi\partial_i\phi\,.
\end{aligned} \tag{8.39}$$

By using the explicit expansions of the conjugate momentum density π (Eq. 8.12) and ϕ (Eq. 5.51), we can rewrite this in terms of the operators $a(\vec{k})$ and $a^\dagger(\vec{k})$:

$$\hat{P}_i = \int_V \frac{d^3k}{(2\pi)^3}\, k_i a^\dagger(\vec{k})a(\vec{k})\,. \tag{8.40}$$

This is demonstrated in Appendix A.6. If we act with this momentum operator on our particle state $|1_{\vec{k}}\rangle$, we find

$$
\begin{aligned}
\hat{P}_i \, |1_{\vec{k}}\rangle &= \hat{P}_i\Big(a^\dagger(\vec{k})\,|0\rangle\Big) \\
&\quad \text{(Eq. 8.40)} \\
&= \Big(\int_V \frac{d^3k'}{(2\pi)^3}\, k_i a^\dagger(\vec{k}') a(\vec{k}')\Big)\Big(a^\dagger(\vec{k})\,|0\rangle\Big) \\
&\quad \text{(Eq. 8.14)} \\
&= \int_V \frac{d^3k'}{(2\pi)^3}\, k_i a^\dagger(\vec{k}')\Big(a^\dagger(\vec{k})a(\vec{k}') + (2\pi)^3\delta(\vec{k}-\vec{k}')\Big)\,|0\rangle \\
&\quad \left(a(\vec{k}')\,|0\rangle = 0 \text{ (Eq. 8.31)}\right) \\
&= \int_V \frac{d^3k'}{(2\pi)^3}\, k_i a^\dagger(\vec{k}')(2\pi)^3\delta(\vec{k}-\vec{k}')\,|0\rangle \\
&\quad \left(\int dx' f(x')\delta(x-x') = f(x)\right) \\
&= k_i a^\dagger(\vec{k})\,|0\rangle \\
&\quad \left(a^\dagger(\vec{k})\,|0\rangle \equiv |1_{\vec{k}}\rangle\right) \\
&= k_i\,|1_{\vec{k}}\rangle \quad \checkmark
\end{aligned}
\tag{8.41}
$$

This tells us that $|1_{\vec{k}}\rangle$ is indeed a momentum eigenstate with momentum $\vec{k}$.

In summary, we discovered that if we act with a creation operator $a^\dagger(\vec{k})$ on the ground state ket $|0\rangle$, the result is an energy and momentum eigenstate:

$$
\boxed{
\begin{aligned}
& |1_{\vec{k}}\rangle \equiv a^\dagger(\vec{k})\,|0\rangle \\
\text{with}\quad & H\,|1_{\vec{k}}\rangle = \omega_k\,|1_{\vec{k}}\rangle && \text{(this is Eq. 8.29)}\;, \\
& \hat{P}_i\,|1_{\vec{k}}\rangle = k_i\,|1_{\vec{k}}\rangle && \text{(this is Eq. 8.41)}\;, \\
\text{and}\quad & a(\vec{k})\,|0\rangle = 0 && \text{(this is Eq. 8.31)}\;.
\end{aligned}
}
\tag{8.42}
$$

It is conventional to say that $|1_{\vec{k}}\rangle$ describes a particle with momentum $\vec{k}$ and energy ω_k. In the following section, we will discuss why and how this statement must be refined for real-world particles.

8.4 Particle States

We can define that the ground state $|0\rangle$ is normalized

$$\langle 0|0\rangle = 1\,. \tag{8.43}$$

But what about all of the other kets that we get by acting with a ladder operator $a^\dagger(\vec{k})$ on this ground state?

By using the commutation relation in Eq. 8.14 and the fact that $|1_{\vec{k}}\rangle \equiv a^\dagger(\vec{k})\,|0\rangle$ implies[12] $\langle 1_{\vec{k}}| = \langle 0|\, a(\vec{k})$, we can calculate

[12] This follows because $\langle\psi| \equiv |\psi\rangle^\dagger$ and therefore $\langle 1_{\vec{k}}| \equiv (|1_{\vec{k}}\rangle)^\dagger = (a^\dagger(\vec{k})\,|0\rangle)^\dagger = \langle 0|\, a(\vec{k})$.

$$\begin{aligned}
\langle 1_{\vec{k}}|1_{\vec{k}'}\rangle &= \langle 0|a(\vec{k})a^\dagger(\vec{k}')|0\rangle \\
&\quad \text{(} -a^\dagger(\vec{k}')a(\vec{k}) + a^\dagger(\vec{k}')a(\vec{k}) = 0 \text{)} \\
&= \langle 0|\Big(a(\vec{k})a^\dagger(\vec{k}') - a^\dagger(\vec{k}')a(\vec{k}) + a^\dagger(\vec{k}')a(\vec{k})\Big)|0\rangle \\
&\quad \text{(} a(\vec{k})\,|0\rangle = 0 \text{ (Eq. 8.31))} \\
&= \langle 0|[a(\vec{k}), a^\dagger(\vec{k}')]|0\rangle \\
&\quad \text{(Eq. 8.14)} \\
&= \langle 0|\Big((2\pi)^3\delta(\vec{k}-\vec{k}')\Big)|0\rangle \\
&= \Big((2\pi)^3\delta(\vec{k}-\vec{k}')\Big)\,\langle 0|0\rangle \\
&\quad \text{(} \langle 0|0\rangle = 1 \text{ (Eq. 8.43))} \\
&= (2\pi)^3\delta(\vec{k}-\vec{k}')\,.
\end{aligned} \tag{8.44}$$

In words, this means that the kets describing particles with different momenta are orthogonal since $\delta(\vec{k}-\vec{k}')$ yields zero except for $\vec{k} = \vec{k}'$.

In addition, recall that we introduced $a(\vec{k})$, $a^\dagger(\vec{k})$ in Eq. 5.52 as rescaled versions of the original coefficients:

$$\begin{aligned}
a(k) &\equiv \sqrt{2\omega_k}\,a(\vec{k}) \\
a^\dagger(k) &\equiv \sqrt{2\omega_k}\,a^\dagger(\vec{k})\,.
\end{aligned} \tag{8.45}$$

We can define

$$a^\dagger(k)\,|0\rangle \equiv |1_k\rangle\,. \tag{8.46}$$

These states are related to the particle states we worked with so

far by

$$
\begin{aligned}
|1_k\rangle &\equiv a^\dagger(k)\,|0\rangle \\
&\quad \text{↷ Eq. 8.45} \\
&= \sqrt{2\omega_k} a^\dagger(\vec{k})\,|0\rangle \\
&\quad \text{↷ } |1_{\vec{k}}\rangle \equiv a^\dagger(\vec{k})\,|0\rangle \\
&= \sqrt{2\omega_k}\,|1_{\vec{k}}\rangle\,.
\end{aligned} \tag{8.47}
$$

This implies that states like $|1_k\rangle$ are normalized as follows

$$
\begin{aligned}
\langle 1_k | 1_{k'} \rangle &\overset{\text{Eq. 8.47}}{=} 2\sqrt{\omega_k}\sqrt{\omega_{k'}}\,\langle 1_{\vec{k}} | 1_{\vec{k}'} \rangle \\
&\quad \text{↷ Eq. 8.44} \\
&= 2\sqrt{\omega_k}\sqrt{\omega_{k'}}(2\pi)^3\delta(\vec{k}-\vec{k}') \\
&\quad \text{↷ } \delta(\vec{k}-\vec{k}') = 0 \text{ for } k \neq k' \\
&= 2\omega_k(2\pi)^3\delta(\vec{k}-\vec{k}')\,.
\end{aligned} \tag{8.48}
$$

What we just discovered is interesting because we learn that we cannot observe the states described by $|1_k\rangle$ or $|1_{\vec{k}}\rangle$ in the real world. In quantum theories, we always use a probabilistic interpretation. The probability to find a system in the state ψ_2 if we prepare it in the state ψ_1 reads in the quantum framework $P(\psi_1 \to \psi_2) = |\langle \psi_2 | \psi_1 \rangle|^2$. This probabilistic interpretation only makes sense if the probability to find the system in the state ψ_1 if we prepare it (at the same moment in time) in the state ψ_1 is 100%:

$$
P(\psi_1 \to \psi_1) = |\langle \psi_1 | \psi_1 \rangle|^2 = 1\,. \tag{8.49}
$$

In mathematical terms this implies that we need normalized states in order to get sensible probabilities. But we just discovered that

$$
\langle 1_k | 1_k \rangle = 2\omega_k(2\pi)^3\delta(\vec{k}-\vec{k}) = 2\omega_k(2\pi)^3\delta(\vec{0})\,. \tag{8.50}
$$

Since $\delta(\vec{0})$ represents formally an infinitely large peak, there is no way how we can normalize a state like $|1_k\rangle$ (and analogously $|1_{\vec{k}}\rangle$).

The physical reason for this strange fact is that $|1_{\vec{k}}\rangle$ describes a particle with perfectly known momentum $|\vec{k}\rangle$. In quantum theories, however, this implies that we have no information about the particle's location due to the uncertainty relation.[13] Therefore this is not a realistic setup. How can we talk about a particle if we have absolutely no idea where it is located? Let's try to understand this difficulty a bit better.

[13] We will discuss the uncertainty relation in more detail in Section 8.4.2.

8.4.1 Plane Waves

We discussed in Section 7.1.6 that it is often illuminating to expand a given abstract ket $|\psi\rangle$ in terms of basis vectors. Mathematically this is possible by inserting a complete basis:

$$|\psi\rangle = \int dx' \, |x'\rangle \, \langle x'|\psi\rangle$$

$$\quad \text{↷ } \psi(x') \equiv \langle x'|\psi\rangle$$

$$= \int dx' \psi(x') \, |x'\rangle \,, \tag{8.51}$$

where we used that $\int dx \, |x\rangle \, \langle x| = 1$ (Eq. 7.41). Moreover, we can project out the amplitude for one specific location x, as usual, by using the corresponding bra $\langle x|$:

$$\langle x|\psi\rangle = \langle x| \Big(\int dx' \psi(x') \, |x'\rangle \Big)$$

$$\quad \text{↷ we integrate over } x' \text{ not } x$$

$$= \int dx' \psi(x') \, \langle x|x'\rangle$$

$$\quad \text{↷ } \langle x|x'\rangle = \delta(x - x')$$

$$= \int dx' \psi(x') \delta(x - x')$$

$$\quad \text{↷ } \int dx' f(x') \delta(x - x') = f(x)$$

$$= \psi(x) \,. \tag{8.52}$$

Thus it would be nice if we could somehow understand our newly defined states $|1_{\vec{k}}\rangle$ similarly in terms of a concrete basis.

To that end, we do something that is long overdue: we discuss what happens when a field ϕ (and not just one of the coefficients $a^\dagger(\vec{k})$) acts on the ground state $|0\rangle$. First of all, we introduce the notation

$$|1_{\vec{x}}\rangle \equiv \phi(\vec{x}) \, |0\rangle \,. \tag{8.53}$$

It is quite tempting to say that $|1_{\vec{x}}\rangle$ describes a particle that is localized at $\vec{x}$. One motivation for this point of view is the formal similarity between the operator (Eq. 5.51 with $t = 0$)[14]

$$\phi(\vec{x}) = \int dk^3 \frac{1}{(2\pi)^3 \sqrt{2\omega_k}} \Big(e^{-i(\vec{k}\cdot\vec{x})} a(\vec{k}) + e^{i(\vec{k}\cdot\vec{x})} a^\dagger(\vec{k}) \Big) \tag{8.54}$$

and the position operator of a quantum mechanical harmonic oscillator (Eq. 7.59)

$$x = \sqrt{\frac{\hbar}{2m\omega}} (a + a^\dagger) \,. \tag{8.55}$$

[14] For simplicity, we evaluate our field in this section at one specific moment in time. We will discuss the time evolution of fields in the next chapter.

Moreover, we will see below that we can use the basis vectors $|1_{\vec{x}}\rangle$ defined in Eq. 8.53 quite analogously to how we use $|x\rangle$ in Eq. 8.52.

However, there are still quite a few poorly understood technical issues with such an interpretation. Most importantly, the state that we label in quantum field theory by $|1_{\vec{x}}\rangle$ is definitely not the same state that we label by $|\vec{x}\rangle$ in quantum mechanics.[15]

[15] Most standard textbooks tell their readers that $\phi(\vec{x})\,|0\rangle$ represents a particle at $\vec{x}$. This is certainly a perfectly valid attitude if you're just starting out. But if you're a bit further in your studies it's worth going down the rabbit hole and reading about the problems we encounter if we try to interpret $|1_{\vec{x}}\rangle \equiv \phi(\vec{x})\,|0\rangle$ this way. Technically, the quantum-mechanical $|\vec{x}\rangle$ is "δ"-localized, while $|1_{\vec{x}}\rangle$ is only *almost* localized at a point. We will see this more explicitly in Section 8.5. For an extensive discussion see

T. Padmanabhan. Obtaining the Non-relativistic Quantum Mechanics from Quantum Field Theory: Issues, Folklores and Facts. *Eur. Phys. J.*, C78(7):563, 2018. DOI: 10.1140/epjc/s10052-018-6039-y

Nevertheless, let's try to understand the state defined in Eq. 8.53 by using the explicit field expansion (Eq. 5.51)

$$
\begin{aligned}
|1_{\vec{x}}\rangle &\equiv \phi(\vec{x})\,|0\rangle \\
&\quad \text{(Eq. 5.51)} \\
&= \left(\int dk^3 \frac{1}{(2\pi)^3\sqrt{2\omega_k}} \left(e^{-i(\vec{k}\cdot\vec{x})}a(\vec{k}) + e^{i(\vec{k}\cdot\vec{x})}a^\dagger(\vec{k})\right)\right)|0\rangle \\
&\quad a(\vec{k})\,|0\rangle = 0 \text{ (Eq. 8.31)} \\
&= \int dk^3 \frac{1}{(2\pi)^3\sqrt{2\omega_k}} e^{i(\vec{k}\cdot\vec{x})}a^\dagger(\vec{k})\,|0\rangle \\
&\quad |1_{\vec{k}}\rangle \equiv a^\dagger(\vec{k})\,|0\rangle \text{ (Eq. 8.38)} \\
&= \int dk^3 \frac{1}{(2\pi)^3\sqrt{2\omega_k}} e^{i(\vec{k}\cdot\vec{x})}\,|1_{\vec{k}}\rangle\,. \qquad (8.56)
\end{aligned}
$$

Here, we act with the ladder operator $a^\dagger(\vec{k})$ on our empty state ket $|0\rangle$. This way we create a field excitation with momentum $\vec{k}$. However, we integrate over all possible momenta $\vec{k}$ and thus create a superposition of field excitations of all possible momenta.

Schematically, we have

$$
\begin{aligned}
|1_{\vec{x}}\rangle &\sim \sum_i e^{i(\vec{k}_i\cdot\vec{x})}a^\dagger(\vec{k}_i)\,|0\rangle \\
&= e^{i(\vec{k}_1\cdot\vec{x})}a^\dagger(\vec{k}_1)\,|0\rangle + e^{i(\vec{k}_2\cdot\vec{x})}a^\dagger(\vec{k}_2)\,|0\rangle + \ldots \\
&\quad a^\dagger(\vec{k}_1)\,|0\rangle \equiv |1_{\vec{k}}\rangle \text{ (Eq. 8.29)} \\
&= e^{i(\vec{k}_1\cdot\vec{x})}\,|1_{\vec{k}_1}\rangle + e^{i(\vec{k}_2\cdot\vec{x})}\,|1_{\vec{k}_2}\rangle + \ldots\,. \qquad (8.57)
\end{aligned}
$$

Each field excitation in this superposition is weighted by a plane wave factor $\mathrm{e}^{-i(\vec{k}_i\cdot\vec{x})}$.[16]

[16] Take note that this does not mean that $|1_{\vec{x}}\rangle$ consists of infinitely many field excitations. Instead, we learn that different field configurations with definite momenta are in principle possible if we prepare a field in the state $|1_{\vec{x}}\rangle$.

Therefore, we learn here that the state described by $|1_{\vec{x}}\rangle$ is a superposition of all possible field excitations with well-defined momentum values. This means that for the state described by $|1_{\vec{x}}\rangle$ it's possible to measure, in principle any momentum value. This is exactly what we would expect for a particle that is perfectly localized in space, as a result of the quantum mechanical uncertainty relation.[17]

[17] Roughly, the (Heisenberg) uncertainty relation tells us that the more a particle is localized in space, the less localized it is in momentum space and vice versa.

But before we talk about uncertainty in more detail, let's finish our discussion of the definite momentum states $|1_{\vec{k}}\rangle$. In particular, as suggested at the beginning of this section, we want to understand them better by expanding them in terms of a concrete basis.

Motivated by the result in Eq. 8.52, we multiply $|1_{\vec{k}}\rangle$ by $\langle 1_{\vec{x}}|$ in order to determine the position representation of the abstract ket $|1_{\vec{k}}\rangle$:[18]

[18] Reminder: in quantum mechanics, we have (Eq. 8.52)

$$\langle x|\psi\rangle = \psi(x)\,,$$

where $\psi(x)$ is the position representation of the abstract ket $|\psi\rangle$.

$$\begin{aligned}
\langle 1_{\vec{x}}|1_{\vec{k}}\rangle &\overset{\text{Eq. 8.38}}{=} \langle 1_{\vec{x}}|\Big(a^\dagger(\vec{k})\,|0\rangle\Big) \\
&\qquad \text{Eq. 8.56 and } \langle\psi| \equiv |\psi\rangle^\dagger \\
&= \Big(\int dk'^3 \frac{1}{(2\pi)^3\sqrt{2\omega_{k'}}}\mathrm{e}^{i(\vec{k}'\cdot\vec{x})}a^\dagger(\vec{k}')\,|0\rangle\Big)^\dagger\Big(a^\dagger(\vec{k})\,|0\rangle\Big) \\
&\qquad \langle\psi|\hat{O} \equiv (\hat{O}^\dagger\,|\psi\rangle)^\dagger \\
&= \Big(\int dk'^3 \frac{1}{(2\pi)^3\sqrt{2\omega_{k'}}}\mathrm{e}^{-i(\vec{k}'\cdot\vec{x})}\,\langle 0|\,a(\vec{k}')\Big)\Big(a^\dagger(\vec{k})\,|0\rangle\Big) \\
&\qquad \text{Eq. 8.14} \\
&= \int dk'^3 \frac{1}{(2\pi)^3\sqrt{2\omega_{k'}}}\mathrm{e}^{-i(\vec{k}'\cdot\vec{x})}\,\langle 0|\Big(a^\dagger(\vec{k})a(\vec{k}') + (2\pi)^3\delta(\vec{k}'-\vec{k})\Big)\,|0\rangle \\
&\qquad a(\vec{k}')\,|0\rangle = 0 \text{ (Eq. 8.31)} \\
&= \int dk'^3 \frac{1}{\sqrt{2\omega_{k'}}}\mathrm{e}^{-i(\vec{k}'\cdot\vec{x})}\delta(\vec{k}'-\vec{k})\,\langle 0|0\rangle \\
&\qquad \int dx' f(x')\delta(x-x') = f(x) \\
&= \frac{1}{\sqrt{2\omega_k}}\mathrm{e}^{-i(\vec{k}\cdot\vec{x})}\,.
\end{aligned} \tag{8.58}$$

This is almost exactly the wave function that describes a particle with momentum $\vec{k}$ in quantum mechanics (Eq. 5.44):

$$\psi_k(\vec{x}) \equiv \langle\vec{x}|\vec{k}\rangle = \mathrm{e}^{-i\vec{k}\cdot\vec{x}}\,. \tag{8.59}$$

The only difference is the normalization factor $\frac{1}{2\omega_k}$. We can get rid of this factor by using the rescaled momentum eigenstates that we already introduced in Eq. 8.45:

$$|1_k\rangle \equiv \sqrt{2\omega_k}\,|1_{\vec{k}}\rangle = \sqrt{2\omega_k}a^\dagger(\vec{k})\,|0\rangle \ . \tag{8.60}$$

If we repeat the calculation in Eq. 8.58 with this modified state, we find

$$\langle 1_{\vec{x}}|1_k\rangle = e^{-i\vec{k}\cdot\vec{x}} \,. \tag{8.61}$$

In any case, what we've discovered here lends further support to the idea that $|1_{\vec{x}}\rangle \equiv \phi(\vec{x})\,|0\rangle$ is at least somewhat analogous to the position eigenstates $|\vec{x}\rangle$ that we use in quantum mechanics.

As a final comment, note that we can understand why it's sometimes more convenient to work with $a(k)$, $a^\dagger(k)$, $|1_k\rangle$ instead of $a(\vec{k})$, $a^\dagger(\vec{k})$, $|1_{\vec{k}}\rangle$. In the latter case, we have a simpler inner product of momentum eigenstates (Eq. 8.44)

$$\langle 1_{\vec{k}}|1_{\vec{k}'}\rangle = (2\pi)^3\delta(\vec{k}-\vec{k}')\,, \tag{8.62}$$

compared to (Eq. 8.48)

$$\langle 1_k|1_{k'}\rangle = 2\omega_k(2\pi)^3\delta(\vec{k}-\vec{k}')\,. \tag{8.63}$$

However, if we use $a(k)$, $a^\dagger(k)$, $|1_k\rangle$ we find proper plane waves (Eq. 8.61)

$$\langle 1_{\vec{x}}|1_k\rangle = e^{-i\vec{k}\cdot\vec{x}} \tag{8.64}$$

which we can compare with (Eq. 8.58)

$$\langle 1_{\vec{x}}|1_{\vec{k}}\rangle = \frac{1}{\sqrt{2\omega_k}}e^{-i(\vec{k}\cdot\vec{x})}\,. \tag{8.65}$$

Ultimately, it's just a matter of taste which of the two conventions we use as long as we keep everything consistent.

8.4.2 The Uncertainty Relation

Now let's revisit the topic of uncertainty. On the one hand, we've discovered that the ket $|1_{\vec{x}}\rangle$ which describes an (almost) localized field excitation can be thought of as a superposition of infinitely many states with well-defined momenta (Eq. 8.56). In physical terms, this means that while we can be quite certain to find the field excitation at $\vec{x}$, we have no idea what its momentum is. Formulated differently, the field excitation is completely delocalized in momentum space. On the other hand, we discovered that a momentum eigenstate $|1_{\vec{k}}\rangle$ can be represented as a plane wave (Eq. 8.58). A plane wave spreads out all over space with equal amplitude. Thus, for a particle described by a plane wave, there is no way to answer the question: where exactly is the particle located?

This interplay between states with well-defined momentum and states with well-defined position is a key feature of quantum theories.

To understand why, let's consider a rope. We can generate a wave in a long rope by shaking it rhythmically up and down:

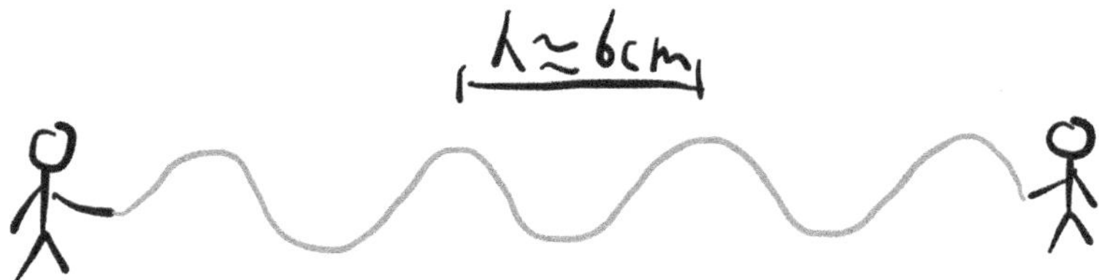

If someone were to ask us where the wave is, we wouldn't have a good answer since the wave is spread out. But if we are asked: "What's the wavelength of the wave?", we could easily answer this question and state: "It's around 6cm."

We can also generate a different kind of wave in a rope by jerking it only once.

This way, we get a narrow bump that travels down the line. For this kind of wave, we can easily answer the question: "Where precisely is the wave?". But we have a hard time answering the question: "What's the wavelength of this wave?", since the wave isn't periodic and it's completely unclear how (or if) we can assign a wavelength to it. Analogously, we can generate any kind of wave in between these two edge cases and there is always a trade-off. The more precisely the position of the wave is localized, the more ambiguous the wavelength becomes, and vice versa. To make this idea more precise, recall that we can think of a localized wave as a superposition of dozens of other waves with well-defined wave-lengths[19].

[19] Such waves with well-defined waves lengths are known as **plane waves**. The expansion of a general bump in terms of such plane waves is exactly the idea behind the Fourier transform. The uncertainty we end up with this way is a general feature of waves and known as the **bandwidth theorem**.

If we add lots of waves with different wavelengths, they will average out almost everywhere. But we can arrange the waves such that, in a small region, they don't cancel each other out. This is true for all waves. Since in quantum theories, we describe particles as field excitations, it also applies here. In quantum theories, the wavelength is directly related to its momentum (Eq. 7.1.7)

$$\lambda = \frac{h}{p} \tag{8.66}$$

The larger the momentum p, the smaller the wavelength λ of the wave that describes the particle. Therefore, a spread in wavelength corresponds to a spread in momentum. What this means in physical terms is exactly what we talked about above: We can't know the location and momentum of particles with arbitrary precision:

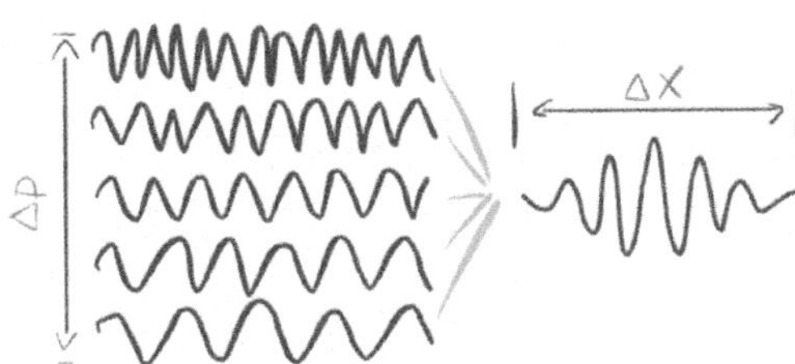

The uncertainty relation that we arrive at tells us:

> The more precisely we determine the location of a particle, the less precisely we are able to determine its momentum and vice versa.

8.4.3 Dealing with Non-Normalizable States

Above, we have learned that in the position basis the states with perfectly known momentum are represented by plane waves $\langle 1_{\vec{x}}|1_{\vec{k}}\rangle = e^{i\vec{k}\cdot\vec{x}}$.[20] As mentioned in the previous section, a problematic aspect of plane waves that already pops up in quantum mechanics is that they fill the entire space with equal amplitude. This implies that plane wave states are not normalizable.

[20] To unclutter the notation, we use the rescaled momentum vectors introduced in Eq. 8.60.

$$\begin{aligned}\langle 1_{\vec{k}}|1_{\vec{k}}\rangle &= \int_{-\infty}^{\infty} d^3x\, \langle 1_{\vec{k}}|1_{\vec{x}}\rangle\langle 1_{\vec{x}}|1_{\vec{k}}\rangle \quad \text{(Eq. 8.61)} \\ &= \int_{-\infty}^{\infty} d^3x\, e^{-i\vec{k}\cdot\vec{x}}e^{i\vec{k}\cdot\vec{x}} \\ &= \int_{-\infty}^{\infty} d^3x\, 1 = \infty\,. \end{aligned} \tag{8.67}$$

This nonsensical result shouldn't be too surprising. Whenever we talk about particles in the real-world we have at least some idea where they are localized in space. Thus plane wave states aren't something that we can observe in Nature. In the following section, we will discuss more realistic particle states. However, plane waves are extremely convenient from a mathematical point of view and therefore it makes sense to discuss how we can use them despite their problems.

One way out of this difficulty is to restrict ourselves to systems with finite volume V.[21] In this case, we find

[21] If we consider dynamical fields, we need to introduce a finite spacetime volume. This means that we imagine that our system lives in a finite box of volume V and that everything happens during a finite time span T. The corresponding spacetime volume reads VT.

$$\begin{aligned}\langle 1_k|1_k\rangle &= \int_V d^3x\, \langle 1_k|1_{\vec{x}}\rangle\langle 1_{\vec{x}}|1_k\rangle \\ &= \int_V d^3x\, 1 = V\,. \end{aligned} \tag{8.68}$$

Since V is some possibly large but finite number, we can normalize our plane wave states. The idea to only consider finite volumes is, of course, quite reasonable. In real-world experiments we always isolate a tiny subsystem from the rest of the universe and then try to predict what is going on within the isolated box. In addition, the actual volume of the box doesn't matter since it drops out from all of our predictions. For example, if we want to calculate the probability of finding the system in the state f after preparing it in the state i, we can work with non-normalized states as long as we restrict ourselves to ratios of probabilities

$$P(i \to f) = \frac{|\langle|f|U|i\rangle|^2}{\langle f|f\rangle \langle i|i\rangle}, \tag{8.69}$$

where U is an operator that describes how $|i\rangle$ changes in time. The factor $\langle f|f\rangle \langle i|i\rangle$ in the denominator makes sure that all dependencies on possible norms and thus on the spacetime volume V drop out from our predictions.

If we recall the integral representation of $\delta(\vec{k})$:

$$\delta(\vec{k}) = \int \frac{d^3x}{(2\pi)^3} e^{-i\vec{k}\cdot\vec{x}}, \tag{8.70}$$

we can use exactly the same steps as in Eq. 8.67 to derive a relation that is used quite often in quantum field theory:

$$\begin{aligned}
\delta(\vec{0}) &= \int_{-\infty}^{\infty} \frac{d^3x}{(2\pi)^3} e^{-i\vec{0}\cdot\vec{k}} \\
&= \lim_{V\to\infty} \int_V \frac{d^3x}{(2\pi)^3} 1 \\
&= \frac{1}{(2\pi)^3} \lim_{V\to\infty} \int_V d^3x \\
&= \frac{1}{(2\pi)^3} \lim_{V\to\infty} V\,.
\end{aligned} \tag{8.71}$$

This is often used to replace occurrences of $(2\pi)^3\delta(\vec{0})$ by V. If we do this everywhere, the volume V drops out and we can eventually take the limit $\lim_{V\to\infty}$ without problems.

The trick we just discussed is, in fact, standard practice in quantum field theory. The whole procedure can be summarized as follows:

1. We work with non-normalizable states like $|1_{\vec{k}}\rangle$ and infinite spacetime volumes because this simplifies many calculations.
2. Once most of the work is done, we make sure that we don't predict nonsensical things like a probability $\sim \infty$. Since a cancellation $\frac{\infty}{\infty}$ is not a sensible mathematical thing to do, we temporarily introduce a finite spacetime volume V which allows us to cancel all occurrences of V.
3. Finally, we can go back to an infinite spacetime volume ($V \to \infty$) if we want because V no longer plays a role in our formulas.

This may sound quite awkward and cumbersome, but you will quickly get used to it. Once we discuss explicit examples, you will see that this procedure is actually simpler than the alternatives.

In the next section, we will discuss an alternative way to handle non-normalizable states which is mathematically a bit more cumbersome but physically quite illuminating.

8.4.4 Wave Packets

When we observe and describe particles in the real world, we have at least some idea where they are located and know their momenta fairly well but not exactly. In the quantum framework, we describe such a situation by using a superposition of possible states

$$|1\rangle^{\text{sup}} = \sum_i c_i \, |\vec{k}_i\rangle = c_1 \, |\vec{k}_1\rangle + c_2 \, |\vec{k}_2\rangle + \ldots \qquad (8.72)$$

where c_i is the probability amplitude for the momentum vector $\vec{k}_i$. In words, this formula indicates that several values for the momentum of the particle are possible. Realistically, we usually only know that the momentum lies within some range around some central value $\vec{k}$. Therefore, we replace the sum by an integral and end up with

$$|1_{\vec{k}}\rangle^{\text{range}} = \int \frac{d^3k'}{(2\pi)^3} f(\vec{k},\vec{k}')\, |1_{\vec{k}'}\rangle\,, \tag{8.73}$$

where $f(\vec{k},\vec{k}')$ is a smearing function that describes how certain we are about different possible momenta. The most famous example is a Gaussian smearing function

$$f^{\text{Gauss}}(\vec{k},\vec{k}') \equiv N e^{-\frac{(\vec{k}-\vec{k}')^2}{2\sigma^2}}\,, \tag{8.74}$$

where N is a normalization constant. The ket in Eq. 8.73 represents a wave packet that encodes that we are somewhat certain to find our particle with momentum $\vec{k}$. The uncertainty is encoded in the width of the wave packet σ. We can check that $|1_{\vec{k}}\rangle^{\text{range}}$ is indeed properly normalized

$$
\begin{aligned}
&{}^{\text{range}}\langle 1_{\vec{k}}|1_{\vec{k}}\rangle^{\text{range}} \\
&= \left(\int \frac{d^3k'}{(2\pi)^3} f(\vec{k},\vec{k}')\, \langle 1_{\vec{k}'}|\right)\left(\int \frac{d^3k''}{(2\pi)^3} f(\vec{k},\vec{k}'')\, |1_{\vec{k}''}\rangle\right) && \text{Eq. 8.73} \\
&= \int \frac{d^3k'}{(2\pi)^3} \int \frac{d^3k''}{(2\pi)^3} f(\vec{k},\vec{k}') f(\vec{k},\vec{k}'')\, \langle 1_{\vec{k}'}|1_{\vec{k}''}\rangle && \\
&= \int \frac{d^3k'}{(2\pi)^3} \int \frac{d^3k''}{(2\pi)^3} f(\vec{k},\vec{k}') f(\vec{k},\vec{k}'') \Big((2\pi)^3 \delta(\vec{k}'-\vec{k}'')\Big) && \text{Eq. 8.44} \\
&= \int \frac{d^3k'}{(2\pi)^3} f(\vec{k},\vec{k}') f(\vec{k},\vec{k}') && \int dx' f(x')\delta(x-x') = f(x),\ \cancel{(2\pi)^3} \\
&= \int \frac{d^3k'}{(2\pi)^3} N^2 e^{-\frac{(\vec{k}-\vec{k}')^2}{\sigma^2}} && \text{Eq. 8.74} \\
&= \frac{N^2 \pi^{3/2} \sigma^3}{(2\pi)^3}\,. && \int_{-\infty}^{\infty} dx\, e^{-x^2} = \sqrt{\pi}
\end{aligned}
\tag{8.75}
$$

Therefore, we find

$$^{\text{range}}\langle 1_{\vec{k}} | 1_{\vec{k}} \rangle^{\text{range}} = 1 \tag{8.76}$$

if $N^2 = \frac{\pi^{3/2} 2^3}{\sigma^3}$. The exact value of this normalization is not that important for us. Far more important is that $|1_{\vec{k}}\rangle^{\text{range}}$ can indeed be normalized as opposed to the more idealized states $|1_{\vec{k}}\rangle$.

In summary, we use a ket of the form given in Eq. 8.73 whenever we are somewhat uncertain about the particle's momentum. In the real world, this is always the case. There are, however, as discussed in the previous section, tricks that are often used to avoid working with wave packets.

In the following section, we will talk about some of the most powerful tools in quantum field theory.

8.5 Propagators

We have discovered in the previous section that it's quite tempting to say that the ket (Eq. 8.53)

$$|1_{\vec{x}}\rangle \equiv \phi(\vec{x}) |0\rangle \tag{8.77}$$

describes a particle located at $\vec{x}$. In this section, we will see why this is not quite right. In quantum mechanics, we can define a position eigenstate $|\vec{x}\rangle$ which describes a particle located at $\vec{x}$. A defining property of this ket is that for all position eigenstates evaluated at equal times, we have

$$\langle \vec{x}' | \vec{x} \rangle = \delta(\vec{x}' - \vec{x}) \,. \tag{8.78}$$

In words this formula encodes that the particle is localized exactly at $\vec{x}$ since the probability amplitude to find it anywhere else is zero.[22] Therefore, to check if the field configuration described by $|1_{\vec{x}}\rangle$ is localized, we need to evaluate $\langle 1_{\vec{x}'} | 1_{\vec{x}} \rangle$. This is possible by using the explicit definition of $|1_{\vec{x}}\rangle$ in Eq. 8.56:

[22] This formula is only valid for a fixed moment in time. More explicitly we can write $\langle t, \vec{x}' | t, \vec{x} \rangle = \delta(\vec{x}' - \vec{x})$. In contrast, $\langle t', \vec{x}' | t, \vec{x} \rangle$ for $t' \neq t$ is not necessarily zero for $\vec{x}' \neq \vec{x}$ since the particle can travel from $\vec{x}$ to $\vec{x}'$ during the interval $\Delta t = t' - t$. For $t' = t$, the time interval is zero and thus there is no way our particle can travel anywhere as a result of the speed limit imposed by special relativity.

$$
\begin{aligned}
&D(t,\vec{x}',t,\vec{x}) \\
&\equiv \langle 1_{\vec{x}'}|1_{\vec{x}}\rangle && \text{definition} \\
&= \Big(\phi(\vec{x}')\,|0\rangle\Big)^\dagger \Big(\phi(\vec{x})\,|0\rangle\Big) \\
&= \Big(\int dk'^3 \frac{1}{(2\pi)^3\sqrt{2\omega_{k'}}} e^{i(\vec{k}'\cdot\vec{x}')}\,|1_{\vec{k}'}\rangle\Big)^\dagger \Big(\int dk^3 \frac{1}{(2\pi)^3\sqrt{2\omega_k}} e^{i(\vec{k}\cdot\vec{x})}\,|1_{\vec{k}}\rangle\Big) && \text{Eq. 8.56} \\
&= \Big(\int dk'^3 \frac{1}{(2\pi)^3\sqrt{2\omega_{k'}}} e^{-i(\vec{k}'\cdot\vec{x}')}\,\langle 1_{\vec{k}'}|\Big) \Big(\int dk^3 \frac{1}{(2\pi)^3\sqrt{2\omega_k}} e^{i(\vec{k}\cdot\vec{x})}\,|1_{\vec{k}}\rangle\Big) && |\psi\rangle^\dagger = \langle\psi| \\
&= \int dk'^3 \int dk^3 \frac{1}{(2\pi)^6\sqrt{2\omega_{k'}}\sqrt{2\omega_k}} e^{-i(\vec{k}'\cdot\vec{x}')} e^{i(\vec{k}\cdot\vec{x})}\,\langle 1_{\vec{k}'}|1_{\vec{k}}\rangle && \text{sorting} \\
&= \int dk'^3 \int dk^3 \frac{1}{(2\pi)^6\sqrt{2\omega_{k'}}\sqrt{2\omega_k}} e^{-i(\vec{k}'\cdot\vec{x}')} e^{i(\vec{k}\cdot\vec{x})}\big((2\pi)^3\delta(\vec{k}-\vec{k}')\big) && \text{Eq. 8.44} \\
&= \int \frac{dk^3}{(2\pi)^3 2\omega_k} e^{-i(\vec{k}\cdot\vec{x}')} e^{i(\vec{k}\cdot\vec{x})} && \int dx' f(x')\delta(x-x') = f(x) \\
&= \int \frac{dk^3}{(2\pi)^3 2\omega_k} e^{-i\vec{k}\cdot(\vec{x}'-\vec{x})}\,, && (8.79)
\end{aligned}
$$

where, as usual, $\omega_k \equiv \sqrt{\vec{k}^2+m^2}$. The most important observation in Eq. 8.79 is that it is not exactly an integral representation of the delta distribution, which reads

$$\delta(\vec{x}-\vec{x}') = \int \frac{dk^3}{(2\pi)^3} e^{-i\vec{k}\cdot(\vec{x}'-\vec{x})}\,. \tag{8.80}$$

The difference between Eq. 8.79 and Eq. 8.80 is the factor $2\omega_k$ in the denominator. This detail is important because it tells us that $\langle 1_{\vec{x}'}|1_{\vec{x}}\rangle$ is not equal to a delta distribution. Therefore, we can conclude that the field excitation described by $|1_{\vec{x}}\rangle$ is not localized at a single point.

This becomes even more obvious if we believe our colleagues from the math department who tell us that in the limit of large distances $r \gg 1$ the complicated integral here behaves like e^{-mr}. Moreover, they tell us that there is a singularity for $r \to 0$.[23]

[23] To see that the integral diverges for $r \to 0$, we observe that $r \to 0$ implies $\vec{x} \to \vec{x}'$ and thus the integral reduces to

$$\int \frac{dk^3}{(2\pi)^3 2\omega_k} e^{-i\vec{k}\cdot(\vec{x}-\vec{x})} = \int \frac{dk^3}{(2\pi)^3 2\omega_k}\,.$$

This integral diverges for the same reasons the integral $\int_{-\infty}^{\infty} dx \frac{1}{\sqrt{x^2+m^2}}$ diverges since $\omega_k \equiv \sqrt{\vec{k}^2+m^2}$. While this may seem problematic, take note that the same comments as for the result (Eq. 8.44) $\langle 1_{\vec{k}}|1_{\vec{k}'}\rangle = (2\pi)^3\delta(\vec{k}-\vec{k}')$ apply. We get diverging probability amplitudes because we consider unrealistic states that we cannot observe in the real world.

Thus even though there is a peak at $r = 0$, we only find an exponentially decaying amplitude if we move away from $r = 0$ and not a completely vanishing amplitude.

We can also see this more visually by evaluating the integral numerically.[24] The result of such a numerical integration is schematically shown in the following figure:

[24] Note that the integral in Eq. 8.79 can be solved analytically

$$\langle 1_{\vec{x}'} | 1_{\vec{x}} \rangle = \frac{m}{4\pi^2 r} K_1(mr), \qquad (8.81)$$

where $r \equiv |\vec{x} - \vec{x}'|$ and K_1 denotes the so-called modified Bessel function. Since the Bessel function cannot be expressed in terms of elementary functions this is probably not very illuminating.

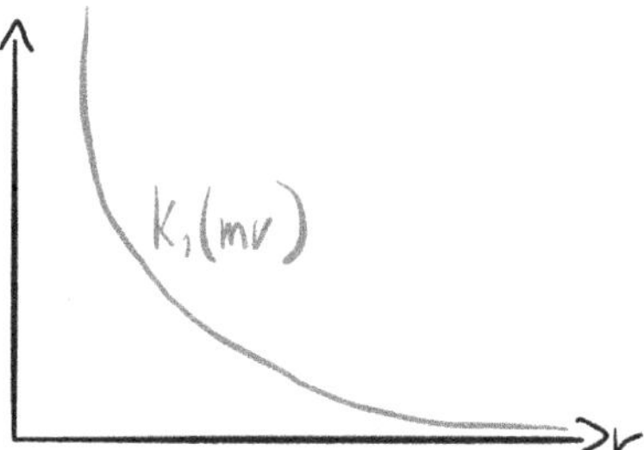

In physical terms this implies that there is a non-zero probability to find a non-zero field excitation at other locations $\vec{x}'$, as long as they are sufficiently close to $\vec{x}$. For a real delta peak, the probability is exactly zero except for $\vec{x}' = \vec{x}$. In summary, a particle-like field excitation is not completely localized in quantum field theory.

8.5.1 Dynamical Propagators

In the previous section, we've talked about the probability amplitude of finding the particle at location x' at the same moment in time that it was prepared at the location x. For the sake of clarity, from here on we will say that $|1_{\vec{x}}\rangle$ describes a particle $\vec{x}$. By using the particle language, we say that $\langle 1_{\vec{x}'} | 1_{\vec{x}} \rangle$ is the probability amplitude to find the particle that we prepared at the location $\vec{x}$ at the same moment in time at the location $\vec{x}'$.

The situation gets even more interesting if we consider the probability amplitudes for transitions between different moments in time. Completely analogous to what we did in Eq. 8.79, we can calculate that this more general probability amplitude reads

$$D(t',\vec{x}',t,\vec{x}) \equiv \langle 1_{t',\vec{x}'}|1_{t,\vec{x}}\rangle = \int \frac{dk^3}{(2\pi)^3 2\omega_k} e^{i\left(\omega_k\cdot(t'-t)-\vec{k}\cdot(\vec{x}'-\vec{x})\right)}$$
$$= \int \frac{dk^3}{(2\pi)^3 2\omega_k} e^{ik^\mu(x'_\mu - x_\mu)} \,. \qquad (8.82)$$

This is the probability amplitude to find a particle that we prepared at $\vec{x}$ at t, at the position $\vec{x}'$ at t'. We call $D(t',\vec{x}',t,\vec{x})$ the **propagator**.[25] For equal times $t = t'$ this is exactly the amplitude that we found in Eq. 8.79. In words, the amplitude in Eq. 8.79 contains information about the static structure of our field, while the amplitude in Eq. 8.82 also contains information about how a field changes dynamically.

[25] We will discuss several special propagators below. This is the basic building block of all propagators.

Instead of studying the general amplitude in Eq. 8.82 it makes sense to isolate the dynamical behavior by keeping the location we consider fixed. In other words, analogous to how we considered the equal times ($t = t'$) special case in the previous section, we now consider the equal positions ($\vec{x} = \vec{x}'$) special case of Eq. 8.82. By using Eq. 8.82 we can immediately write down the amplitude of finding the particle at a possibly different moment in time at the same location:

$$D(t',\vec{x},t,\vec{x}) \equiv \langle 1_{t',\vec{x}}|1_{t,\vec{x}}\rangle$$

(Eq. 8.82 with $\vec{x} = \vec{x}'$)

$$= \int \frac{dk^3}{(2\pi)^3 2\omega_k} e^{i\left(\omega_k\cdot(t'-t)-\vec{k}\cdot(\vec{x}-\vec{x})\right)}$$

($\vec{x} - \vec{x} = 0$)

$$= \int \frac{dk^3}{(2\pi)^3 2\omega_k} e^{i\omega_k\cdot(t'-t)}$$

($\omega_k \equiv \sqrt{\vec{k}^2 + m^2}$)

$$= \int \frac{dk^3}{(2\pi)^3 2\sqrt{\vec{k}^2+m^2}} e^{i\sqrt{\vec{k}^2+m^2}\cdot(t'-t)} \qquad (8.83)$$

This amplitude is very different from the static amplitude (Eq. 8.79) that we considered in the previous section.[26] This becomes especially obvious if we ask our friends from the math

[26] For your convenience: Eq. 8.79 reads

$$\langle 1_{t,\vec{x}'}|1_{t,\vec{x}}\rangle = \int \frac{dk^3}{(2\pi)^3 2\omega_k} e^{-i\vec{k}\cdot(\vec{x}'-\vec{x})} \,.$$

department once more who tell us that for long time spans $T \equiv |t' - t| \gg 1$, the integral in Eq. 8.83 behaves like e^{imT}. In contrast, the static amplitude (Eq. 8.79) behaves in the long range limit $r \gg 1$ like e^{-mr}. The imaginary unit in the exponent makes all the difference. While e^{-mr} is a rapidly vanishing function, e^{-imT} oscillates up and down forever.

This makes perfect sense from a physical point of view. The fact that the static amplitude (Eq. 8.79) vanishes rapidly tells us that elementary field excitations are quite localized (but not completely). In contrast, the fact that the dynamical equal position amplitude oscillates indefinitely means that its quite likely to find an elementary field excitation at a different moment in time at the same location.

We are almost ready to talk about the general amplitude (Eq. 8.82) which encodes information about the likelihood that a particle moves from one location $\vec{x}$ at t to a different location $\vec{x}'$ at a different moment in time t'. But first, we need to talk about one subtlety.

8.5.2 Advanced and Retarded Propagators

In the previous section, I've tried to be careful and only talked about *different* moments in time and never about earlier or later moments in time. In this section, we will try to introduce notions like "earlier" and "later" into our formalism.

From a mathematical point of view, we can consider the amplitude $D(t', \vec{x}', t, \vec{x}) \equiv \langle 1_{t',\vec{x}'} | 1_{t,\vec{x}} \rangle$ (Eq. 8.82) for $t' > t$, for $t = t'$ and for $t' < t$ without problems. But let's try to put into words what the amplitude describes in these cases:

▷ For $t' > t$, the amplitude $D(t', \vec{x}', t, \vec{x})$ tells us how likely it is that we find the particle at $\vec{x}'$ at some *later* point in time t' if we prepare it at $\vec{x}$ at time t.

- ▷ For $t' = t$, the amplitude $D(t', \vec{x}', t, \vec{x})$ tells us how likely it is that we find the particle at $\vec{x}'$ if we prepare it at $\vec{x}$ at the same moment in time t.
- ▷ For $t' < t$, the amplitude $D(t', \vec{x}', t, \vec{x})$ tells us how likely it is that the particle was at $\vec{x}'$ at some *earlier* point in time t' if it is at $\vec{x}$ at time t. This case can be quite confusing because here we consider a "final state" which is located at an earlier moment in time.

If we want to use the amplitude $\langle 1_{t',\vec{x}} | 1_{t,\vec{x}} \rangle$ to predict how a given field configuration evolves in time, we need to make sure that $t' > t$. In contrast, for $t' < t$ we can use the amplitude $\langle 1_{t',\vec{x}} | 1_{t,\vec{x}} \rangle$ to find out where a given field configuration came from.

Mathematically, we can describe this by using the so-called Heaviside step function $\Theta(x)$ which is zero for $x < 0$ and equal to one for $x > 0$.[27] This can be summarized by writing

[27] In case it is needed, it is conventional to define that $\Theta(0) = \frac{1}{2}$.

$$\theta = \begin{cases} 0, & x < 0, \\ 1, & x > 0. \end{cases} \tag{8.84}$$

Or graphically

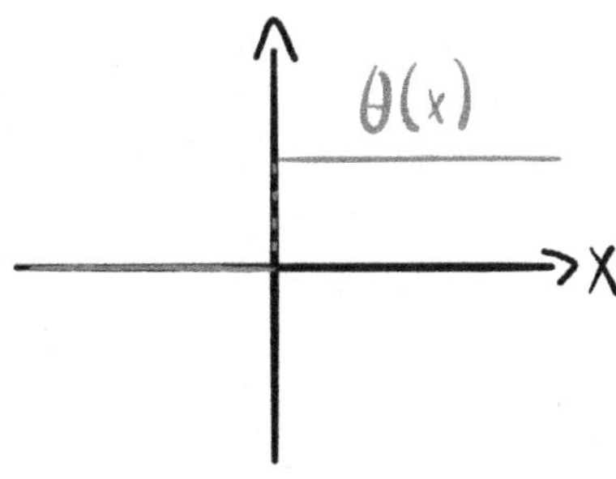

With this new tool at hand, we can make sure that $t' > t$ by

writing

$$D_R(t',\vec{x}',t,\vec{x}) \equiv \Theta(t'-t)D(t',\vec{x}',t,\vec{x})\,, \tag{8.85}$$

which is called the **retarded propagator**. This amplitude is zero for $t' < t$ since in this case $t' - t < 0$ and therefore $\Theta(t'-t) = 0$. Thus we can write it equivalently as

$$D_R(t',\vec{x}',t,\vec{x}) = \begin{cases} D(t',\vec{x}',t,\vec{x}) & t' > t \\ 0 & t' < t \end{cases}. \tag{8.86}$$

In summary, by multiplying the general propagator $D(t',\vec{x}',t,\vec{x})$ (Eq. 8.82) by the Heaviside function $\Theta(t'-t)$ we can make sure that we only consider final states which live in spacetime at a future point in time. Formulated differently, the retarded propagator allows us to understand how a field configuration influences the field configuration in the future.[28]

[28] Take note that different books call different objects *the* retarded propagator. One object that is often called the retarded propagator is

$\tilde{D}_R(t',\vec{x}',t,\vec{x}) \equiv$
$\Theta(t'-t)\Big(D(t',\vec{x}',t,\vec{x}) - D(t,\vec{x},t',\vec{x}')\Big)$

The reason for this definition is that this object is a (retarded) Green's function of the Klein-Gordon equation, while the object I called the retarded propagator is not a Green's function. We will discuss this more explicitly below in the context of the Feynman propagator which plays a more important role in quantum field theory than the retarded propagator. A closely related way of motivating this more complicated retarded propagator is by recalling that we observed that the elementary equal-time propagator $D(t,\vec{x},t,\vec{x}')\Big)$ behaves in the long distance limit $r = \sqrt{(\vec{x}-\vec{x}')^2} \gg 1$ like e^{-mr}. This is somewhat problematic because it implies that distant points can influence each other even though no time passes which is against the spirit of special relativity.
But if we consider the difference $D(t,\vec{x}',t,\vec{x}) - D(t,\vec{x},t,\vec{x}')$ we get an object that vanishes in the long distance limit since the two factors of e^{-mr} cancel. In words this implies that the amplitude for a particle to go from $\vec{x}$ to $\vec{x}'$ cancels exactly with the amplitude for a particle to go from $\vec{x}'$ to $\vec{x}$. Thus, we get an object this way that is no longer at odds with the laws of special relativity. For this reason the object defined above is often also called the causal propagator.

Analogously, we can define the **advanced propagator**[29]

$$D_A(t',\vec{x}',t,\vec{x}) \equiv \Theta(t-t')D(t',\vec{x}',t,\vec{x})\,. \tag{8.87}$$

[29] The comments made in the sidenote above about alternative objects that are called the retarded propagator also apply for the advanced propagator.

The only difference to the retarded propagator is that we switched the place of t and t' in the argument of the Heaviside function. Therefore, this amplitude is only non-zero for $t' < t$. We can write it equivalently as

$$D_R(t',\vec{x}',t,\vec{x}) = \begin{cases} 0 & t' > t \\ D(t',\vec{x}',t,\vec{x}) & t' < t \end{cases}. \tag{8.88}$$

We can use the advanced propagator to understand how a given field configuration was influenced by field configurations in the past.

8.5.3 The Feynman Propagator

There is another propagator that we should talk about since it will become incredibly important in subsequent chapters. We will discover that if we want to calculate the probabilities of different scattering processes, we regularly encounter expressions of the form[30]

$$\int d^4x \int d^4x' \langle 0|T\phi(t,\vec{x})\phi(t',\vec{x}')|0\rangle \,, \tag{8.89}$$

[30] We will derive in Section 9.3 why the time ordering operator enters our description.

where T is the time ordering operator that is defined as follows:

$$T\phi(t,\vec{x})\phi(t',\vec{x}') = \begin{cases} \phi(t,\vec{x})\phi(t',\vec{x}') & \text{for } t > t' \\ \phi(t',\vec{x}')\phi(t,\vec{x}) & \text{for } t < t' \end{cases} . \tag{8.90}$$

This motivates us to consider the time-ordered propagator

$$D_F(t',\vec{x}',t,\vec{x}) \equiv \langle 0|T\phi(t,\vec{x})\phi(t',\vec{x}')|0\rangle \,, \tag{8.91}$$

which is commonly called the **Feynman propagator**.

To understand the Feynman propagator a bit better, take note that we can write down time-ordered products in more explicit terms by using the Heaviside function (Eq. 8.84):

$$T\phi(t,\vec{x})\phi(t',\vec{x}') = \Theta(t-t')\phi(t,\vec{x})\phi(t',\vec{x}') + \Theta(t'-t)\phi(t',\vec{x}')\phi(t,\vec{x}) \,. \tag{8.92}$$

This is correct because $\Theta(t-t')$ is only non-zero for $t > t'$ and therefore t' describes an earlier moment in time. Similarly the Heaviside function that appears in the second term $\Theta(t'-t)$ is only non-zero for $t < t'$ and therefore $\phi(t',\vec{x}')\phi(t,\vec{x})$ only contributes something if t is indeed an earlier moment in time.

Therefore, we can write the Feynman propagator as

$$D_F(t',\vec{x}',t,\vec{x}) \equiv \Theta(t'-t)D(t',\vec{x}',t,\vec{x}) + \Theta(t-t')D(t,\vec{x},t',\vec{x}') \,. \tag{8.93}$$

where $D(t', \vec{x}', t, \vec{x}) \equiv \langle 0|\phi(t', \vec{x}')\phi(t, \vec{x})|0\rangle = \langle 1_{t',\vec{x}'}|1_{t,\vec{x}}\rangle$ (Eq. 8.82).

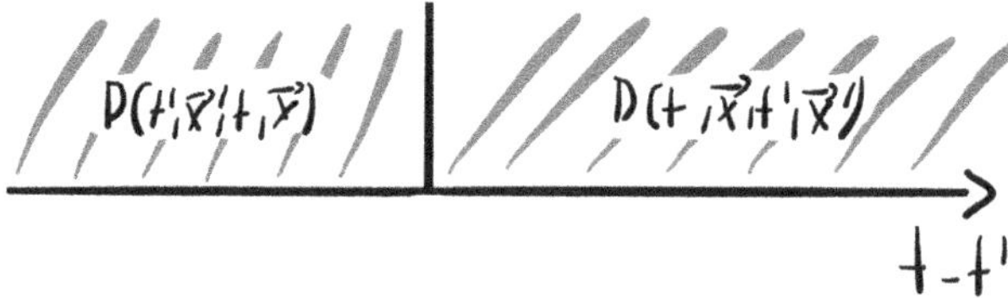

In words, the Feynman propagator is the probability amplitude that for $t' > t$ a field excitation moves from $\vec{x}$ to $\vec{x}'$ and that for $t > t'$ an excitation moves from $\vec{x}'$ to $\vec{x}$. If we look at the Feynman propagator in isolation it's quite hard to understand why we should care about this particular amplitude. However, as mentioned above, we care about the Feynman propagator because it appears in formulas that we use to calculate the probabilities of different scattering processes. Thus it is important to keep in mind that the role of the Feynman propagator is quite different from the role played by the retarded propagator discussed in the previous section. We use the retarded propagator to calculate the probability of finding a particle at a specific location at a later point in time. In contrast, the role played by the Feynman propagator is analogous to the role played by the Green's functions discussed in Chapter 6.[31]

[31] In fact, the Feynman propagator *is* a Green's function as we will discuss below.

A Green's function is a damping factor that allows us to calculate how the field value at a specific location is influenced by the field values elsewhere. The impact of non-zero field values gets smaller if we move further away from the location in question. How exactly the impact gets smaller depends on the field at hand and is described in mathematically precise terms by the corresponding Green's function.

The prototypical situation that we consider in quantum field theory is two particles scattering off of each other. In our framework, particles are field excitations and the Feynman propagator is, like the classical Green's functions, a damping factor that tells us exactly how the particles influence each other.

Let's say particle A is located at $\vec{x}_0$ at time t_0, at $\vec{x}_1$ at time t_1 and at $\vec{x}_2$ at time t_2, where $t_0 < t_1 < t_2$. Moreover, we imagine that a second particle B flies by and is at $\vec{y}_0$ at time t_0, at $\vec{y}_1$ at time t_1 and at $\vec{y}_2$ at time t_2.

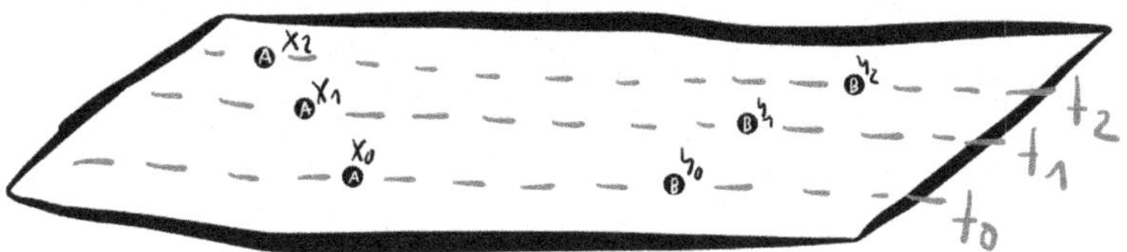

Since in quantum theories we always make probabilistic predictions, we need to take all possible ways the two particles can interact with each other into account if we want to describe the scattering process properly. This means that we need to take into account how the non-zero field value at $\vec{y}_0, \vec{y}_1, \vec{y}_2$ at different times influences the field values at $\vec{x}_0, \vec{x}_1, \vec{x}_2$.[32]

[32] For the sake of argument, we say that a particle corresponds to a non-zero field value.

To start with, let's consider particle A at a fixed moment in time t_1. How is it influenced by the second particle B? A first idea could be that we only need to know that the second particle B is at t_1 at $\vec{y}_1$ and then use an appropriate damping factor to calculate how this influences particle A. But this isn't correct. To understand why, let's imagine that the two particles represent quite localized spikes in the field that cause little ripples in the field all the time. It's through these ripples that particles influence each other.[33] But we know from special relativity that there is an upper speed limit and thus these ripples need time to travel from the location of particle B to the location of particle A. Moreover, since particle B sends out these ripples all the time, all of its past positions potentially play a role.

[33] This is just an illustrative picture and please don't take it too seriously. In addition, take note that it is conventional to talk about these ripples by using the notion of virtual particles. We will discuss this in more detail below.

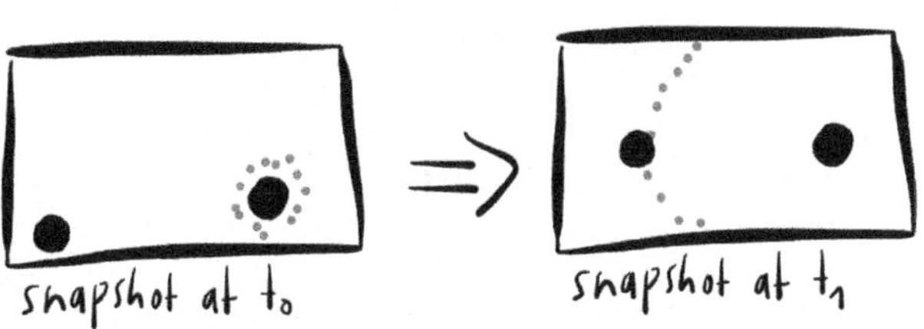

Mathematically, this means we need to integrate over t in order to take all the ways particle B influences particle A into account. If we say for concreteness that $\vec{x}'$, t' describe the spacetime point of particle A and $\vec{x}$, t describe the spacetime point of particle B. The first term in the Feynman propagator (Eq. 8.93) $\Theta(t' - t)D(t', \vec{x}', t, \vec{x})$ describes how ripples move from past locations of particle B to the present location of particle A. The Heaviside function makes sure that we only include past locations.

In contrast, the second term in the Feynman propagator (Eq. 8.93) $\Theta(t - t')D(t, \vec{x}, t', \vec{x}')$ yields the probability amplitude that a field excitation that starts at the location of A hits exactly the future position of B. This may seem extremely puzzling at first but can be understood as follows.

First of all, take note that a particle is not only affected when a ripple hits it but also when it sends out a ripple. This is somewhat analogous to how the trajectory of a boat changes if it is hit by a ball, but also when we throw a ball whilst we are standing on the boat.

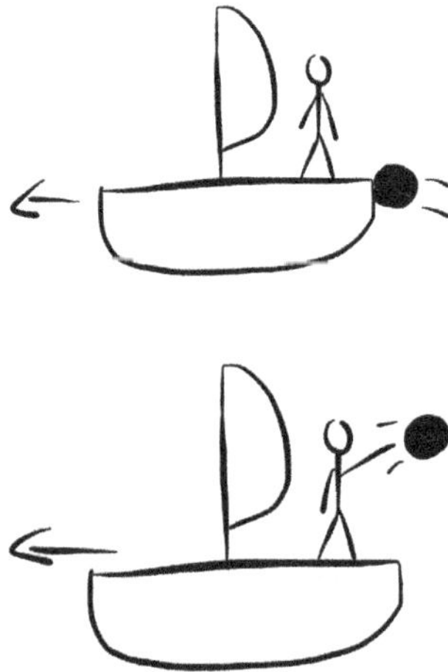

A key idea in our quantum framework is that while we can

imagine that each particle sends out ripples all the time, only those ripples that hit other particles have an impact on the particle that sent them.

Think of the ripples as probes that each particle sends out all the time. This continuous process of sending out probes has no immediate effect on the particle. If, however, one of the probes hits another particle, the particle that sent the probe is affected too.[34] This makes sense if we think, for example, about conservation of momentum. If one of the probes hits another particle, its momentum gets changed and hence, if momentum is conserved, the particle that sent the probe must provide the required momentum and thus is also affected.[35]

[34] A reader (Eran Zamir) suggested that it might be useful to think of the probes as being somewhat analogous to the spokes of a bike wheel. Using this metaphor, we have to imagine that these spokes get longer as time moves on. The metaphor is helpful since it makes clearer that the sending particle can "feel" what happens to the probes.

[35] As usual in quantum theory it's best to not take all of this too literally. There are no probes that are sent out continuously. This follows because they have absolutely no effect unless they hit another particle. We will see in the next chapter in mathematical terms how these "virtual particles" (probes) enter the stage.

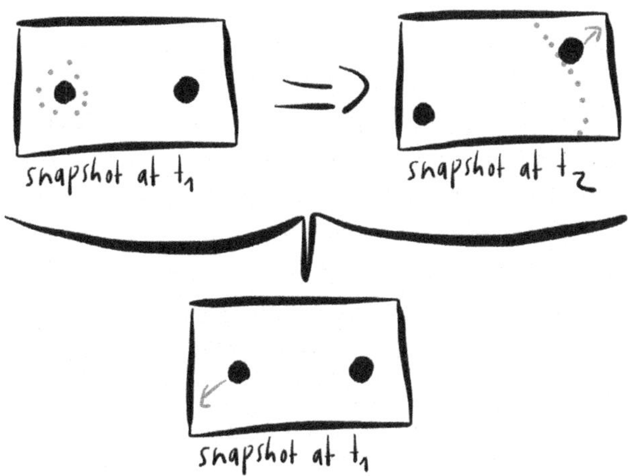

This is where the second term in the Feynman propagator comes into play. As mentioned above, this second term is the probability amplitude that a field excitation that starts at the location of particle A hits exactly the future position of particle B. Thus, this is precisely what we need to calculate (in probabilistic terms) which probe will hit particle B and thus affects the state of particle A.

The total effect on a particle is therefore determined by two factors:

▷ How it is hit by the probes that are sent out by other particles. We can calculate this contribution by using the first factor in the Feynman propagator that encodes the probability amplitude that a probe moves from a location in the past to the present location of the particle.

▷ How the probes it sends out itself hit other particles. This contribution requires that we calculate how the probes move to different locations in the future. The second term in the Feynman propagator encodes the probability amplitude for this to happen.

For completeness, let me mention another way to think about the Feynman propagator which is more standard but also more puzzling. In this interpretation (known as the Feynman-Stückelberg interpretation), we imagine that particle A is affected by "virtual particles" (ripples) that were sent out by particle B in the past and by virtual antiparticles that are sent out by particle B in the future. In other words, in this interpretation we imagine that particle A is only affected when it is hit by virtual particles that are sent out by particle B. However, some of these probes move backwards in time. They start from a future position of B at some future point in time and then hit exactly the location of particle A in the present.

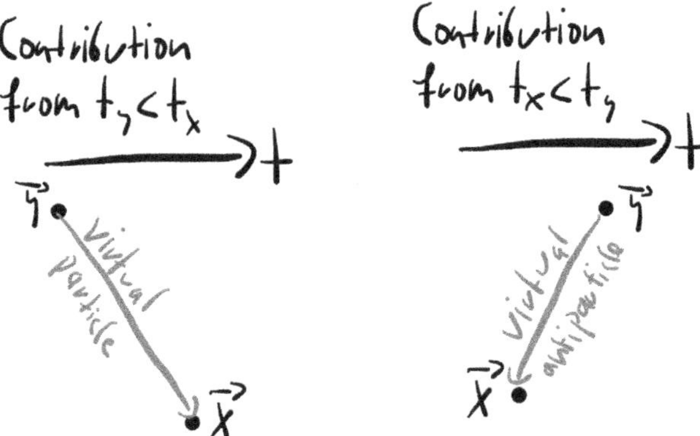

We will talk about antiparticles in more detail in Section 8.6.

The Feynman propagator $D_F(y_\mu, x_\mu)$ has an illuminating property. It's a Green's function of the Klein-Gordon equation:[36]

$$\left(\partial_\mu \partial^\mu + m^2\right) D_F(y_\mu, x_\mu) = i\delta(x_\mu - y_\mu)\,, \tag{8.94}$$

where the factor i is a convention that we could equally absorb into our definition of $D_F(y_\mu, x_\mu)$. This is why the Feynman propagator plays such an important role in our description of how quantum fields interact with each other.

[36] To unclutter the notation we define here $x_\mu \equiv (t, \vec{x})$ and $y_\mu \equiv (t', \vec{x}')$. Reminder: the defining property of a Green's function is that it yields the delta distribution if we plug it into the corresponding equation. In intuitive terms, a Green's function encodes the field's response to a delta-shaped source. We discussed this in Section 6.1.2.

We already learned in Chapter 6 that Green's functions are exactly what we need to describe how fields behave in the presence of interactions. We will see in the next chapter that this is again true in quantum field theory. An important observation is that it's the time-ordering that makes the Feynman propagator a Green's function. One hint of why this is true is the fact that the derivative of the Heaviside function is the delta distribution

$$\frac{d\Theta(x)}{dx} = \delta(x)\,. \tag{8.95}$$

Intuitively this follows because the slope of $\Theta(x)$ is only non-zero at $x = 0$ where it is infinitely steep since the jump from 0 to 1 is discontinuous. We explicitly check in Appendix A.7 that the Feynman propagator is a Green's function.

In contrast, the elementary propagator (Eq. 8.82)[37]

$$D(t', \vec{x}', t, \vec{x}) \equiv \langle 0|\phi(t, \vec{x})\phi(t', \vec{x}')|0\rangle = \langle 1_{t',\vec{x}'}|1_{t,\vec{x}}\rangle \tag{8.96}$$

is not a Green's function. This follows immediately if we plug it into the Klein-Gordon equation, as shown in Appendix A.7. Instead, we find that the elementary propagator is a solution of the free Klein-Gordon equation.[38] In other words, if we plug $D(t', \vec{x}', t, \vec{x})$ into the Klein-Gordon equation, we find zero and not a delta distribution:

$$\left(\partial_\mu \partial^\mu + m^2\right) D(y_\mu, x_\mu) = 0\,. \tag{8.97}$$

[37] Take note that what I call the elementary propagator here is usually known as the Wightman function or two-point correlation function.

[38] Mathematically, $D(t', \vec{x}', t, \vec{x})$ is the kernel of the Klein-Gordon equation. In many cases the Green's function of an equation can be understood as the product of the kernel times a Heaviside function.

This is why the more complicated looking Feynman propagator plays a more important role than the elementary propagator for interacting quantum fields — even though, of course, the elementary propagator is an essential building block of the Feynman propagator.

A somewhat confusing aspect of the Feynman propagator is that it has many faces. We have already encountered two of them (Eq. 8.91, Eq. 8.93).[39] The most popular way to write the Feynman propagator, however, looks like this:

$$D_F(y_\mu, x_\mu) = \int \frac{d^4k}{(2\pi)^4} \frac{i\, e^{-ik^\mu(x_\mu - y_\mu)}}{k_\mu k^\mu - m^2 + i\epsilon} . \tag{8.98}$$

We will not discuss the steps that allow us to bring Eq. 8.93 into the form given in Eq. 8.98 since this requires a lot of mathematical machinery that we don't really need for our modest purposes in this book.[40] However, we can understand the final form of the propagator given here because we've discussed above that the Feynman propagator is a Green's function of the Klein-Gordon equation (Eq. 8.94) and the formula given here is almost exactly the Klein-Gordon Green's function (Eq. 6.14) that we discussed in Section 6.1.2. [41] The only significant difference is the term $i\epsilon$ in the denominator which encodes time-ordering in an extremely sophisticated mathematical way.

Since we talked about quite a few similar but still different notions in the previous section, it makes sense to quickly recap what we've learned about propagators.

[39] For your convenience: Eq. 8.91 reads

$$D_F(y_\mu, x_\mu) \equiv \langle 0|T\phi(x_\mu)\phi(y_\mu)|0\rangle$$

and Eq. 8.93 reads

$$D_F(y_\mu, x_\mu) \equiv \Theta(t'-t)D(y_\mu, x_\mu) + \Theta(t-t')D(x_\mu, y_\mu).$$

Take note that, as before, we use the notation $x_\mu \equiv (t, \vec{x})$ and $y_\mu \equiv (t', \vec{x}')$.

[40] An important hint is the integral representation of the Heaviside function:

$$\Theta(t-t') = i\int_{-\infty}^{\infty} \frac{dz}{2\pi} \frac{e^{iz(t-t')}}{z + i\epsilon} .$$

You can find an understandable discussion at http://www.quantumfieldtheory.info/Derivation_of_the_Propagator.pdf

[41] Reminder: Eq. 6.14 reads

$$\phi_s(x_\mu, y_\mu) = \int \frac{d^4k}{(2\pi)^4} \frac{e^{-ik^\mu(x_\mu - y_\mu)}}{-k_\mu k^\mu + m^2} .$$

Moreover take note that the conventional form of the Feynman propagator given here yields $-i\delta(x_\mu - y_\mu)$ if we plug it into the Klein-Gordon equation, while the Green's function in Eq. 6.14 yields $\delta(x_\mu - y_\mu)$. The additional factor $-i$ is really just a convention with no deeper meaning.

8.5.4 Summary

The basic building block of all of the propagators that we discussed in this section is the elementary propagator $D(t', \vec{x}', t, \vec{x})$ (Eq. 8.82). This propagator is the probability amplitude for an elementary field excitation to move from $\vec{x}$ at time t to $\vec{x}'$ at time t'. We considered two special cases to get a better understanding of it. Firstly, we discussed the static propagator $D(t, \vec{x}', t, \vec{x})$ (Eq. 8.79), which is the elementary propagator for equal time ($t = t'$) but possibly different locations ($\vec{x} \neq \vec{x}'$).[42] The static propagator is the probability amplitude that we find an elementary field excitation that we prepared at $\vec{x}$ at the same moment in time at another location $\vec{x}'$. Surprisingly, this amplitude is non-zero for $\vec{x} \neq \vec{x}'$. But this doesn't mean that a particle can move around even though no time passes which would imply a velocity above the speed limit imposed by special relativity. Instead, this result suggests that it's impossible to localize a field excitation in quantum field theory beyond a certain limit.[43] Moreover, we discussed that $D(t, \vec{x}', t, \vec{x})$ vanishes like e^{-mr} for large distances $r \equiv |\vec{x} - \vec{x}'| \gg 1$.

[42] Alternative names for what I call the static propagator are equal-times propagator or spacelike propagator.

[43] A popular explanation is that this is a result of the non-trivial vacuum structure of quantum fields (think: boiling sea) which we will discuss in more detail in Chapter 14.

The second special case that we considered was for a fixed position ($\vec{x} = \vec{x}'$) at different times ($t \neq t'$). The probability amplitude to find a field excitation at a later moment in time at the same position is given by the dynamical propagator $D(t', \vec{x}, t, \vec{x})$ (Eq. 8.83).[44] In this case, we found that in the long timespan limit $T \equiv |t - t'| \gg 1$ the amplitude oscillates like $\sim e^{-imT}$. We then moved on and talked about other propagators that we can construct by using the elementary propagator. An important example is the retarded propagator $D_R(t', \vec{x}', t, \vec{x})$ (Eq. 8.85) which describes the probability amplitude that a field excitation moves from $\vec{x}$ at time t to $\vec{x}'$ at time t' and is only non-zero for $t' > t$. Thus, the retarded propagator allows us to calculate how a field excitation evolves in the future. A second example is the advanced propagator $D_A(t', \vec{x}', t, \vec{x})$ (Eq. 8.87)) which is only non-zero for $t' < t$ and thus allows us to understand the past of a given field configuration.

[44] An alternative name for this propagator is a timelike propagator.

The final propagator we talked about is the Feynman propagator $D_F(t', \vec{x}', t, \vec{x})$ (Eq. 8.91). We construct it by time-ordering the elementary propagator.[45] The Feynman propagator is primarily important in scattering processes as we will see in the next chapter. A strong hint for this role of the Feynman propagator is that it's, unlike the elementary propagator, a Green's function of the Klein-Gordon equation.[46] Although we postponed a proper discussion of scattering processes to the next chapter, we already developed some rough understanding of what the Feynman propagator describes. First of all, the Feynman propagator consists of two parts. The first one is the probability amplitude that a field excitation starts at a specific location in the past and ends up exactly at the location that we are interested in. The second part is the probability amplitude that a field excitation starts at the location that we are interested in and then moves exactly to a specific location in the future. These two probability amplitudes are important if we want to understand how different particles interact with each other. The first part of the Feynman propagator encodes how a particle is affected by the virtual particles that are sent out by a second particle. The second part encodes how the particle is affected by the virtual particles that it sends out itself which hit exactly the second particle in the future. All of this is summarized in the following diagram:

[45] Just for completeness, take note that there is also an anti-time ordered propagator which is commonly known as the Dyson propagator.

[46] We learned in Chapter 6 that Green's functions are essential tools when we want to describe how fields interact with each other or with themselves. Moreover, take note that it's really the time ordering which turns the Feynman propagator into a Green's function. This is demonstrated explicitly in Appendix A.7.

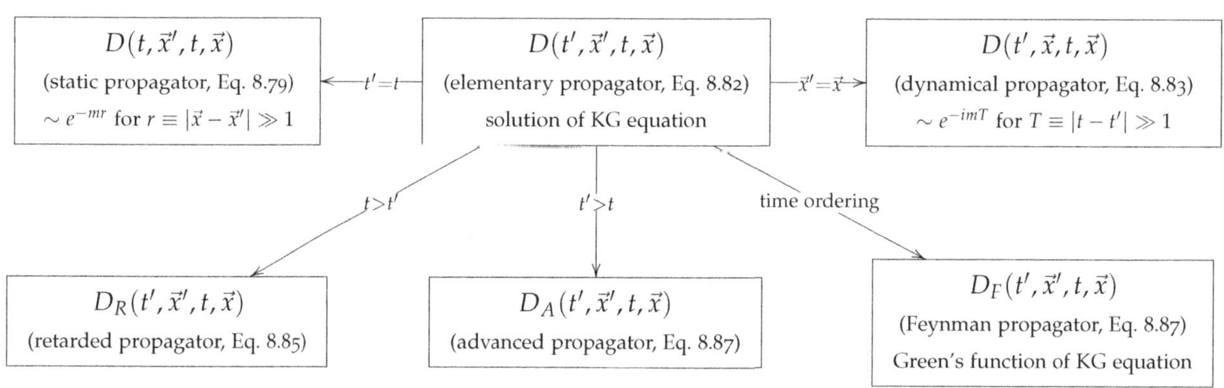

8.6 Complex Scalar Fields

So far, we've only talked about real (scalar) fields. In the real world, however, complex fields are just as (if not more) important as real fields. While many of the things that we just discussed also apply to complex fields, there is one major difference with incredibly important consequences. This is what this section is about.

First of all, recall that a general complex solution of the Klein-Gordon equation can be written as (Eq. 5.53)

$$\phi(x) = \int dk^3 \frac{1}{(2\pi)^3\sqrt{2\omega_k}} \left(a(\vec{k})e^{-ikx} + b(\vec{k})e^{ikx} \right) . \tag{8.99}$$

The only difference to the real solution (Eq. 5.51) we discussed so far is that the coefficients in front of e^{ikx} and e^{-ikx} are independent of each other.[47] For reasons that will become clear in a moment, we adopt the usual convention and denote the coefficient in front of e^{ikx} by $b^\dagger(\vec{k})$:

$$\phi(x) = \int dk^3 \frac{1}{(2\pi)^3\sqrt{2\omega_k}} \left(a(\vec{k})e^{-ikx} + b^\dagger(\vec{k})e^{ikx} \right) . \tag{8.100}$$

The corresponding expansion of the conjugated field $\phi^\dagger$ reads

$$\phi^\dagger(x) = \int dk^3 \frac{1}{(2\pi)^3\sqrt{2\omega_k}} \left(a^\dagger(\vec{k})e^{ikx} + b(\vec{k})e^{-ikx} \right) . \tag{8.101}$$

since $(b^\dagger)^\dagger = b$ and $(e^{ix})^\dagger = e^{-ix}$. Equipped with these expansions of a complex scalar field and its conjugate, we can repeat the same steps that allowed us to understand real-valued quantum scalar fields.

[47] For your convenience: Eq. 5.51 reads

$$\phi(x) = \int dk^3 \frac{1}{(2\pi)^3\sqrt{2\omega_k}} \times \left(a(\vec{k})e^{-ikx} + a^\dagger(\vec{k})e^{ikx} \right) .$$

Moreover, we checked in Eq. 5.50 that for $b = a^\dagger$ our field is indeed real ($\phi^\star = \phi$).

First of all, by using that the Lagrangian for a complex scalar field reads

$$\mathcal{L} = \partial_\mu\phi^\dagger\partial^\mu\phi - m^2\phi^\dagger\phi , \tag{8.102}$$

we can calculate the corresponding conjugate momentum density (Eq. 4.52):

$$\begin{aligned}\pi &= \frac{\partial \mathcal{L}}{\partial(\partial_0 \phi)} \\ &\quad \text{Eq. 8.102} \\ &= \frac{\partial\left(\partial_\mu \phi^\dagger \partial^\mu \phi - m^2 \phi^\dagger \phi\right)}{\partial(\partial_0 \phi)} \\ &\quad \text{sum convention} \\ &= \frac{\partial\left(\partial_0 \phi^\dagger \partial_0 \phi - \partial_i^\dagger \phi \partial_i \phi - m^2 \phi^\dagger \phi\right)}{\partial(\partial_0 \phi)} \\ &= \partial_0 \phi^\dagger . \end{aligned} \tag{8.103}$$

Analogously, we find that

$$\begin{aligned}\pi^\dagger &= \frac{\partial \mathcal{L}}{\partial(\partial_0 \phi^\dagger)} \\ &= \partial_0 \phi . \end{aligned} \tag{8.104}$$

By using these results and the canonical commutation relations (Eq. 8.6)[48]

$$\begin{aligned}[\phi(x_\mu), \pi(y_\mu)] &= i\delta(x_\mu - y_\mu) \\ [\phi^\dagger(x_\mu), \pi^\dagger(y_\mu)] &= i\delta(x_\mu - y_\mu) , \end{aligned} \tag{8.105}$$

we find for the coefficients $a, a^\dagger, b, b^\dagger$ that appear in the expansion of ϕ and $\phi^\dagger$:[49]

$$\begin{aligned} &[a(\vec{k}), a^\dagger(\vec{k}')] = (2\pi)^3 \delta(\vec{k} - \vec{k}') , [b(\vec{k}), b^\dagger(\vec{k}')] = (2\pi)^3 \delta(\vec{k} - \vec{k}') , \\ &[a(\vec{k}), a(\vec{k}')] = 0 , \quad [a^\dagger(\vec{k}), a^\dagger(\vec{k}')] = 0, \quad [a(\vec{k}), b(\vec{k}')] = 0 , \\ &[b(\vec{k}), b(\vec{k}')] = 0 , \quad [b^\dagger(\vec{k}), b^\dagger(\vec{k}')] = 0, \quad [a^\dagger(\vec{k}), b^\dagger(\vec{k}')] = 0 \\ &[a(\vec{k}), b^\dagger(\vec{k}')] = 0 . \end{aligned} \tag{8.106}$$

This may look quite frightening but we just get the commutation relations that we are already familiar with twice. Thus we can again interpret $a, a^\dagger, b, b^\dagger$ as creation and annihilation operators. In physical terms, what we've just discovered is that there are two types of particles associated with a complex scalar field. The first kind is created by $a^\dagger(\vec{k})$ and destroyed by $a(\vec{k})$, while the second one is created by $b^\dagger(\vec{k})$ and destroyed by $b(\vec{k})$. Since both kinds of particles are related to the same field they are closely related to each other.

[48] As before, we treat ϕ and $\phi^\dagger$ as independent fields. Thus following the same arguments as in Section 8.2 we can derive these two commutation relations.

[49] Compare the commutation relations given here with those for a real scalar field (Eq. 8.14):

$$[a(\vec{k}), a^\dagger(\vec{k}')] = (2\pi)^3 \delta(\vec{k} - \vec{k}')$$
$$[a(\vec{k}), a(\vec{k}')] = 0 , \quad [a^\dagger(\vec{k}), a^\dagger(\vec{k}')] = 0 .$$

8.6.1 Antiparticles

In particular, the particle states (c.f. Eq. 8.42)

$$|1_{\vec{k}}\rangle \equiv a^{\dagger}(\vec{k})\,|0\rangle$$
$$|\tilde{1}_{\vec{k}}\rangle \equiv b^{\dagger}(\vec{k})\,|0\rangle \tag{8.107}$$

are extremely similar. Both describe a single particle with momentum $\vec{k}$, mass m, and energy $\omega_k = \sqrt{\vec{k}^2 + m^2}$. For the energy this follows because the Hamiltonian for a complex scalar field reads [50]

$$\hat{H} \equiv \int_V dk^3 \frac{\omega_k}{(2\pi)^3}\left(a^{\dagger}(\vec{k})a(\vec{k}) + b^{\dagger}(\vec{k})b(\vec{k})\right), \tag{8.108}$$

which we can calculate by using the general definition (Eq. 8.22). This implies that the total energy is given by the number of a-particles, as counted by $N_a \equiv a^{\dagger}(\vec{k})a(\vec{k})$ (Eq. 7.71) plus the number of b-particles, as counted by the number operator $N_b \equiv b^{\dagger}(\vec{k})b(\vec{k})$, times ω_k. Thus each b-particle, just as each a-particle, contributes ω_k to the total energy.[51]

There is, however, in general a difference between a-particles and b-particles. This difference becomes only apparent if we consider another label associated with certain fields: electric charge. We discovered in Section 4.3.2 that electric charge is the conserved quantity that follows via Noether's theorem from the invariance under phase shifts.[52] Moreover, we calculated that the total electric charge carried by a complex scalar field is given by (Eq. 4.61)

$$\tilde{Q}_q = iq \int d^3x \left(\frac{\partial \mathcal{L}}{\partial(\partial_0 \phi^{\dagger})}\phi^{\dagger} - \frac{\partial \mathcal{L}}{\partial(\partial_0 \phi)}\phi\right), \tag{8.109}$$

where q is the electric charge parameter associated with the fields. If we plug the Lagrangian (Eq. 8.102) and the explicit expansions of ϕ and $\phi^{\dagger}$ (Eq. 8.100, Eq. 8.101) into this formula, we can calculate that

$$\tilde{Q}_q = q \int \frac{dk^3}{(2\pi)^3}\left(a^{\dagger}(\vec{k})a(\vec{k}) - b^{\dagger}(\vec{k})b(\vec{k})\right). \tag{8.110}$$

This is demonstrated in Appendix A.8. In words, this result tells us that each a-particle contributes a factor q to the total charge,

[50] Compare this to the Hamiltonian for a real scalar field (Eq. 8.32)

$$\hat{H} \equiv \int_V dk^3 \frac{\omega_k}{(2\pi)^3} a^{\dagger}(\vec{k})a(\vec{k})\,.$$

[51] In addition, the momenta of the two states can be calculated completely analogously to how we did it in Eq. 8.41.

[52] Reminder: a phase shift is a transformation of the form (Eq. 4.54)

$$\phi \to e^{i\varphi}\phi$$
$$\phi^{\dagger} \to e^{-i\varphi}\phi^{\dagger}\,.$$

while each b-particle contributes a factor of $-q$. In other words, a-particles and b-particles carry opposite electric charges.

We call the particles that are created by $b^\dagger(\vec{k})$ the **antiparticles** of the particles created by $a^\dagger(\vec{k})$. For example, if ϕ describes a pion field, the particles created by $a^\dagger(\vec{k})$ are pions with electric charge q while the particles created by $b^\dagger(\vec{k})$ are anti-pions with electric charge $-q$.[53]

[53] This is just a convention. We could equally call the field excitation with charge $-q$ the pion and the field excitation with charge q the anti-pion.

The main point to take away is that there are two kinds of particle-like field excitations associated with a complex scalar field. We call them particles and antiparticles. One defining difference between them is that they carry opposite electric charges.[54]

[54] This is not only true for electric charge but also for all other "gauge" charges like isospin or color charge.

An important special case are fields that don't carry any charge that could allow a distinction between particles and antiparticles. We then say that the associated particles are their own antiparticles. Mathematically, we describe this by defining that $a^\dagger(\vec{k}) = b^\dagger(\vec{k})$ (and equivalently $a(\vec{k}) = b(\vec{k})$), which implies that the particles created by these operators are equal. If we plug this into the field expansion (Eq. 8.100), we find

$$\begin{aligned} \phi(x) &= \int \frac{dk^3}{(2\pi)^3\sqrt{2\omega_k}} \left(a(\vec{k})e^{-ikx} + b^\dagger(\vec{k})e^{ikx} \right) && \text{this is Eq. 8.100} \\ & && \curvearrowright \; a^\dagger(\vec{k}) = b^\dagger(\vec{k}) \\ &= \int \frac{dk^3}{(2\pi)^3\sqrt{2\omega_k}} \left(a(\vec{k})e^{-ikx} + a^\dagger(\vec{k})e^{ikx} \right) . && (8.111) \end{aligned}$$

This is exactly the field expansion of a real scalar field that we discussed in the previous sections. From this perspective, we say that the particle-like field excitations associated with a real scalar field are their own antiparticles.

While, in principle, particles described by a complex scalar field can be treated analogously to the real case, there is a subtlety that we need to talk about.

8.6.2 Complex Scalar Field Propagators

The elementary propagator of a real scalar field reads (Eq. 8.82)

$$D(t',\vec{x}',t,\vec{x}) \equiv \langle 1_{t',\vec{x}'}|1_{t,\vec{x}}\rangle = \langle 0|\phi(t',\vec{x}')\phi(t,\vec{x})|0\rangle \ . \tag{8.112}$$

Thus it seems natural that we try to use the same formula for the elementary propagator of a complex scalar field. It turns out, however, that $\langle 0|\phi(t',\vec{x}')\phi(t,\vec{x})|0\rangle$ is not a particularly interesting quantity for a complex scalar field. To understand why, we recall the general expansion of a complex scalar field (Eq. 8.100)

$$\begin{aligned}\phi(x) &= \int dk^3 \frac{1}{(2\pi)^3\sqrt{2\omega_k}}\left(a(\vec{k})e^{-ikx} + b^\dagger(\vec{k})e^{ikx}\right) \\ &\qquad \text{(definition)} \\ &\equiv \phi_a^- + \phi_b^+ \ .\end{aligned} \tag{8.113}$$

The first term consist of particle annihilation operators while the second term consists of antiparticle-creation operators.

This implies that

$$\phi_a^- |0\rangle = 0 \qquad \text{since } a|0\rangle = 0 \text{ (Eq. 8.31)} \tag{8.114}$$

Moreover,

$$\begin{aligned} 0 &= (b|0\rangle)^\dagger \\ &\qquad \left(\langle\psi| = |\psi\rangle^\dagger\right) \\ &= \langle 0| b^\dagger \end{aligned} \tag{8.115}$$

and therefore

$$\langle 0|\phi_b^+ = 0 \ . \tag{8.116}$$

Using these results, we can calculate

$$\begin{aligned}\langle 0|\phi(t',\vec{x}')\phi(t,\vec{x})|0\rangle &= \langle 0|\left(\phi_a^-(t',\vec{x}') + \phi_b^+(t',\vec{x}')\right)\left(\phi_a^-(t,\vec{x}) + \phi_b^+(t,\vec{x})\right)|0\rangle \\ &= \langle 0|\phi_a^-(t',\vec{x}')\phi_a^-(t,\vec{x})|0\rangle + \langle 0|\phi_b^+(t',\vec{x}')\phi_a^-(t,\vec{x})|0\rangle \\ &\quad + \langle 0|\phi_a^-(t',\vec{x}')\phi_b^+(t,\vec{x})|0\rangle + \langle 0|\phi_b^+(t',\vec{x}')\phi_b^+(t,\vec{x})|0\rangle \\ &\qquad \text{(Eq. 8.114, Eq. 8.116)} \\ &= \langle 0|\phi_a^-(t',\vec{x}')\phi_b^+(t,\vec{x})|0\rangle \\ &= 0 \ .\end{aligned} \tag{8.117}$$

To get to the final line, we used that $\phi_b^+(t,\vec{x})$ creates an antiparticle state and thus if we act with $\phi_a^-(t',\vec{x}')$ on the resulting ket, we try to annihilate something which isn't there (a particle) and thus get zero.[55]

[55] Alternatively, we can use that $[a,b^\dagger]=0$ (Eq. 8.106) and therefore

$$\begin{aligned}&\langle 0|\phi_a^-(t',\vec{x}')\phi_b^+(t,\vec{x})|0\rangle\\&=\langle 0|\phi_b^+(t,\vec{x})\phi_a^-(t',\vec{x}')|0\rangle\\&=0\end{aligned}$$

since $|\phi_a^-(t',\vec{x}')|0\rangle=0$.

Only terms of the form $\langle 0|\phi_a^-(t',\vec{x}')\phi_a^+(t,\vec{x})|0\rangle$ and $\langle 0|\phi_b^-(t',\vec{x}')\phi_b^+(t,\vec{x})|0\rangle$ would be non-zero, where ϕ_a^+,ϕ_b^+ consist of creation operators while ϕ_b^-,ϕ_a^- consist of annihilation operators. We have just seen that these non-zero terms are not contained in $\langle 0|\phi(t',\vec{x}')\phi(t,\vec{x})|0\rangle$. For a real scalar field, the situation is different. The expansion of a real scalar field contains the creation and annihilation operators for only one type of particle at a time. Thus, we necessarily find the non-trivial term $\langle 0|\phi_a^-(t',\vec{x}')\phi_a^+(t,\vec{x})|0\rangle$ in $\langle 0|\phi(t',\vec{x}')\phi(t,\vec{x})|0\rangle$.

For a complex scalar field, we can construct a non-trivial elementary propagator by using the conjugated field (Eq. 8.101)

$$\begin{aligned}\phi^\dagger(x)&=\int dk^3\frac{1}{(2\pi)^3\sqrt{2\omega_k}}\left(a^\dagger(\vec{k})e^{ikx}+b(\vec{k})e^{-ikx}\right)\\&\quad\text{definition}\\&\equiv\phi_a^+ + \phi_b^-\,.\end{aligned}\tag{8.118}$$

For example, let's have a look at

$$\begin{aligned}\langle 0|\phi^\dagger(t',\vec{x}')\phi(t,\vec{x})|0\rangle&=\langle 0|\left(\phi_a^+(t',\vec{x}')+\phi_b^-(t',\vec{x}')\right)\left(\phi_a^-(t,\vec{x})+\phi_b^+(t,\vec{x})\right)|0\rangle\\&=\langle 0|\phi_a^+(t',\vec{x}')\phi_a^-(t,\vec{x})|0\rangle+\langle 0|\phi_b^-(t',\vec{x}')\phi_a^-(t,\vec{x})|0\rangle\\&\quad+\langle 0|\phi_a^+(t',\vec{x}')\phi_b^+(t,\vec{x})|0\rangle+\langle 0|\phi_b^-(t',\vec{x}')\phi_b^+(t,\vec{x})|0\rangle\\&\quad a|0\rangle=0\\&=\langle 0|\phi_b^-(t',\vec{x}')\phi_b^+(t,\vec{x})|0\rangle\neq 0\,.\end{aligned}\tag{8.119}$$

In words, $\langle 0|\phi^\dagger(t',\vec{x}')\phi(t,\vec{x})|0\rangle$ is the probability amplitude that we prepare an *antiparticle* at $\vec{x}$ at time t and find it at $\vec{x}'$ at time t'.

Similarly, we can consider

$$\langle 0|\phi(t',\vec{x}')\phi^\dagger(t,\vec{x})|0\rangle=\langle 0|\phi_a^-(t',\vec{x}')\phi_a^+(t,\vec{x})|0\rangle\neq 0\,,\tag{8.120}$$

which is the probability amplitude to find a *particle* at $\vec{x}'$ at t' that we prepared at $\vec{x}$ at time t.

Last but not least, we can consider the Feynman propagator for a complex scalar field, which reads

$$D_F \equiv \langle 0|T\phi(t',\vec{x}')\phi^\dagger(t,\vec{x})|0\rangle\ , \tag{8.121}$$

where T is again the time-ordering operator (Eq. 8.90).

So far we've only talked about scalar fields. However, gauge fields and spinor fields play an equally important role and thus we will discuss them in a quantum context next.

8.7 Quantized Spinor Fields

Most of the things that we discussed in the previous sections for quantized scalar fields also apply to spinor fields. This is necessarily the case because the spacetime structure of spinor fields can also be described in terms of plane waves. In particular, the general solution of the Dirac equation reads (Eq. 5.106)

$$\Psi = \sum_{r=1}^{2} \int \frac{d^3k}{(2\pi)^3\sqrt{2\omega_k}} \left(c_r(\vec{k}) u_r(k) e^{-ik_\mu x^\mu} + d_r(\vec{k}) v_r(k) e^{+ik_\mu x^\mu} \right) \tag{8.122}$$

which is extremely similar to the solution of the Klein-Gordon equation that we used in the previous sections. The main difference is the occurrence of basis spinors $u_r(k)$, $v_r(k)$. But before we discuss the implications of this difference, we rename, for exactly the same reasons as in the previous section, the operator in front of $e^{ik_\mu x^\mu}$ to $d_r^\dagger(\vec{k})$:[56]

[56] We do this because now $d_r^\dagger(\vec{k})$ describes the creation of antiparticles while $c_r^\dagger(\vec{k})$ describes the creation of particles. We could, of course, continue to work with $d_r(\vec{k})$ in the expansion, but then need to live with the fact that for antiparticles it's $d_r(\vec{k})$ and not $d_r^\dagger(\vec{k})$ that acts as a creation operator. Since this is quite confusing, we work with $d_r^\dagger(\vec{k})$ in the expansion.

$$\Psi = \sum_{r=1}^{2} \int \frac{d^3k}{(2\pi)^3\sqrt{2\omega_k}} \left(c_r(\vec{k}) u_r(k) e^{-ik_\mu x^\mu} + d_r^\dagger(\vec{k}) v_r(k) e^{+ik_\mu x^\mu} \right) \tag{8.123}$$

We will learn below that we can again interpret the coefficients that appear in this expansion ($c_r(\vec{k}), d_r^\dagger(\vec{k})$) as annihilation and creation operators.

However, we start our discussion of spinor fields by talking about a somewhat subtle but incredibly important property of them that sets them apart from all other fields.

First of all, recall that a Dirac spinor consists of two Weyl spinors (Eq. 3.35):

$$\Psi = \begin{pmatrix} \chi \\ \xi \end{pmatrix} . \tag{8.124}$$

Moreover, the scalar product of two Weyl spinors reads (Eq. 3.63):

$$\xi\chi \equiv \xi_a \epsilon^{ab} \chi_b , \tag{8.125}$$

where ϵ^{ab} is the spinor metric (Eq. 3.57)

$$\epsilon^{ab} = \begin{pmatrix} 0 & 1 \\ -1 & 0 \end{pmatrix} . \tag{8.126}$$

The scalar product of two Dirac spinors reads (Eq. 5.58)

$$\bar{\Psi}\Psi \equiv \Psi^{\dagger}\gamma_0\Psi . \tag{8.127}$$

All of this is important, if we want to think about how the canonical commutation relations (Eq. 8.6,Eq. 8.7) apply to spinor fields. In particular, Eq. 8.7 seems to suggest that spinor fields commute

$$\begin{aligned} 0 &\stackrel{?}{=} [\chi(t,\vec{x}),\chi(t,\vec{y})] \\ &\quad \curvearrowright \quad [A,B] \equiv AB - BA \\ &= \chi(t,\vec{x})\chi(t,\vec{y}) - \chi(t,\vec{y})\chi(t,\vec{x}) \\ &\quad \curvearrowright \\ \chi(t,\vec{x})\chi(t,\vec{y}) &= \chi(t,\vec{y})\chi(t,\vec{x}) . \end{aligned} \tag{8.128}$$

On the other hand, if we use the explicit form of the spinor product and swap the position of the two spinors to learn something about their commutation behavior, we find

$$\begin{aligned} \chi(t,\vec{x})\chi(t,\vec{y}) &\stackrel{?}{=} \chi_a(t,\vec{x})\epsilon^{ab}\chi_b(t,\vec{y}) \qquad \text{this is Eq. 8.125} \\ &\quad \curvearrowright \quad \text{position swap} \\ &= \chi_b(t,\vec{y})\epsilon^{ab}\chi_a(t,\vec{x}) \\ &\quad \curvearrowright \quad \epsilon^{ab} = -\epsilon^{ba} \\ &= -\chi_b(t,\vec{y})\epsilon^{ba}\chi_a(t,\vec{x}) \\ &\quad \curvearrowright \\ &= -\chi(t,\vec{y})\chi(t,\vec{x}) , \end{aligned} \tag{8.129}$$

where we used that the spinor metric is antisymmetric $\epsilon^T = -\epsilon$.[57]

We can reconcile these two seemingly conflicting equations by proposing that the components of spinor fields pick up an additional minus sign if we swap their positions:[58]

$$\chi_b(t,\vec{y})\chi_a(t,\vec{x}) = -\chi_a(t,\vec{x})\chi_b(t,\vec{y}) . \tag{8.130}$$

[57] Swapping the indices corresponds to transposing a matrix: $M^T_{ab} = M_{ba}$. We need to swap the indices in order for them to match up and yield a proper product in index notation.

[58] Below, we will talk about a more physical reason why this should be the case.

If we now repeat the calculation in Eq. 8.129, we find

$$\begin{aligned}\chi(t,\vec{x})\chi(t,\vec{y}) &\equiv \chi_a(t,\vec{x})\epsilon^{ab}\chi_b(t,\vec{y}) && \text{this is Eq. 8.125} \\ & && \text{position swap, Eq. 8.130} \\ &= -\chi_b(t,\vec{y})\epsilon^{ab}\chi_a(t,\vec{x}) \\ & && \epsilon^{ab} = -\epsilon^{ba} \\ &= \chi_b(t,\vec{y})\epsilon^{ba}\chi_a(t,\vec{x}) \\ &= \chi(t,\vec{y})\chi(t,\vec{x}) . \end{aligned} \tag{8.131}$$

The anti-commutation relation (Eq. 8.130)

$$\begin{aligned} &\chi_a(t,\vec{x})\chi_b(t,\vec{y}) + \chi_b(t,\vec{y})\chi_a(t,\vec{x}) = 0 \\ & && \text{definition} \\ &\{\chi_a(t,\vec{x}),\chi_b(t,\vec{y})\} = 0 \end{aligned} \tag{8.132}$$

has wide-ranging consequences for the particles that are described by spinor fields. Moreover, analogously we can derive that

$$\begin{aligned}\{\pi_a(t,\vec{x}),\chi_b(t,\vec{y})\} &= i\delta(\vec{x}-\vec{y})\delta_{ab} \\ \{\pi_a(t,\vec{x}),\pi_b(t,\vec{y})\} &= 0 ,\end{aligned} \tag{8.133}$$

where π denotes the conjugate momentum density (Eq. 4.52)

$$\pi = \frac{\partial \mathcal{L}}{\partial(\partial_0 \chi)} . \tag{8.134}$$

Since a Dirac spinor consists of Weyl spinors, we can immediately write down the **anticommutation relations for Dirac spinors**

$$\begin{aligned}\{\pi_a(t,\vec{x}),\Psi_b(t,\vec{y})\} &= i\delta(\vec{x}-\vec{y})\delta_{ab} \\ \{\pi_a(t,\vec{x}),\pi_b(t,\vec{y})\} &= 0 \\ \{\Psi_a(t,\vec{x}),\Psi_b(t,\vec{y})\} &= 0 ,\end{aligned} \tag{8.135}$$

where

$$\pi = \frac{\partial \mathcal{L}}{\partial(\partial_0 \Psi)} . \tag{8.136}$$

Equipped with these anticommutation relations, we can discuss the implications for the coefficients $c_r(\vec{k})$, $d_r^\dagger(\vec{k})$ that appear in the general solution of the Dirac equation (Eq. 8.123). We start by calculating the conjugate momentum density for a spinor field (Eq. 4.52)

$$\begin{aligned}
\pi &= \frac{\partial \mathcal{L}}{\partial(\partial_0 \Psi)} && \text{Eq. 5.54} \\
&= \frac{\partial\Big(\bar{\Psi}(i\gamma^\mu\partial_\mu - m)\Psi\Big)}{\partial(\partial_0\Psi)} && \\
&= i\bar{\Psi}\gamma^0 && \bar{\Psi} \equiv \Psi^\dagger\gamma^0 \text{ (Eq. 5.55)} \\
&= i\Psi^\dagger\gamma^0\gamma^0 && \gamma^0\gamma^0 = 1 \\
&= i\Psi^\dagger . && (8.137)
\end{aligned}$$

Therefore, the first anticommutation relation in Eq. 8.135 reads in more explicit terms

$$\begin{aligned}
\{\pi_a(t,\vec{x}), \Psi_b(t,\vec{y})\} &= i\delta(\vec{x}-\vec{y})\delta_{ab} && \text{Eq. 8.137} \\
\{i\Psi_a^\dagger(t,\vec{x}), \Psi_b(t,\vec{y})\} &= i\delta(\vec{x}-\vec{y})\delta_{ab} && /i \\
\{\Psi_a^\dagger(t,\vec{x}), \Psi_b(t,\vec{y})\} &= \delta(\vec{x}-\vec{y})\delta_{ab} . && (8.138)
\end{aligned}$$

Moreover, by using the field expansion in Eq. 8.123 we calculate that $\Psi^\dagger$ can be written as

$$\begin{aligned}
\Psi &= \sum_{r=1}^{2}\int \frac{d^3k}{(2\pi)^3\sqrt{2\omega_k}}\left(c_r(\vec{k})u_r(k)e^{ik_\mu x^\mu} + d_r^\dagger(\vec{k})v_r(k)e^{-ik_\mu x^\mu}\right) && \text{this is Eq. 8.123} \\
& && \dagger \\
\Psi^\dagger &= \left(\sum_{r=1}^{2}\int \frac{d^3k}{(2\pi)^3\sqrt{2\omega_k}}\left(c_r(\vec{k})u_r(k)e^{ik_\mu x^\mu} + d_r^\dagger(\vec{k})v_r(k)e^{-ik_\mu x^\mu}\right)\right)^\dagger && (d^\dagger)^\dagger = d,\ (e^{ix})^\dagger = e^{-ix} \\
&= \sum_{r=1}^{2}\int \frac{d^3k}{(2\pi)^3\sqrt{2\omega_k}}\left(c_r^\dagger(\vec{k})u_r^\dagger(k)e^{-ik_\mu x^\mu} + d_r(\vec{k})v_r^\dagger(k)e^{ik_\mu x^\mu}\right) . && (8.139)
\end{aligned}$$

The next step is that we conclude analogous to what we did for scalar fields in Section 8.6 that the anticommutation relations in Eq. 8.135 imply for the coefficients $c, c^\dagger, d, d^\dagger$:[59]

[59] It is instructive to compare these relations to the canonical commutation relations for a complex scalar field (Eq. 8.106).

$$\begin{aligned}
&\{c(\vec{k}),c^\dagger(\vec{k}')\} = (2\pi)^3\delta(\vec{k}-\vec{k}')\,, \{d(\vec{k}),d^\dagger(\vec{k}')\} = (2\pi)^3\delta(\vec{k}-\vec{k}')\,,\\
&\{c(\vec{k}),c(\vec{k}')\} = 0\,, \quad \{c^\dagger(\vec{k}),c^\dagger(\vec{k}')\} = 0\,, \quad \{c(\vec{k}),d(\vec{k}')\} = 0\,,\\
&\{d(\vec{k}),d(\vec{k}')\} = 0\,, \quad \{c^\dagger(\vec{k}),d^\dagger(\vec{k}')\} = 0\,, \quad \{d^\dagger(\vec{k}),d^\dagger(\vec{k}')\} = 0\\
&\{d(\vec{k}),d^\dagger(\vec{k}')\} = 0\,,
\end{aligned} \tag{8.140}$$

where, as before, $\{A,B\} = AB + BA$ denotes the anticommutator.[60]

[60] The proof is completely analogous to the one discussed in Appendix A.4.

Before we can talk about the meaning of the operators $c, c^\dagger, d, d^\dagger$, we need to talk about the spinor Hamiltonian.

8.7.1 Spinor Hamiltonian

The spinor Hamiltonian can be calculated by using the general definition as the Noether charge following from invariance under temporal translations $t \to t + \epsilon$ (Eq. 4.38):

$$\begin{aligned}
H &\equiv \int_V d^3x\, T^0_0\\
&\quad \text{Eq. 4.35}\\
&= \int_V d^3x\, \frac{\partial \mathcal{L}}{\partial(\partial_0\psi)}\partial_0\psi - \mathcal{L}
\end{aligned} \tag{8.141}$$

and reads in terms of the coefficients[61]

$$H \equiv \int_V \mathrm{d}k^3 \frac{\omega_k}{(2\pi)^3}\Big(c_r^\dagger(\vec{k})c_r(\vec{k}) + d_r^\dagger(\vec{k})d_r(\vec{k})\Big)\,. \tag{8.142}$$

[61] Compare this to the Hamiltonian for a real scalar field (Eq. 8.17) and the Hamiltonian for a complex scalar field (Eq. 8.108)

$$H \equiv \int_V \mathrm{d}k^3 \frac{\omega_k}{(2\pi)^3}\Big(a^\dagger(\vec{k})a(\vec{k}) + b^\dagger(\vec{k})b(\vec{k})\Big)\,.$$

Moreover, note that (as for scalar fields) we simply ignore here a potentially infinite contribution to the total energy coming from the non-zero ground state energy of each harmonic oscillator. In addition, there is an implicit sum over the index r.

An interesting aspect of this Hamiltonian is that if we try to use commutation relations instead of the anticommutation relations in Eq. 8.140 in its derivation, we find

$$\hat{H}_{\text{wrong}} \equiv \int_V \mathrm{d}k^3 \frac{\omega_k}{(2\pi)^3}\Big(c_r^\dagger(\vec{k})c_r(\vec{k}) - d_r^\dagger(\vec{k})d_r(\vec{k})\Big)\,. \tag{8.143}$$

In physical terms, this would imply that antiparticles contribute negatively to the total energy. Luckily, this is not the case because otherwise energy wouldn't be bound from below. Formulated differently, if we use (wrongly) commutation relations instead of anticommutation relations, we find a formula for the total energy that can be arbitrarily negative. This is bad because there wouldn't be any stable states if this were correct as every state could decay into lower energy states forever. In particular, there wouldn't be any stable matter in the universe because each particle it consists of could decay into more and more antiparticles to lower the energy further.

This lends further support to the idea that spinor fields anticommute (Eq. 8.130).

Now that we have the Hamiltonian, we can start to investigate the meaning of the operators $c_r, c_r^\dagger, d_r, d_r^\dagger$

8.7.2 Spinor Particles

As in the Section 8.3.1, the first key ingredient is the commutator of the Hamiltonian with the operators $c_r^\dagger, d_r^\dagger$. The result is exactly the same as for scalar particles (Eq. 8.24)

$$\begin{aligned} [\hat{H}, c_r^\dagger(\vec{k})] &= \omega_k c_r^\dagger(\vec{k}) \\ [\hat{H}, d_r^\dagger(\vec{k})] &= \omega_k d_r^\dagger(\vec{k}) \,. \end{aligned} \tag{8.144}$$

Therefore, we can conclude that $c_r^\dagger, d_r^\dagger$ are creation operators. We say that $c_r^\dagger$ creates particles, while $d_r^\dagger$ creates the corresponding antiparticles associated with the same spinor field.[62]

[62] This is analogous to what we discovered in Section 8.6 for a complex scalar field.

It follows from the commutation relations (c.f. Eq. 8.25)

$$\begin{aligned} [\hat{H}, c_r(\vec{k})] &= -\omega_k c_r(\vec{k}) \\ [\hat{H}, d_r(\vec{k})] &= -\omega_k d_r(\vec{k}) \end{aligned} \tag{8.145}$$

that c_r, d_r are annihilation operators.

Therefore, we define the ground state through its property (c.f. Eq. 8.31)

$$\begin{aligned} c_r(\vec{k})\,|0\rangle &= 0 \\ d_r(\vec{k})\,|0\rangle &= 0\,. \end{aligned} \tag{8.146}$$

We then denote the one-particle state by

$$|1_{\vec{k}}\rangle \equiv c_r^\dagger(\vec{k})\,|0\rangle \tag{8.147}$$

and the one-antiparticle state by

$$|\bar{1}_{\vec{k}}\rangle \equiv d_r^\dagger(\vec{k})\,|0\rangle\ . \tag{8.148}$$

So far, everything seems completely analogous to what we've already discussed for scalar fields. However, the fact that spinorial creation and annihilation operators obey an anticommutation relation instead of a commutation relation leads to an important feature of spinor field components.

The key observation is that if we evalulate the anticommutation relation $\{c^\dagger(\vec{k}), c^\dagger(\vec{k}')\} = 0$ (Eq. 8.140) for equal momenta $\vec{k} = \vec{k}'$, we find

$$\begin{aligned} 0 &= \{c^\dagger(\vec{k}), c^\dagger(\vec{k})\} \\ &\qquad \text{↷ } \{A,B\} \equiv AB + BA \\ &= c^\dagger(\vec{k})c^\dagger(\vec{k}) + c^\dagger(\vec{k})c^\dagger(\vec{k}) \\ &\qquad \text{↷ } c + c = 2c \\ &= 2c^\dagger(\vec{k})c^\dagger(\vec{k}) \\ &\qquad \text{↷ } \not{2} \\ &= c^\dagger(\vec{k})c^\dagger(\vec{k})\,. \end{aligned} \tag{8.149}$$

This implies, that if we act twice with the same creation operator on the ground state we find zero

$$c_r^\dagger(\vec{k})c_r^\dagger(\vec{k})\,|0\rangle = 0 \tag{8.150}$$

instead of a two-particle state.

This is famously known as the **Pauli exclusion principle**. In words, it means

> There can never be two spinorial particles in exactly the same state.

This is not just some crude feature of our formalism but an established experimental fact.

However, take note that we *can* create two particle states as long as the momenta are different

$$c_r^\dagger(\vec{k})c_r^\dagger(\vec{k}')\,|0\rangle \equiv |1_{\vec{k}}1_{\vec{k}'}\rangle \neq 0\,. \tag{8.151}$$

We can also create particle-antiparticle states with equal momenta

$$d_r^\dagger(\vec{k})c_r^\dagger(\vec{k})\,|0\rangle \equiv |\bar{1}_{\vec{k}}1_{\vec{k}'}\rangle \neq 0\,. \tag{8.152}$$

Now that we've established a notation for spinorial particles, we can investigate how they move around.

8.7.3 Spinor Propagator

Analogous to what we discussed in Section 8.5 for scalar fields, we can talk about the spinor propagator. Since our spinor field Ψ is complex, we know that the naive elementary propagator $\langle 0|\Psi(y_\mu)|\Psi(x_\mu)|0\rangle$ vanishes.[63] Instead, analogous to what we discovered in Section 8.6.2 for a complex scalar field, the correct non-vanishing elementary propagators are of the form $\langle 0|\bar{\Psi}(y_\mu)\Psi(x_\mu)|0\rangle$ and $\langle 0|\Psi(y_\mu)\bar{\Psi}(x_\mu)|0\rangle$. If we plug in the explicit field expansions, we find

$$\begin{aligned}
\langle 0|\Psi(y_\mu)\bar{\Psi}(x_\mu)|0\rangle &= \int \frac{d^3k}{(2\pi)^3 2\omega_k}(k_\mu\gamma^\mu + m)\mathrm{e}^{-ik(x-y)} \\
\langle 0|\bar{\Psi}(y_\mu)\Psi(x_\mu)|0\rangle &= \int \frac{d^3k}{(2\pi)^3 2\omega_k}(k_\mu\gamma^\mu - m)\mathrm{e}^{ik(x-y)}\,.
\end{aligned} \tag{8.153}$$

[63] Exactly the same arguments as in Eq. 8.117 apply.

We can then define the spinorial Feynman propagator[64]

$$\Delta_F(y_\mu, x_\mu) \equiv \langle 0|T\Psi(y_\mu)\bar{\Psi}(x_\mu)|0\rangle \,, \tag{8.154}$$

where T denotes the time-ordering operator (Eq. 8.90). This propagator is known as the **fermion propagator** since the particles associated with spinor fields are usually called fermions.

[64] This definition is analogous to the definition of the Feynman propagator for a complex scalar field in Eq. 8.121.

Since we know already that there is a close connection between Feynman propagators and Green's functions, it's hopefully somewhat plausible that the fermion propagator can be rewritten as[65]

$$\Delta_F(y_\mu, x_\mu) = i\int \frac{d^4k}{(2\pi)^4}\, e^{-ik^\mu(x_\mu - y_\mu)} \frac{(k_\rho\gamma^\rho + m)}{k_\lambda k^\lambda - m^2 + i\epsilon} \,. \tag{8.155}$$

which is, except for the "time-ordering term" $+i\epsilon$ and a conventional overall factor i, exactly the Green's function for the Dirac equation (Eq. 6.48) that we discussed in Section 6.3.2.

[65] We noted already in Section 8.5 that the Feynman propagator for scalar fields is a Green's function of the Klein-Gordon equation and can be written like the Green's function we considered previously. The calculation for the fermion propagator works analogously.

So far, we have talked about quantized (real and complex) scalar fields and spinor fields. The final puzzle piece that we will talk about before we consider scattering processes are quantized gauge fields.

8.8 Quantized Gauge Fields

For ordinary vector fields, we could proceed exactly as for scalar fields. In modern physics, however, we are primarily interested in a special kind of vector field known as gauge fields. We've learned already in Section 3.9 that the defining property of gauge fields is that they don't have four independent polarization states. For massive gauge fields there are only three, while for massless gauge fields there are two.

The main difficulty in talking about quantized gauge fields is describing this fact consistently in the quantum framework.

For massive gauge fields, the procedure is relatively straightforward. But for massless gauge fields, the whole issue is subtle due to gauge symmetry.[66] Thus we will start by talking about massive fields.

[66] Reminder: we talked about gauge symmetry in Section 5.3.3. The main observation was that we have the freedom to redefine our gauge field as follows (Eq. 5.137):

$$A_\mu(x_\mu) \rightarrow A'_\mu(x_\mu) = A_\mu(x_\mu) + \partial_\mu \eta(x_\mu)\,, \tag{8.156}$$

where $\eta(x_\mu)$ is an ordinary function.

8.8.1 Quantized Massive Gauge Fields

We learned in Section 5.3.2 that it follows directly from the Lorenz condition (Eq. 5.116) that there are only three independent polarization states.[67] To understand why this is potentially problematic in our quantum framework, we start by looking at the Lagrangian for massive gauge fields (Eq. 5.107)

[67] Reminder: the Lorenz condition is a direct consequence of the Proca equation and reads $\partial_\mu A^\mu = 0$.

$$\mathcal{L}_{\text{Proca}} = -\frac{1}{2}F_{\mu\nu}F^{\mu\nu} + m^2 A_\mu A^\mu\,, \tag{8.157}$$

where $F_{\mu\nu} = (\partial_\mu A_\nu - \partial_\nu A_\mu)$ (Eq. 3.103) is the field strength tensor. We observe that

$$F_{00} = (\partial_0 A_0 - \partial_0 A_0) = 0\,. \tag{8.158}$$

This implies that there is no $\partial_0 A_0$ term in the Lagrangian. Therefore, the corresponding conjugate momentum density (Eq. 4.52) vanishes:

$$\pi^0 = \frac{\partial \mathcal{L}}{\partial(\partial_0 A^0)} = 0\,. \tag{8.159}$$

Thus, we run into a problem if we try to write down commutation relations for the massive gauge field A_μ (Eq. 8.6)

$$[A_\mu(t,\vec{x}), \pi^\mu(t,\vec{y})] = i\delta(\vec{x}-\vec{y}), \tag{8.160}$$

where

$$\pi^\mu = \frac{\partial \mathcal{L}}{\partial(\partial_0 A^\mu)}. \tag{8.161}$$

If we evaluate this formula for $\mu = 0$ and use that π_0 vanishes, we find

$$\begin{aligned} [A_0(t,\vec{x}), \pi^0(t,\vec{y})] &= i\delta(\vec{x}-\vec{y}) \\ & \quad \text{↷ } \pi_0 = 0 \text{ (Eq. 8.159)} \\ [A_0(t,\vec{x}), 0] &= i\delta(\vec{x}-\vec{y}) \\ & \quad \text{↷ } [A,0] = A0 - 0A = 0 \\ 0 &= i\delta(\vec{x}-\vec{y}). \end{aligned} \tag{8.162}$$

This is a contradiction.

The source of the problem is that we wrote down the commutation relations (Eq. 8.160) without thinking first. The result $\pi_0 = 0$ tells us something important. It occurs because there is no $\partial_0 A_0$ term in the Lagrangian. Since $\partial_0 \equiv \partial_t$, there is no kinetic term for the field A_0. This suggests that A_0 is not a proper dynamical variable. Therefore, we shouldn't be surprised that we run into a problem when we try to promote it to a quantum field.

We have, in fact, discovered this already in Section 5.3.2. We calculated that in the rest frame ($\vec{k} = (0,0,0)^T$), the Lorenz condition implies $\epsilon_0 = 0$ (Eq. 5.134). Since ϵ_μ encodes the complete internal structure of our field (Eq. 5.115), this means that in the rest frame a massive vector field has no temporal polarization component, $A_0 = 0$.[68] While in other frames $A_0 \neq 0$ it's still not an independent variable. On the one hand, this follows immediately because physics must be the same in all frames of reference. Therefore, a boost to a different frame cannot promote A_0 from a vanishing quantity to an important dynamical player. Instead, the fact that $A_0 \neq 0$ in general frames of reference is an artifact that occurs because a little bit of the other field components is shifted to A_0. On the other hand, we

[68] Reminder: in Eq. 5.115 we made the ansatz

$$A_\mu(x_\mu) = \underbrace{\epsilon_\mu}_{\text{internal structure}} \times \underbrace{f(x_\mu)}_{\text{spacetime structure}}.$$

checked this explicitly for a field excitation that moves in the z-direction ($\vec{k} = (0,0,k_z)^T$). In this case we found that the Lorenz condition implies $\epsilon_0\sqrt{m^2+k_z^2} = \epsilon_3 k_z$ (Eq. 5.128). Therefore, A_0 can be calculated immediately once A_3 and k_z are known.

The resolution of the "paradox" that we've stumbled upon above (Eq. 8.162) is therefore that we use

$$[A_i(t,\vec{x}), \pi^j(t,\vec{y})] = i\delta(\vec{x}-\vec{y})\delta_{ij} \tag{8.163}$$

instead of Eq. 8.160. This is exactly a three-dimensional version of the scalar commutation relation (Eq. 8.14). We can then proceed exactly as before.

In particular, we can use the general expansion (Eq. 5.156)

$$A_\mu(x) = \sum_{r=1}^{3}\int \frac{d^3p}{(2\pi)^3}\frac{1}{\sqrt{2k_0}}\left(\epsilon^r_\mu a^r(\vec{k})e^{-ik_\mu x^\mu} + \epsilon^r_\mu a^{r\dagger}(\vec{k})e^{ik_\mu x^\mu}\right), \tag{8.164}$$

to discover that the coefficients $a^r(\vec{k}), a^{r\dagger}(\vec{k})$ are creation and annihilation operators. Moreover, it's again possible to define corresponding particle states and to write down propagators like the Feynman propagator

$$D_F^{\nu\zeta}(x,y) = \langle 0|TA_\mu(x)A_\nu(y)|0\rangle$$

cumbersome calculation

$$= i\int \frac{d^4k}{(2\pi)^4} e^{-ik^\mu(x_\mu - y_\mu)}\frac{\eta^{\nu\zeta} - \frac{k^\nu k^\zeta}{k_\rho k^\rho}}{k_\mu k^\mu - m^2 - i\epsilon}. \tag{8.165}$$

This is again a Green's function of the corresponding equation of motion, which in this case is the Proca equation. In addition, take note that this is quite similar to the Green's function of the Maxwell equation, except for the usual mass term $-m^2$ and the time-ordering term $-i\epsilon$. The only surprising difference is the factor $(\eta^{\mu\nu} - \frac{k^\mu k^\nu)}{k_\rho k^\rho}$ in the numerator. This factor shows up because when we calculate a product like $A_\mu(x)A_\nu(y)$, we encounter sums over products of polarization vectors. These can be rewritten by using the so-called **completeness relation**

$$\sum_{r=1}^{3} \epsilon^r_\mu \epsilon^r_\nu = -\left(\eta^{\mu\nu} - \frac{k^\mu k^\nu}{k_\rho k^\rho}\right) . \tag{8.166}$$

By using the explicit polarization vectors that we derived in Section 5.3.2, we can verify explicitly that this relation is correct. For example, for $\mu = \nu = 0$, we find

$$\begin{aligned}\sum_{r=1}^{3} \epsilon^r_0 \epsilon^r_0 &= \epsilon^1_0\epsilon^1_0 + \epsilon^2_0\epsilon^2_0 + \epsilon^3_0\epsilon^3_0 \\ &\quad \text{Eq. 5.130, Eq. 5.129} \\ &= 0 + 0 + \left(\frac{k_z}{m}\right)^2 ,\end{aligned} \tag{8.167}$$

which we compare with

$$\begin{aligned}-\left(\eta^{00} - \frac{k^0k^0}{k_\rho k^\rho}\right) &= -\left(1 - \frac{k^0k^0}{k_\rho k^\rho}\right) \\ &\quad k_\rho k^\rho = m^2 \text{ (Eq. 5.124)} \\ &= -\left(1 - \frac{k^0k^0}{m^2}\right) \\ &\quad \text{Eq. 5.126} \\ &= -\left(1 - \frac{m^2 + k_z^2}{m^2}\right) \\ &\quad \frac{m^2}{m^2} = 1 \\ &= -\left(\frac{m^2}{m^2} - \frac{m^2 + k_z^2}{m^2}\right) \\ &= \frac{k_z^2}{m^2} \quad \checkmark\end{aligned} \tag{8.168}$$

Of course, the completeness relation can not only be verified on a case by case basis but also in general terms. But since the proof is quite formal and not very illuminating, we will not discuss it here.

There is, however, a nice way to understand Eq. 8.166. The first puzzle piece is that the Lorenz condition implies (Eq. 5.125)

$$\epsilon_\rho k^\rho = 0 . \tag{8.169}$$

Geometrically this means that all allowed polarization vectors are orthogonal to the wave four-vector k^ρ, completely analogously to how $\vec{v} \cdot \vec{w} = 0$ implies that $\vec{v}$ and $\vec{w}$ are orthogonal.[69]

[69] Geometrically, the scalar product $\vec{v} \cdot \vec{w}$ is the projection of $\vec{v}$ onto $\vec{w}$. In other words, $\vec{v} \cdot \vec{w}$ tells us how much $\vec{v}$ spreads out in the direction in which $\vec{w}$ points. For example, by using $\vec{w} \cdot \vec{e}_x$ we can calculate how much $\vec{w}$ spreads out in the x-direction. Thus if $\vec{v} \cdot \vec{w} = 0$ the projection is zero which means that the two vectors are orthogonal.

The second puzzle piece is that the sum that we defined in Eq. 8.166 is a projection operator

$$P^{\mu\nu} \equiv \sum_{r=1}^{3} \epsilon^r_\mu \epsilon^r_\nu$$

$$\overset{\text{Eq. 8.166}}{=} -\left(\eta^{\mu\nu} - \frac{k^\mu k^\nu}{k_\rho k^\rho}\right) . \tag{8.170}$$

We already talked about projection operators in Section 7.1.6. In particular, we observed that we can rewrite any vector in terms of a new basis by using the projection operator $P = \sum_i \vec{e}_i \vec{e}_i$ (Eq. 7.36):[70]:

$$\vec{v}_{\text{new basis}} = P\vec{v} = \sum_i (\vec{e}_i)(\vec{e}_i \cdot \vec{v}) . \tag{8.171}$$

[70] Take note that there is no scalar product of the two basis vectors. Instead, the right basis vector acts via the scalar product on any vector $\vec{v}$ we throw at the projection operator.

In index notation, this projection operator reads

$$P^{ab} = \sum_i e^a_i e^b_i , \tag{8.172}$$

where i labels different basis vectors and a and b their components. If P^{ab} acts on a vector component v_b, we get the a-th component in the new basis. Therefore, the sum on the left-hand side in Eq. 8.166 is simply a four-dimensional version of this projection operator.

Formulated more precisely, we can now understand that $P^{\mu\nu}$ is a projection operator that projects any given vector onto the subspace spanned by the polarization vectors. Since the polarization vectors are all orthogonal to the wave four-vector k_μ (Eq. 8.169), we know that this subspace is given by all vectors orthogonal to k_μ. This implies that the projection operator $P^{\mu\nu}$ allows us to "remove" from any four-vector v_μ all components that are parallel to k_μ. In other words, if we act with $P^{\mu\nu}$ on a four-vector, the result is a four-vector that is orthogonal to k_μ.

Now that we know that the operator $P^{\mu\nu}$, defined as the sum $\sum_{r=1}^3 \epsilon^r_\mu \epsilon^r_\nu$ (Eq. 8.170), should have this property, we can check that the expression given on the right-hand side in Eq. 8.166 has the desired effect. To that end, we act with the expression given on the right-hand side in Eq. 8.166 on an arbitrary four vector v_ν

and then check if the result is really orthogonal to k_μ:

$$
\begin{aligned}
P^{\mu\nu}v_\nu &= \Big(- \Big(\eta^{\mu\nu} - \frac{k^\mu k^\nu}{k_\rho k^\rho}\Big)\Big)v_\nu \\
&\qquad \text{↷ } \eta^{\mu\nu}v_\nu \equiv v^\mu \\
&= - \Big(v^\mu - \frac{k^\mu k^\nu v_\nu}{k_\rho k^\rho}\Big) \\
&\qquad \text{↷ definition} \\
&\equiv v_\perp^\mu \,.
\end{aligned} \tag{8.173}
$$

If $v_\perp^\mu k_\mu = 0$ the two four-vectors are orthogonal and we can conclude that the projection operator $P^{\mu\nu}$ works as expected. Thus we calculate

$$
\begin{aligned}
0 &\stackrel{!}{=} v_\perp^\mu k_\mu \\
&\qquad \text{↷ Eq. 8.173} \\
&= \Big(- \Big(v^\mu - \frac{k^\mu k^\nu v_\nu}{k_\rho k^\rho}\Big)\Big)k_\mu \\
&\qquad \text{↷} \\
&= - \Big(v^\mu k_\mu - \frac{k^\mu k_\mu k^\nu v_\nu}{k_\rho k^\rho}\Big) \\
&\qquad \text{↷ } \cancel{k^2} \\
&= - \big(v^\mu k_\mu - k^\nu v_\nu\big) \\
&\qquad \text{↷ } k^\nu v_\nu = v^\mu k_\mu \\
&= - (0) \quad \checkmark
\end{aligned} \tag{8.174}
$$

This lends further support that the formula given in Eq. 8.166 is indeed correct.

What we've just discussed may seem like a huge detour. In the next section, however, we will see that projection operators of the kind that we just discussed play an incredibly important role for massless gauge fields.[71]

[71] Take note that there are many problematic technical aspects of massive gauge fields that we didn't talk about. In short, a quantum theory of massive gauge fields is not renormalizable. This means that certain infinities cannot be removed and thus it's hard to make sense of such a model. However, it makes perfect sense to consider massive gauge fields in the context of the Higgs mechanism. Moreover, take note that the propagator of a massive gauge fields blows up as $m \to 0$ due to the $\frac{1}{k_\rho k^\rho} = \frac{1}{m^2}$ term in the numerator. This implies that the transition from massive to massless gauge fields is quite subtle.

8.8.2 Quantized Massless Gauge Fields

In the previous section we learned that we run into a problem if we try to introduce quantized massive gauge fields in exactly the same way that allowed us to introduce quantized scalar fields. The main difficulty is that we need to take into account that for massive gauge fields there are three independent polarizations. We run into exactly the same kind of problem when we want to talk about quantized massless gauge fields. We discovered in Section 5.3.3 that for massless gauge fields there are only two independent polarizations. Therefore, our main task will be to figure out a way to take this into account in our quantum framework.

For massless gauge fields the procedure is a bit more subtle than in the massive case. To understand why, recall that we discussed in Section 5.3.3 that our model of massless gauge fields is invariant under gauge transformations (Eq. 5.137)

$$A_\mu(x_\mu) \to A'_\mu(x_\mu) = A_\mu(x_\mu) + \partial_\mu \eta(x_\mu)\,, \tag{8.175}$$

where $\eta(x_\mu)$ is an ordinary function. Depending on the context, we can use this gauge freedom to accomplish different things. For example, in Section 5.3.3 we used it to restrict ourselves to gauge fields that fulfill the Lorenz condition $\partial_\mu A^\mu = 0$ (see Eq. 5.142), just as in the massive case. We say that in this case, we work in the Lorenz gauge.

While it is also possible to talk about quantized massless gauge fields in the Lorenz gauge, the discussion is much simpler if we use the gauge freedom a bit differently. A first hint is that in the Lagrangian for massless gauge fields

$$\mathcal{L}_{\text{Maxwell}} = -\frac{1}{2} F_{\mu\nu} F^{\mu\nu}\,, \tag{8.176}$$

there is, just as in the massive case, no term $\partial_0 A_0$.[72] This implies that the corresponding conjugate momentum $\pi^0 = \frac{\partial \mathcal{L}}{\partial(\partial_0 A^0)}$ vanishes and we can conclude again that A_0 is not an independent dynamical parameter. Thus it would be great if we could use our gauge freedom to get rid of A_0 altogether. This is, in fact, possible. For any gauge field configuration it's possible to find a gauge function $\eta(x_\mu)$ such that $A_0 = 0$. This is known as the **temporal gauge**.[73] This is already a great first step because this way we effectively eliminate one degree of freedom from the gauge field. Only one more to go.

[72] This follows again since

$$F_{00} = (\partial_0 A_0 - \partial_0 A_0) = 0\,.$$

[73] The argument that this is possible is exactly the same one that justified the use of the Lorenz gauge in Eq. 5.142.

Luckily, our gauge freedom is not completely exhausted by fixing A_0. It's additionally possible to restrict ourselves to gauge fields that fulfill $\partial_i A_i = 0$ which is a three-dimensional version of the Lorenz condition. The restriction $\partial_i A_i = 0$ is known as the Coulomb condition and if we restrict ourselves to gauge fields that simultaneously fulfill

$$A_0 = 0\,, \quad \partial_i A_i = 0\,, \tag{8.177}$$

we say that we work in the **radiation gauge**.[74]

[74] Take note that the radiation gauge is more restrictive than the Lorenz gauge and really removes all gauge freedom while the Lorenz gauge leaves some residual gauge freedom. In particular, field configurations that fulfill the radiation gauge condition automatically fulfill the Lorenz condition $\partial_\mu A^\mu = 0$ since $\partial_\mu A^\mu = \partial_0 A_0 - \partial_i A_i = \partial_0 0 - \partial_i A_i = 0$.

If we plug our usual ansatz (Eq. 5.115)[75]

$$A_i(x_\mu) = \epsilon_i e^{ik_\mu x^\mu} \tag{8.178}$$

[75] Take note that since $A_0 = 0$ we only use this ansatz for the spatial components.

into the temporal condition, we find

$$\begin{aligned} 0 &= A_0 \\ &\quad \text{Eq. 8.178} \\ &= \epsilon_0 e^{ik_\mu x^\mu} \\ &\quad \cancel{e^{ik_\mu x^\mu}} \\ &= \epsilon_0 \end{aligned} \tag{8.179}$$

Therefore, all allowed polarization vectors have a vanishing zeroth component. In words, this implies that massless gauge fields can't have a temporal polarization.

If we plug the ansatz into the Coulomb condition, we find

$$\begin{aligned} 0 &= \partial_i A_i \\ &\quad \text{Eq. 8.178} \\ &= \partial_i \epsilon_i e^{ik_\mu x^\mu} \\ &\quad \partial_x e^{ikx} = ike^{ikx} \\ &= ik_i \epsilon_i e^{ik_\mu x^\mu} \\ &\quad \cancel{ie^{ik_\mu x^\mu}} \\ &= k_i \epsilon_i\,. \end{aligned} \tag{8.180}$$

For a field excitation that moves in the z-direction ($\vec{k} = (0, 0, k_z)^t$), this implies

$$\begin{aligned} 0 &= k_i \epsilon_i \\ &\quad \vec{k} = (0,0,k_z)^t \\ &= k_z \epsilon_3 \\ &\quad \cancel{k_z} \\ &= \epsilon_3\,. \end{aligned} \tag{8.181}$$

We can therefore conclude again that massless gauge fields cannot be polarized in the direction in which they are traveling. In other words, massless gauge fields can only be transversally polarized but not longitudinally. Since there is no restriction on ϵ_1 and ϵ_2 and we have $\epsilon_0 = 0$ as a result of $A_0 = 0$, we can conclude that for a field excitation that moves in the z-direction, all allowed polarizations can be described by using the basis vectors (Eq. 5.129)

$$\epsilon^1_\mu \equiv \begin{pmatrix} 0 \\ 1 \\ 0 \\ 0 \end{pmatrix}, \quad \epsilon^2_\mu \equiv \begin{pmatrix} 0 \\ 0 \\ 1 \\ 0 \end{pmatrix}. \tag{8.182}$$

Now that we understand what we want to achieve, we can discuss how we consistently take this into account in the quantum theory.

The condition $A_0 = 0$ implies that we don't write down a canonical commutation relation for A_0. The commutation relations for the remaining components A_i is a bit more tricky. Above, we've discovered that for a field excitation that moves in the z-direction, we have $A_3 = 0$. This seems to suggest that it's sufficient to only write down canonical commutation relations for A_1 and A_2.

However, if our field excitation moves in another direction, say, the x-direction, we have $A_1 = 0$. Therefore, the commutation relations we wrote down for the previous case are no longer valid.

We need some tool that allows us to write down for all possible cases that only transverse polarizations become genuine quantum degrees of freedom. Luckily, we already know exactly the right kind of tool: projection operators.

In the previous section we discussed that we can use the operator (Eq. 8.170)

$$P^{\mu\nu} \equiv -\left(\eta^{\mu\nu} - \frac{k^\mu k^\nu}{k_\rho k^\rho}\right) \tag{8.183}$$

to turn any vector v_μ into a vector $v_\mu^\perp \equiv P^{\mu\nu} v_\nu$ that is orthogonal to k_μ:[76]

$$v_\mu^\perp k^\mu = P^{\mu\nu} v_\nu k^\mu = 0\,. \tag{8.184}$$

[76] We checked this explicitly in Eq. 8.173 and Eq. 8.174.

Now we need a projection operator P_{ij} that removes from any given three-vector A_i all components that are parallel to k_i. This would allow us to write down a generally valid formula for the physical degrees of freedom contained in A_i that we can then promote to quantum fields. Formulated differently, we want an operator P_{ij} such that $A_i^\perp k_i = 0$ where $A_i^\perp \equiv P_{ij} A_j$. As soon as we have this operator, we can use it to isolate the two physical transverse components among the remaining three components of the gauge field A_i.

The projection operator that we are looking for is completely analogous to the one that we discussed above:

$$P_{ij} \equiv \left(\delta_{ij} - \frac{k_i k_j}{k_l k_l}\right), \tag{8.185}$$

where δ_{ij} (the Kronecker delta) is the spatial part of the Minkowski metric $\eta^{\mu\nu}$ (modulo a minus sign). We can check explicitly that this operator has the desired effect:

$$\begin{aligned}
0 &\overset{!}{=} A_i^\perp k_i \\
&\quad \text{【 } A_i^\perp \equiv P_{ij} A_j \text{ 】} \\
&= P_{ij} A_j k_i \\
&\quad \text{【 Eq. 8.185 】} \\
&= \left(\delta_{ij} - \frac{k_i k_j}{k_l k_l}\right) A_j k_i \\
&= \left(A_j k_j - \frac{k_i k_i k_j A_j}{k_l k_l}\right) \\
&\quad \text{【 } \not{k}^2 \text{ 】} \\
&= (A_j k_j - k_j A_j) = 0 \quad \checkmark
\end{aligned} \tag{8.186}$$

The newly defined object

$$A_i^\perp = P_{ij} A_j = \left(\delta_{ij} - \frac{k_i k_j}{k_l k_l}\right) A_j \tag{8.187}$$

contains all of the physical degrees of freedom of the massless gauge field. Therefore, we only introduce canonical commutation relations for $A_i^\perp$.

We can calculate the commutation relations by recalling our mantra (Eq. 7.15)

quantum operator $\leftrightarrow$ generator of symmetry.

In particular, we identify the conjugate momentum density with the corresponding generator $\pi_i = -i\frac{\partial}{\partial A_i}$. If we now repeat the calculation in Eq. 8.5 for the physical field $A_i^\perp$, we find

$$
\begin{aligned}
&[A_i^\perp(t,\vec{x}), \pi_j(t,\vec{y})] \, |\Psi\rangle \\
&\quad \text{Eq. 8.4} \\
&= \left[A_i^\perp(t,\vec{x}), -i\frac{\partial}{\partial A_j(t,\vec{y})} \right] |\Psi\rangle \\
&\quad [A,B] \equiv AB - BA \\
&= A_i^\perp(t,\vec{x}) \left(-i\frac{\partial}{\partial A_j(t,\vec{y})} \right) |\Psi\rangle - \left(-i\frac{\partial}{\partial A_j(t,\vec{y})} \right) A_i^\perp(t,\vec{x}) \, |\Psi\rangle \\
&\quad \text{product rule} \\
&= A_i^\perp(t,\vec{x}) \left(-i\frac{\partial}{\partial A_j(t,\vec{y})} \right) |\Psi\rangle - \left(-i\frac{\partial}{\partial A_j(t,\vec{y})} A_i^\perp(t,\vec{x}) \right) |\Psi\rangle \\
&\quad - A_i^\perp(t,\vec{x}) \left(-i\frac{\partial}{\partial A_j(t,\vec{y})} |\Psi\rangle \right) \\
&\quad \cancel{A_i^\perp(x_\mu) \left(-i\frac{\partial}{\partial A_j(t,\vec{y})} \right) |\Psi\rangle} \\
&= - \left(-i\frac{\partial}{\partial A_j(t,\vec{y})} A_i^\perp(t,\vec{x}) \right) |\Psi\rangle \\
&\quad \text{Eq. 8.187} \\
&= i\frac{\partial}{\partial A_j(t,\vec{y})} \left(\left(\delta_{ij} - \frac{k_i k_j}{k_l k_l} \right) A_j(t,\vec{x}) \right) |\Psi\rangle \\
&\quad \frac{\partial A_j(t,\vec{y})}{\partial A_j(t,\vec{y})} = \delta(\vec{x}-\vec{y}) \\
&= i \left(\delta_{ij} - \frac{k_i k_j}{k_l k_l} \right) \delta(\vec{x}-\vec{y}) \, |\Psi\rangle \\
&\quad \text{definition} \\
&= \delta_{ij}^\perp(\vec{x}-\vec{y}) \, |\Psi\rangle \, . \qquad (8.188)
\end{aligned}
$$

The object that we defined in the final step, $\delta^{\perp}(\vec{x}-\vec{y})$, is commonly known as the **transverse delta**. Moreover, the formula that we derived here

$$[A_i^{\perp}(t,\vec{x}), \pi_j(t,\vec{y})] = \delta_{ij}^{\perp}(\vec{x}-\vec{y}) \tag{8.189}$$

is the canonical commutation relation for massless gauge fields in the Coulomb gauge.

With this relation at hand, we can proceed exactly as in the previous sections. We can use the general expansion of our massless gauge field (Eq. 5.156)

$$A_i^{\perp}(x) = \sum_{r=1}^{2} \int \frac{d^3p}{(2\pi)^3} \frac{1}{\sqrt{2k_0}} \left(\epsilon_\mu^r a^r(\vec{k}) e^{-ik_\mu x^\mu} + \epsilon_\mu^r a^{r\dagger}(\vec{k}) e^{ik_\mu x^\mu} \right), \tag{8.190}$$

to introduce the operators $a^r(\vec{k}), a^{r\dagger}(\vec{k})$. By using Eq. 8.189 we can then derive that the operators fulfill the usual commutation relations[77]

$$\begin{aligned} [a^r(\vec{k}), a^{s\dagger}(\vec{k}')] &= (2\pi)^3 \delta^{rs} \delta(\vec{k}-\vec{k}'), \\ [a^r(\vec{k}), a^s(\vec{k}')] = 0, \quad & [a^{r\dagger}\vec{k}), a^{s\dagger}(\vec{k}')] = 0. \end{aligned} \tag{8.192}$$

[77] In this derivation we need the three-dimensional version of the completeness relation that we discussed above (Eq. 8.166)

$$\sum_{r=1}^{2} \epsilon_i^r \epsilon_j^r = -\left(\delta^{ij} - \frac{k^i k^j}{k_l k^l}\right). \tag{8.191}$$

This means that $a^r(\vec{k}), a^{r\dagger}(\vec{k})$ are creation and annihilation operators and we can again introduce a ground state and particle states:

$$\begin{aligned} a^r(\vec{k}) |0\rangle &= 0 \\ a^{r\dagger}(\vec{k}) |0\rangle &\equiv |1_{\vec{k}}^r\rangle . \end{aligned} \tag{8.193}$$

Last but not least, we can once more introduce propagators and in particular, the Feynman propagator

$$\begin{aligned} D_{ij}^{\perp} &\equiv \langle 0|TA_i^{\perp}(x)A_j^{\perp}(y)|0\rangle \\ &\quad \text{cumbersome calculation} \\ &= \int \frac{d^4k}{(2\pi)^4} \frac{i}{k^2+i\epsilon} \left(\delta_{ij} - \frac{k_i k_j}{k_l k_l}\right) e^{-ik(y-x)} . \end{aligned} \tag{8.194}$$

With all the tools introduced in this chapter in line, we are ready to discuss how we can use quantum field theory to predict things that we observe in experiments.

9

Interacting Quantum Fields

So far, we've only talked about free quantum fields. In this section, we start discussing how they interact with each other and with themselves. However, we will only introduce the most important concepts that are commonly used to describe interacting quantum fields and discuss further details in the next part of the book. In other words, in this chapter we lay the groundwork for practical applications of quantum field theory. In particular, we will discuss:

▷ How we can calculate the probability that one given initial field configuration evolves into a specific final configuration.

▷ How these calculations can be simplified by using the interacting picture which allows us, in particular, to reuse everything we learned about free fields in the context of interacting fields.

▷ Moreover, we introduce the Dyson series which allows us to calculate transition amplitudes using a perturbative approach.

▷ Last but not least we have to discuss how the ground state energy changes in the presence of interactions and how we can get sensible results nevertheless.

9.1 Transition Amplitudes and Time Evolution

There are two puzzle pieces when it comes to time evolution. Firstly, we've already discussed the equations of motion that describe how free fields evolve classically. For example, the time evolution of scalar fields is described by the Klein-Gordon equation. Secondly, we discussed that the time evolution of state vectors $|\psi\rangle$ is described by the Schrödinger equation.

As we will see in a moment, this is all we need to know to understand how quantum fields evolve in time.

Let's start by formulating what we want to achieve in mathematical terms. The first ingredient is a ket $|i(0)\rangle$ that describes the initial configuration of the system at some initial moment in time $t = 0$. For example, we can prepare our system in a way such that it contains one particle with momentum k and another particle with momentum k'. We denote the corresponding ket by $|1_k, 1_{k'}\rangle$. Our next task is to figure out how this ket evolves in time. We discussed already in Section 7.1.4 that the time evolution of kets is described by the Schrödinger equation (Eq. 7.26)

$$i\hbar\partial_t |i(t)\rangle = H |i(t)\rangle \,, \tag{9.1}$$

where H denotes the Hamiltonian operator.[1]

[1] In (somewhat abstract) words this equation encodes the fact that the Hamiltonian H is the generator of temporal translations. This can be understood because the Hamiltonian is (for most systems) the energy operator and energy is the Noether charge associated with temporal translations.

Moreover, we discovered in Section 7.1.5 that it's equally possible to describe the time evolution by using a time evolution operator (Eq. 7.27)[2]

$$|\Psi(x,t)\rangle = U(0,t) |\Psi(x,0)\rangle \,. \tag{9.2}$$

[2] We use two arguments for the time evolution operator to indicate that it takes us from $t_i = 0$ to $t_f = t$. These points in time are completely arbitrary and below we start at a different time ($t_i = -\infty$).

In general, the time evolution operator reads (Eq. 7.30)[3]

$$U(0,t) = \mathrm{e}^{-\frac{i}{\hbar}\int_0^t dt' H(t')} \,. \tag{9.3}$$

[3] Reminder: we derived this by plugging the ansatz in Eq. 7.27 into the Schrödinger equation (Eq. 7.26).

Therefore, we have

$$|i(t)\rangle = U(0,t) |i(0)\rangle \,, \tag{9.4}$$

where $|i(t)\rangle$ describes the system at a later moment in time t.

A hallmark of quantum theories is that there is an intrinsic uncertainty that we seemingly can't get rid of. This implies that we are only able to make probabilistic predictions. As discussed in Section 7.1 this is possible in the quantum framework by acting with a bra $\langle f(t)|$ that describes a specific outcome on the ket that describes the system:[4]

$$P(i \to f, t) = |\langle f(t)|i(t)\rangle|^2, \tag{9.5}$$

where $P(i \to f, t)$ denotes the probability for finding the system in the state described by $|f\rangle$. By acting with the bra $\langle f| \equiv |f\rangle^\dagger$ on our ket $|i(t)\rangle$ we project out the probability amplitude we are looking for. The absolute square of this probability amplitude yields the corresponding probability.

[4] Reminder: this is analogous to how we can determine how much a given vector spreads out, say, in the z-direction by multiplying it by the basis vector $\vec{e}_z$:

$$\vec{e}_z \cdot \vec{v} = \vec{e}_z^T \vec{v} = \begin{pmatrix} 0 & 0 & 1 \end{pmatrix} \begin{pmatrix} 1 \\ 3 \\ 5 \end{pmatrix} = 5.$$

This step is necessary because even if we prepare our system in a specific configuration, after a while there will usually be a non-zero probability amplitude for various different final configurations. Schematically

$$|i(t)\rangle = c_1 |f_1(t)\rangle + c_2 |f_2(t)\rangle + c_3 |f_3(t)\rangle + \ldots, \tag{9.6}$$

where $f_1, f_2, \ldots$ describe different possible final configurations and $c_1, c_2, \ldots$ are the corresponding probability amplitudes. By calculating

$$\begin{aligned} \langle f_1(t)|i(t)\rangle &= \langle f_1(t)| \Big(c_1 |f_1(t)\rangle + c_2 |f_2(t)\rangle + c_3 |f_3(t)\rangle + \ldots \Big) \\ &= c_1 \langle f_1(t)|f_1(t)\rangle + c_2 \langle f_1(t)|f_2(t)\rangle + c_3 \langle f_1(t)|f_3(t)\rangle + \ldots \\ &= c_1, \end{aligned} \tag{9.7}$$

$\langle f_1(t)|f_1(t)\rangle = 1$, $\langle f_1(t)|f_2(t)\rangle = 0$

we project out exactly the probability amplitude c_1 that we are looking for.

In summary, we want to evaluate expressions of the form

$$P(i \to f, t) = |\langle f(t)|i(t)\rangle|^2 \tag{9.8}$$

by using the time evolution operator $U(0,t) = e^{-\frac{i}{\hbar}\int_0^t dt' H(t')}$. The object $\langle f(t)|e^{-\frac{i}{\hbar}\int_0^t dt' H(t')}|i(0)\rangle$ is known as a **transition amplitude**.

At this point you might be wondering: where exactly do quantum fields enter the stage here? The answer is: in the Hamiltonian H which depends on the fields. For example, we calculated in Eq. 8.16 that the Hamiltonian operator for a free scalar field reads

$$H = \frac{1}{2}\int_V d^3x \left(\pi^2 + (\partial_i\phi)^2 + m^2\phi^2\right) . \tag{9.9}$$

One of the main tasks in quantum field theory is to calculate the transition amplitude for different initial and final configurations. In the following section, we will talk about a smart trick that is extremely helpful in these calculations.

9.2 The Interaction Picture

What we measure in experiments is not described by a ket $|\psi\rangle$, but by the product of a ket with a bra with possibly some operator $\hat{O}$ in between[5]

$$A(t) = \langle f(t)|\,\hat{O}\,|i(t)\rangle . \tag{9.10}$$

[5] This is the standard formula for an expectation value in quantum theories that we discussed on page 274.

So far we've only talked about the Schrödinger equation which describes how state vectors evolve in time, while there is no equation of motion for the operator $\hat{O}$. This is a perfectly valid approach known as the **Schrödinger picture**. However, by using the observation that we are usually only interestered in expressions of the form given in Eq. 9.10 we can construct different "pictures". While this is merely a neat trick in ordinary quantum mechanics, it is absolutely essential in quantum field theory. In particular, in quantum field theory the fields are the operators that we are interested in and therefore it would be nice if we could somehow take their time evolution into account.

To see how this is possible we rewrite Eq. 9.10 by using the time-evolution operator (Eq. 9.3):[6]

$$A = \langle f(0)| U^{\dagger}(0,t)\hat{O}U(0,t) |i(0)\rangle \,. \tag{9.11}$$

[6] Reminder: $\langle f| = |f\rangle^{\dagger}$ and therefore $\langle f(t)| = \langle f(0)| U^{\dagger}(t)$

Now we can *define* that the time evolution of the operator $\hat{O}$ is described by

$$\hat{O}(t) \equiv U^{\dagger}(0,t)\hat{O}U(0,t)\,. \tag{9.12}$$

In words this means that we absorb all the time dependence into a new definition of the operator. This is interesting because in this case there is no time dependence left for the states which therefore stay as they are:

$$\langle f(0)| U^{\dagger}(0,t)\hat{O}U(0,t) |i(0)\rangle = \langle f(0)| \hat{O}(t) |i(0)\rangle \,. \tag{9.13}$$

This is known as the **Heisenberg picture**.

There is a third picture which is a mix of the Heisenberg picture and the Schrödinger picture. The idea is that we split the time evolution operator U into two parts

$$\begin{aligned} U(t) &\equiv U_{\mathrm{f}}(0,t)U_{\mathrm{i}}(0,t) \\ \mathrm{e}^{-\frac{i}{\hbar}\int_0^t dt' H(t')} &\equiv \mathrm{e}^{-\frac{i}{\hbar}\int_0^t dt' H_{\mathrm{f}}(t')}\mathrm{e}^{-\frac{i}{\hbar}\int_0^t dt' H_{\mathrm{i}}(t')}\,, \end{aligned} \tag{9.14}$$

which is possible if we split the Hamiltonian into two parts

$$H(t) = H_{\mathrm{f}}(t) + H_{\mathrm{i}}(t). \tag{9.15}$$

This splitting is motivated by the observation that the Hamiltonians we are usually interested in consist of a free part and an interaction part. The free Hamiltonian $H_{\mathrm{f}}(t)$ describes the system if all interactions are ignored, while $H_{\mathrm{i}}(t)$ contains all interaction terms.[7]

[7] We discussed interaction terms in Chapter 6.

We then let $U_{\mathrm{i}}(t)$ act on our state vectors and $U_{\mathrm{f}}(t)$ on the operators

$$\begin{aligned} A &= \langle f(0)| \, U^\dagger(0,t)\hat{O}U(0,t) \, |i(0)\rangle \\ &= \langle f(0)| \, U_\mathrm{i}^\dagger(0,t)U_\mathrm{f}^\dagger(0,t)\hat{O}U_\mathrm{f}(0,t)U_\mathrm{i}(0,t) \, |i(0)\rangle \\ &\equiv \langle f_i(t)| \, \hat{O}_i(t) \, |i_i(t)\rangle \, , \end{aligned} \tag{9.16}$$

▷ Eq. 9.14, $(AB)^\dagger = B^\dagger A^\dagger$

▷ definitions

where

$$\begin{aligned} \hat{O}_i(t) &\equiv U_\mathrm{f}^\dagger(0,t)\hat{O}U_\mathrm{f}(0,t) \\ |i_i(t)\rangle &\equiv U_\mathrm{i}(0,t) \, |i(0)\rangle \\ \langle f_i(t)| &\equiv \langle f(0)| \, U_\mathrm{i}^\dagger(0,t) \end{aligned} \tag{9.17}$$

denote the bra, ket, and operator in the **interaction picture**. In words, this means that in the interaction picture the time evolution of our operators is as if they were free, while the time evolution of states is governed entirely by the interaction terms.

This is useful because as long as we stick to the interaction picture, we can use everything we learned about the time evolution of free fields. For example, we can use that the time evolution of free scalar fields is governed by the Klein-Gordon equation.

With this in mind, let's go back to the problem that we really want to solve.

9.3 The Dyson Series

The prototypical setup that we want to describe in quantum field theory is a scattering process. We shoot particles onto each other and then want to predict which particles are produced this way. We start by preparing our system in a specific way at an initial time t_i and we want to predict what the system looks like at a later moment in time t_f.[8] In our framework, we describe the system's state at t_i by $|i(t_i)\rangle$ and a possible outcome at t_f by $\langle f(t_f)|$. Therefore, when we want to describe scattering processes we calculate amplitudes of the form

[8] The subscripts "i" and "f" denote initial and final respectively.

$$A(i \to f) \equiv \langle f(t_f)|i(t_i)\rangle \tag{9.18}$$

In the interaction picture, these amplitudes read

$$\begin{aligned} A(i \to f) &= \langle f(t_f)|U_i(t_i,t_f)|i(t_i)\rangle \\ &\quad \text{Eq. 9.14} \\ &= \langle f(t_f)|e^{-\frac{i}{\hbar}\int_{t_i}^{t_f} dt' H_i(t')}|i(t_i)\rangle \,, \end{aligned} \tag{9.19}$$

where all fields that appear in the interaction Hamiltonian H_i evolve in time as if they were free.

It is convenient to consider the time evolution between $t_i = -\infty$ and $t_f = \infty$. On the one hand this simplifies many calculations. On the other hand, this choice is motivated by the observation that we are usually not interested in what is going on during a scattering process but only in the final outcome since this is what we can observe in our detectors. So we start at $t_i = -\infty$ before scattering has happened and consider the final outcome at $t_f = \infty$ which symbolically represents a moment in time at which all scattering is over.

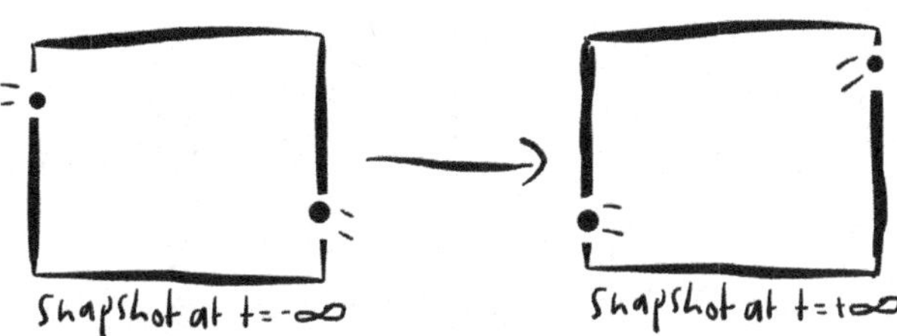

In addition, it is conventional in this context to use the symbol $\hat{S}$ for the time evolution operator. Therefore, we now consider[9]

[9] This is Eq. 9.19 with $t_i = -\infty$ and $t_f = \infty$.

$$\begin{aligned} A(i \to f) &= \langle f(\infty)|e^{-\frac{i}{\hbar}\int_{-\infty}^{\infty} dt' H_i(t')}|i(-\infty)\rangle \\ &\quad |i\rangle \equiv |i(-\infty)\rangle,\ \langle f| \equiv |f(\infty)\rangle \\ &= \langle f|e^{-\frac{i}{\hbar}\int_{-\infty}^{\infty} dt' H_i(t')}|i\rangle \\ &\quad \hat{S} \equiv e^{-\frac{i}{\hbar}\int_{-\infty}^{\infty} dt' H_i(t')} \\ &= \langle f|\hat{S}|i\rangle \,. \end{aligned} \tag{9.20}$$

Schematically, the scattering operator $\hat{S}$ transforms a given initial state into a sum of possible final states that are weighted by the corresponding probability amplitudes. For example, let's assume that we start with two electrons

$$|i\rangle = |e_{k_1}, e_{k_2}\rangle \,, \tag{9.21}$$

where k_1, k_2 denote their momenta. If we act on this initial state with $\hat{S}$, we find something of the form

$$\begin{aligned} \hat{S}\,|i\rangle &= S_{e_{q_1},e_{q_2}}\,|e_{q_1}, e_{q_2}\rangle + S_{e_{q_3},e_{q_4}}\,|e_{q_3}, e_{q_4}\rangle + \ldots \\ &\quad + S_{\mu_{p_1},\mu_{p_2}}\,|\mu_{p_1}, \mu_{p_2}\rangle + S_{\mu_{p_3},\mu_{q_4}}\,|\mu_{p_3}, \mu_{p_4}\rangle + \ldots \,, \end{aligned} \tag{9.22}$$

where $q_1, q_2, \ldots, p_1, p_2$ denote different possible momenta and $|\mu_{p_1}, \mu_{p_2}\rangle$ denotes a state consisting of two muons.[10] Moreover, $S_{e_{q_1},e_{q_2}}$, $S_{\mu_{p_1},\mu_{p_2}}$ etc. are the probability amplitudes for different possible outcomes which we can isolate by multiplying $\hat{S}\,|i\rangle$ by a bra like $\langle e_{q_1}, e_{q_2}|$.

[10] A muon is a heavy cousin of an electron. This means that all properties of the muon are exactly the same as for an electron, except for its mass.

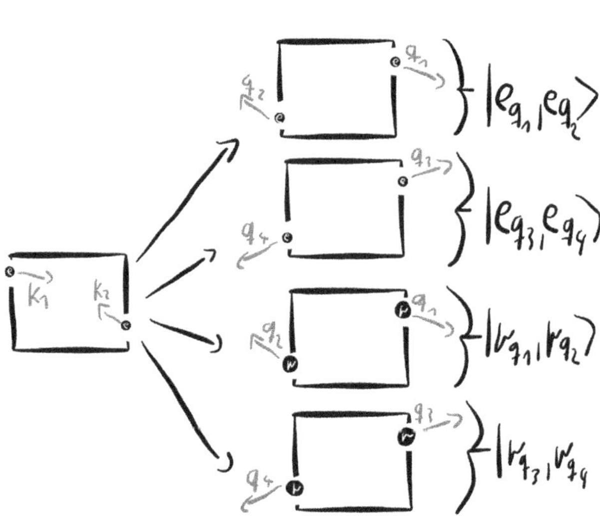

The difficulty in Eq. 9.20 is that the Hamiltonian and therefore our field operators appear in the exponential function. Thus while we already understand what a single field operator does, it's not immediately clear how the exponential function of such field operators acts on a ket. To make sense of such an expression, we need to recall that we can write the exponential function in terms of a series

$$e^x = \sum_{n=0}^{\infty} \frac{x^n}{n!} = 1 + x + \frac{x^2}{2!} + \frac{x^3}{3!} + \frac{x^4}{4!} + \ldots \tag{9.23}$$

Therefore, the scatter operator $\hat{S}$ reads

$$\begin{aligned}\hat{S} &\equiv e^{-\frac{i}{\hbar}\int_{-\infty}^{\infty} dt' H_i(t')} \\ &\quad \text{↷ Eq. 9.23} \\ &= 1 - \frac{i}{\hbar}\int_{-\infty}^{\infty} dt_1 H_i(t_1) \\ &\quad - \frac{1}{\hbar^2 2!}\left(\int_{-\infty}^{\infty} dt_1 H_i(t_1)\right)\left(\int_{-\infty}^{\infty} dt_2 H_i(t_2)\right) - \ldots .\end{aligned} \tag{9.24}$$

9.3.1 Time-Ordering

There is, however, once more a subtlety. So far, we have written the time-evolution operator as being completely analogous to the one we use in quantum mechanics as $U(-\infty, \infty) \equiv e^{-i\int_{-\infty}^{\infty} dt' H(t')}$. But this formula is no longer correct in quantum field theory.[11] Instead, we must use

[11] In fact, it's not always correct in quantum mechanics too. We will understand in a minute why.

$$\tilde{U}(-\infty, \infty) \equiv T e^{-i\int_{-\infty}^{\infty} dt' H(t')}, \tag{9.25}$$

where T denotes the time-ordering operator (Eq. 8.90). To understand why, recall that we discovered in Section 7.1.5 that the time-evolution operator fulfills the equation (Eq. 7.29)

$$i\partial_t U(t) = HU(t). \tag{9.26}$$

The time-evolution operator in the interaction picture, which describes the time-evolution of states, fulfills analogously[12]

[12] The derivation of this equation is analogous to what we did in Section 7.1.5.

$$i\partial_t U_i(t) = H_i U_i(t). \tag{9.27}$$

At first glance, it seems as if $U_i(t) \equiv e^{-i\int_0^t dt' H_i(t')}$ solves this equation. This, however, is not necessarily the case. We only notice this if we evaluate the equation carefully. Let's focus on the left-hand side first:

$$
\begin{aligned}
i\partial_t U_i(t) &= i\partial_t \mathrm{e}^{-i\int_0^t dt' H_i(t')} \\
& \quad \text{↲ } \mathrm{e}^x = \ldots \text{ (Eq. 9.23)} \\
&= i\partial_t \Bigg(1 - i\int_0^t dt_1 H_i(t_1) \\
&\qquad - \frac{1}{2!}\left(\int_0^t dt_1 H_i(t_1)\right)\left(\int_0^t dt_2 H_i(t_2)\right) - \ldots \Bigg) \\
& \quad \text{↲ } \partial_x \int_a^x f(t)dt = f(x) \\
&= -i^2 H_i(t) - i\partial_t \left(\frac{1}{2!}\left(\int_0^t dt_1 H_i(t_1)\right)\left(\int_0^t dt_2 H_i(t_2)\right)\right) - \ldots \\
& \quad \text{↲ product rule} \\
&= H_i(t) - \frac{i}{2!}\Bigg(\left(\partial_t \int_0^t dt_1 H_i(t_1)\right)\left(\int_0^t dt_2 H_i(t_2)\right) \\
&\qquad + \left(\int_0^t dt_1 H_i(t_1)\right)\left(\partial_t \int_0^t dt_2 H_i(t_2)\right)\Bigg) - \ldots \\
& \quad \text{↲ } \partial_x \int_a^x f(t)dt = f(x) \\
&= H_i(t) - \frac{i}{2!}\left(H_i(t)\left(\int_0^t dt_2 H_i(t_2)\right) + \left(\int_0^t dt_1 H_i(t_1)\right) H_i(t)\right) - \ldots \\
& \quad \text{↲} \\
&= H_i(t) - \frac{i}{2!}\left(H_i(t)\left(\int_0^t dt_1 H_i(t_1)\right) + \left(\int_0^t dt_1 H_i(t_1)\right) H_i(t)\right) - \ldots . \qquad (9.28)
\end{aligned}
$$

To get to the last line, we used that we can rename integration variables ("dummy variables") freely. Now compare this to what we have on the right-hand side of Eq. 9.27

$$
\begin{aligned}
H_i(t)U_i(t) &= H_i(t)\mathrm{e}^{-i\int_0^t dt' H_i(t')} \\
& \quad \text{↲ Eq. 9.23} \\
&= H_i(t)\left(1 - i\int_0^t dt_1 H_i(t_1) + \ldots\right) \\
& \quad \text{↲} \\
&= H_i(t) - iH_i(t)\int_0^t dt_1 H_i(t_1) - \ldots . \qquad (9.29)
\end{aligned}
$$

The first term on both right-hand sides of Eq. 9.28 and Eq. 9.29, $H_i(t)$, coincides perfectly. But already the second term is problematic. On the right hand side of Eq. 9.29, we get just one term with $H_i(t)$ on the left-hand side of the integral $\int_0^t dt_1 H_i(t_1)$. While in Eq. 9.28 we also have this term, there is an additional term in which $H_i(t)$ sits on the "wrong" side of the integral.[13] Therefore, the left-hand and right-hand side are only equal if we can can move $H_i(t)$ past the integral such that this term also becomes $H_i(t)\Big(\int_0^t dt_1 H_i(t_1)\Big)$. This, however, is only possible if the Hamiltonian operator evaluated at different moments (here t and t_1) commutes with itself. Formulated differently, only if $[H_i(t), H_i(t')] = 0$, we have

[13] Take note that even if we include higher order terms in Eq. 9.29, there is no comparable term. For example, the next highest order yields something of the form $H_i(t)(\int_0^t dt_1 H_i(t_1))(\int_0^t dt_2 H_i(t_2))$ which is certainly not equal to $\Big(\int_0^t dt_1 H_i(t_1)\Big)H_i(t)$.

$$H_i(t)\Big(\int_0^t dt_1 H_i(t_1)\Big) = \Big(\int_0^t dt_1 H_i(t_1)\Big)H_i(t)\,. \qquad (9.30)$$

This, in turn, implies that only in this case, the left-hand side (Eq. 9.28) and the right-hand side (Eq. 9.29) are actually equal. What can we say about $[H_i(t), H_i(t')]$ in quantum field theory?

We already know that the Hamiltonian contains several products of the fields in question, which themselves are operators.[14] Moreover, we discovered in Section 8.5.1 that

[14] Reminder: in Eq. 8.16 we found that the Hamiltonian for a free scalar field reads

$$H = \frac{1}{2}\int_V d^3x \left(\pi^2 + (\partial_i\phi)^2 + m^2\phi^2\right).$$

$$\begin{aligned} D(t',\vec{x},t,\vec{x}) &\equiv \langle 1_{t',\vec{x}}|1_{t,\vec{x}}\rangle \\ &\equiv \langle 0|\phi(t',\vec{x})\phi(t,\vec{x})|0\rangle \qquad \text{Eq. 8.83} \\ &= \int \frac{dk^3}{(2\pi)^3 2\sqrt{\vec{k}^2+m^2}} e^{i\sqrt{\vec{k}^2+m^2}\cdot(t'-t)}\,. \end{aligned} \qquad (9.31)$$

This implies

$$\begin{aligned} \langle 0|[\phi(t',\vec{x}),\phi(t,\vec{x})]|0\rangle &= \langle 0|\phi(t',\vec{x})\phi(t,\vec{x})|0\rangle - \langle 0|\phi(t,\vec{x})\phi(t',\vec{x})|0\rangle \qquad \text{Eq. 9.31} \\ &= \int \frac{dk^3}{(2\pi)^3 2\sqrt{\vec{k}^2+m^2}} e^{i\sqrt{\vec{k}^2+m^2}\cdot(t'-t)} \\ &\quad - \int \frac{dk^3}{(2\pi)^3 2\sqrt{\vec{k}^2+m^2}} e^{i\sqrt{\vec{k}^2+m^2}\cdot(t-t')} \\ &\neq 0\,. \end{aligned} \qquad (9.32)$$

We can therefore conclude that

$$[\phi(t',\vec{x}),\phi(t,\vec{x})] \neq 0\,. \qquad (9.33)$$

In words, this means that field operators at different moments in time do not commute. Since the Hamiltonian consists of fields, there is no reason why it should commute with itself at different instants of time:

$$[H_i(t), H_i(t')] \neq 0\,. \qquad (9.34)$$

Therefore,

$$H_i(t)\Big(\int_0^t dt_1 H_i(t_1)\Big) \neq \Big(\int_0^t dt_1 H_i(t_1)\Big) H_i(t) \qquad (9.35)$$

and we conclude that the right-hand side (Eq. 9.29) and left-hand side (c.f. Eq. 9.28) in Eq. 9.27 are not equal if we use $U_i(t) \equiv e^{-i\int_0^t dt' H_i(t')}$. In other words, $U_i(t) \equiv e^{-i\int_0^t dt' H_i(t')}$ is not the correct time-evolution operator if the Hamiltonian at different instants in time does not commute with itself.

As already suggested at the beginning of this section, the problem can be solved by using the time-ordering operator T. To understand why this works, we write down explicitly what time-ordering implies for the problematic second term

$$
\begin{aligned}
&T\Big(\int_0^t dt_1\, H_i(t_1) \int_0^t dt_2 H_i(t_2)\Big) \\
&= T\Big(\int_0^t dt_1 \int_0^{t_1} dt_2 H_i(t_1)H_i(t_2) + \int_0^t dt_1 \int_{t_1}^t dt_2\, H_i(t_1)H_i(t_2)\Big) && \text{↷ } \int_a^c = \int_a^b + \int_b^c \\
&= \int_0^t dt_1 \underbrace{\int_0^{t_1} dt_2}_{t_1 > t_2} H_i(t_1)H_i(t_2) + \int_0^t dt_1 \underbrace{\int_{t_1}^t dt_2}_{t_2 > t_1} H_i(t_2)H_i(t_1)\,. && \text{↷ time ordering} \qquad (9.36)
\end{aligned}
$$

We can combine theses two terms into a single term by noting that $t_2 > t_1$ is equivalent to $t_1 < t_2$ and therefore, we have

$$\int_0^t dt_1 \underbrace{\boxed{\int_{t_1}^t dt_2}}_{t_2 > t_1} H_i(t_2)H_i(t_1) = \int_0^t dt_2 \underbrace{\boxed{\int_0^{t_2} dt_1}}_{t_1 < t_2} H_i(t_2)H_i(t_1)$$

renaming integration variables

$$= \int_0^t dt_1 \int_0^{t_1} dt_2\, H_i(t_1)H_i(t_2)\,. \tag{9.37}$$

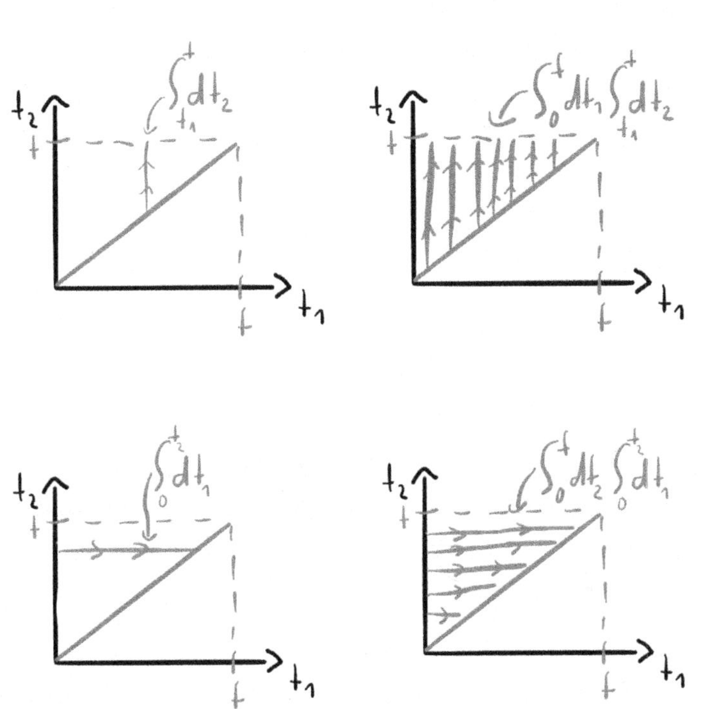

By plugging Eq. 9.37 into Eq. 9.36 we find

$$T\Big(\int_0^t dt_1\, H_i(t_1) \int_0^t dt_2 H_i(t_2)\Big) = 2\int_0^t dt_1 \int_0^{t_1} dt_2\, H_i(t_1)H_i(t_2)\,. \tag{9.38}$$

Therefore, if we plug $\tilde{U}_i(t) \equiv Te^{-i\int_0^t dt' H_i(t')}$ into the left-hand side of our defining equation (Eq. 9.27), we find

$$
\begin{aligned}
i\partial_t \tilde{U}_i(t) &= i\partial_t T e^{-i\int_0^t dt' H_i(t')} \\
&\quad \text{↷ } e^x = \ldots \text{ (Eq. 9.23)} \\
&= i\partial_t T\bigg(1 - i\int_0^t dt_1 H_i(t_1) \\
&\quad - \frac{1}{2!}\left(\int_0^t dt_1 H_i(t_1)\right)\left(\int_0^t dt_2 H_i(t_2)\right) - \ldots\bigg) \\
&\quad \text{↷ } \partial_x \int_a^x f(t)dt = f(x) \\
&= -i^2 H_i(t) - i\partial_t T\left(\frac{1}{2!}\left(\int_0^t dt_1 H_i(t_1)\right)\left(\int_0^t dt_2 H_i(t_2)\right)\right) - \ldots \\
&\quad \text{↷ Eq. 9.38} \\
&= H_i(t) - \frac{i}{2!}\partial_t\left(2\int_0^t dt_1\, H_i(t_1) \underbrace{\int_0^{t_1} dt_2\, H_i(t_2)}_{\text{does not depend on } t}\right) - \ldots \\
&\quad \text{↷ } \partial_x \int_a^x f(t)dt = f(x) \\
&= H_i(t) - iH_i(t)\int_0^t dt_2\, H_i(t_2) - \ldots,
\end{aligned}
\tag{9.39}
$$

To get to the final line, we used $\partial_t \int_0^t f(t_1)dt_1 = f(t)$ with $f(t_1) \equiv H_i(t_1)\int_0^{t_1} dt_2\, H_i(t_2)$ since the upper limit of the second integral also depends on t_1. Thus after we take the derivative this upper limit becomes t. Moreover, we don't need to use the product rule since t only appears in the first integral.

We need to compare this to what we find when we plug $\tilde{U}_i(t) \equiv Te^{-i\int_0^t dt' H_i(t')}$ into the right-hand side of our defining equation (Eq. 9.27):

$$
\begin{aligned}
H_i(t)\tilde{U}(t) &= H_i T e^{-i\int_0^t dt' H_i(t')} \\
&\quad \text{↷ Eq. 9.23} \\
&= H_i(t) T\left(1 - i\int_0^t dt_1 H_i(t_1) - \ldots\right) \\
&\quad \text{↷} \\
&= H_i(t) - iH_i(t)\int_0^t dt_1 H_i(t_1) - \ldots.
\end{aligned}
\tag{9.40}
$$

Since the final lines in Eq. 9.39 and Eq. 9.40 are exactly equal, we can conclude that the correct time evolution operator indeed reads

$$\boxed{\tilde{U}_i(t) \equiv Te^{-i\int_0^t dt' H_i(t')}\,.} \tag{9.41}$$

This implies that the correct scattering operator $\hat{S}$ (Eq. 9.24) reads

$$\begin{aligned}
\hat{S} &\equiv Te^{-i\int_{-\infty}^{\infty} dt' H_i(t')} \\
&\quad \text{(Eq. 9.23)} \\
&= T\left(1 - i\int_{-\infty}^{\infty} dt_1 H_i(t_1)\right. \\
&\quad \left. - \frac{1}{2!}\left(\int_{-\infty}^{\infty} dt_1 H_i(t_1)\right)\left(\int_{-\infty}^{\infty} dt_2 H_i(t_2)\right) - \ldots\right).
\end{aligned} \tag{9.42}$$

We can therefore write the probability amplitudes that we are usually interested in as

$$\begin{aligned}
A(i \to f) &\overset{\text{Eq. 9.20}}{=} \langle f|\hat{S}|i\rangle \\
&\quad \text{(Eq. 9.42)} \\
&= \langle f|i\rangle - i\langle f|\int_{-\infty}^{\infty} dt_1 H_i(t_1)|i\rangle \\
&\quad - \frac{1}{2!}\langle f|T\left(\int_{-\infty}^{\infty} dt_1 H_i(t_1)\right)\left(\int_{-\infty}^{\infty} dt_2 H_i(t_2)\right)|i\rangle - \ldots \\
&\quad \text{(definitions)} \\
&= A^{(0)} + A^{(1)} + A^{(2)} + \ldots\,.
\end{aligned} \tag{9.43}$$

This is known as the **Dyson series**. It is useful because it allows us to evaluate the action of $\hat{S}$ on the given initial state $|i\rangle$ by considering the individual terms in Eq. 9.43 one after another. Moreover, the interaction terms that appear in H_i always involve a coupling constant g which, in many cases, is smaller than one. This implies that higher order terms will contribute less and less to the total probability amplitude.[15] Thus we can calculate approximately correct probability amplitudes by focusing on the first few terms in this series.

[15] For $0 < g < 1$ we have $g > g^2 > g^3 > \ldots$. For example, for $g = 0.1$, we have $g^2 = 0.01$ and $g^3 = 0.001$ etc.

A final aspect that we need to take into account as soon as we talk about interacting quantum fields, is that the ground state gets modified. This is important because we interpret every particle state as an excitation above the ground state $|1_k\rangle \equiv a^\dagger(k)|0\rangle$ (Eq. 8.46). In the following section we will see how we can make this interpretation work for interacting models.

9.4 Ground State Energy in the Presence of Interactions

We discussed in Section 8.3.1 that the energy of the ground state $|0\rangle$ is formally infinite in quantum field theory (Eq. 8.19). Before we discuss how the situation changes if we take interactions into account, let's recap what we've learned about this issue so far. We discovered that if we plug our general field expansion (Eq. 5.51)

$$\phi(x) = \int \mathrm{d}k^3 \frac{1}{(2\pi)^3\sqrt{2\omega_k}} \left(a(\vec{k})\mathrm{e}^{i(kx)} + a^\dagger(\vec{k})\mathrm{e}^{-i(kx)} \right) \tag{9.44}$$

into the general definition (Eq. 8.16):

$$H = \int_V d^3x \left(\frac{\partial \mathcal{L}}{\partial(\partial_0\phi)} \partial_0\phi - \mathcal{L} \right) \tag{9.45}$$

we find (Eq. 8.17)

$$H = \frac{1}{2} \int_V \mathrm{d}k^3 \frac{\omega_k}{(2\pi)^3} \left(a^\dagger(\vec{k})a(\vec{k}) + a(\vec{k})a^\dagger(\vec{k}) \right) . \tag{9.46}$$

This implies that the expected ground state energy is infinitely large:

$$\langle 0|H|0\rangle \sim \infty . \tag{9.47}$$

We can see this because

$$\langle 0|a(\vec{k})a^\dagger(\vec{k})|0\rangle = \left(a^\dagger(\vec{k})\,|0\rangle\right)^\dagger \left(a^\dagger(\vec{k})\,|0\rangle\right)$$

↷ Eq. 8.46

$$= \left(|1_{\vec{k}}\rangle\right)^\dagger \left(|1_{\vec{k}}\rangle\right)$$

↷ $\langle\psi| \equiv |\psi\rangle^\dagger$

$$= \langle 1_{\vec{k}}|1_{\vec{k}}\rangle$$

↷ Eq. 8.44

$$= (2\pi)^3\delta(\vec{k}-\vec{k}) = (2\pi)^3\delta(0) \sim \infty\,. \qquad (9.48)$$

Alternatively, we can also use the commutation relations (Eq. 8.14)

$$[a(k), a^\dagger(k')] = (2\pi)^3\delta(\vec{k}-\vec{k}') \qquad (9.49)$$

to rewrite the Hamiltonian as follows (Eq. 8.19)

$$H = \frac{1}{2}\int_V \mathrm{d}k^3 \frac{\omega_k}{(2\pi)^3}\left(2a^\dagger(\vec{k})a(\vec{k}) + [a(\vec{k}), a^\dagger(\vec{k}')]\right)$$

↷

$$= \int_V \mathrm{d}k^3 \frac{\omega_k}{(2\pi)^3} a^\dagger(\vec{k})a(\vec{k}) + \frac{1}{2}\int_V \mathrm{d}k^3 \omega_k \delta(\vec{0})\,. \qquad (9.50)$$

The first term depends on the configuration of the system in question and yields zero if we apply it to the ground state since $a(k)\,|0\rangle = 0$ (Eq. 8.31).

In contrast, the second term yields exactly the same number (infinity) for any state, even for the ground state. Thus we argued that this is a constant energy offset that we can ignore since what usually matters for us are energy differences. A constant energy offset — even it is infinitely large — makes no difference.

This settled the issue for the free Hamiltonian. However, as soon as we take interactions into account, we need to revisit the issue.

If we take interactions into account, the Hamiltonian contains new terms (Eq. 9.15):

$$H = H_{\mathrm{f}} + H_{\mathrm{i}}, \qquad (9.51)$$

where H_f is the Hamiltonian that we use if we ignore all interactions and H_i contains all interaction terms. One example that we already encountered is[16]

$$H_i = \frac{\lambda}{4!}\phi^4 . \tag{9.52}$$

[16] We discussed the ϕ^4-term in Section 6.2. To derive the Hamiltonian, we can again use the general definition (Eq. 8.16):

$$H = \int_V d^3x \left(\frac{\partial \mathcal{L}}{\partial(\partial_0\phi)}\partial_0\phi - \mathcal{L} \right) .$$

If we plug the ϕ^4-Lagrangian (Eq. 6.26)

$$\mathcal{L} = \frac{1}{2}\partial_\mu\phi\partial^\mu\phi - \frac{1}{2}\mu^2\phi^2 + \frac{1}{4!}\lambda\phi^4 ,$$

into this formula, we find the free Hamiltonian plus a new $\frac{\lambda}{4!}\phi^4$ term which we call the interaction Hamiltonian.

If we now plug the general field expansion (Eq. 5.51) into this formula in order to understand the interaction Hamiltonian in terms of creation and annihilation operators, we find new infinitely large contributions to the ground state energy.

To see this, we introduce the notation

$$\begin{aligned}\phi(x) &= \int dq_1^3 \frac{1}{(2\pi)^3\sqrt{2\omega_{q_1}}} \left(a(\vec{q}_1)e^{-i(q_1x)} + a^\dagger(\vec{q}_1)e^{i(q_1x)} \right) \\ &\equiv \phi_{1-} + \phi_{1+} ,\end{aligned} \tag{9.53}$$

where ϕ_{1-} is an integral over annihilation operators and ϕ_{1+} an integral over creation operators. The interesting part of the interaction Hamiltonian then reads

$$\begin{aligned}\phi^4 &\overset{\text{Eq. 9.53}}{=} (\phi_{1-} + \phi_{1+})(\phi_{2-} + \phi_{2+})(\phi_{3-} + \phi_{3+})(\phi_{4-} + \phi_{4+}) \\ &= \phi_{1+}\phi_{2+}\phi_{3-}\phi_{4-} + \phi_{1-}\phi_{2-}\phi_{3+}\phi_{4+} + \phi_{1-}\phi_{2+}\phi_{3-}\phi_{4+} \\ &\quad + \phi_{1-}\phi_{2+}\phi_{3+}\phi_{4-} + \phi_{1+}\phi_{2-}\phi_{3-}\phi_{4+} + \phi_{1+}\phi_{2-}\phi_{3+}\phi_{4-} + \dots\end{aligned} \tag{9.54}$$

where the dots indicate terms that we ignore for the moment.[17] While the first term in this sum yields zero if we apply it to the ground state since $\phi_- |0\rangle = 0$, the second term, for example, doesn't.

[17] We will see in Chapter 10 that we can ignore these additional terms because they contain an uneven number of creation and annihilation operator terms and therefore necessarily yield zero when we sandwich them between $\langle 0|$ and $|0\rangle$.

However, analogous to what we did for the free Hamiltonian, we can bring the remaining five terms into exactly the same form as the first term by using the commutation relations (Eq. 8.14). The price we have to pay for this are a "few" additional commutators.

For example, for the second term the calculation works as follows[18]

[18] Feel free to jump directly to the final line.

$$
\begin{aligned}
\phi_{1-}\phi_{2-}\phi_{3+}\phi_{4+} &= \phi_{1-}\Big(\phi_{3+}\phi_{2-} + [\phi_{2-},\phi_{3+}]\Big)\phi_{4+} \\
&= \phi_{1-}\phi_{3+}\phi_{2-}\phi_{4+} + [\phi_{2-},\phi_{3+}]\phi_{1-}\phi_{4+} \\
&= \phi_{1-}\phi_{3+}\Big(\phi_{4+}\phi_{2-} + [\phi_{2-},\phi_{4+}]\Big) \\
&\quad + [\phi_{2-},\phi_{3+}]\Big(\phi_{4+}\phi_{1-} + [\phi_{1-},\phi_{4+}]\Big) \\
&= \phi_{1-}\phi_{3+}\phi_{4+}\phi_{2-} + \phi_{1-}\phi_{3+}[\phi_{2-},\phi_{4+}] \\
&\quad + [\phi_{2-},\phi_{3+}]\phi_{4+}\phi_{1-} + [\phi_{2-},\phi_{3+}][\phi_{1-},\phi_{4+}] \\
&= \Big(\phi_{3+}\phi_{1-} + [\phi_{1-},\phi_{3+}]\Big)\phi_{4+}\phi_{2-} \\
&\quad + \Big(\phi_{3+}\phi_{1-} + [\phi_{1-},\phi_{3+}]\Big)[\phi_{2-},\phi_{4+}] \\
&\quad + [\phi_{2-},\phi_{3+}]\phi_{4+}\phi_{1-} + [\phi_{2-},\phi_{3+}][\phi_{1-},\phi_{4+}] \\
&= \phi_{3+}\phi_{1-}\phi_{4+}\phi_{2-} + [\phi_{1-},\phi_{3+}]\phi_{4+}\phi_{2-} \\
&\quad + [\phi_{2-},\phi_{4+}]\phi_{3+}\phi_{1-} + [\phi_{1-},\phi_{3+}][\phi_{2-},\phi_{4+}] \\
&\quad + [\phi_{2-},\phi_{3+}]\phi_{4+}\phi_{1-} + [\phi_{2-},\phi_{3+}][\phi_{1-},\phi_{4+}] \\
&= \phi_{3+}\Big(\phi_{4+}\phi_{1-} + [\phi_{1-},\phi_{4+}]\Big)\phi_{2-} \\
&\quad + [\phi_{1-},\phi_{3+}]\phi_{4+}\phi_{2-} + [\phi_{2-},\phi_{4+}]\phi_{3+}\phi_{1-} \\
&\quad + [\phi_{1-},\phi_{3+}][\phi_{2-},\phi_{4+}] + [\phi_{2-},\phi_{3+}]\phi_{4+}\phi_{1-} \\
&\quad + [\phi_{2-},\phi_{3+}][\phi_{1-},\phi_{4+}] \\
&= \phi_{3+}\phi_{4+}\phi_{1-}\phi_{2-} + [\phi_{1-},\phi_{4+}]\phi_{3+}\phi_{2-} \\
&\quad + [\phi_{1-},\phi_{3+}]\phi_{4+}\phi_{2-} + [\phi_{2-},\phi_{4+}]\phi_{3+}\phi_{1-} \\
&\quad + [\phi_{1-},\phi_{3+}][\phi_{2-},\phi_{4+}] + [\phi_{2-},\phi_{3+}]\phi_{4+}\phi_{1-} \\
&\quad + [\phi_{2-},\phi_{3+}][\phi_{1-},\phi_{4+}]\,. \qquad (9.55)
\end{aligned}
$$

The first term here has exactly the same structure as the first term in Eq. 9.54, $(\phi_{1+}\phi_{2+}\phi_{3-}\phi_{4-})$, and yields zero if we apply it to the ground state $|0\rangle$.

All the remaining terms formally yield infinitely large contributions to the energy of any state. This follows because the field ϕ is evaluated in the product $\phi^4 = \phi^4(x)$ four times at exactly the same spacetime point x. Therefore, when we evaluate the commutators in Eq. 9.55, we find

$$\begin{aligned}
[\phi_{1-}(x),\phi_{2+}(x)] &= \phi_{1-}(x)\phi_{2+}(x) - \phi_{2+}(x)\phi_{1-}(x) \\
&\quad \text{Eq. 9.53} \\
&= \Big(\int dq_1^3 \frac{1}{(2\pi)^3\sqrt{2\omega_{q_1}}} a(\vec{q}_1)e^{-i(q_1x)}\Big)\Big(\int dq_2^3 \frac{1}{(2\pi)^3\sqrt{2\omega_{q_2}}} a^\dagger(\vec{q}_2)e^{i(q_2x)}\Big) \\
&\quad - \Big(\int dq_2^3 \frac{1}{(2\pi)^3\sqrt{2\omega_{q_2}}} a^\dagger(\vec{q}_2)e^{i(q_2x)}\Big)\Big(\int dq_1^3 \frac{1}{(2\pi)^3\sqrt{2\omega_{q_1}}} a(\vec{q}_1)e^{-i(q_1x)}\Big) \\
&= \int \frac{dq_1^3 dq_2^3}{(2\pi)^6\sqrt{4\omega_{q_1}\omega_{q_2}}} a(\vec{q}_1)a^\dagger(\vec{q}_2)e^{-i(q_1-q_2)x} \\
&\quad - \int \frac{dq_1^3 dq_2^3}{(2\pi)^6\sqrt{4\omega_{q_1}\omega_{q_2}}} a^\dagger(\vec{q}_2)a(\vec{q}_1)e^{-i(q_1-q_2)x} \\
&= \int \frac{dq_1^3 dq_2^3}{(2\pi)^6\sqrt{4\omega_{q_1}\omega_{q_2}}} [a(\vec{q}_1),a^\dagger(\vec{q}_2)]e^{-i(q_1-q_2)x} \\
&\quad \text{Eq. 8.14} \\
&= \int \frac{dq_1^3 dq_2^3}{(2\pi)^6\sqrt{4\omega_{q_1}\omega_{q_2}}} \Big((2\pi)^3\delta(\vec{q}_1-\vec{q}_2\Big)e^{-i(q_1-q_2)x} \\
&= \int \frac{dq_1^3}{(2\pi)^3\sqrt{4\omega_{q_1}\omega_{q_1}}} e^{-i(q_1-q_1)x} \\
&\quad e^0 = 1 \\
&= \int \frac{dq_1^3}{(2\pi)^3 2\omega_{q_1}} .
\end{aligned} \tag{9.56}$$

This integral yields infinity if we integrate it from $-\infty$ to ∞ since $\omega_{q_1} = \sqrt{\vec{q}_1^2 + m^2}$ and[19]

$$\int_{-\infty}^{\infty} \frac{1}{\sqrt{x^2+m^2}} = \log\left(\sqrt{x^2+m^2}+x\right)\Big|_{-\infty}^{\infty} \sim \infty . \tag{9.57}$$

Therefore, all terms in Eq. 9.55 that involve a $[\phi_-(x),\phi_+(x)]$ commutator yield an infinitely large contribution to the energy of any state. How can we handle this problem?

Infinitely large contributions to the energy levels of all states are a general problem that occurs in different ways for all kinds of

[19] We assume once more that a trustworthy colleague from the math department confirms that the integral diverges, i.e. yields infinity.

interactions. Thus it makes sense to develop a general strategy that allows us to separate the terms that we are really interested in (e.g. in the free case $a^\dagger a$ and $\phi_{1+}\phi_{2+}\phi_{3-}\phi_{4-} \sim a^\dagger a^\dagger aa$ in the ϕ^4 case) from the ones that represent constant, infinitely large energy shifts. A strategy that works well in many cases is **normal ordering**. We say that an operator product is normal-ordered if all annihilation operators are located to the very right. A few examples

$$\begin{aligned} : aa^\dagger : &\equiv a^\dagger a \\ : a^\dagger aa^\dagger : &\equiv a^\dagger a^\dagger a \\ : aa^\dagger aa^\dagger : &\equiv a^\dagger a^\dagger aa \\ : aaa^\dagger a : &\equiv a^\dagger aaa \,, \end{aligned} \tag{9.58}$$

where the colons denote normal ordering.

The general idea is that a given Hamiltonian in normal order contains all the terms that we are really interested in. For example

$$\begin{aligned} : H_{\text{f}} : &\overset{8.17}{=} : \frac{1}{2}\int_V \mathrm{d}k^3 \frac{\omega_k}{(2\pi)^3}\Big(a^\dagger(\vec{k})a(\vec{k}) + a(\vec{k})a^\dagger(\vec{k})\Big) : \\ &= \frac{1}{2}\int_V \mathrm{d}k^3 \frac{\omega_k}{(2\pi)^3}\Big(: a^\dagger(\vec{k})a(\vec{k}) : + : a(\vec{k})a^\dagger(\vec{k}) :\Big) \\ &= \frac{1}{2}\int_V \mathrm{d}k^3 \frac{\omega_k}{(2\pi)^3}\Big(a^\dagger(\vec{k})a(\vec{k}) + a^\dagger(\vec{k})a(\vec{k})\Big) \\ &= \int_V \mathrm{d}k^3 \frac{\omega_k}{(2\pi)^3} a^\dagger(\vec{k})a(\vec{k}) \,, \end{aligned} \tag{9.59}$$

which is exactly the Hamiltonian that we already identified in Eq. 8.22 as the relevant one.

Similarly, we find for the relevant part of the ϕ^4 interaction Hamiltonian

$$
\begin{aligned}
:\phi^4: \overset{9.54}{=} &: \phi_{1+}\phi_{2+}\phi_{3-}\phi_{4-} : + : \phi_{1-}\phi_{2-}\phi_{3+}\phi_{4+} : + : \phi_{1-}\phi_{2+}\phi_{3-}\phi_{4+} : \\
&+ : \phi_{1-}\phi_{2+}\phi_{3+}\phi_{4-} : + : \phi_{1+}\phi_{2-}\phi_{3-}\phi_{4+} : + : \phi_{1+}\phi_{2-}\phi_{3+}\phi_{4-} : \\
&+ \ldots \\
&= \phi_{1+}\phi_{2+}\phi_{3-}\phi_{4-} + \phi_{3+}\phi_{4+}\phi_{1-}\phi_{2-} + \phi_{2+}\phi_{4+}\phi_{1-}\phi_{3-} \\
&\quad + \phi_{2+}\phi_{3+}\phi_{1-}\phi_{4-} + \phi_{1+}\phi_{4+}\phi_{2-}\phi_{3-} + \phi_{1+}\phi_{3+}\phi_{2-}\phi_{4-} + \ldots \\
&= 6\phi_{1+}\phi_{2+}\phi_{3-}\phi_{4-} + \ldots\,. \qquad (9.60)
\end{aligned}
$$

To get to the final line, we used that the indices $1, 2, 3, 4$ only label different integration variables (Eq. 9.53) that we can always rename freely. Moreover, we used that ϕ_- is defined as an integral over annihilation operators while ϕ_+ is defined as an integral over creation operators. Therefore $: \phi_-\phi_+ : = \phi_+\phi_-$.

One observation that lends further support to the idea that normal ordering our Hamiltonian may be the way to go, is that a normal-ordered Hamiltonian yields zero if we sandwich it between $\langle 0|$ and $|0\rangle$:

$$\langle 0| : H : |0\rangle = 0\,. \qquad (9.61)$$

This follows because H is a sum over products of creation and annihilation operators and in normal order, we either have an annihilation operator to the very right and thus can use $a\,|0\rangle = 0$, or encounter terms that do not contain any annihilation operators but can then use

$$\langle 0| \, a^\dagger = 0\,, \qquad (9.62)$$

which is true since $(|0\rangle\, a^\dagger)^\dagger = a\,|0\rangle = 0$. In words, Eq. 9.61 tells us that the expected energy value for a system in the ground state is zero. This is exactly what we want to be able to interpret particles as finite energy excitation above the vanishing ground state energy.

In summary, whenever it is possible we should use normal-ordered Hamiltonians to avoid infinitely large terms. This will become especially important in the next section, since our probability amplitudes depend directly on the Hamiltonian. Therefore, if our Hamiltonian contains infinitely large terms, we will also find infinitely large contributions to our probability amplitudes. This doesn't make much sense and thus we will use $:H:$ instead of H.

Now it's time to see how all this works in practice. In the following chapters, we will talk about some of the most important applications of quantum field theory.

Part II
Essential Applications

"You can't cross the sea merely by standing and staring at the water."

Rabindranath Tagore

PS: You can discuss the content of Part II with other readers and give feedback at `www.nononsensebooks.com/qft/bonus`.

One of the core ideas in modern physics is that we can dive deeper into Nature's secrets by smashing particles onto each other. If we accelerate our particles sufficiently before the collision, they "break" and we can get a glimpse of what lies behind.[1] Thus, in some sense, we can say that particle colliders are the most powerful microscopes of our time.

[1] Of course, particles don't really break because we understand them as excitations of quantum fields. Therefore, what this really means is that if the energy of the colliding particles is sufficiently high, we can excite additional quantum fields. And theses new excitations show up as new particles in our detectors. Since it costs energy to excite quantum fields, it's possible that the original quantum field excitations (the colliding particles) vanish.

For this reason, applications of quantum field theory are often focused around tools to describe scattering processes. Here, we start with a given set of particles which we prepare in a collider experiment, for example, two electrons. Then our task is to calculate the probability for a given end result after the collision. For example, two electrons with a different momentum or two different particles like two muons. The main tool which allows us to calculate these probabilities is the time-evolution operator. We evolve our initial state in time and then project out the probability amplitude for the final state in question.

While this may sound simple, in practice it isn't. In fact, we can't calculate the probabilities exactly but have to use a perturbative approach. As we've seen in the previous part, we rewrite our time-evolution operator in terms of a series expansion and then evaluate the terms individually. To evaluate a given term, we often use the fact that if two operators A, B do not commute $[A, B] \neq 0$, we can still switch their position as long as we include an additional term:[2]

$$[A, B] = AB - BA$$

$$AB = BA + [A, B] .$$

[2] We will discuss in detail below why switching the position of operators is an important step. The key idea is that we try to move annihilation operators to the right, where they annihilate the ground state $a|0\rangle = 0$ (Eq. 8.31). This implies that only the terms that we get when we switch the operators around (the commutator terms) yield something non-zero.

Usually, the terms that we encounter contain not just two but many operators. Hence, we must use this trick multiple times and get lots of commutator terms as a result. While it is possible to do this manually, it's much smarter to simplify the calculation by using specific tools that we will discuss in the subsequent chapter.

To understand how all of this works, let's consider an example. We will gloss over many important details here in order to build some intuition for what is going on. Afterwards, we will refine our understanding and improve the workflow step by step.

10

Scattering - a First Look

We imagine that we have isolated a small part of the universe in such a way that we can focus on a single scalar field ϕ. Moreover, we assume that we can describe the field and its self-interactions by using the Lagrangian density (Eq. 6.26)[3]

$$\mathcal{L} = \frac{1}{2}\partial_\mu\phi\partial^\mu\phi - \frac{1}{2}m^2\phi^2 - \frac{1}{4!}\lambda\phi^4 \,, \tag{10.1}$$

[3] In comparison with Eq. 6.26 there is an additional minus sign in front of the ϕ^4 term. This is purely conventional since the minus sign can be absorbed into a redefinition of the parameter λ.

that we discussed already in Section 6.2. The corresponding Hamiltonian reads

$$\begin{aligned} H &= \int d^3x \left(\frac{1}{2}\left(\partial_0\phi\right)^2 + \frac{1}{2}(\partial_i\phi)^2 + \frac{1}{2}m^2\phi^2 + \frac{1}{4!}\lambda\phi^4\right) \\ &\equiv H_f + H_i \,, \end{aligned} \tag{10.2}$$

↷ definitions

which can be derived by following exactly the same steps as in Eq. 8.16.

In this case,

$$H_f \equiv \frac{1}{2}\int d^3x \left(\left(\partial_0\phi\right)^2 + (\partial_i\phi)^2 + m^2\phi^2\right) \tag{10.3}$$

is the Hamiltonian that we would use if there were no interactions (Eq. 8.16), and

$$H_i \equiv \int d^3x \left(\frac{1}{4!}\lambda\phi^4\right) \tag{10.4}$$

is the interaction Hamiltonian. For the following discussion to make sense, we assume that λ is a small parameter. In physical terms this implies that the field only interacts weakly with itself.

We call the particles associated with the field ϕ pions, π^0. A typical situation is that we prepare two pions and assume that their momenta $(\vec{k}_1, \vec{k}_2)$ are well known. We then bring them sufficiently close together and want to describe how they scatter off each other.

Since we consider a single scalar field with only one possible type of elementary excitation (that we call pions), we only expect to see pions (possibly with different momenta) after the scattering processes.

In mathematical terms, we start by preparing $|\pi^0_{k_1}, \pi^0_{k_2}\rangle$ and want to calculate, for example, the probability amplitude for finding two pions with different momenta $(\vec{k}_3, \vec{k}_4)$ after the scattering process:

$$A(\pi^0_{k_1}, \pi^0_{k_2} \to \pi^0_{k_3}, \pi^0_{k_4}) = \langle \pi^0_{k_3}, \pi^0_{k_4} | \hat{S} | \pi^0_{k_1}, \pi^0_{k_2} \rangle \,. \tag{10.5}$$

Plugging in the series expansion for the scattering operator $\hat{S}$ (Eq. 9.42) yields

$$\begin{aligned}
&A(\pi^0_{k_1}, \pi^0_{k_2} \to \pi^0_{k_3}, \pi^0_{k_4}) \\
&= \langle \pi^0_{k_3}, \pi^0_{k_4} | \hat{S} | \pi^0_{k_1}, \pi^0_{k_2} \rangle && \text{Eq. 10.5} \\
&= \langle \pi^0_{k_3}, \pi^0_{k_4} | T\Big(1 - i\int_{-\infty}^{\infty} dt_1 H_i(t_1) - \ldots\Big) | \pi^0_{k_1}, \pi^0_{k_2} \rangle && \text{Eq. 9.24} \\
&= \langle \pi^0_{k_3}, \pi^0_{k_4} | \pi^0_{k_1}, \pi^0_{k_2} \rangle - i \langle \pi^0_{k_3}, \pi^0_{k_4} | \int_{-\infty}^{\infty} dt_1 H_i(t_1) | \pi^0_{k_1}, \pi^0_{k_2} \rangle - \ldots \\
&\equiv A^{(0)} + A^{(1)} + \ldots \,. && \text{definition}
\end{aligned} \tag{10.6}$$

Take note that the time ordering operator T makes no difference for the first two terms.

10.1 Zeroth-Order Approximation

If we assume that the momenta of the two pions are completely unchanged by the scattering process $\vec{k}_1, \vec{k}_2 = \vec{k}_3, \vec{k}_4$, the first term, $A^{(0)}$, is non-vanishing and we find[4]

[4] This is only a first order approximation for the probability amplitude since we ignore all higher order terms. Thus we use the symbol $\approx$.

$$\begin{aligned}
A(\pi^0_{k_1}, \pi^0_{k_2} \to \pi^0_{k_1}, \pi^0_{k_2}) &\approx A^0 && \text{Eq. 10.6}\\
&= \langle \pi^0_{k_1}, \pi^0_{k_2} | \pi^0_{k_1}, \pi^0_{k_2} \rangle && |\psi_1, \psi_2\rangle \equiv |\psi_1\rangle |\psi_2\rangle\\
&= \Big(\langle \pi^0_{k_2} | \langle \pi^0_{k_1} | \Big) \Big(|\pi^0_{k_1}\rangle |\pi^0_{k_2}\rangle \Big)\\
&= \langle \pi^0_{k_2} | \pi^0_{k_2} \rangle \langle \pi^0_{k_1} | \pi^0_{k_1} \rangle && \text{Eq. 8.48}\\
&= \Big(2\omega_{k_1} (2\pi)^3 \delta(\vec{k}_1 - \vec{k}_1) \Big) \Big(2\omega_{k_2} (2\pi)^3 \delta(\vec{k}_2 - \vec{k}_2) \Big)\\
&= 4\omega_{k_1} \omega_{k_2} \Big((2\pi)^3 \delta(\vec{0}) \Big)^2 . \qquad (10.7)
\end{aligned}$$

This result doesn't make much sense. But this is not surprising since we started with the unrealistic assumption that the momenta of the two pions that we start with are exactly known. We discussed this issue already in Section 8.4.3. One solution is to assume that the system we consider is confined to a finite volume V.

If this is the case, states with exactly known momentum (plane wave states) are, in principle, normalizable and instead of $(2\pi)^3\delta(\vec{0})$ we get V (Eq. 8.68, Eq. 8.71). As discussed in Section 8.4.3 it is conventional to rewrite all formulas in such a way that the volume V drops out. For example, in this case we could write the probability for the transition $\pi^0_{k_1}, \pi^0_{k_2} \to \pi^0_{k_1}, \pi^0_{k_2}$ as

$$
\begin{aligned}
P(\pi^0_{k_1}, \pi^0_{k_2} &\to \pi^0_{k_1}, \pi^0_{k_2}) \\
&= \frac{|A(\pi^0_{k_1}, \pi^0_{k_2} \to \pi^0_{k_1}, \pi^0_{k_2})|^2}{\langle \pi^0_{k_1}, \pi^0_{k_2} | \pi^0_{k_1}, \pi^0_{k_2} \rangle \langle \pi^0_{k_1}, \pi^0_{k_2} | \pi^0_{k_1}, \pi^0_{k_2} \rangle} && \text{Eq. 8.69} \\
&= \frac{|\langle \pi^0_{k_1}, \pi^0_{k_2} | \pi^0_{k_1}, \pi^0_{k_2} \rangle|^2}{\langle \pi^0_{k_1}, \pi^0_{k_2} | \pi^0_{k_1}, \pi^0_{k_2} \rangle \langle \pi^0_{k_1}, \pi^0_{k_2} | \pi^0_{k_1}, \pi^0_{k_2} \rangle} && \text{Eq. 10.5} \\
&= \frac{\big(V\big)^2}{\big(V\big)^2} && \text{Eq. 10.7} \\
&= 1 . && (10.8)
\end{aligned}
$$

This is really just a trick that allows us to avoid working with wave packets. A second possibility is to use the more realistic smeared initial and final states (Eq. 8.76) that we introduced in Section 8.4.4. In this case, we find

$$
\begin{aligned}
A(\pi^0_{k_1}, \pi^0_{k_2} \to \pi^0_{k_1}, \pi^0_{k_2}) &\approx \Big({}^{\mathrm{r}}\langle \pi^0_{k_2} | \, {}^{\mathrm{r}}\langle \pi^0_{k_1} | \Big) \Big(| \pi^0_{k_1} \rangle^{\mathrm{r}} \, | \pi^0_{k_2} \rangle^{\mathrm{r}} \Big) \\
&= {}^{\mathrm{r}}\langle \pi^0_{k_2} | \, {}^{\mathrm{r}}\langle \pi^0_{k_1} | \pi^0_{k_1} \rangle^{\mathrm{r}} \, | \pi^0_{k_2} \rangle^{\mathrm{r}} \\
&= {}^{\mathrm{r}}\langle \pi^0_{k_2} | \pi^0_{k_2} \rangle^{\mathrm{r}} \, {}^{\mathrm{r}}\langle \pi^0_{k_1} | \pi^0_{k_1} \rangle^{\mathrm{r}} \\
&= 1 , && (10.9)
\end{aligned}
$$

where we used that ${}^{\mathrm{r}}\langle \pi^0_{k_1} | \pi^0_{k_1} \rangle^{\mathrm{r}}$ is a number and we can move numbers around freely. If we allow that the momenta of the particles in the final state can be different, we find

$$\begin{aligned}
&A(\pi^0_{k_1}, \pi^0_{k_2} \to \pi^0_{k_3}, \pi^0_{k_4}) \\
&\approx A^0 \\
&= \langle \pi^0_{k_3}, \pi^0_{k_4} | \pi^0_{k_1}, \pi^0_{k_2} \rangle \\
&= \Big(\langle \pi^0_{k_4} | \langle \pi^0_{k_3} | \Big) \Big(| \pi^0_{k_1} \rangle | \pi^0_{k_2} \rangle \Big) \\
&= \langle \pi^0_{k_4} | \pi^0_{k_2} \rangle \langle \pi^0_{k_3} | \pi^0_{k_1} \rangle \\
&= \Big(2\sqrt{\omega_{k_1}\omega_{k_3}} (2\pi)^3 \delta(\vec{k}_1 - \vec{k}_3) \Big) \Big(2\sqrt{\omega_{k_2}\omega_{k_4}} (2\pi)^3 \delta(\vec{k}_2 - \vec{k}_4) \Big) .
\end{aligned} \tag{10.10}$$

Eq. 10.6

$|\psi_1, \psi_2\rangle \equiv |\psi_1\rangle |\psi_2\rangle$

Eq. 8.48

This is only non-zero for $\vec{k}_1 = \vec{k}_3$ and $\vec{k}_2 = \vec{k}_4$, which is the case we considered above.

The zeroth order term we considered in this section describes the scattering of two particles if all interactions are turned off. With all interactions turned off, there is a 100% probability that the two particles have at the end of the scattering process exactly the same momenta as at the beginning. The probability for any other state (two particles with different momenta etc.) is zero. This is true for the zeroth order term in any scattering process and therefore it is conventional to isolate the trivial part of the scattering operator by defining

$$\hat{S} \equiv 1 + i\hat{T} , \tag{10.11}$$

where $\hat{T}$ is known as the transfer operator.

10.2 First-Order Approximation

It is instructive to evaluate the first nontrivial term in Eq. 10.6 explicitly since there are many new aspects

$$\begin{aligned}
A^{(1)} &\equiv -i \langle \pi^0_{k_1}, \pi^0_{k_2}| \int_{-\infty}^{\infty} dt_1 H_i(t_1) |\pi^0_{k_1}, \pi^0_{k_2}\rangle \\
&\quad \text{Eq. 10.4} \\
&= -i \langle \pi^0_{k_1}, \pi^0_{k_2}| \int_{-\infty}^{\infty} dt_1 \Big(\int_V d^3x \left(\frac{1}{4!} \lambda \phi^4 \right) \Big) |\pi^0_{k_1}, \pi^0_{k_2}\rangle \\
&= \frac{-i\lambda}{4!} \int_{-\infty}^{\infty} d^4x \, \langle \pi^0_{k_1}, \pi^0_{k_2}| \phi^4 |\pi^0_{k_1}, \pi^0_{k_2}\rangle \, .
\end{aligned} \tag{10.12}$$

To evaluate $\langle \pi^0_{k_1}, \pi^0_{k_2}| \phi^4 |\pi^0_{k_1}, \pi^0_{k_2}\rangle$, we need to recall that our general field expansion reads (Eq. 5.51)

$$\begin{aligned}
\phi(x) &= \int \mathrm{d}k^3 \frac{1}{(2\pi)^3 \sqrt{2\omega_k}} \left(a(\vec{k}) \mathrm{e}^{-i(kx)} + a^\dagger(\vec{k}) \mathrm{e}^{i(kx)} \right) \\
&\equiv \phi_- + \phi_+ \, ,
\end{aligned} \tag{10.13}$$

where ϕ_- is an integral over annihilation operators, while ϕ_+ is an integral over creation operators. The factor ϕ^4 therefore reads

$$\phi^4 \overset{\text{Eq. 10.13}}{=} (\phi_- + \phi_+)(\phi_- + \phi_+)(\phi_- + \phi_+)(\phi_- + \phi_+) \, . \tag{10.14}$$

Before we discuss more subtle aspects of this expression, take note that most of the terms yield zero if we sandwich them between $\langle \pi^0_{k_1}, \pi^0_{k_2}|$ and $|\pi^0_{k_1}, \pi^0_{k_2}\rangle$. For example, let's consider the term ϕ_-^4. This terms contains a product of four annihilation operators a^4. Two of them are sufficient to annihilate the two particles contained in $a^2 |\pi^0_{k_1}, \pi^0_{k_2}\rangle \sim |0\rangle$. Afterwards, we are left with the ground state and two additional annihilation operators. When they act on the ground state, we necessarily find zero: $a|0\rangle = 0$ (Eq. 8.31). Similarly, a term of the form ϕ_+^4 will yield zero since it contains a product of four creation operators $a^{\dagger 4}$. When they act on our initial state $|\pi^0_{k_1}, \pi^0_{k_2}\rangle$, they create four further particles. If we then act with the bra $\langle \pi^0_{k_1}, \pi^0_{k_2}|$, which describes a final state consisting of just two particles, on the resulting state we find zero. Analogous arguments apply to all terms that do not contain an equal number of creation and annihilation terms. Only terms of the form $\phi_+\phi_+\phi_-\phi_- \sim a^\dagger a^\dagger aa$ have a chance of yielding something non-zero since they contain products of an equal number of creation and annihilation operators.[5] The annihilation operators act on $|\pi^0_{k_1}, \pi^0_{k_2}\rangle$, which leaves us with the ground state $|0\rangle$ (times some numerical factors). The remaining two operators $a^\dagger a^\dagger$ then act on this ground state and create two new particles. Thus, we possibly find something non-zero if we then act on this final ket with the two particle final state $\langle \pi^0_{k_1}, \pi^0_{k_2}|$. If we want to evaluate the product in Eq. 10.14, we need to recall that operators, in general, do not commute: (Eq. 8.14)

[5] Take note that this is only the case because we consider an equal number of particles in the initial and final state. If we considered, for example, a transition from two to three particles we would need a term of the form $\phi_+\phi_+\phi_+\phi_-\phi_-$ to get something non-zero.

$$[a(\vec{k}), a^\dagger(\vec{k}')] = (2\pi)^3\delta(\vec{k} - \vec{k}')$$
$$[a(\vec{k}), a(\vec{k}')] = 0\,, \quad [a^\dagger(\vec{k}), a^\dagger(\vec{k}')] = 0\,. \tag{10.15}$$

As in Section 9.4, we must use different integration parameters, q_1, q_2, q_3, q_4, when we expand the four field factors that appear in ϕ^4 and thus introduce the notation

$$\phi(x) = \int \mathrm{d}q_1^3 \frac{1}{(2\pi)^3\sqrt{2\omega_{q_1}}} \left(a(\vec{q}_1)\mathrm{e}^{-i(q_1x)} + a^\dagger(\vec{q}_1)\mathrm{e}^{i(q_1x)} \right)$$

definitions

$$\equiv \phi_{1-} + \phi_{1+}\,. \tag{10.16}$$

Using this more careful notation, we write our product again as

$$\phi^4 \overset{\text{Eq. 10.16}}{=} (\phi_{1-} + \phi_{1+})(\phi_{2-} + \phi_{2+})(\phi_{3-} + \phi_{3+})(\phi_{4-} + \phi_{4+})$$
$$= \phi_{1+}\phi_{2+}\phi_{3-}\phi_{4-} + \phi_{1-}\phi_{2-}\phi_{3+}\phi_{4+} + \phi_{1-}\phi_{2+}\phi_{3-}\phi_{4+}$$
$$+ \phi_{1-}\phi_{2+}\phi_{3+}\phi_{4-} + \phi_{1+}\phi_{2-}\phi_{3-}\phi_{4+} + \phi_{1+}\phi_{2-}\phi_{3+}\phi_{4-} + \ldots \tag{10.17}$$

where the dots indicate all terms with an uneven number of creation and annihilation terms like, for example, $\phi_{1-}\phi_{2-}\phi_{3-}\phi_{4-}$. Let's focus on the first term here for a moment. The expression we want to evaluate reads

$$\langle \pi^0_{k_1}, \pi^0_{k_2} | \phi_{1+}\phi_{2+}\phi_{3-}\phi_{4-} | \pi^0_{k_1}, \pi^0_{k_2} \rangle\,. \tag{10.18}$$

To that end, we need the definition of our initial state[6]

[6] The ordering of the operators here is not important since $[a^\dagger(\vec{k}), a^\dagger(\vec{k}')] = 0$ (Eq. 8.14).

$$\begin{aligned} |\pi^0_{k_1}, \pi^0_{k_2}\rangle &= a^\dagger(k_1) a^\dagger(k_2) |0\rangle \\ &\quad \text{Eq. 8.47} \\ &= \sqrt{2\omega_{k_1}} a^\dagger(\vec{k}_1) \sqrt{2\omega_{k_2}} a^\dagger(\vec{k}_2) |0\rangle \,. \end{aligned} \tag{10.19}$$

Analogously, our final state is defined as[7]

[7] Reminder: $\langle\psi| = |\psi\rangle^\dagger$

$$\langle \pi^0_{k_1}, \pi^0_{k_2}| = \langle 0| \sqrt{2\omega_{k_1}} a(\vec{k}_1) \sqrt{2\omega_{k_2}} a(\vec{k}_2) \,. \tag{10.20}$$

A smart idea is now that we use the commutation relations in Eq. 8.14 to move the annihilation operators to the right side. Once this is done, they act on the ground state and thus yield zero ($a|0\rangle = 0$, Eq. 8.31). What we are then left with, is the contribution to the amplitude that we are looking for. This surely sounds a bit strange at first, but will make a lot of sense as soon as we go through the motions:[8]

[8] Be warned that the following calculation is quite cumbersome. But it is worth the effort since it is instructive to see everything spelled out in explicit terms at least once.

$$\begin{aligned} &\langle \pi^0_{k_1}, \pi^0_{k_2} | \phi_{1+}\phi_{2+}\phi_{3-}\phi_{4-} | \pi^0_{k_1}, \pi^0_{k_2}\rangle \\ &\quad \text{Eq. 10.19, Eq. 10.20} \\ &= \Big(\langle 0| \sqrt{2\omega_{k_1}} a(\vec{k}_1) \sqrt{2\omega_{k_2}} a(\vec{k}_2) \Big) \phi_{1+}\phi_{2+}\phi_{3-}\phi_{4-} \\ &\quad \times \Big(\sqrt{2\omega_{\vec{k}_1}} a^\dagger(\vec{k}_1) \sqrt{2\omega_{\vec{k}_2}} a^\dagger(\vec{k}_2) |0\rangle \Big) \\ &= 4\omega_{k_1}\omega_{k_2} \langle 0| a(\vec{k}_1) a(\vec{k}_2) \phi_{1+}\phi_{2+}\phi_{3-}\phi_{4-} a^\dagger(\vec{k}_1) a^\dagger(\vec{k}_2) |0\rangle \\ &\quad \text{Eq. 9.53} \\ &= 4\omega_{k_1}\omega_{k_2} \langle 0| a(\vec{k}_1) a(\vec{k}_2) \Big(\int dq_1^3 \frac{1}{(2\pi)^3 \sqrt{2\omega_{q_1}}} a^\dagger(\vec{q}_1) e^{i(q_1 x)} \Big) \\ &\quad \times \Big(\int dq_2^3 \frac{1}{(2\pi)^3 \sqrt{2\omega_{q_2}}} a^\dagger(\vec{q}_2) e^{i(q_2 x)} \Big) \Big(\int dq_3^3 \frac{1}{(2\pi)^3 \sqrt{2\omega_{q_3}}} a(\vec{q}_3) e^{-i(q_3 x)} \Big) \\ &\quad \times \Big(\int dq_4^3 \frac{1}{(2\pi)^3 \sqrt{2\omega_{q_4}}} a(\vec{q}_4) e^{-i(q_4 x)} \Big) a^\dagger(\vec{k}_1) a^\dagger(\vec{k}_2) |0\rangle \\ &= 4\omega_{k_1}\omega_{k_2} \int \frac{dq_1^3}{(2\pi)^3 \sqrt{2\omega_{q_1}}} \int \frac{dq_2^3}{(2\pi)^3 \sqrt{2\omega_{q_2}}} \int \frac{dq_3^3}{(2\pi)^3 \sqrt{2\omega_{q_3}}} \int \frac{dq_4^3}{(2\pi)^3 \sqrt{2\omega_{q_4}}} \\ &\quad \times \langle 0| a(\vec{k}_1) a(\vec{k}_2) a^\dagger(\vec{q}_1) a^\dagger(\vec{q}_2) a(\vec{q}_3) a(\vec{q}_4) a^\dagger(\vec{k}_1) a^\dagger(\vec{k}_2) |0\rangle \, e^{i(q_1+q_2-q_3-q_4)x} \,. \end{aligned} \tag{10.21}$$

We now use the commutation relations (Eq. 8.14) to move the annihilation operators to the right side. We have, for example,

$$\begin{aligned} [a(\vec{q}_4), a^\dagger(\vec{k}_1)] &\overset{\text{Eq. 8.14}}{=} (2\pi)^3 \delta(\vec{k}_1 - \vec{q}_4) \\ a(\vec{q}_4) a^\dagger(\vec{k}_1) &= a^\dagger(\vec{k}_1) a(\vec{q}_4) + (2\pi)^3 \delta(\vec{k}_1 - \vec{q}_4) \,. \end{aligned} \tag{10.22}$$

This yields

$$\begin{aligned}
&\langle 0| a(\vec{k}_1)a(\vec{k}_2)a^\dagger(\vec{q}_1)a^\dagger(\vec{q}_2)a(\vec{q}_3)a(\vec{q}_4)a^\dagger(\vec{k}_1)a^\dagger(\vec{k}_2)|0\rangle \\
&= \langle 0| a(\vec{k}_1)a(\vec{k}_2)a^\dagger(\vec{q}_1)a^\dagger(\vec{q}_2)a(\vec{q}_3)\Big(a^\dagger(\vec{k}_1)a(\vec{q}_4) + (2\pi)^3\delta(\vec{k}_1-\vec{q}_4)\Big)a^\dagger(\vec{k}_2)|0\rangle \\
&= \langle 0| a(\vec{k}_1)a(\vec{k}_2)a^\dagger(\vec{q}_1)a^\dagger(\vec{q}_2)a(\vec{q}_3)a^\dagger(\vec{k}_1)a(\vec{q}_4)a^\dagger(\vec{k}_2)|0\rangle \\
&\quad + (2\pi)^3\delta(\vec{k}_1-\vec{q}_4)\langle 0| a(\vec{k}_1)a(\vec{k}_2)a^\dagger(\vec{q}_1)a^\dagger(\vec{q}_2)a(\vec{q}_3)a^\dagger(\vec{k}_2)|0\rangle \\
&= \langle 0| a(\vec{k}_1)a(\vec{k}_2)a^\dagger(\vec{q}_1)a^\dagger(\vec{q}_2)a(\vec{q}_3)a^\dagger(\vec{k}_1)\Big(a^\dagger(\vec{k}_2)a(\vec{q}_4) + (2\pi)^3\delta(\vec{k}_2-\vec{q}_4)\Big)|0\rangle \\
&\quad + (2\pi)^3\delta(\vec{k}_1-\vec{q}_4)\langle 0| a(\vec{k}_1)a(\vec{k}_2)a^\dagger(\vec{q}_1)a^\dagger(\vec{q}_2)\Big(a^\dagger(\vec{k}_2)a(\vec{q}_3) + (2\pi)^3\delta(\vec{k}_2-\vec{q}_3)\Big)|0\rangle \\
&= (2\pi)^3\delta(\vec{k}_2-\vec{q}_4)\langle 0| a(\vec{k}_1)a(\vec{k}_2)a^\dagger(\vec{q}_1)a^\dagger(\vec{q}_2)a(\vec{q}_3)a^\dagger(\vec{k}_1)|0\rangle \\
&\quad + (2\pi)^6\delta(\vec{k}_1-\vec{q}_4)\delta(\vec{k}_2-\vec{q}_3)\langle 0| a(\vec{k}_1)a(\vec{k}_2)a^\dagger(\vec{q}_1)a^\dagger(\vec{q}_2)|0\rangle \\
&= (2\pi)^6\delta(\vec{k}_2-\vec{q}_4)\delta(\vec{k}_1-\vec{q}_3)\langle 0| a(\vec{k}_1)a(\vec{k}_2)a^\dagger(\vec{q}_1)a^\dagger(\vec{q}_2)|0\rangle \\
&\quad + (2\pi)^6\delta(\vec{k}_1-\vec{q}_4)\delta(\vec{k}_2-\vec{q}_3)\langle 0| a(\vec{k}_1)a(\vec{k}_2)a^\dagger(\vec{q}_1)a^\dagger(\vec{q}_2)|0\rangle \\
&= (2\pi)^6\delta(\vec{k}_2-\vec{q}_4)\delta(\vec{k}_1-\vec{q}_3)\langle 0| a(\vec{k}_1)\Big(a^\dagger(\vec{q}_1)a(\vec{k}_2) + (2\pi)^3\delta(\vec{k}_2-\vec{q}_1)\Big)a^\dagger(\vec{q}_2)|0\rangle \\
&\quad + (2\pi)^6\delta(\vec{k}_1-\vec{q}_4)\delta(\vec{k}_2-\vec{q}_3)\langle 0| a(\vec{k}_1)\Big(a^\dagger(\vec{q}_1)a(\vec{k}_2) + (2\pi)^3\delta(\vec{k}_2-\vec{q}_1)\Big)a^\dagger(\vec{q}_2)|0\rangle \\
&= (2\pi)^6\delta(\vec{k}_2-\vec{q}_4)\delta(\vec{k}_1-\vec{q}_3)\langle 0| a(\vec{k}_1)a^\dagger(\vec{q}_1)a(\vec{k}_2)a^\dagger(\vec{q}_2)|0\rangle \\
&\quad + (2\pi)^9\delta(\vec{k}_2-\vec{q}_4)\delta(\vec{k}_1-\vec{q}_3)\delta(\vec{k}_2-\vec{q}_1)\langle 0| a(\vec{k}_1)a^\dagger(\vec{q}_2)|0\rangle \\
&\quad + (2\pi)^6\delta(\vec{k}_1-\vec{q}_4)\delta(\vec{k}_2-\vec{q}_3)\langle 0| a(\vec{k}_1)a^\dagger(\vec{q}_1)a(\vec{k}_2)a^\dagger(\vec{q}_2)|0\rangle \\
&\quad + (2\pi)^9\delta(\vec{k}_1-\vec{q}_4)\delta(\vec{k}_2-\vec{q}_1)\delta(\vec{k}_2-\vec{q}_3)\langle 0| a(\vec{k}_1)a^\dagger(\vec{q}_2)|0\rangle \\
&= (2\pi)^6\delta(\vec{k}_2-\vec{q}_4)\delta(\vec{k}_1-\vec{q}_3)\langle 0| a(\vec{k}_1)a^\dagger(\vec{q}_1)\Big(a^\dagger(\vec{q}_2)a(\vec{k}_2) + (2\pi)^3\delta(\vec{k}_2-\vec{q}_2)\Big)|0\rangle \\
&\quad + (2\pi)^9\delta(\vec{k}_2-\vec{q}_4)\delta(\vec{k}_1-\vec{q}_3)\delta(\vec{k}_2-\vec{q}_1)\langle 0|\Big(a^\dagger(\vec{q}_2)a(\vec{k}_1) + (2\pi)^3\delta(\vec{k}_1-\vec{q}_2)\Big)|0\rangle \\
&\quad + (2\pi)^6\delta(\vec{k}_1-\vec{q}_4)\delta(\vec{k}_2-\vec{q}_3)\langle 0| a(\vec{k}_1)a^\dagger(\vec{q}_1)\Big(a^\dagger(\vec{q}_2)a(\vec{k}_2) + (2\pi)^3\delta(\vec{k}_2-\vec{q}_2)\Big)|0\rangle \\
&\quad + (2\pi)^9\delta(\vec{k}_1-\vec{q}_4)\delta(\vec{k}_2-\vec{q}_1)\delta(\vec{k}_2-\vec{q}_3)\langle 0|\Big(a^\dagger(\vec{q}_2)a(\vec{k}_1) + (2\pi)^3\delta(\vec{k}_1-\vec{q}_2)\Big)|0\rangle \\
&= (2\pi)^9\delta(\vec{k}_2-\vec{q}_4)\delta(\vec{k}_1-\vec{q}_3)\delta(\vec{k}_2-\vec{q}_2)\langle 0| a(\vec{k}_1)a^\dagger(\vec{q}_1)|0\rangle \\
&\quad + (2\pi)^{12}\delta(\vec{k}_2-\vec{q}_4)\delta(\vec{k}_1-\vec{q}_3)\delta(\vec{k}_2-\vec{q}_1)\delta(\vec{k}_1-\vec{q}_2)\langle 0|0\rangle \\
&\quad + (2\pi)^9\delta(\vec{k}_1-\vec{q}_4)\delta(\vec{k}_2-\vec{q}_3)\delta(\vec{k}_2-\vec{q}_2)\langle 0| a(\vec{k}_1)a^\dagger(\vec{q}_1)|0\rangle \\
&\quad + (2\pi)^{12}\delta(\vec{k}_1-\vec{q}_4)\delta(\vec{k}_2-\vec{q}_1)\delta(\vec{k}_1-\vec{q}_2)\delta(\vec{k}_2-\vec{q}_3)\langle 0|0\rangle \\
&= (2\pi)^{12}\delta(\vec{k}_2-\vec{q}_4)\delta(\vec{k}_1-\vec{q}_3)\delta(\vec{k}_2-\vec{q}_2)\delta(\vec{k}_1-\vec{q}_1)\langle 0|0\rangle \\
&\quad + (2\pi)^{12}\delta(\vec{k}_2-\vec{q}_4)\delta(\vec{k}_1-\vec{q}_3)\delta(\vec{k}_2-\vec{q}_1)\delta(\vec{k}_1-\vec{q}_2)\langle 0|0\rangle \\
&\quad + (2\pi)^{12}\delta(\vec{k}_1-\vec{q}_4)\delta(\vec{k}_2-\vec{q}_3)\delta(\vec{k}_2-\vec{q}_2)\delta(\vec{k}_1-\vec{q}_1)\langle 0|0\rangle \\
&\quad + (2\pi)^{12}\delta(\vec{k}_1-\vec{q}_4)\delta(\vec{k}_2-\vec{q}_1)\delta(\vec{k}_1-\vec{q}_2)\delta(\vec{k}_2-\vec{q}_3)\langle 0|0\rangle\,. \qquad (10.23)
\end{aligned}$$

Margin notes: ↷ Eq. 10.22; ↷ $a|0\rangle = 0$; ↷ $a|0\rangle = 0$

If we now use that $\langle 0|0\rangle = 1$ (Eq. 8.43), we are ultimately left with

$$\begin{aligned}&(2\pi)^{12}\delta(\vec{k}_2-\vec{q}_4)\delta(\vec{k}_1-\vec{q}_3)\delta(\vec{k}_2-\vec{q}_2)\delta(\vec{k}_1-\vec{q}_1)\\&+(2\pi)^{12}\delta(\vec{k}_2-\vec{q}_4)\delta(\vec{k}_1-\vec{q}_3)\delta(\vec{k}_2-\vec{q}_1)\delta(\vec{k}_1-\vec{q}_2))\\&+(2\pi)^{12}\delta(\vec{k}_1-\vec{q}_4)\delta(\vec{k}_2-\vec{q}_3)\delta(\vec{k}_2-\vec{q}_2)\delta(\vec{k}_1-\vec{q}_1)\\&+(2\pi)^{12}\delta(\vec{k}_1-\vec{q}_4)\delta(\vec{k}_2-\vec{q}_1)\delta(\vec{k}_1-\vec{q}_2)\delta(\vec{k}_2-\vec{q}_3)\end{aligned}\tag{10.24}$$

If we plug this into Eq. 10.21, we find

$$\begin{aligned}&\langle\pi^0_{k_1},\pi^0_{k_2}|\phi_{1+}\phi_{2+}\phi_{3-}\phi_{4-}|\pi^0_{k_1},\pi^0_{k_2}\rangle\\&\quad \text{↷ Eq. 10.21}\\&=4\omega_{k_1}\omega_{k_2}\int\frac{dq_1^3}{(2\pi)^3\sqrt{2\omega_{q_1}}}\int\frac{dq_2^3}{(2\pi)^3\sqrt{2\omega_{q_2}}}\int\frac{dq_3^3}{(2\pi)^3\sqrt{2\omega_{q_3}}}\int\frac{dq_4^3}{(2\pi)^3\sqrt{2\omega_{q_4}}}\\&\quad\times\langle 0|\,a(\vec{k}_1)a(\vec{k}_2)a^\dagger(\vec{q}_1)a^\dagger(\vec{q}_2)a(\vec{q}_3)a(\vec{q}_4)a^\dagger(\vec{k}_1)a^\dagger(\vec{k}_2)\,|0\rangle\, e^{i(q_1+q_2-q_3-q_4)x}\\&\quad \text{↷ Eq. 10.24}\\&=4\omega_{k_1}\omega_{k_2}\int\frac{dq_1^3}{(2\pi)^3\sqrt{2\omega_{q_1}}}\int\frac{dq_2^3}{(2\pi)^3\sqrt{2\omega_{q_2}}}\int\frac{dq_3^3}{(2\pi)^3\sqrt{2\omega_{q_3}}}\int\frac{dq_4^3}{(2\pi)^3\sqrt{2\omega_{q_4}}}\\&\quad\times\Bigg((2\pi)^{12}\delta(\vec{k}_2-\vec{q}_4)\delta(\vec{k}_1-\vec{q}_3)\delta(\vec{k}_2-\vec{q}_2)\delta(\vec{k}_1-\vec{q}_1)\\&\quad+(2\pi)^{12}\delta(\vec{k}_2-\vec{q}_4)\delta(\vec{k}_1-\vec{q}_3)\delta(\vec{k}_2-\vec{q}_1)\delta(\vec{k}_1-\vec{q}_2))\\&\quad+(2\pi)^{12}\delta(\vec{k}_1-\vec{q}_4)\delta(\vec{k}_2-\vec{q}_3)\delta(\vec{k}_2-\vec{q}_2)\delta(\vec{k}_1-\vec{q}_1)\\&\quad+(2\pi)^{12}\delta(\vec{k}_1-\vec{q}_4)\delta(\vec{k}_2-\vec{q}_1)\delta(\vec{k}_1-\vec{q}_2)\delta(\vec{k}_2-\vec{q}_3)\Bigg)e^{i(q_1+q_2-q_3-q_4)x}\,.\end{aligned}\tag{10.25}$$

Let's focus on the first term

$$\begin{aligned}&4\omega_{k_1}\omega_{k_2}\int\frac{dq_1^3}{(2\pi)^3\sqrt{2\omega_{q_1}}}\int\frac{dq_2^3}{(2\pi)^3\sqrt{2\omega_{q_2}}}\int\frac{dq_3^3}{(2\pi)^3\sqrt{2\omega_{q_3}}}\int\frac{dq_4^3}{(2\pi)^3\sqrt{2\omega_{q_4}}}\\&\quad\times\Big((2\pi)^{12}\delta(\vec{k}_2-\vec{q}_4)\delta(\vec{k}_1-\vec{q}_3)\delta(\vec{k}_2-\vec{q}_2)\delta(\vec{k}_1-\vec{q}_1)\Big)e^{i(q_1+q_2-q_3-q_4)x}\\&\quad \text{↷ } \int dx' f(x')\delta(x-x') = f(x)\\&=4\omega_{k_1}\omega_{k_2}\frac{1}{\sqrt{2\omega_{k_1}}\sqrt{2\omega_{k_2}}\sqrt{2\omega_{k_1}}\sqrt{2\omega_{k_2}}}e^{i(k_1+k_2-k_2-k_1)x}\\&\quad \text{↷}\\&=1\,.\end{aligned}\tag{10.26}$$

The result for the remaining three terms is exactly the same. Therefore, we can conclude that

$$\langle \pi^0_{k_1}, \pi^0_{k_2} | \phi_{1+}\phi_{2+}\phi_{3-}\phi_{4-} | \pi^0_{k_1}, \pi^0_{k_2} \rangle = 4 \,. \tag{10.27}$$

For the remaining five contributing terms in Eq. 10.17 ($\phi_{1-}\phi_{2-}\phi_{3+}\phi_{4+}$, $\phi_{1-}\phi_{2+}\phi_{3-}\phi_{4+}$ etc.), we need to recall from Section 9.4 that we should work with normal-ordered Hamiltonians to avoid problems that stem from infinitely large contributions to the energy levels of all states. In particular, we discovered for the relevant terms in our ϕ^4 model (Eq. 9.60)

$$\begin{aligned} :\phi^4: &\overset{9.54}{=} :\phi_{1+}\phi_{2+}\phi_{3-}\phi_{4-}: + :\phi_{1-}\phi_{2-}\phi_{3+}\phi_{4+}: + :\phi_{1-}\phi_{2+}\phi_{3-}\phi_{4+}: \\ &\quad + :\phi_{1-}\phi_{2+}\phi_{3+}\phi_{4-}: + :\phi_{1+}\phi_{2-}\phi_{3-}\phi_{4+}: + :\phi_{1+}\phi_{2-}\phi_{3+}\phi_{4-}: + \ldots \\ &= 6\phi_{1+}\phi_{2+}\phi_{3-}\phi_{4-} + \ldots \,. \end{aligned} \tag{10.28}$$

This implies that if we work with $:H_i:$ instead of H_i in the Dyson series, we encounter six times the term that we already evaluated instead of six different terms.

Formulated differently, if we work with H_i in the Dyson series, we encounter six different terms that potentially contribute something to the probability amplitude (Eq. 10.17). All of them can be brought into the same form as the term that we evaluated above ($\phi_{1+}\phi_{2+}\phi_{3-}\phi_{4-}$) by using the commutation relations (Eq. 8.14). The price we have to pay for this is additional terms that involve commutators of the form $[\phi_{1-}(x), \phi_{2+}(x)]$. But we discovered already in Eq. 9.56 that this yields infinitely large contributions. This is certainly not something that we want in our probability amplitudes, just as we don't want infinitely large contributions to all energy levels. Thus we should really work with normal-ordered Hamiltonians whenever it is possible to avoid such problems.

We can therefore conclude that if we use the normal-ordered interaction Hamiltonian in the Dyson series, the total result reads

$$
\begin{aligned}
A^{(1)} &\equiv -i\,\langle \pi^0_{k_1}, \pi^0_{k_2}| \int_{-\infty}^{\infty} dt_1 : H_i(t_1) : |\pi^0_{k_1}, \pi^0_{k_2}\rangle && \text{Eq. 10.12} \\
&= \frac{-i\lambda}{24} \int_{-\infty}^{\infty} d^4x\, \langle \pi^0_{k_1}, \pi^0_{k_2}| : \phi^4 : |\pi^0_{k_1}, \pi^0_{k_2}\rangle && 6\times \text{ Eq. 10.27, Eq. 10.28} \\
&= \frac{-i\lambda}{24} (6 \cdot 4) \int_{-\infty}^{\infty} d^4x && \int_{-\infty}^{\infty} d^4x = V \\
&= -i\lambda V\,.
\end{aligned}
\tag{10.29}
$$

The factor $\int_{-\infty}^{\infty} d^4x$ is formally infinite, which is again an artifact of our non-normalizable states. We therefore only integrate over a finite spacetime volume V which eventually drops out from our predictions.

This was an extremely long-winded road to an almost trivial result. However, I think it's important to see at least once that everything works even without any reference to theorems and sophisticated arguments (although, admittedly, it's a bit cumbersome). We will talk about a helpful theorem and more sophisticated arguments in the following chapter.

Let's finish this section with a few short comments on what we've just learned:

▷ By looking at Eq. 10.29, we can understand why it's conventional to define the interaction term $\frac{\lambda\phi^4}{4!}$ with a numerical factor $\frac{1}{4!}$ as we did it above. A factor of 4! is exactly what we need to cancel the combinatorial 4! factor that arises in our calculations. This factor $\frac{1}{4!}$ in the definition of the Hamiltonian and Lagrangian is purely conventional since we could easily get rid of it by redefining the coupling constant $\tilde{\lambda} \equiv \frac{\lambda}{4!}$. However, especially at higher orders in perturbation theory, it's often helpful to use a clever numerical factor to avoid working with unnecessarily large factors.

▷ Interestingly, our result in Eq. 10.29 is constant and only depends on the coupling constant. In particular, there is no dependence on the angle at which the outgoing particles emerge. This implies that the scattering process happens in all directions with equal probability. This is not too surprising since we are considering scalar particles which have no internal structure (spin) that could help to single out specific directions.

▷ If we consider the closely related case in which we again get two particles but allow different momenta ($k_3, k_4 \neq k_1, k_2$) at the end of the scattering process, the result is quite similar. The only difference is that in Eq. 10.26 we find instead of $e^{i(k_1+k_2-k_2-k_1)x} = e^0 = 1$ a factor $e^{i(k_1+k_2-k_3-k_4)x}$. If we then carry out the spacetime integration in Eq. 10.29 this yields a delta distribution $\delta(k_1 + k_2 - k_3 - k_4)$ which encodes the conservation of momentum. To get real-world predictions, we then typically integrate over some momentum region for the final states. We will discuss this aspect of scattering processes in more detail below.

▷ We integrate over all possible locations within the system. This is necessary since we are dealing with plane waves in the initial and final state. This implies that the corresponding particles are delocalized in space. Therefore, we must take possible scattering processes at each possible point within the system into account.

11

Amplitude Technology

The calculations in the previous chapter were quite cumbersome. Moreover, if we want to include higher order corrections in the Dyson series (Eq. 9.43) or describe how different fields interact with each other the calculations are even more cumbersome. Thus it makes sense to formalize our general strategy.

The main difficulty we've encountered so far is that even if we use a normal-ordered Hamiltonian, we need to switch lots of operators around. A typical contribution to the probability amplitude reads schematically

$$A \approx \langle f| : H_i : |i\rangle = \langle 0|aa \ldots : H_i : \ldots a^\dagger a^\dagger |0\rangle \,. \tag{11.1}$$

To evaluate it, we normal order the operator product between $\langle 0|$ and $|0\rangle$. This is non-trivial because in the expressions we start with only the Hamiltonian is normal-ordered. In particular, all annihilation operators that show up in our definition of the final state must be moved to the very right.[1] If we use the commutator relations (Eq. 8.14) to reorder the operators, we eventually find a normal-ordered term plus dozens of terms that involve commutators:

[1] Reminder: $\langle\psi| = |\psi\rangle^\dagger$ and therefore $|\psi\rangle \sim a^\dagger \ldots a^\dagger |0\rangle$ implies $\langle\psi| \sim (a^\dagger \ldots a^\dagger |0\rangle)^\dagger = \langle 0|\, a \ldots a$. This is why annihilation operators show up in the definition of the final state.

$$
\begin{aligned}
A &\approx \langle f| : H_i : |i\rangle \\
&= \langle 0|aa\ldots : H_i : \ldots a^\dagger a^\dagger|0\rangle \\
&= \langle 0| : aa\ldots H_i \ldots a^\dagger a^\dagger : |0\rangle + \langle 0|[a,a^\dagger]\ldots[a,a^\dagger]|0\rangle + \ldots \, . \qquad \text{AB = BA + [AB]}
\end{aligned} \tag{11.2}
$$

We've learned in the previous section that the reordering is quite cumbersome if we do it by brute force.

Therefore, we will discuss in this chapter a tool that allows us to simplify these kinds of calculations. The tool is known as Wick's theorem and allows us to understand the problem of switching operators around as a pure combinatorics problem which we can then solve systematically.

Additionally, we will learn that the combinatorics problem can be simplified by using Feynman diagrams. Instead of thinking about abstract combinatorics, we only have to draw all Feynman diagrams that contribute to a given order in the perturbation series. Each Feynman diagram represents a specific "contraction" term that appears if we apply Wick's theorem. The only remaining task is then to evaluate all basic contractions that can appear in our formulas. As a final improvement, we will discover that the basic contractions can be translated into so-called Feynman rules. These rules allow us to deduce directly from a given Feynman diagram the corresponding factors in the perturbation series.

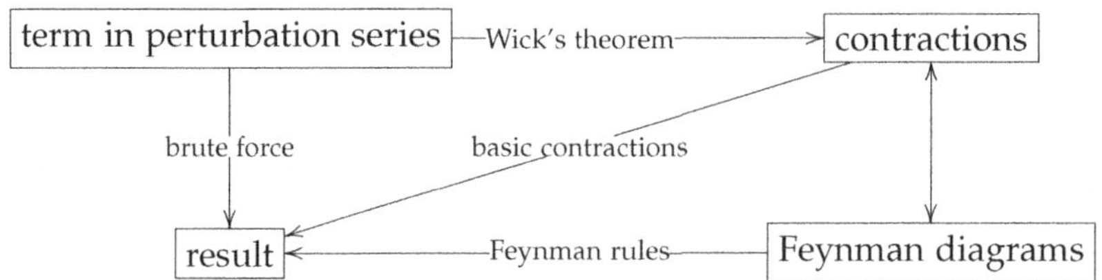

With this plan in mind, let's dive in.

11.1 Contractions

We discovered in the previous chapter that it's a smart strategy to move all terms that contain annihilation operators to the very right. Let's recap how and why this works. We again use the notation that we introduced in Eq. 10.13

$$\phi(x) = \int dk^3 \frac{1}{(2\pi)^3\sqrt{2\omega_k}} \left(a(\vec{k})e^{-i(kx)} + a^\dagger(\vec{k})e^{i(kx)}\right)$$

$$= \phi_- + \phi_+ , \qquad (11.3)$$

where ϕ_- is an integral over annihilation operators, while ϕ_+ is an integral over creation operators. Whenever we encounter a product of the form $\phi(x)\phi(y)$, we can bring it into the desired form at the price of introducing commutators[2]

[2] Take note that in the previous section, we considered the special case of a point-like interaction $\sim \phi(x)\phi(x)\phi(x)\phi(x)$ for which the fields in the product are evaluated at exactly the same spacetime point x. In general, we can also encounter products of fields evaluated at different spacetime points. Thus we consider the more general case here.

$$\phi(x)\phi(y) = \Big(\phi_-(x) + \phi_+(x)\Big)\Big(\phi_-(y) + \phi_+(y)\Big)$$

$$= \phi_-(x)\phi_-(y) + \phi_+(x)\phi_-(y) + \phi_-(x)\phi_+(y) + \phi_+(x)\phi_+(y)$$

$$\equiv \phi_-(x)\phi_-(y) + \phi_+(x)\phi_-(y) + [\phi_-(x), \phi_+(y)] + \phi_+(y)\phi_-(x) + \phi_+(x)\phi_+(y)$$

$$\equiv: \phi(x)\phi(y) : + [\phi_-(x), \phi_+(y)] . \qquad (11.4)$$

(definition)

We say that we bring $\phi(x)\phi(y)$ into normal order which we again denote by[3]

$$: \phi(x)\phi(y) : \equiv \text{all annihilation operators in } \phi(x)\phi(y) \text{ moved to the right} . \qquad (11.5)$$

In words, Eq. 11.4 therefore tells us that the price we have to pay for normal ordering $\phi(x)\phi(y)$ is the commutator $[\phi_-(x), \phi_+(y)]$.

[3] We discussed normal ordering already in the context of infinitely large contributions to the ground state energy in Section 9.4.

Normal ordering is useful because in our calculation of scattering amplitudes, we typically encounter products like $\phi(x)\phi(y)$ sandwiched between the ground state $\langle 0|\phi(x)\phi(y)|0\rangle$ and thus all terms except for the commutator term $[\phi_-, \phi_+]$ vanish. This follows because $a\,|0\rangle = 0$ (Eq. 8.31) which automatically implies that

$$\langle 0|\, a^\dagger = 0 \qquad (11.6)$$

since $(|0\rangle\, a^\dagger)^\dagger = a\,|0\rangle = 0$. That's the whole point of normal ordering. Normal-ordered terms yield zero if we sandwich them between $\langle 0|$ and $|0\rangle$:

$$\langle 0| : \phi(x)\phi(y) : |0\rangle = 0\,. \tag{11.7}$$

By using the explicit formula for the normal-ordered product in Eq. 11.4, we can check this explicitly

$$\begin{aligned}
&\langle 0| : \phi(x)\phi(y) : |0\rangle \\
&\quad \text{(Eq. 11.4)} \\
&= \langle 0| \Big(\phi_-(x)\phi_-(y) + \phi_+(x)\phi_-(y) \\
&\qquad + \phi_+(y)\phi_-(x) + \phi_+(x)\phi_+(y)\Big)\,|0\rangle \\
&= \underbrace{\langle 0|\phi_-(x)\phi_-(y)|0\rangle}_{=0 \text{ since } a|0\rangle = 0} + \underbrace{\langle 0|\phi_+(x)\phi_-(y)|0\rangle}_{=0 \text{ since } a|0\rangle = 0} \\
&\quad + \underbrace{\langle 0|\phi_+(y)\phi_-(x)|0\rangle}_{=0 \text{ since } a|0\rangle = 0} + \underbrace{\langle 0|\phi_+(x)\phi_+(y)|0\rangle}_{=0 \text{ since } \langle 0|a^\dagger = 0} \\
&= 0\,.
\end{aligned} \tag{11.8}$$

By using Eq. 11.4 and Eq. 11.8, we can conclude

$$\begin{aligned}
\langle 0|\phi(x)\phi(y)|0\rangle &\overset{\text{Eq. 11.4}}{=} \langle 0| : \phi(x)\phi(y) : + [\phi_-(x), \phi_+(y)]|0\rangle \\
&= \langle 0| : \phi(x)\phi(y) : |0\rangle + \langle 0|[\phi_-(x), \phi_+(y)]|0\rangle \\
&= \langle 0|[\phi_-(x), \phi_+(y)]|0\rangle\,.
\end{aligned} \tag{11.9}$$

Moreover, if we use the definitions of $\phi_-(x), \phi_+(y)$ in Eq. 11.3, we can calculate this commutator explicitly

$$
\begin{aligned}
[\phi_-(x), \phi_+(y)] &= \phi_-(x)\phi_+(y) - \phi_+(y)\phi_-(x) \\
&\quad \text{Eq. 11.3} \\
&= \Big(\int dk^3 \frac{1}{(2\pi)^3\sqrt{2\omega_k}} a(\vec{k})e^{-i(kx)}\Big)\Big(\int dq^3 \frac{1}{(2\pi)^3\sqrt{2\omega_q}} a^\dagger(\vec{q})e^{i(qy)}\Big) \\
&\quad - \Big(\int dq^3 \frac{1}{(2\pi)^3\sqrt{2\omega_q}} a^\dagger(\vec{q})e^{i(qy)}\Big)\Big(\int dk^3 \frac{1}{(2\pi)^3\sqrt{2\omega_k}} a(\vec{k})e^{-i(kx)}\Big) \\
&= \int\int \frac{dk^3}{(2\pi)^3\sqrt{2\omega_q}} \frac{dq^3}{(2\pi)^3\sqrt{2\omega_k}} e^{-i(kx)}e^{i(qy)}[a(\vec{k}), a^\dagger(\vec{q})] \\
&\quad \text{Eq. 8.14} \\
&= \int\int \frac{dk^3}{(2\pi)^3\sqrt{2\omega_q}} \frac{dq^3}{(2\pi)^3\sqrt{2\omega_k}} e^{-i(kx)}e^{i(qy)}\Big((2\pi)^3\delta(\vec{k}-\vec{q})\Big) \\
&= \int \frac{dk^3}{(2\pi)^3\sqrt{2\omega_k}\sqrt{2\omega_k}} e^{-i(kx)}e^{i(ky)} \\
&= \int \frac{dk^3}{(2\pi)^3 2\omega_k} e^{-ik(x-y)} \,. \qquad (11.10)
\end{aligned}
$$

This is exactly the elementary propagator that we already encountered in Eq. 8.83. This makes perfect sense if we recall that we defined the elementary propagator as $D(x,y) \equiv \langle 0|\phi(x)\phi(y)|0\rangle$ and now plug Eq. 11.10 back into Eq. 11.8:

$$
\begin{aligned}
D(x,y) &\equiv \langle 0|\phi(x)\phi(y)|0\rangle \\
&\quad \text{Eq. 11.9} \\
&= [\phi_-(x), \phi_+(y)] \\
&\quad \text{Eq. 11.10} \\
&= \int \frac{dk^3}{(2\pi)^3 2\omega_k} e^{-ik(x-y)} \,. \qquad (11.11)
\end{aligned}
$$

The point of all of this is that the general strategy we just discussed always works and not just for simple products of the form $\phi(x)\phi(y)$. We normal order the fields and the price that we have to pay for this are commutators. One of the main tasks in quantum field theory is to formalize this process to make sure that we don't have to repeat dozens of steps each time and are still able to figure out the correct commutators.

Before we discuss a general algorithm to accomplish this, we need to discuss a small detail that we ignored in the calculations above. Usually in quantum field theory we don't encounter products of the form $\phi(x)\phi(y)$ but instead, time-ordered products $T\phi(x)\phi(y)$.[4] Recall that (Eq. 8.90)

$$T\phi(x)\phi(y) = \begin{cases} \phi(x)\phi(y) & \text{for } x_0 > y_0 \\ \phi(y)\phi(x) & \text{for } y_0 > x_0 \end{cases} \tag{11.12}$$

[4] Recall that we derived in Section 9.3.1 that the time ordering operator necessarily appears in the Dyson series (Eq. 9.43).

The result we calculated above (Eq. 11.11) is valid for $x_0 > y_0$, while for $y_0 > x_0$ we find analogously

$$D(x,y) \equiv \langle 0|\phi(y)\phi(x)|0\rangle = [\phi_-(y), \phi_+(x)]\,. \tag{11.13}$$

If we sandwich $T\phi(x)\phi(y)$ between $\langle 0|$ and $|0\rangle$, we get exactly the definition of the Feynman propagator (Eq. 8.93) which we again can write a bit differently[5]

[5] I already warned you above that the Feynman propagator has many, many faces.

$$\begin{aligned} D_F(x,y) &\equiv \langle 0|T\phi(x)\phi(y)|0\rangle \\ &\quad \text{(explicit time ordering)} \\ &= \theta(x_0 - y_0)\,\langle 0|\phi(x)\phi(y)|0\rangle + \theta(y_0 - x_0)\,\langle 0|\phi(y)\phi(x)|0\rangle \\ &\quad \text{(Eq. 11.11, Eq. 11.13)} \\ &= \theta(x_0 - y_0)\,\langle 0|[\phi_-(x), \phi_+(y)]|0\rangle + \theta(y_0 - x_0)\,\langle 0|[\phi_-(y), \phi_+(x)]|0\rangle \\ &= \theta(x_0 - y_0)[\phi_-(x), \phi_+(y)]\,\langle 0|0\rangle + \theta(y_0 - x_0)[\phi_-(y), \phi_+(x)]\,\langle 0|0\rangle \\ &\quad (\langle 0|0\rangle = 1 \text{ (Eq. 8.43)}) \\ &= \theta(x_0 - y_0)[\phi_-(x), \phi_+(y)] + \theta(y_0 - x_0)[\phi_-(y), \phi_+(x)]\,. \end{aligned} \tag{11.14}$$

This motivates the following new notation

$$\overbrace{\phi(x)\phi(y)} \equiv \begin{cases} [\phi_-(x), \phi_+(y)] & \text{for } x_0 > y_0 \\ [\phi_-(y), \phi_+(x)] & \text{for } y_0 > x_0 \end{cases}\,. \tag{11.15}$$

We call $\overbrace{\phi(x)\phi(y)}$ the **contraction** of the two fields.

Take note that Eq. 11.14 tells us that

$$\overbrace{\phi(x)\phi(y)} = D_F(x,y)\,. \tag{11.16}$$

Thus it may seem as if we've introduced just another way to write the Feynman propagator. However, we will see in a moment that thinking in terms of contractions will help us to keep track of cumbersome calculations.

In summary, by using all the new notations introduced so far we can write

$$T\phi(x)\phi(y) =: \phi(x)\phi(y) : + \overbracket{\phi(x)\phi(y)}\,. \tag{11.17}$$

In words this formula tells us that we can rewrite a time-ordered product of two fields as a normal-ordered product plus their contraction. As discussed above, a formula like this is useful because normal-ordered terms yield zero if we sandwich them between $\langle 0|$ and $|0\rangle$ (Eq. 11.7):

$$\begin{aligned}
\langle 0|T\phi(x)\phi(y)|0\rangle &\overset{\text{Eq. 11.17}}{=} \langle 0| : \phi(x)\phi(y) : + \overbracket{\phi(x)\phi(y)}|0\rangle \\
&= \langle 0| : \phi(x)\phi(y) : |0\rangle + \langle 0|\overbracket{\phi(x)\phi(y)}|0\rangle \qquad \text{Eq. 11.7} \\
&= \langle 0|\overbracket{\phi(x)\phi(y)}|0\rangle
\end{aligned} \tag{11.18}$$

Thus all that's left is the contraction which, as we've just seen, we can understand in this case as the Feynman propagator.

As a final remark take note that, in more general terms, we can also say that the contraction of two fields is defined as all the terms that are left over when we compare the fields in normal ordering versus time ordering

$$\overbracket{\phi(x)\phi(y)} = T\phi(x)\phi(y) - : \phi(x)\phi(y) : \,. \tag{11.19}$$

This implies that the contraction of two operators is equal to what we find when we sandwich their time-ordered product between $\langle 0|$ and $|0\rangle$:

$$\begin{aligned}
\langle 0|\overbracket{\phi(x)\phi(y)}|0\rangle &= \langle 0|T\phi(x)\phi(y)|0\rangle - \langle 0| : \phi(x)\phi(y) : |0\rangle \qquad \text{Eq. 11.7} \\
\overbracket{\phi(x)\phi(y)}\,\langle 0|0\rangle &= \langle 0|T\phi(x)\phi(y)|0\rangle \qquad \text{(Eq. 8.43)} \\
\overbracket{\phi(x)\phi(y)} &= \langle 0|T\phi(x)\phi(y)|0\rangle\,.
\end{aligned} \tag{11.20}$$

In the next section, we will see why contractions are extremely useful if we want to consider more complicated time-ordered products.[6]

[6] More complicated time-ordered products routinely appear in calculations of scattering amplitudes. We will discuss this explicitly below.

11.2 Wick's Theorem

The usefulness of the notion "contraction" primarily stems from the general result:

$$T\hat{A}_1 \ldots \hat{A}_n =: \hat{A}_1 \ldots \hat{A}_n : + : \text{ all possible contractions } :, \tag{11.21}$$

This is known as **Wick's theorem**. In words, it tells us that the difference between a time-ordered product and a normal-ordered product of a given number of operators is given by a sum over all possible contractions of the operators. Formulated differently, if we switch from time-ordering to normal-ordering, the price we have to pay is additional terms that we can understand as the sum over all possible contractions of the fields that appear in the product. Moreover, all fields that appear in the contraction terms that are not themselves contracted, are normal-ordered too.

For a time-ordered product of quantum fields, Wick's theorem tells us

$$T\phi(x_1)\ldots\phi(x_n) =: \phi(x_1)\ldots\phi(x_n) : + : \text{ all possible contractions } :, \tag{11.22}$$

where $x_1, \ldots x_n$ denote different spacetime points.

Since for two fields $\phi(x_1)\phi(x_2)$ there is just one possible contraction $\wick{\c\phi(x_1)\c\phi(x_2)}$, we have encountered one instance of Wick's theorem already in the previous section (Eq. 11.17)

$$T\phi(x)\phi(y) =: \phi(x)\phi(y) : + \wick{\c\phi(x)\c\phi(y)} . \tag{11.23}$$

Moreover, for example, for a product of three fields at different spacetime points (x_1, x_2, x_3), Wick's theorem tells us that

$$\begin{aligned} T\phi(x_1)\phi(x_2)\phi(x_3) &=: \phi(x_1)\phi(x_2)\phi(x_3) : + \wick{\c\phi(x_1)\c\phi(x_2)}\phi(x_3) \\ &+ \wick{\c\phi(x_1)\phi(x_2)\c\phi(x_3)} + \phi(x_1)\wick{\c\phi(x_2)\c\phi(x_3)} \end{aligned} \tag{11.24}$$

Since there is always only one field which isn't contracted, there is no need to normal order anything in the contraction terms.

In contrast, for a product of four fields we have

$$
\begin{aligned}
&T\phi(x_1)\phi(x_2)\phi(x_3)\phi(x_4) \\
&=: \phi(x_1)\phi(x_2)\phi(x_3)\phi(x_4) : + : \Big(\wick{\c{\phi}(x_1)\c{\phi}(x_2)}\phi(x_3)\phi(x_4) \\
&\quad + \wick{\c{\phi}(x_1)\phi(x_2)\c{\phi}(x_3)}\phi(x_4) + \wick{\c{\phi}(x_1)\phi(x_2)\phi(x_3)\c{\phi}(x_4)} \\
&\quad + \phi(x_1)\wick{\c{\phi}(x_2)\c{\phi}(x_3)}\phi(x_4) + \phi(x_1)\wick{\c{\phi}(x_2)\phi(x_3)\c{\phi}(x_4)} + \phi(x_1)\phi(x_2)\wick{\c{\phi}(x_3)\c{\phi}(x_4)} \\
&\quad + \wick{\c1{\phi}(x_1)\c1{\phi}(x_2)\c2{\phi}(x_3)\c2{\phi}(x_4)} + \wick{\c1{\phi}(x_1)\c2{\phi}(x_2)\c1{\phi}(x_3)\c2{\phi}(x_4)} + \wick{\c1{\phi}(x_1)\c2{\phi}(x_2)\c2{\phi}(x_3)\c1{\phi}(x_4)} \Big) : .
\end{aligned}
\tag{11.25}
$$

We can see here that there are many terms which contain two fields that are not contracted. Thus it is important to include the colons to indicate that they are normal-ordered. For example,

$$
\begin{aligned}
: \Big(\wick{\c{\phi}(x_1)\c{\phi}(x_2)}\phi(x_3)\phi(x_4) \Big) : &= \wick{\c{\phi}(x_1)\c{\phi}(x_2)} : \phi(x_3)\phi(x_4) : \\
&\quad \text{⤸ Eq. 11.16} \\
&= D_F(x_1, x_2) : \phi(x_3)\phi(x_4) : ,
\end{aligned}
\tag{11.26}
$$

where we used that the contraction of two fields yields the Feynman propagator (Eq. 11.16).

This is especially important if we recall that we usually consider time-ordered products that are sandwiched between $\langle 0|$ and $|0\rangle$. If we then recall that the Feynman propagator is a complex function and thus has no effect on $\langle 0|$ and $|0\rangle$, we can pull it in front of the brakets and are then only left with the normal-ordered terms:

$$
\begin{aligned}
&\langle 0| : \wick{\c{\phi}(x_1)\c{\phi}(x_2)}\phi(x_3)\phi(x_4) : |0\rangle \\
&\quad \text{⤸ Eq. 11.26} \\
&= \langle 0| D_F(x_1, x_2) : \phi(x_3)\phi(x_4) : |0\rangle \\
&\quad \text{⤸} \\
&= D_F(x_1, x_2) \langle 0| : \phi(x_3)\phi(x_4) : |0\rangle \\
&\quad \text{⤸ } \langle 0| : \phi(x_3)\phi(x_4) : |0\rangle = 0 \text{ (Eq. 11.7)} \\
&= 0 .
\end{aligned}
\tag{11.27}
$$

This means that only terms in which all fields are contracted contribute something to probability amplitudes. For example, by using Eq. 11.25, we find

$$
\begin{aligned}
&\langle 0|T\phi(x_1)\phi(x_2)\phi(x_3)\phi(x_4)|0\rangle \\
&= \langle 0| :\phi(x_1)\phi(x_2)\phi(x_3)\phi(x_4): |0\rangle \qquad \text{Eq. 11.25}\\
&+ \langle 0| : \Big(\wick{\c1\phi(x_1)\c1\phi(x_2)}\phi(x_3)\phi(x_4) + \wick{\c1\phi(x_1)\phi(x_2)\c1\phi(x_3)}\phi(x_4) + \wick{\c1\phi(x_1)\phi(x_2)\phi(x_3)\c1\phi(x_4)} \\
&+ \phi(x_1)\wick{\c1\phi(x_2)\c1\phi(x_3)}\phi(x_4) + \phi(x_1)\wick{\c1\phi(x_2)\phi(x_3)\c1\phi(x_4)} + \phi(x_1)\phi(x_2)\wick{\c1\phi(x_3)\c1\phi(x_4)} \\
&+ \wick{\c1\phi(x_1)\c1\phi(x_2)\c2\phi(x_3)\c2\phi(x_4)} + \wick{\c1\phi(x_1)\c2\phi(x_2)\c1\phi(x_3)\c2\phi(x_4)} + \wick{\c1\phi(x_1)\c2\phi(x_2)\c2\phi(x_3)\c1\phi(x_4)} \Big) : |0\rangle \\
&\qquad \text{Eq. 11.7}\\
&= \langle 0|\wick{\c1\phi(x_1)\c1\phi(x_2)\c2\phi(x_3)\c2\phi(x_4)}|0\rangle + \langle 0|\wick{\c1\phi(x_1)\c2\phi(x_2)\c1\phi(x_3)\c2\phi(x_4)}|0\rangle + \langle 0|\wick{\c1\phi(x_1)\c2\phi(x_2)\c2\phi(x_3)\c1\phi(x_4)}|0\rangle \qquad \text{Eq. 11.26}\\
&= D_F(x_1,x_2)D_F(x_3,x_4)\,\langle 0|0\rangle + D_F(x_1,x_3)D_F(x_2,x_4)\,\langle 0|0\rangle + D_F(x_1,x_4)D_F(x_2,x_3)\,\langle 0|0\rangle \qquad \text{Eq. 8.43}\\
&= D_F(x_1,x_2)D_F(x_3,x_4) + D_F(x_1,x_3)D_F(x_2,x_4) + D_F(x_1,x_4)D_F(x_2,x_3)
\end{aligned}
\tag{11.28}
$$

To get a bit more confidence in the validity of Wick's theorem beyond the two field case (Eq. 11.17), we check the three field case $T\phi(x_1)\phi(x_2)\phi(x_3)$ (Eq. 11.24) explicitly in Appendix B.1. The proof for arbitrary field products works analogously and the general formula can be proven by induction.[7]

[7] You can find a rigorous proof in

Luca Guido Molinari. Notes on Wick's theorem in many-body theory, 2017

11.3 Important Contractions

So far, we've only talked about one very special kind of contraction which we identified as the Feynman propagator (Eq. 11.16)

$$\wick{\c1\phi(x)\c1\phi(y)} = D_F(x,y)\,. \tag{11.29}$$

Before we can really make use of Wick's theorem, we need to talk about other kinds of contractions. To understand why, take note that in our formulas for scattering amplitudes we don't get expression of the form

$$\langle 0|T\phi(x_1)\dots\phi(x_n)|0\rangle \tag{11.30}$$

but rather something like

$$\langle f|T\phi(x_1)\dots\phi(x_n)|i\rangle\ , \tag{11.31}$$

where $\langle f|$ denotes a specific final state, for example, $\langle \pi^0_{k_3}, \pi^0_{k_4}|$ and $|i\rangle$ denotes the initial state, for example, $|\pi^0_{k_1}, \pi^0_{k_2}\rangle$. These states are defined in terms of creation and annihilation operators that act on the ground state (Eq. 10.19)

$$|\pi^0_{k_1}, \pi^0_{k_2}\rangle \equiv \sqrt{2\omega_{k_1}}a^\dagger(\vec{k}_1)\sqrt{2\omega_{k_2}}a^\dagger(\vec{k}_2)\,|0\rangle \tag{11.32}$$

and (Eq. 10.20)

$$\langle \pi^0_{k_1}, \pi^0_{k_2}| \equiv \langle 0|\,\sqrt{2\omega_{k_1}}a(\vec{k}_1)\sqrt{2\omega_{k_2}}a(\vec{k}_2)\,. \tag{11.33}$$

Thus even though we get nicely normal-ordered terms by applying Wick's theorem to the field operators $(\phi(x_1)\dots\phi(x_n))$, there is a lot of work left to be done since we still need to move these creation and annihilation operators around to get a fully normal-ordered expression.

Schematically, we have

$$\langle f|T\phi(x_1)\dots\phi(x_n)|i\rangle \sim \langle 0|a(\vec{k}_3)a(\vec{k}_4)\Big(T\phi(x_1)\dots\phi(x_n)\Big)a^\dagger(\vec{k}_1)a^\dagger(\vec{k}_2)|0\rangle\ . \tag{11.34}$$

A key observation is that the creation and annihilation operators in these products automatically appear at the position at which the time-ordering operator T would put them. The operators that create the final state act at the final time $t = \infty$ and thus are already at the correct position to the very left. Similarly the operators that are part of our definition of the initial state act at time $t = -\infty$ and thus are correctly located at the very right. This means that we can write

$$\begin{aligned}&\langle 0|a(\vec{k}_3)a(\vec{k}_4)\Big(T\phi(x_1)\dots\phi(x_n)\Big)a^\dagger(k_1)a^\dagger(k_2)|0\rangle\\ &= \langle 0|Ta(\vec{k}_3)a(\vec{k}_4)\phi(x_1)\dots\phi(x_n)a^\dagger(\vec{k}_1)a^\dagger(\vec{k}_2)|0\rangle\ .\end{aligned}$$

This is useful because we can now use Wick's theorem to simplify this time-ordered product. Wick's theorem also applies to the creation and annihilation operators because the only part of our fields that makes them non-commutative are exactly these creation and annihilation operators. Thus, when we commute a creation operator and a field, we also get commutators that we can denote as contractions.[8] In other words, Wick's theorem works for operators in general. Wick's theorem is basically only a combinatorial tool that allows us to keep track of all the commutations we need to perform to bring a given time-ordered product into normal order.

[8] We saw this explicitly in Section 10.

This, however, implies that we need to investigate the meaning of a contraction between creation and annihilation operators (e.g., $\overbracket{a(\vec{k}_4)a}^\dagger(\vec{k}_2)$) and the meaning of a contraction between a field and a creation or annihilation operator (e.g., $\overbracket{\phi(x_1)a}^\dagger(\vec{k}_1)$).

To calculate a contraction like $\overbracket{\phi(x)a}^\dagger(\vec{k})$ we use the general formula (Eq. 11.20)

$$\overbracket{\phi(x)a}^\dagger(\vec{k}) = \langle 0|T\phi(x)a^\dagger(\vec{k})|0\rangle \,. \tag{11.35}$$

As mentioned above, factors like $\phi(x)a^\dagger(\vec{k})$ are already time-ordered in our formulas since $a^\dagger(\vec{k})$ creates the initial state at the earliest possible time that we consider. Moreover, we need the general field expansion (Eq. 10.13)[9] and the canonical commutation relations (Eq. 8.14)[10]. By using these results, we find

[9] Reminder: Eq. 10.13 reads

$$\phi(x) = \int dq^3 \frac{1}{(2\pi)^3\sqrt{2\omega_q}}\Big(a(\vec{q})e^{-i(qx)} + a^\dagger(\vec{q})e^{i(qx)}\Big)\,.$$

[10] Reminder: Eq. 8.14 reads

$$[a(\vec{k}), a^\dagger(\vec{k}')] = (2\pi)^3\delta(\vec{k}-\vec{k}')$$
$$[a(\vec{k}), a(\vec{k}')] = 0\,, \quad [a^\dagger(\vec{k}), a^\dagger(\vec{k}')] = 0\,.$$

$$
\begin{aligned}
\overbracket{\phi(x)a^\dagger}(\vec{k}) &= \langle 0|T\phi(x)a^\dagger(\vec{k})|0\rangle \\
&= \langle 0|\phi(x)a^\dagger(\vec{k})|0\rangle \\
&= \langle 0|\left(\int \frac{dq^3}{(2\pi)^3\sqrt{2\omega_q}}\left(a(\vec{q})e^{-i(qx)} + a^\dagger(\vec{q})e^{i(qx)}\right)\right)a^\dagger(\vec{k})|0\rangle \\
&= \int \frac{dq^3}{(2\pi)^3\sqrt{2\omega_q}}e^{-i(qx)}\langle 0|a(\vec{q})a^\dagger(\vec{k})|0\rangle \\
&\quad + \int \frac{dq^3}{(2\pi)^3\sqrt{2\omega_q}}e^{i(qx)}\langle 0|a^\dagger(\vec{q})a^\dagger(\vec{k})|0\rangle \\
&= \int \frac{dq^3}{(2\pi)^3\sqrt{2\omega_q}}e^{-i(qx)}\langle 0|a(\vec{q})a^\dagger(\vec{k})|0\rangle \\
&= \int \frac{dq^3}{(2\pi)^3\sqrt{2\omega_q}}e^{-i(qx)}\langle 0|\left(a^\dagger(\vec{k})a(\vec{q}) + [a(\vec{q}),a^\dagger(\vec{k})]\right)|0\rangle \\
&= \int \frac{dq^3}{(2\pi)^3\sqrt{2\omega_q}}e^{-i(qx)}\langle 0|(2\pi)^3\delta(\vec{q}-\vec{k})|0\rangle \\
&= \int \frac{dq^3}{\sqrt{2\omega_q}}e^{-i(qx)}\delta(\vec{q}-\vec{k}) \\
&= \frac{1}{\sqrt{2\omega_k}}e^{-i(kx)}\,. \qquad (11.36)
\end{aligned}
$$

↷ already time-ordered

↷ Eq. 10.13

↷

↷ $\langle 0|\, a^\dagger = 0$ (Eq. 11.6)

↷

↷ $a\,|0\rangle = 0$ (Eq. 8.31), Eq. 8.14

↷ $\langle 0|0\rangle = 1$ (Eq. 8.43)

↷

In words, this represents an incoming wave. By using the definition of an initial state

$$|1_k\rangle \equiv \sqrt{2\omega_k}a^\dagger(\vec{k})\,|0\rangle \qquad (11.37)$$

we can also define the contraction of a field with a ket

$$
\begin{aligned}
\overbracket{\phi(x)|1}_{\vec{k}}\rangle &= \overbracket{\phi(x)\left(\sqrt{2\omega_k}a\right.}^\dagger(\vec{k})\,|0\rangle\Big) \\
&= \frac{1}{\sqrt{2\omega_k}}e^{-i(kx)}\sqrt{2\omega_k}\,|0\rangle \\
&= e^{-i(kx)}\,|0\rangle \qquad (11.38)
\end{aligned}
$$

↷ Eq. 11.36

↷ $\cancel{\sqrt{2\omega_k}}$

Analogously, we can calculate

$$\overbracket{a(\vec{k})\phi}(x) = \frac{1}{\sqrt{2\omega_k}}e^{i(kx)} \qquad (11.39)$$

and

$$\langle 1_k | \phi(x) = \langle 0 | \, e^{i(kx)} \,, \tag{11.40}$$

which represents an outgoing wave.

Another puzzle piece is the contraction of an annihilation operator with a creation operator. To calculate this, we use once more the general formula (Eq. 11.20) and then bring the right-hand side into normal order:

$$\begin{aligned}
a(\vec{q})a^\dagger(\vec{k}) &\overset{11.20}{=} \langle 0|Ta(\vec{q})a^\dagger(\vec{k})|0\rangle \\
&\quad \text{already time-ordered} \\
&= \langle 0|a(\vec{q})a^\dagger(\vec{k})|0\rangle \\
&\quad AB = BA + [A,B] \\
&= \langle 0|a^\dagger(\vec{k})a(\vec{q}) + [a(\vec{q}),a^\dagger(\vec{k})]|0\rangle \\
&\quad a(\vec{q})\,|0\rangle = 0 \text{ (Eq. 8.31)} \\
&= \langle 0|[a(\vec{q}),a^\dagger(\vec{k})]|0\rangle \\
&\quad \text{Eq. 8.14} \\
&= \langle 0|(2\pi)^3\delta(\vec{q}-\vec{k})|0\rangle \\
&= (2\pi)^3\delta(\vec{q}-\vec{k})\,\langle 0|0\rangle \\
&\quad \langle 0|0\rangle = 1 \text{ (Eq. 8.43)} \\
&= (2\pi)^3\delta(\vec{q}-\vec{k})\,.
\end{aligned} \tag{11.41}$$

This implies that when we contract a particle in an initial state with a particle in the final state, we find

$$\begin{aligned}
\langle 1_q| \dots |1_k\rangle &\overset{\text{Eq. 10.19}}{=} \sqrt{2\omega_q}\sqrt{2\omega_k}\langle 0|a(\vec{q})\dots a^\dagger(\vec{k})|0\rangle \\
&\quad \text{Eq. 11.41} \\
&= \sqrt{2\omega_q}\sqrt{2\omega_k}\langle 0|(2\pi)^3\delta(\vec{q}-\vec{k})|0\rangle \\
&\quad \text{Eq. 8.43} \\
&= \sqrt{2\omega_q}\sqrt{2\omega_k}(2\pi)^3\delta(\vec{q}-\vec{k})\,.
\end{aligned} \tag{11.42}$$

In addition, we need to consider the contraction of an annihilation operator with an annihilation operator and the contraction of a creation operator with a creation operator:

$$\begin{aligned}
a(\vec{q})a(\vec{k}) &\overset{11.20}{=} \langle 0|Ta(\vec{q})a(\vec{k})|0\rangle \\
&\quad \text{already time-ordered} \\
&= \langle 0|a(\vec{q})a(\vec{k})|0\rangle \\
&\quad a(\vec{k})\,|0\rangle = 0 \\
&= 0\,.
\end{aligned} \tag{11.43}$$

This implies

$$\langle \overbracket{1_q, 1_k} | = 0 \,. \tag{11.44}$$

Analogously, we find

$$\overbracket{a^\dagger(q) a^\dagger}(k) = 0 \,. \tag{11.45}$$

This implies

$$| \overbracket{1_q, 1_k} \rangle = 0 \,. \tag{11.46}$$

A final puzzle piece that we need to talk about is the contraction of a field with itself at exactly the same spacetime point, $\overbracket{\phi(x)\phi}(x)$. Such contractions appear if we evaluate, for example, $\phi^4 = \phi^4(x)$ interactions. By using Eq. 11.16:

$$\overbracket{\phi(x)\phi}(y) = D_F(x,y) \,, \tag{11.47}$$

we can immediately conclude that

$$\begin{aligned}
\overbracket{\phi(x)\phi}(x) &= D_F(x,x) \\
&\qquad\qquad \text{(Eq. 8.93)} \\
&= \Theta(x-x)D(x,x) + \Theta(x-x)D(x,x) \\
&\qquad\qquad \left(\Theta(0) \equiv \tfrac{1}{2}\right) \\
&= D(x,x) \\
&\qquad\qquad \text{(Eq. 8.82)} \\
&= \int \frac{dk^3}{(2\pi)^3 2\omega_k} e^{-ik(x-x)} \\
&\qquad\qquad \left(e^0 = 1\right) \\
&= \int \frac{dk^3}{(2\pi)^3 2\omega_k} \,.
\end{aligned} \tag{11.48}$$

This is exactly the divergent integral that we already encountered in Eq. 9.56 in the context of infinitely large contributions to the Hamiltonian operator. Therefore, we can conclude that our restriction to normal-ordered Hamiltonians implies for Wick's theorem that we do not allow contractions of a field with itself at the same spacetime point. We can also understand why by noting that Eq. 11.15

$$\overbracket{\phi(x)\phi}(x) \equiv \begin{cases} [\phi_-(x), \phi_+(x)] & \text{for } x_0 > y_0 \\ [\phi_-(x), \phi_+(x)] & \text{for } y_0 > x_0 \end{cases} \,, \tag{11.49}$$

which are exactly the commutator terms that we encounter if we don't work with a normal-ordered Hamiltonian.[11]

[11] We discussed this in the text below Eq. 10.28.

In summary

$$
\begin{aligned}
\overbracket{\phi(x)\phi(y)} &= D_F(x,y) && \text{(Eq. 11.16)}\\
\overbracket{\phi(x)|1_k\rangle} &= e^{-i(kx)}\,|0\rangle && \text{(Eq. 11.38)}\\
\overbracket{\langle 1_k|\phi(x)} &= \langle 0|\,e^{i(kx)} && \text{(Eq. 11.40)}\\
\overbracket{\langle 1_q|\ldots|1_k\rangle} &= \sqrt{2\omega_q\sqrt{2\omega_k}}(2\pi)^3\delta(\vec{q}-\vec{k}) && \text{(Eq. 11.42)}\\
\overbracket{|1_q,1_k\rangle} &= 0 && \text{(Eq. 11.46)}\\
\overbracket{\langle 1_q,1_k|} &= 0 && \text{(Eq. 11.44)}
\end{aligned}
\qquad (11.50)
$$

11.4 Scattering - a Second Look

Equipped with Wick's theorem and the formulas in Eq. 11.50 it is instructive to take a second look at the scattering process $\pi^0_{k_1}, \pi^0_{k_2} \to \pi^0_{k_3}, \pi^0_{k_4}$ for a single scalar field ϕ with interaction term $\sim \phi^4$ that we considered in Section 10.

Recall that we want to evaluate (Eq. 10.6)

$$
\begin{aligned}
&A(\pi^0_{k_1}, \pi^0_{k_2} \to \pi^0_{k_3}, \pi^0_{k_4}) \\
&= \langle \pi^0_{k_3}, \pi^0_{k_4} | \hat{S} | \pi^0_{k_1}, \pi^0_{k_2} \rangle \\
&= \langle \pi^0_{k_3}, \pi^0_{k_4} | T\Big(1 - i\int_{-\infty}^{\infty} dt_1 : H_i(t_1) : - \ldots \Big) | \pi^0_{k_1}, \pi^0_{k_2} \rangle \\
&= T\,\langle \pi^0_{k_3}, \pi^0_{k_4} | \pi^0_{k_1}, \pi^0_{k_2} \rangle - iT\,\langle \pi^0_{k_3}, \pi^0_{k_4} | \int_{-\infty}^{\infty} dt_1 : H_i(t_1) : | \pi^0_{k_1}, \pi^0_{k_2} \rangle - \ldots \\
&\equiv A^{(0)} + A^{(1)} + \ldots . \qquad (11.51)
\end{aligned}
$$

↓ Eq. 10.5

↓ Eq. 9.42

↓

↓ definition

11.4.1 Zeroth-Order Approximation

Again, let's start by focusing on the first term in the expansion:[12]

[12] We neglect all terms in which not all of the operators are contracted since we know already (Eq. 11.27) that these yield zero.

$$
\begin{aligned}
A^{(0)} &\equiv T\,\langle \pi^0_{k_3}, \pi^0_{k_4} | \pi^0_{k_1}, \pi^0_{k_2} \rangle \\
&=: \langle \pi^0_{k_3}, \pi^0_{k_4} | \pi^0_{k_1}, \pi^0_{k_2} \rangle : + \langle \pi^0_{k_3}, \pi^0_{k_4} | \pi^0_{k_1}, \pi^0_{k_2} \rangle \\
&\quad + \langle \pi^0_{k_3}, \pi^0_{k_4} | \pi^0_{k_1}, \pi^0_{k_2} \rangle + \langle \pi^0_{k_3}, \pi^0_{k_4} | \pi^0_{k_1}, \pi^0_{k_2} \rangle \\
&= \langle \pi^0_{k_3}, \pi^0_{k_4} | \pi^0_{k_1}, \pi^0_{k_2} \rangle + \langle \pi^0_{k_3}, \pi^0_{k_4} | \pi^0_{k_1}, \pi^0_{k_2} \rangle \\
&= \Big(\sqrt{2\omega_{k_3}}\sqrt{2\omega_{k_1}}(2\pi)^3\delta(\vec{k}_3 - \vec{k}_1) \Big) \Big(\sqrt{2\omega_{k_4}}\sqrt{2\omega_{k_2}}(2\pi)^3\delta(\vec{k}_4 - \vec{k}_2) \Big) \\
&\quad + \Big(\sqrt{2\omega_{k_3}}\sqrt{2\omega_{k_2}}(2\pi)^3\delta(\vec{k}_3 - \vec{k}_2) \Big) \Big(\sqrt{2\omega_{k_4}}\sqrt{2\omega_{k_1}}(2\pi)^3\delta(\vec{k}_4 - \vec{k}_1) \Big)
\end{aligned}
\qquad (11.52)
$$

↓ Wick's theorem

↓ Eq. 11.7, Eq. 11.46

↓

For the case that the final two particle have exactly the same momenta as the initial two states ($\vec{k}_3, \vec{k}_4 = \vec{k}_1, \vec{k}_2$) this reduces to

$$A^{(0)} = 2\omega_{k_1} 2\omega_{k_2} (2\pi)^6 \delta(\vec{k}_1 - \vec{k}_1)\delta(\vec{k}_2 - \vec{k}_2)$$
$$= 4\omega_{k_1}\omega_{k_2} \Big((2\pi)^3 \delta(\vec{0}) \Big)^2 . \tag{11.53}$$

This is exactly the same result that we found in Section 10.1 (Eq. 10.7). Admittedly, this calculation was not really simpler than the naive approach in Section 10.1. The real power of the more sophisticated approach only becomes apparent once we consider higher order terms. Thus, let's evaluate the first order term $A^{(1)}$ next.

For simplicity, we focus in the following sections on the case that the final two particle have exactly the same momenta as the initial two states ($\vec{k}_3, \vec{k}_4 = \vec{k}_1, \vec{k}_2$).

11.4.2 First Order Approximation

The next term in our expansion of the probability amplitude then reads (Eq. 10.12)

$$A^{(1)} \equiv \frac{-i\lambda}{4!} \int_{-\infty}^{\infty} d^4x T \left\langle \pi^0_{k_1}, \pi^0_{k_2} \right| : \phi^4 : \left| \pi^0_{k_1}, \pi^0_{k_2} \right\rangle . \tag{11.54}$$

We want to evaluate the time-ordered product that appears here by applying Wick's theorem. But first, let's make some general observations.

As before, we can neglect all terms in which some operators remain uncontracted since we know that they yield zero (Eq. 11.27). Moreover, as before, we know that all contractions of two particles in the initial state yield zero (Eq. 11.46). Similarly, a contraction of the two particles in the final state yields zero (Eq. 11.44). Therefore, all terms that contain such a contraction can be neglected.

But of course there are many contractions that do not vanish. Luckily many of them yield exactly the same factors which makes our calculation much simpler. Since the four fields in the product $\phi^4 = \phi(x)\phi(x)\phi(x)\phi(x)$ are evaluated at exactly the same spacetime point x, each contraction of the initial or final state with one of the four fields yields exactly the same term. For example

$$\langle \pi^0_{k_1}, \pi^0_{k_2} | \phi\phi\phi\phi | \pi^0_{k_1}, \pi^0_{k_2} \rangle = \langle \pi^0_{k_1}, \pi^0_{k_2} | \phi\phi\phi\phi | \pi^0_{k_1}, \pi^0_{k_2} \rangle \qquad (11.55)$$

Thus we only need to evaluate one of these terms

$$\begin{aligned} &\langle \pi^0_{k_1}, \pi^0_{k_2} | \phi\phi\phi\phi | \pi^0_{k_1}, \pi^0_{k_2} \rangle && \text{Eq. 11.50} \\ &= \Big(\langle 0 | e^{ik_1x} e^{ik_2x} \Big) \Big(e^{-ik_1x} e^{-ik_2x} | 0 \rangle \Big) && e^0 = 1 \\ &= \langle 0 | 0 \rangle && \langle 0|0 \rangle = 1 \text{ (Eq. 8.43)} \\ &= 1\,. && (11.56) \end{aligned}$$

To count how many such terms there are, we start with the particle $\pi^0_{k_1}$ in the final state, which we can connect to four different fields. For the second particle in the final state $\pi^0_{k_2}$ there are then three uncontracted fields that it can still contract with. For the particle in the initial state $\pi^0_{k_1}$, there remain two possible contractions. The contraction of $\pi^0_{k_2}$ in the initial state is then completely fixed by the previous contractions. Thus, in total, there are $4! = 4 \cdot 3 \cdot 2 \cdot 1 = 24$ contractions of this type.

All other terms in which all of the operators are contracted involve contractions of the four fields contained in ϕ^4 with each other. For example

$$\begin{aligned} &\langle \pi^0_{k_1}, \pi^0_{k_2} | \phi\phi\phi\phi | \pi^0_{k_1}, \pi^0_{k_2} \rangle\,, \langle \pi^0_{k_1}, \pi^0_{k_2} | \phi\phi\phi\phi | \pi^0_{k_1}, \pi^0_{k_2} \rangle \\ &\langle \pi^0_{k_1}, \pi^0_{k_2} | \phi\phi\phi\phi | \pi^0_{k_1}, \pi^0_{k_2} \rangle\,, \langle \pi^0_{k_1}, \pi^0_{k_2} | \phi\phi\phi\phi | \pi^0_{k_1}, \pi^0_{k_2} \rangle \end{aligned} \qquad (11.57)$$

Or

$$\langle \pi^0_{k_1}, \pi^0_{k_2} | \phi\phi\phi\phi | \pi^0_{k_1}, \pi^0_{k_2} \rangle\,, \langle \pi^0_{k_1}, \pi^0_{k_2} | \phi\phi\phi\phi | \pi^0_{k_1}, \pi^0_{k_2} \rangle\,. \qquad (11.58)$$

However, we've discussed already in Section 11.3 that if we work with normal-ordered Hamiltonians these kind of contractions do not occur since they represent precisely the commutators that are necessary to bring the Hamiltonian into normal order.[13] In other words, the 24 contractions that we discussed above describe already all physically relevant contributions to the probability amplitude.

[13] Take note that only the Hamiltonian is normal-ordered from the start and we will need to normal order the complete expression including the initial and final state by using Wick's theorem.

Therefore, we can conclude

$$\begin{aligned}
&T\langle \pi^0_{k_1},\pi^0_{k_2}|\phi^4|\pi^0_{k_1},\pi^0_{k_2}\rangle \\
&\quad \text{(Wick's theorem)} \\
&=:\langle \pi^0_{k_1},\pi^0_{k_2}|\phi^4|\pi^0_{k_1},\pi^0_{k_2}\rangle : + \langle \pi^0_{k_1},\pi^0_{k_2}|\phi\phi\phi\phi|\pi^0_{k_1},\pi^0_{k_2}\rangle \\
&\quad + \langle \pi^0_{k_1},\pi^0_{k_2}|\phi\phi\phi\phi|\pi^0_{k_1},\pi^0_{k_2}\rangle + \ldots \\
&\quad \text{(24× Eq. 11.56)} \\
&=:\langle \pi^0_{k_1},\pi^0_{k_2}|\phi^4|\pi^0_{k_1},\pi^0_{k_2}\rangle : +24 \\
&\quad \text{(Eq. 11.7)} \\
&= 24\,.
\end{aligned} \tag{11.59}$$

If we plug this back into Eq. 11.54, we find

$$\begin{aligned}
A^{(1)} &\equiv \frac{-i\lambda}{4!}\int d^4x T\langle \pi^0_{k_1},\pi^0_{k_2}|\phi^4|\pi^0_{k_1},\pi^0_{k_2}\rangle \\
&\quad \text{(Eq. 11.59)} \\
&= \frac{-i\lambda}{24}\int d^4x\big(24\big) \\
&= -i\lambda\int d^4x \\
&\quad \text{(finite spacetime volume)} \\
&= -i\lambda V\,.
\end{aligned} \tag{11.60}$$

This is exactly the same result that we already calculated in Eq. 10.29.

The calculation in this section demonstrates how useful Wick's theorem can be once we've organized all relevant puzzle pieces. Instead of juggling dozens of commutators around, we just have to do a bit of combinatorics. But it gets even better. The combinatorics part of the calculation can be tremendously simplified by representing each possible term diagrammatically. We will discuss how this works in the next section.

11.5 Feynman Diagrams

A powerful tool to make sense of long winded quantum field theory calculations are **Feynman diagrams**. For a given initial and final state, each Feynman diagram represents one term in the corresponding Dyson series.

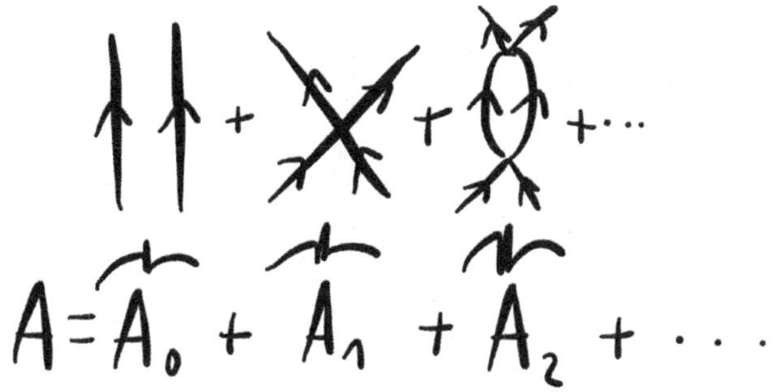

$$A = A_0 + A_1 + A_2 + \dots$$

The elements that Feynman diagrams consists of (external lines, internal lines, and vertices) are directly related to the different kinds of contractions that we discussed in Section 11.3:

- ▷ The contraction of a field with a particle in the initial state, $\phi(x)|1_k\rangle$, yields an **incoming external line** that starts at some external outside location and ends at x.
- ▷ The contraction of a field with a particle in the final state, $\langle 1_k|\phi(x)$, yields an **outgoing external line** that starts at x and ends at some unspecific external location.

▷ The contraction of a field with itself, $\phi(x)\phi(y)$, represents an internal line that goes from x to y.

▷ Moreover, we call each point at which different lines meet a vertex and denote it by a dot.

By using these rules, we can immediately translate the terms that we encountered in the previous sections into Feynman diagrams. In general, an n-th order term in the Dyson series corresponds to a Feynman diagram with n vertices.

For example, in our zeroth order approximation of the probability amplitude for the process $\pi^0_{k_1}, \pi^0_{k_2} \to \pi^0_{k_1}, \pi^0_{k_2}$, we found that (Eq. 11.52)

$$A^{(0)} = \langle \pi^0_{k_1}, \pi^0_{k_2} | \pi^0_{k_1}, \pi^0_{k_2} \rangle + \langle \pi^0_{k_1}, \pi^0_{k_2} | \pi^0_{k_1}, \pi^0_{k_2} \rangle \,. \tag{11.61}$$

In diagrammatic form, the first term looks like this

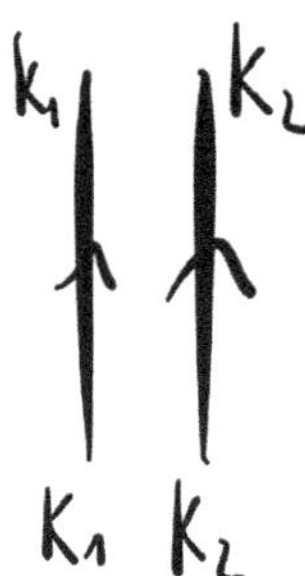

while the second term looks like this

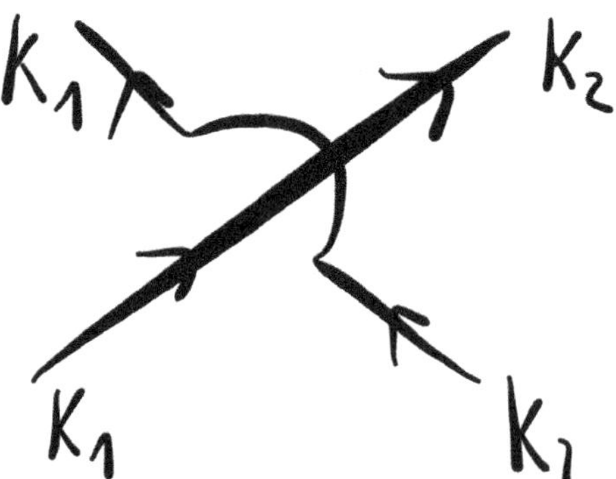

Similarly, we can draw Feynman diagrams that represent the various terms that contribute to our first order correction $A^{(1)}$. In Section 11.4.2, we discovered that there is really only one relevant type of contraction (Eq. 11.59)

$$\langle \pi^0_{k_1}, \pi^0_{k_2} | \phi\phi\phi\phi | \pi^0_{k_1}, \pi^0_{k_2} \rangle \,. \tag{11.62}$$

In diagrammatic form, we represent this contraction as follows

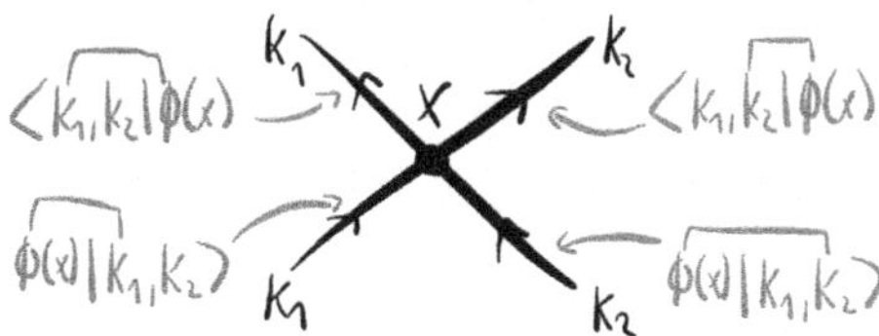

A diagram like this is known as a **tree-level diagram.**[14]

[14] More generally, a tree-level diagram is a diagram without loops. We discuss loops below.

Even though we've discarded terms that involve contractions $\phi(x)\phi(x)$ as mere artifacts, it is instructive to translate them into Feynman diagrams.[15] One example that we encountered in Section 11.4.2 when we tried to calculate $A^{(1)}$ was the term (Eq. 11.57)

$$\langle \pi^0_{k_1}, \pi^0_{k_2} | \phi\phi\phi\phi | \pi^0_{k_1}, \pi^0_{k_2} \rangle \,. \tag{11.63}$$

[15] Reminder: we discarded all terms that contain a contraction of a field with itself at the same spacetime point, because they represent commutators that only occur if we use a Hamiltonian that isn't normal-ordered.

In diagrammatic form this term contains a loop that closes at exactly the same location it starts at.

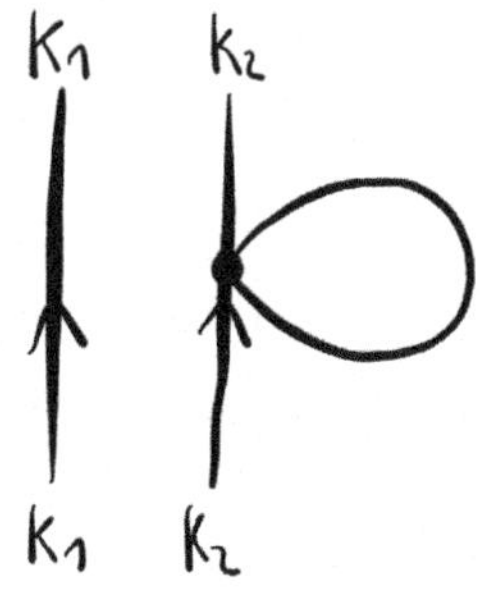

This is known as a **self-loop diagram**. In fact, all diagrams that correspond to a term, which contains a contraction of the form $\overbrace{\phi(x)\phi(x)}$, contain a self-loop. Thus we can say that when we normal order the Hamiltonian, we remove all self-loop diagrams from the perturbation series.[16] From a slightly different perspective, we can say that self-loop diagrams represent the infinitely large contributions to the ground state energy that we wish to ignore.

[16] We saw in Section 11.4.2 that this is necessary because they yield an infinitely large contribution to the probability amplitude and probabilities larger than 1 = 100% do not make sense.

If we evaluate higher order terms in the Dyson series, we encounter more complicated diagrams which, however, all consist of the basic ingredients that we introduced above. The second order correction $A^{(2)}$, for example, reads (Eq. 9.43)

$$\begin{aligned}
A^{(2)} &= -\frac{1}{2!}T\langle f|\left(\int_{-\infty}^{\infty} dt_1 H_i(t_1)\right)\left(\int_{-\infty}^{\infty} dt_2 H_i(t_2)\right)|i\rangle \\
&= -\frac{1}{2!}T\langle f|\left(\int_{-\infty}^{\infty} dx_1^4 \frac{\lambda}{4!}\phi(x_1)^4\right)\left(\int_{-\infty}^{\infty} dx_2^4 \frac{\lambda}{4!}\phi(x_2)^4\right)|i\rangle \\
&= -\frac{1}{2!}\left(\frac{\lambda}{4!}\right)^2 \int_{-\infty}^{\infty} dx_1^4\, dx_2^4\, T\langle f|\phi(x_1)^4\phi(x_2)^4|i\rangle\,.
\end{aligned} \tag{11.64}$$

If we use Wick's theorem to rewrite the time-ordered product $T\langle f|\phi(x_1)^4\phi(x_2)^4|i\rangle$, we encounter contractions $\overbrace{\phi(x_1)\phi(x_2)}$. As mentioned above, we represent these kinds of contractions in our Feynman diagrams by internal lines that start at x_1 and end at x_2. This implies that the diagrams that correspond to these second order corrections involve **loops** and look as follows:

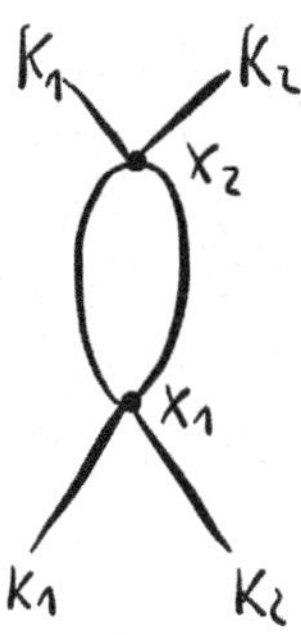

On the one hand, Feynman diagrams are useful because they allow us to develop some visual understanding of the various terms in our perturbation series and to drape words around them. For example:

- By looking at the diagrams that contribute to our zeroth-order probability amplitude $A^{(0)}$, we imagine that the two particles leave the system without any interaction going on.

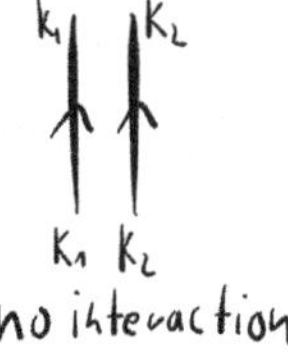

- If we include the first order correction $A^{(1)}$, we take into account that exactly one interaction happens between the two particles.

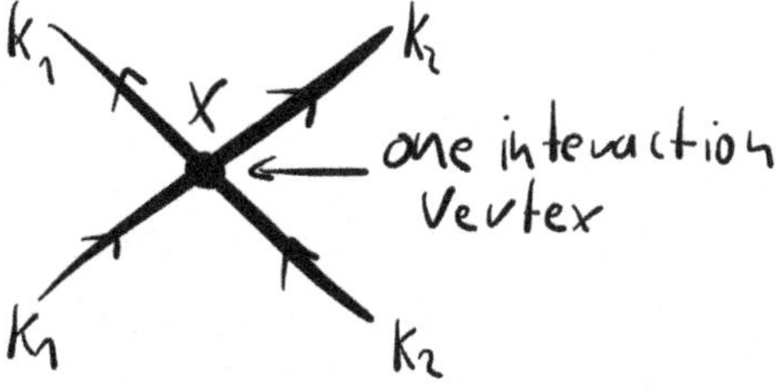

▷ Some of the self-loop diagrams represent situations in which a particle emits and then absorbs a virtual particle.

▷ Other self-loop diagrams represent situations in which the particles enter and leave the system without any interaction. At the same time, a vacuum-to-vacuum loop (a "vacuum bubble") that is completely separated from the scattering process happens. A popular way to describe these vacuum loops is by saying that a virtual particle pair pops shortly into existence before they annihilate each other again.

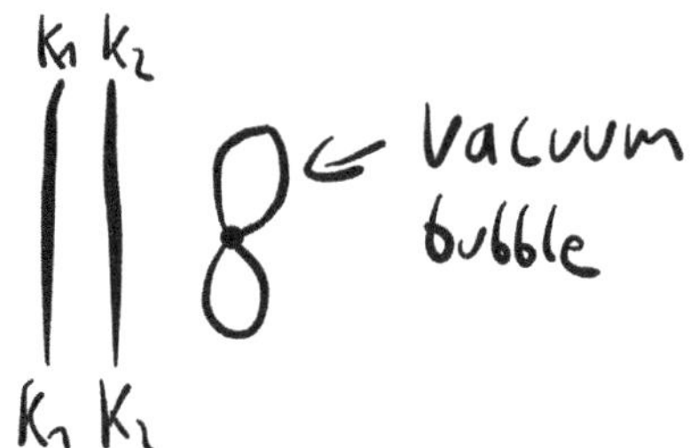

▷ At higher order in perturbation theory there are new self-loop diagrams that represent, for example, a situation in which two vacuum bubbles pop in and out of existence.

▷ Moreover, we can describe the loop diagrams that appear at higher orders in perturbation theory, by saying that the two particles interact, create a virtual particle pair as a result of their interaction, which then annihilates again and produces this way the two particles that leave the system.

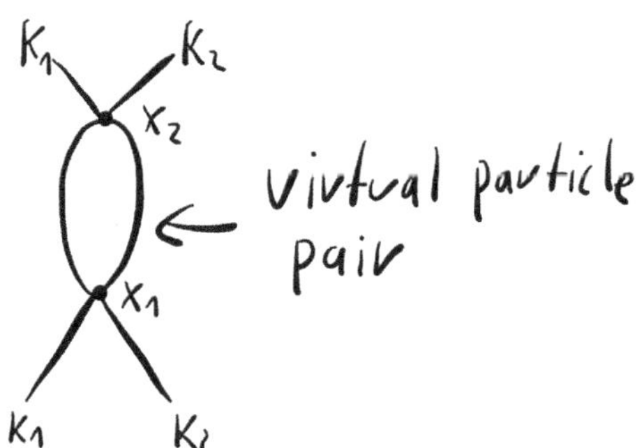

This use case is analogous to how we used diagrams to understand the terms that appear in our classical perturbation series.[17]

[17] We discussed a diagrammatic interpretation of terms that appear in our perturbation series that describes interacting classical fields in Chapter 6.

On the other hand, the real reason why Feynman diagrams are used everywhere in modern particle physics is that they allow us to write down the correct terms that appear in our perturbation series without referring to the complicated Dyson series at all. In other words, usually we start by drawing Feynman diagrams and use them to deduce the correct terms that appear in perturbation series. As soon as we know how to draw the correct diagrams, we can use the rules given above to write down the corresponding perturbation series terms. But it gets even better. Since we've already evaluated all of the relevant contractions (Eq. 11.50), we can immediately write down the correct factor for each Feynman diagram element:[18]

▷ Each incoming external line corresponds to a factor of e^{-ipx} (Eq. 11.38).

▷ Each outgoing external line corresponds to a factor of e^{ipx} (Eq. 11.40).

▷ Each internal line corresponds to a factor of $D_F(x,y)$ (Eq. 11.16).

▷ Each vertex corresponds to a factor of $-i\lambda$. (Take note that there is no factor $\frac{1}{4!}$ because of the 4! ways the four particles that meet at a ϕ^4-vertex can pair up with the four field factors $\phi(x)\phi(x)\phi(x)\phi(x)$. We discussed this in the text below Eq. 11.56.)

▷ Each line that enters and leaves the system without any interaction, contributes a factor $\sqrt{2\omega_q}\sqrt{2\omega_k}(2\pi)^3\delta(\vec{q}-\vec{k})$ (Eq. 11.42).

[18] Take note that in addition, we need to integrate over all possible locations x at which the interaction can happen. We saw this explicitly in Section 10 and Section 11.4.2, but we can also understand it in more intuitive terms. As mentioned before, in our initial and final state we use particles with exactly known momenta. According to the uncertainty relation, this implies that we have no information about their location. Thus, in principle the interaction can happen anywhere in the system. In a quantum context we take this into account by summing/integrating the probability amplitude that the interaction happens at a specific location x over all allowed values of x.

These are known as the **Feynman rules for the ϕ^4 model.**[19]

[19] Different models require different Feynman rules. We will discuss this in more detail below.

In most cases there is a natural hierarchy among Feynman diagrams: the more vertices, the less important (at least if $0 < \lambda < 1$). In particular

▷ No vertex $\leftrightarrow$ no factor $-i\lambda$ $\leftrightarrow$ most important term in perturbation series (but only relevant if no momentum transfer happens).

▷ One vertex $\leftrightarrow$ one factor $-i\lambda$ $\leftrightarrow$ first order correction in perturbation series.

▷ Two vertices ↔ two factors $-i\lambda$ ↔ second order correction in perturbation series.

⋮

For a given number of initial and final particles, we then draw all possible diagrams that involve a specific number of vertices. These diagrams represent all possible terms that contribute to the probability amplitude at the desired level of accuracy.

In summary:

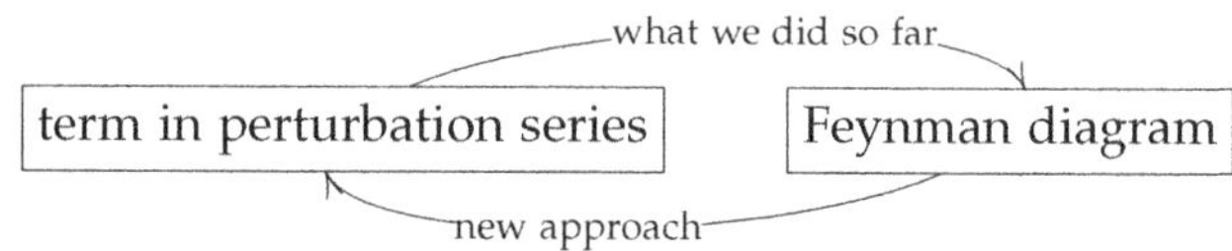

In the following section, we will see how this works by using the $\pi^0_{k_1}, \pi^0_{k_2} \to \pi^0_{k_1}, \pi^0_{k_2}$ example that we discussed two times already.

11.6 Scattering - a Third Look

Let's forget for a moment everything we know already about the probability amplitude for the process $\pi^0_{k_1}, \pi^0_{k_2} \to \pi^0_{k_1}, \pi^0_{k_2}$. In our new approach, we want to start by drawing Feynman diagrams.

11.6.1 Zeroth order Approximation

At zeroth order in perturbation theory, there are exactly two diagrams that we can draw.

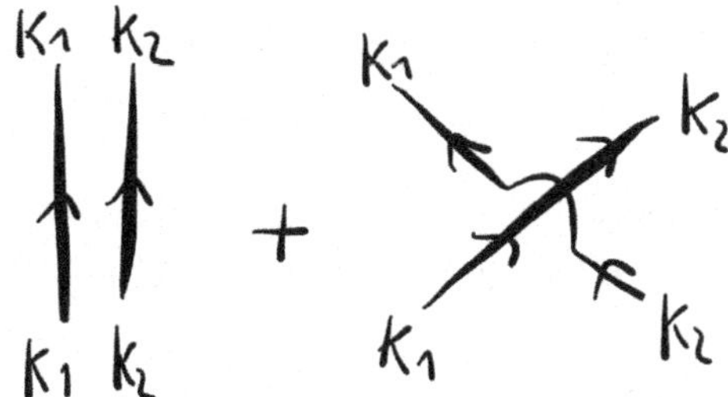

In the first case, the first particle enters with momentum k_1 and leaves with momentum k_1. Similarly, the momentum of the second particle remains unchanged, $k_2 \to k_2$. In the second case, the momentum of the first particle changes from $k_1 \to k_2$ while the momentum of the second particle changes from $k_2 \to k_1$. This may seem odd because no interaction happens. However, we are dealing with a quantum theory and the two particles that enter and leave the system are indistinguishable except for their momenta. Hence, there is no way for us to tell if it's the first particle that leaves with momentum k_1 or if it's the second particle. Therefore, we need to take both possibilities into account.[20] This is analogous to how we are unable to tell which path a particle takes in a double slit experiment and thus need to take paths through both slits into account.

[20] This is, of course, just one way to drape words around the fact that we need both diagrams to get all terms that appear in the perturbation series.

By using the Feynman rules and assuming $k_1 \neq k_2$, we find

$$
\begin{aligned}
A^{(0)} &= \text{first Feynman diagram} + \text{second Feynman diagram} \\
&= \Big((\text{line } k_1 \to k_1) \times (\text{line } k_2 \to k_2)\Big) + \Big((\text{line } k_1 \to k_2) \times (\text{line } k_2 \to k_1)\Big) \\
&= \Big(\sqrt{2\omega_{k_1}}\sqrt{2\omega_{k_1}}(2\pi)^3\delta(\vec{k}_1 - \vec{k}_1)\Big)\Big(\sqrt{2\omega_{k_2}}\sqrt{2\omega_{k_2}}(2\pi)^3\delta(\vec{k}_2 - \vec{k}_2)\Big) \\
&\quad + \Big(\sqrt{2\omega_{k_1}}\sqrt{2\omega_{k_2}}(2\pi)^3\delta(\vec{k}_1 - \vec{k}_2)\Big)\Big(\sqrt{2\omega_{k_2}}\sqrt{2\omega_{k_1}}(2\pi)^3\delta(\vec{k}_2 - \vec{k}_1)\Big) \\
&= 4\omega_{k_1}\omega_{k_2}\Big((2\pi)^3\delta(\vec{0})\Big)^2 . \qquad (11.65)
\end{aligned}
$$

Feynman rules

This is exactly the same result that we calculated in Eq. 10.7 and Eq. 11.53.

11.6.2 First order Approximation

If we allow exactly one interaction vertex, there is one possible diagram (at least, if we ignore self-loop diagrams):[21]

[21] Take note that switching $k_1 \leftrightarrow k_2$ for the incoming or outgoing particles doesn't lead to a new diagram.

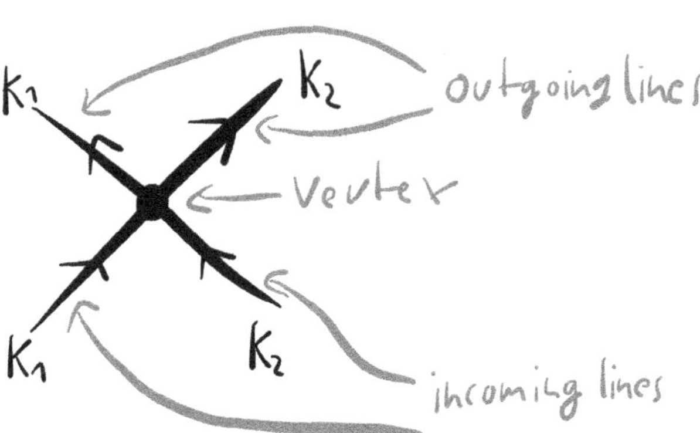

By using the Feynman rules, we find immediately

$$
\begin{aligned}
A^{(1)} &= \text{Feynman diagram} \\
&= \text{incoming } k_1 \text{ line } \times \text{ incoming } k_2 \text{ line } \times \text{ vertex} \\
&\quad \times \text{ outgoing } k_1 \text{ line } \times \text{ outgoing } k_2 \text{ line} && \text{Feynman rules} \\
&= \int d^4x\, e^{ik_1x} e^{ik_2x} (-i\lambda) e^{-ik_1x} e^{-ik_2x} && e^0 = 1 \\
&= -i\lambda \int d^4x && \text{finite } V \\
&= -i\lambda V \,.
\end{aligned}
\tag{11.66}
$$

This is the result that we already found in Eq. 10.29 and Eq. 11.60.

11.6.3 Second-Order Approximation

Let's risk a quick glance beyond the first order approximation. Instead of a complete discussion, we draw just one viable diagram with two vertices because this already reveals an important feature of higher order corrections.

Using the Feynman rules, we can write down the corresponding contribution to the probability amplitude

$$
\begin{aligned}
&(-i\lambda)^2 \int d^4x_1 d^4x_2 \, e^{-ik_1x_1} e^{-ik_2x_1} D_F(x_1,x_2) D_F(x_1,x_2) e^{ik_3x_2} e^{ik_4x_2} \\
&= -\lambda^2 \int d^4x_1 d^4x_2 \, e^{-ik_1x_1} e^{-ik_2x_1} \Big(\int \frac{d^4q}{(2\pi)^4} \frac{i\, e^{-iq(x_2-x_1)}}{q^2-m^2+i\epsilon} \Big) \Big(\int \frac{d^4p}{(2\pi)^4} \frac{i\, e^{-ip(x_2-x_1)}}{p^2-m^2+i\epsilon} \Big) e^{ik_3x_2} e^{ik_4x_2} \\
&= \lambda^2 \int d^4x_1 d^4x_2 \frac{d^4q}{(2\pi)^4} \frac{d^4p}{(2\pi)^4} \, e^{-i(k_1+k_2-p-q)x_1} e^{i(k_3+k_4-p-q)x_2} \frac{1}{q^2-m^2+i\epsilon} \frac{1}{p^2-m^2+i\epsilon} \\
&= \lambda^2 \int \frac{d^4q}{(2\pi)^4} \frac{d^4p}{(2\pi)^4} (2\pi)^4 \delta(k_1+k_2-p-q) (2\pi)^4 \delta(k_3+k_4-p-q) \frac{1}{q^2-m^2+i\epsilon} \frac{1}{p^2-m^2+i\epsilon} \\
&= \lambda^2 \int d^4q \, \delta(k_3+k_4-(k_1+k_2-q)-q) \frac{1}{q^2-m^2+i\epsilon} \frac{1}{(k_1+k_2-q)^2-m^2+i\epsilon} \\
&= \lambda^2 \int d^4q \frac{1}{q^2-m^2+i\epsilon} \frac{1}{(k_1+k_2-q)^2-m^2+i\epsilon} \delta(k_3+k_4-k_1-k_2) \,. \qquad (11.67)
\end{aligned}
$$

Eq. 8.98

A key observation here is that the integral is non-trivial because q doesn't appear in the delta distribution. The delta distribution

$\delta(k_3 + k_4 - k_1 - k_2)$ encodes momentum conservation: the total four-momentum of the two incoming particles must be equal to the total four-momentum of the two outgoing particles. Thus we still need to integrate over the "loop momentum" q, which is not restricted by the external momenta. This means, q can take on any value irrespective of what the momenta of the incoming and outgoing particles are.

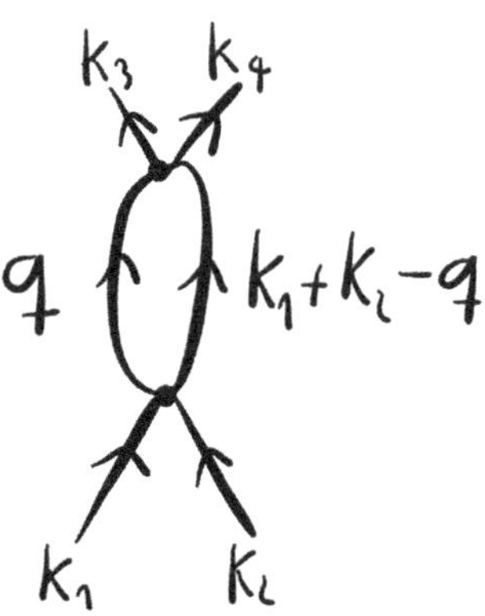

A problematic aspect of the unconstrained loop momentum is that it can take on arbitrarily high values, even $q \to \infty$. Formally, the integration limits are, in fact, $(-\infty, \infty)$. Setting the question if infinitely large momentum values make sense aside, this fact is problematic because it implies that the integral in Eq. 11.67 blows up. Roughly this follows, because[22]

$$\int_0^\infty d^4q \, \frac{1}{q^4} \sim \ln(|q|)\Big|_0^\infty \sim \infty \,, \tag{11.68}$$

[22] Take note that $\ln(\infty) = \infty$ and $\int \frac{1}{x} = \ln(x)$.

which implies that $\int_\infty^\infty \frac{d^4q}{(2\pi)^4} \frac{1}{q^4} \sim \infty$.

If we take this result seriously, we must conclude that the second-order contribution to the probability amplitude is infinitely large. A probability of larger than $100\% = 1$ doesn't make sense and it therefore seems as if our approach breaks down at this point. There are, however, ways to deal with this issue.

One possibility is to introduce a finite upper limit Λ, which encodes the maximum momentum value that is possible. The general idea here is somewhat analogous to how we got rid of infinities that we encountered previously by introducing a finite spacetime volume V. [23] The exact magnitude of V turned out to be unimportant because it drops out from our predictions. Analogously, the maximum momentum limit drops out if we handle our expressions properly. To understand how this works, take note that for a finite upper limit the integral in Eq. 11.67 yields[24]

[23] We discussed the need for a finite spacetime volume in Section 8.4.3.

[24] As before, we will simply assume that a trustworthy mathematician hands us this correct integration result.

$$\lambda^2 \int_{-\Lambda}^{\Lambda} d^4q \, \frac{1}{q^2 - m^2 + i\epsilon} \frac{1}{(k_1 + k_2 - q)^2 - m^2 + i\epsilon}$$

$$= -i\lambda^2 C \ln\left(\frac{(k_1 + k_2)^2}{\Lambda^2}\right)$$

↷ $\ln \frac{a}{b} = \ln a - \ln b$

$$= -i\lambda^2 C\Big(\ln\big((k_1 + k_2)^2 - \ln(\Lambda^2)\big)\Big)$$

↷ definition

$$= -i\lambda^2 C\Big(\ln(s) - \ln(\Lambda^2)\Big) \tag{11.69}$$

where C is a constant factor that isn't important for us here and $s \equiv (k_1 + k_2)^2$ encodes the energy scale at which the scattering process happens. If we shoot the two particles with high energies onto each other, s is large, while for small energies, s is small. This contribution to the scattering amplitude therefore depends primarily on s and we denote it by

$$A^{(2)}(s) = -i\lambda^2 C\Big(\ln(s) - \ln(\Lambda^2)\Big)\delta(k_3 + k_4 - k_1 - k_2) + \ldots, \tag{11.70}$$

where the dots indicate possible additional contributions from different diagrams. The total scattering amplitude for $k_1, k_2 \neq k_3, k_4$ then reads[25]

[25] This definition may look somewhat awkward but we're basically just getting rid of all the irrelevant things.

$$\tilde{A}(s) \equiv \frac{-V - A(s)}{iV} = \frac{1}{iV}\Big(-V - (A^{(0)}(s) + A^{(1)}(s) + A^{(2)}(s) + \ldots)\Big)$$

↷ Eq. 11.65, Eq. 11.66, Eq. 11.70

$$= i - i - \lambda - \lambda^2 C\Big(\ln(s) - \ln(\Lambda^2)\Big) + \ldots$$

↷ $\ln \frac{a}{b} = \ln a - \ln b$

$$= -\lambda - \lambda^2 C \ln\left(\frac{s}{\Lambda^2}\right) + \ldots \tag{11.71}$$

where we divide by V to avoid working with factors of $\delta(\vec{0})$.

While the second contribution to the scattering amplitude is now no longer infinitely large, it's still problematic because it depends on the cutoff Λ. Luckily, as it was the case for the finite spacetime volume V, we can make predictions that are independent of Λ. To understand how this works, take note that if we compare the scattering amplitude at two different scales s_1, s_2, the unknown factor Λ drops out

$$\begin{aligned}
\tilde{A}(s_1) - \tilde{A}(s_2) &= \Bigg(-\lambda - \lambda^2 C\Big(\ln(s_1) - \ln(\Lambda^2)\Big)\Bigg) \\
&\quad - \Bigg(-\lambda - \lambda^2 C\Big(\ln(s_2) - \ln(\Lambda^2)\Big)\Bigg) \\
&= -\lambda^2 C\Big(\ln(s_2) - \ln(s_1)\Big) \\
&= -\lambda^2 C \ln\left(\frac{s_2}{s_1}\right) . \qquad (11.72)
\end{aligned}$$

This is encouraging. But what about the probability amplitude at a given scale s? Isn't $|\tilde{A}(s)|^2$ observable and should therefore be finite even for $\Lambda \to \infty$?

To resolve this issue, we need to rethink the role of the coupling constant λ. In words, it encodes how strongly the scalar field interacts with itself. To measure a coupling constant in an experiment, we rely on scattering processes like the one that we are considering here. Moreover, we saw in the previous section that the parameter λ that appears in the Lagrangian describes the first order approximation perfectly. In experiments, however, we never measure first order approximations but always the full probability amplitude which includes all terms in the perturbation series. This implies, that scattering processes don't tell us something about λ but rather about the **renormalized coupling**

$$\lambda_R(s) \equiv -\tilde{A}(s) = \lambda + \lambda^2 C \ln\left(\frac{s}{\Lambda^2}\right) + \dots . \qquad (11.73)$$

It's this quantity which describes how different excitations of the scalar field interact with each other, while λ is only a first order approximation. We can therefore start by measuring the scattering probability at a specific but arbitrary scale s_0:

$$\lambda_R \equiv -\tilde{A}(s_0) = \lambda + \lambda^2 C \ln\left(\frac{s_0}{\Lambda^2}\right) + \dots \quad (11.74)$$

The left-hand side is fixed by what we measure in the experiment. Since what we measure in experiments are finite numbers, the right-hand side of this equation has to be finite too, even if we send the cutoff to infinity, $\Lambda \to \infty$.

To understand why this is useful, let's invert Eq. 11.74 by making the ansatz[26]

$$\lambda = \lambda_R + a\lambda_R^2 + \dots \quad (11.75)$$

[26] We will see in a moment why a formula of this form will help us to get rid of the scale Λ altogether.

If we plug this ansatz into Eq. 11.74, we find

$$\begin{aligned} \lambda_R &= \lambda + \lambda^2 C \ln\left(\frac{s_0}{\Lambda^2}\right) + \dots \\ &\quad \text{(Eq. 11.75)} \\ &= \left(\lambda_R + a\lambda_R^2 + \dots\right) + \left(\lambda_R + a\lambda_R^2 + \dots\right)^2 C \ln\left(\frac{s_0}{\Lambda^2}\right) + \dots \\ &= \lambda_R + a\lambda_R^2 + \lambda_R^2 C \ln\left(\frac{s_0}{\Lambda^2}\right) + \dots, \end{aligned} \quad (11.76)$$

where we neglected all higher order terms. By comparing the left-hand side with the right-hand side, we can conclude that

$$\begin{aligned} a &= -C \ln\left(\frac{s_0}{\Lambda^2}\right) \\ &\quad \text{(} -\ln\left(\tfrac{a}{b}\right) = \ln\left(\tfrac{b}{a}\right) \text{)} \\ &= C \ln\left(\frac{\Lambda^2}{s_0}\right). \end{aligned} \quad (11.77)$$

Therefore,

$$\begin{aligned} \lambda &\overset{11.75}{=} \lambda_R + a\lambda_R^2 + \dots \\ &\quad \text{(Eq. 11.77)} \\ &= \lambda_R + C \ln\left(\frac{\Lambda^2}{s_0}\right) \lambda_R^2 + \dots. \end{aligned} \quad (11.78)$$

With this formula and a measured value of λ_R at hand, we can predict the scattering probability at any scale s without having to refer to the cutoff Λ:

$$
\begin{aligned}
\tilde{A}(s) &\overset{11.71}{=} -\lambda - \lambda^2 C \ln\left(\frac{s}{\Lambda^2}\right) + \dots \\
&= -\left(\lambda_R + C\ln\left(\frac{\Lambda^2}{s_0}\right)\lambda_R^2\right) \\
&\quad - \left(\lambda_R + C\ln\left(\frac{\Lambda^2}{s_0}\right)\lambda_R^2\right)^2 C\ln\left(\frac{s}{\Lambda^2}\right) + \dots \\
&= -\lambda_R - C\ln\left(\frac{\Lambda^2}{s_0}\right)\lambda_R^2 - \lambda_R^2 C\ln\left(\frac{s}{\Lambda^2}\right) + \dots \\
&= -\lambda_R - C\ln\left(\frac{\Lambda^2}{s_0}\frac{s}{\Lambda^2}\right)\lambda_R^2 + \dots \\
&= -\lambda_R - C\ln\left(\frac{s}{s_0}\right)\lambda_R^2 + \dots .
\end{aligned}
\tag{11.79}
$$

↷ Eq. 11.78

↷

↷ $\ln(ab) = \ln(a) + \ln(b)$

↷ $\cancel{\Lambda^2}$

Let's drape words around what we've just done. We started by calculating the second order correction for the probability amplitude $A(\pi^0_{k_1}, \pi^0_{k_2} \to \pi^0_{k_3}, \pi^0_{k_4})$. We noticed that the correction is formally infinitely large. Since this doesn't make any sense, we introduced a cutoff Λ and simply declared that no momentum larger than Λ is possible. This step is known as **regularization**.[27] As a result, the contribution of the second order term we considered is no longer infinite, but now depends on Λ. This is problematic because we have no idea what value we should plug in for Λ, if such a cutoff really exists at all. We then discovered that the dependence on Λ is an artifact that occurs if we try to write down a probability amplitude that depends on the parameter λ.

[27] An obvious question is: does such a cutoff really exist? Presently, nobody knows the answer to this question. However, take note that since energy scales are inversely related to length scales in quantum theories, an upper energy limit implies a lower length scale limit. In other words, the existence of a cutoff Λ would imply that there is a minimum length scale. This, in turn, implies that spacetime is not continuous but discrete. If the minimum length scale is sufficiently small there is no way to tell using present day technologies if it exists.

This is a bad idea because λ, which appears in the Lagrangian, is not directly measurable. Instead, experimental outcomes only depend on the renormalized coupling $\lambda_R(s)$. We can see this because in an experiment we always measure the (absolute value squared of the) total probability amplitude which includes all order corrections $A = A^{(0)} + A^{(1)} + A^{(2)} + \dots$. The Lagrangian parameter λ, however, only describes the coupling between two excitations of the scalar field at first order $A^{(1)} \sim \lambda$. In contrast, the renormalized coupling $\lambda_R(s)$ is an experimentally measured value and thus takes all order corrections into account.[28]

[28] We will discuss this in more systematic terms in the next section.

We then proceeded by using the experimental value of $\lambda_R(s)$ at one fixed but otherwise arbitrary reference scale s_0: $\lambda_R \equiv \lambda_R(s_0)$. In particular, we discovered that if we rewrite the probability amplitude as a series in λ_R instead of λ, there is no longer any dependence on the cutoff Λ (Eq. 11.79). Thus, if we focus on the coupling constant that we can actually measure (λ_R) instead of on the formal λ parameter, the cutoff scale becomes irrelevant and we can even take the limit $\Lambda \to \infty$.

For completeness, take note that there are two additional diagrams that contribute to the second order correction.

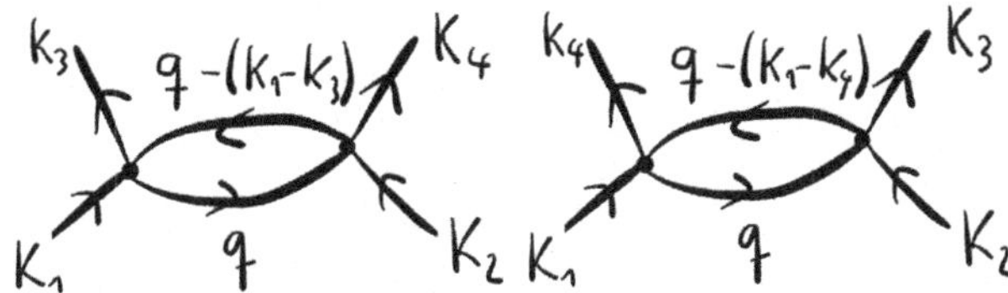

Using our Feynman rules and then following exactly the same steps as in Eq. 11.69, it's possible to derive that the corresponding contributions read

$$\text{2. Feynman diagram} \quad \leftrightarrow \quad -\lambda^2 C\left(\ln(t) - \ln(\Lambda^2) \right)$$

$$\text{3. Feynman diagram} \quad \leftrightarrow \quad -\lambda^2 C\left(\ln(u) - \ln(\Lambda^2) \right), \quad (11.80)$$

where $t \equiv (k_1 - k_3)^2$ and $u \equiv (k_1 - k_4)^2$. These results are analogous to our result for the first Feynman diagram (Eq. 11.69):

$$\text{1. Feynman diagram} \quad \leftrightarrow \quad -\lambda^2 C\left(\ln(s) - \ln(\Lambda^2)\right), \quad (11.81)$$

where $s \equiv (k_1 + k_2)^2$. Since the general structure of the formulas is so similar, we can regularize and renormalize them analogously.

As a final comment, take note that by focusing on specific final momenta k_3 and k_4 it's possible to consider only processes for which $t \equiv (k_1 - k_3)^2 = 0$ and $u \equiv (k_1 - k_4)^2 = 0$, while $s \equiv (k_1 + k_2)^2 \neq 0$. This is known as probing the s-channel since for these specific processes only the diagram that we discussed above contributes something non-zero.

Let's summarize what we've learned in this chapter.

11.7 Summary

We started by noting that it usually makes sense to normal order any given product that we encounter. A product of operators in quantum field theory is normal-ordered when all annihilation operators are moved as far as possible to the right (Eq. 11.5):

$$\begin{aligned} :\phi(x)\phi(y): &\equiv \text{all annihilation operators in } \phi(x)\phi(y) \text{ moved to the right} \\ &\equiv \text{normal-ordered } \phi(x)\phi(y)\,. \end{aligned} \tag{11.82}$$

We are interested in normal-ordered products, since they yield zero if we sandwich them between $\langle 0|$ and $|0\rangle$ (Eq. 11.7)

$$\langle 0| :\phi(x)\phi(y): |0\rangle = 0\,. \tag{11.83}$$

Moreover, the operator products that we are typically interested in appear sandwiched between $\langle 0|$ and $|0\rangle$ because the probability amplitudes that we are interested in are defined as $\langle i|\hat{S}|f\rangle$ and we define particle states as excitations above the ground state $|1_k\rangle \equiv a^\dagger(k)\,|0\rangle$.

If we start with an operator product in arbitrary order, we can normal order it by using commutation relations (Eq. 8.14). This implies that if we want to switch from an arbitrarily ordered product to a normal-ordered product, we find additional terms that contain commutators. These terms do not vanish if we sandwich them between $\langle 0|$ and $|0\rangle$ since a commutator yields a complex function and can therefore be pulled out from the braket. For example

$$\langle 0|[\phi_-(x),\phi_+(y)]|0\rangle = [\phi_-(x),\phi_+(y)]\,\langle 0|0\rangle = [\phi_-(x),\phi_+(y)]\,. \tag{11.84}$$

Thus, in general, we find

$$\phi(x_1)\ldots\phi(x_n) =: \phi(x_1)\ldots\phi(x_n) : + \text{ commutator terms} \tag{11.85}$$

and

$$\begin{aligned}\langle 0|\phi(x_1)\dots\phi(x_n)|0\rangle &= \langle 0| : \phi(x_1)\dots\phi(x_n) : |0\rangle \\ &\quad + \langle 0| \text{ commutator terms } |0\rangle \\ &= 0 + \text{ commutator terms} \\ &= \text{ commutator terms}\,. \end{aligned} \tag{11.86}$$

Eq. 11.83, Eq. 11.84

In words, this means that all relevant information is contained in the commutator terms. We then noted that the products we encounter are typically not in arbitrary order, but time-ordered. This follows because the scattering operator $\hat{S}$ involves the time ordering operator T (Eq. 9.42). We discovered that the commutator terms that we encounter when we bring a time-ordered product to normal order, are exactly equal to the Feynman propagator $D_f(x,y)$. This motivated us to define the contraction of two fields as

$$\overbrace{\phi(x)\phi(y)} \equiv \begin{cases} [\phi_-(x), \phi_+(y)] & \text{for } x_0 > y_0 \\ [\phi_-(y), \phi_+(x)] & \text{for } y_0 > x_0 \end{cases}, \tag{11.87}$$

where (Eq. 11.16)

$$\overbrace{\phi(x)\phi(y)} = D_F(x,y)\,. \tag{11.88}$$

For a time-ordered product of just two fields we therefore write (Eq. 11.17)

$$T\phi(x)\phi(y) =: \phi(x)\phi(y) : + \overbrace{\phi(x)\phi(y)}\,, \tag{11.89}$$

where now only the contraction term on the right-hand side is non-vanishing if we sandwich the product between $\langle 0|$ and $|0\rangle$ (Eq. 11.18)

$$\langle 0|T\phi(x)\phi(y)|0\rangle = \overbrace{\phi(x)\phi(y)}\,. \tag{11.90}$$

This, in turn, implies that if we want to calculate the contraction of two fields, we simply have to evaluate their time-ordered product (Eq. 11.20). Afterwards, we discussed that exactly the same general ideas hold true for more complicated time-ordered products. No matter how many operators are contained in the product, we can always bring it into normal order by using the commutation relations. In addition, the commutators that appear when we rearrange a time-ordered product are precisely the contractions we defined above. This general idea is formalized by Wick's theorem (Eq. 11.21)

$$T\hat{A}_1 \ldots \hat{A}_n =: \hat{A}_1 \ldots \hat{A}_n : + : \text{ all possible contractions } : .$$

The theorem is useful because if we sandwich the product between $\langle 0|$ and $|0\rangle$, it's only the contraction terms that survive. In other words, as long as we're interested in probability amplitudes, the contraction terms contain all relevant information. Thus, Wick's theorem reduces the problem of calculating probability amplitudes (time-ordered products sandwiched between $\langle 0|$ and $|0\rangle$) to a combinatorics problem (writing down all contractions). We then studied all elementary contractions that we typically encounter in our calculations (Eq. 11.50):

$$\begin{aligned}
\overbracket{\phi(x)\phi(y)} &= D_F(x,y) && \text{(Eq. 11.16)} \\
\overbracket{\phi(x)|1_k}\rangle &= e^{-i(kx)}\,|0\rangle && \text{(Eq. 11.38)} \\
\langle\overbracket{1_k|\phi}(x) &= \langle 0|\,e^{i(kx)} && \text{(Eq. 11.40)} \\
\langle\overbracket{1_q|\ldots|1_k}\rangle &= \sqrt{2\omega_q}\sqrt{2\omega_k}(2\pi)^3\delta(\vec{q}-\vec{k}) && \text{(Eq. 11.42)} \\
|\overbracket{1_q,1_k}\rangle &= 0 && \text{(Eq. 11.46)} \\
\langle\overbracket{1_q,1_k}| &= 0 && \text{(Eq. 11.44)}
\end{aligned}$$

Equipped with these general rules, we can immediately evaluate the terms that we encounter after we've applied Wick's theorem.

The final aspect that we talked about was a method to streamline the whole procedure and make it more intuitive. The key idea is that we can represent each type of contraction that we typically encounter by a graphical element. For example, the contraction $\phi(x)|1_k\rangle$ is represented by an incoming line and is interpreted as an incoming particle. Taken together, these graphical elements yield a Feynman diagram that represents one specific term in the perturbation series.

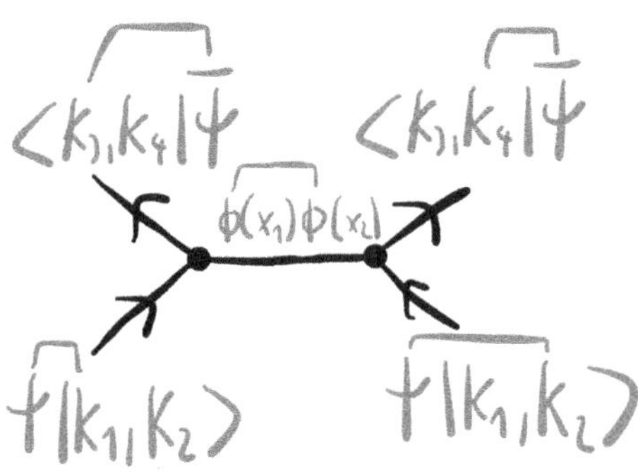

A powerful idea is to turn the whole procedure on its head. Instead of translating terms in the perturbation series into Feynman diagrams, we start by drawing Feynman diagrams and use them to deduce the corresponding terms that appear in the perturbation series. For the ϕ^4 model that we discussed several times in this chapter, the Feynman rules that allow us to do this are[29]

[29] Take note that the Feynman rules depend on the model at hand. In the following chapter, we will encounter different kinds of Feynman rules. Moreover, don't worry if you're still a bit unsure how to draw Feynman diagrams and how to translate them. It takes quite a bit of practice to get this right and the only goal in this chapter was to develop some elementary understanding of the main ideas, and not to turn you into a skillful practitioner.

▷ Each incoming external line corresponds to a factor of e^{-ipx} (Eq. 11.38).

▷ Each outgoing external line corresponds to a factor of e^{ipx} (Eq. 11.40).

▷ Each internal line corresponds to a factor of $D_F(x,y)$ (Eq. 11.16).

▷ Each vertex corresponds to a factor of $-i\lambda$. (Take note that there is no factor $\frac{1}{4!}$ because of the 4! ways the four particles that meet at a ϕ^4-vertex can pair up with the four field factors $\phi(x)\phi(x)\phi(x)\phi(x)$.)[30]

[30] We discussed this in the text below Eq. 11.56.

▷ Each line that enters and leaves the system without any interaction, contributes a factor $\sqrt{2\omega_q}\sqrt{2\omega_k}(2\pi)^3\delta(\vec{q}-\vec{k})$ (Eq. 11.42).

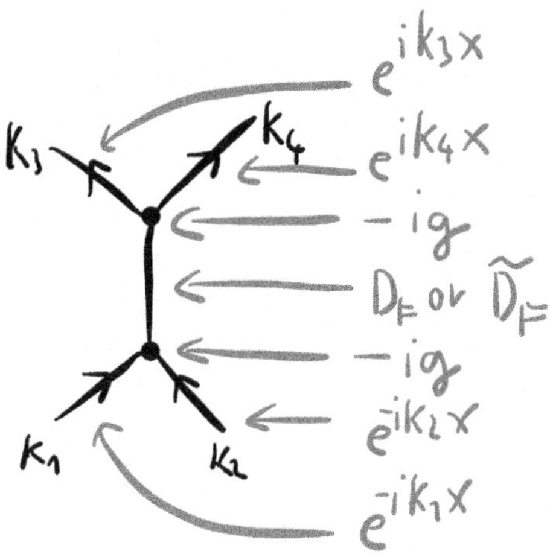

All of this is summarized in the following diagram:

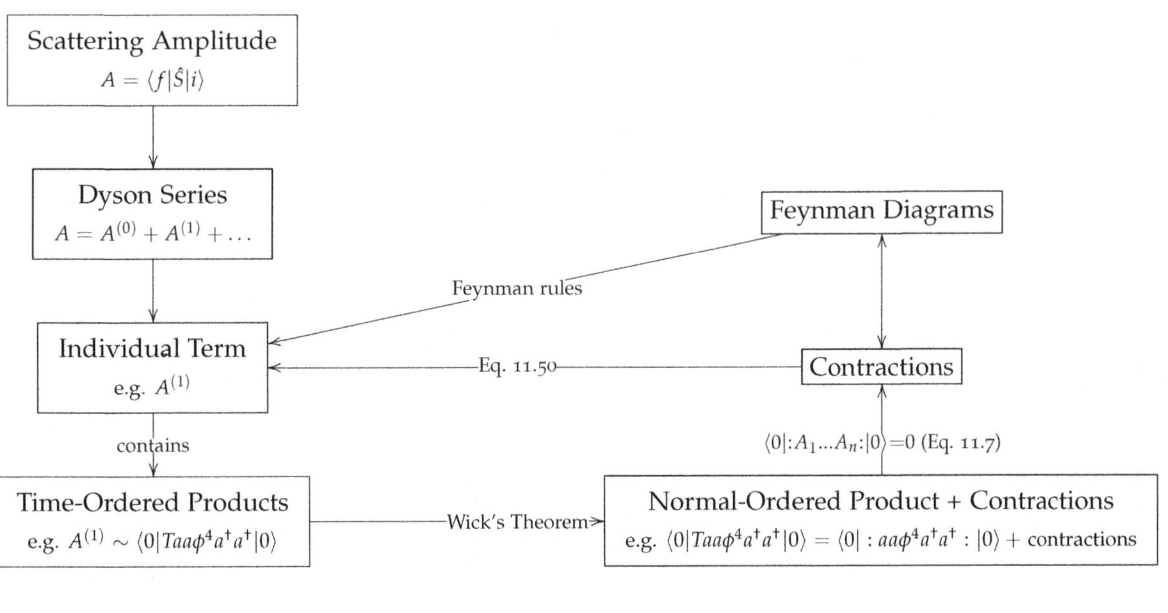

Lastly, we talked about a problem that occurs when we try to evaluate higher order corrections. If we evaluate the expressions naively, we find that higher order corrections that correspond to Feynman diagrams involving loops are infinitely large. The solution to this problem is a two-step process known as regularization and renormalization. Regularization means that we introduce an upper momentum cutoff Λ. This renders the contribution finite. In a second step, we then argued that our predictions are independent of Λ if we focus on the renormalized coupling λ_R that can be measured in experiments, instead of on the "bare" coupling λ that appears in the Lagrangian and is therefore only a feature of our formalism.

12

Elementary Models

In the previous chapter, we already got a first glimpse at how applications of quantum field theory work in practice. So far, we've only discussed one specific scattering process ($\pi^0_{k_1}, \pi^0_{k_2} \to \pi^0_{k_3}, \pi^0_{k_4}$) in one specific model $H_i \sim \phi^4$. Luckily, we can use exactly the same procedure to calculate probability amplitudes for all kinds of processes in different models too.[1]

[1] There are, of course, important differences if we consider alternative models. These primarily originate because if we consider a model that not only contains a scalar field, the probability amplitudes automatically contain more complicated objects like spinors or vectors. We will encounter some examples in the sections below.

But since there are, in principle, infinitely many models and processes that we can consider it's simply impossible to discuss applications of quantum field theory exhaustively. Therefore, we will focus in this chapter on just two additional types of models:

▷ An elementary Yukawa model that describes the interactions between a real scalar field and a complex scalar field.[2]

▷ An elementary gauge model that describes the interactions between a spinor field and a gauge field.

[2] The Yukawa interaction between a real scalar field and a spinor field is extremely similar. However, to avoid complications that arise as soon as we consider spinors, we consider here a complex scalar field to illustrate the main features of Yukawa interactions. At the end of the section, we will discuss shortly which parts of our formula need to be modified if we consider spinor fields.

These elementary models can be used to make real world predictions and are the basic building blocks of the standard model of physics. The full standard model is, however, a bit more complicated as many types of interactions must be considered at the same time. In addition, there are slightly more complicated gauge interactions that allow transitions between different types of particles (e.g, electrons $\leftrightarrow$ neutrinos) which is not possible in the simple models that we consider here. Nevertheless, the following discussion of two elementary models should give you a solid foundation in case you want to dive deeper and study more sophisticated applications of quantum field theory.

Let's start with a useful general observation.

Usually, we define a model by writing down a Lagrangian. Each Lagrangian consists of interaction terms and terms that describe how the fields behave in the absence of interactions:

$$L = L_{\text{free}} + L_{\text{interactions}} \,. \tag{12.1}$$

In most cases, the interaction terms do not contain derivatives. Thus, if we look at the general definition of the Hamiltonian (Eq. 8.16)

$$\begin{aligned} H &\equiv \int d^3x\, T^0_0 \\ &\quad \text{Eq. 4.35} \\ &= \int d^3x \left(\frac{\partial \mathcal{L}}{\partial(\partial_0 \phi)} \partial_0 \phi - \mathcal{L} \right) , \end{aligned} \tag{12.2}$$

we can conclude that the interaction Hamiltonian is in these cases given by

$$H_{\text{interactions}} = -L_{\text{interactions}} \,. \tag{12.3}$$

12.1 Yukawa Interactions

The Lagrangian that describes how a real scalar field ϕ interacts with a complex scalar field ψ reads[3]

$$\mathcal{L} = \mathcal{L}_{\text{free real scalar}} + \mathcal{L}_{\text{free complex scalar}} + \mathcal{L}_{\text{Yukawa}}$$

↷ Eq. 5.2, Eq. 8.102

$$= \frac{1}{2}(\partial_\mu \phi)^2 - \frac{m_\phi^2}{2}\phi^2 + i\partial^\mu \bar{\psi}\partial_\mu \psi - m_\psi^2 \bar{\psi}\psi - g\bar{\psi}\psi\phi\,. \quad (12.4)$$

The most interesting part of this Lagrangian when we want to talk about scattering processes is the interaction term $\mathcal{L}_{\text{Yukawa}} \equiv -g\bar{\psi}\psi\phi$. The corresponding interaction Hamiltonian reads

$$H_{\text{Yukawa}} \overset{12.3}{=} -L_{\text{Yukawa}}$$

↷

$$= g\int d^3x \bar{\psi}\psi\phi\,. \quad (12.5)$$

[3] This Lagrangian is analogous to the one we discussed in Section 6.3. The only difference is that we consider here a complex scalar field instead of a spinor field to simplify the discussion. This makes it much easier to see the forest for the trees because as long as we only consider scalar fields, we don't need to evaluate spinor products and spinor sums.

The remaining terms in the Lagrangian tell us that we can use the free field expansions of the real scalar field ϕ and the complex field ψ that we discussed in Chapter 8:

$$\phi(x) = \int \frac{dk^3}{(2\pi)^3\sqrt{2\omega_k}}\left(a(\vec{k})e^{i(kx)} + a^\dagger(\vec{k})e^{-i(kx)}\right) \quad \text{(Eq. 5.51)}$$

$$\psi = \int \frac{d^3k}{(2\pi)^3\sqrt{2\tilde{\omega}_k}}\left(c(\vec{k})e^{ik_\mu x^\mu} + d^\dagger(\vec{k})e^{-ik_\mu x^\mu}\right) \quad \text{(Eq. 8.100)}$$

$$\bar{\psi} \equiv \psi^\dagger = \int \frac{d^3k}{(2\pi)^3\sqrt{2\tilde{\omega}_k}}\left(c^\dagger(\vec{k})e^{-ik_\mu x^\mu} + d(\vec{k})e^{ik_\mu x^\mu}\right) \quad \text{(Eq. 8.101)}\,,$$

$$(12.6)$$

where $\omega_k \equiv \sqrt{\vec{k}^2 + m_\phi^2}$ and $\tilde{\omega}_k \equiv \sqrt{\vec{k}^2 + m_\psi^2}$.

As before, we say that $a^\dagger(\vec{k})$ creates a pion of momentum $\vec{k}$, while $a(\vec{k})$ annihilates a pion of momentum $\vec{k}$. We denote pions again by π^0. Moreover, for illustrative purposes we say that $c^\dagger(\vec{k})$ creates a kaon, while $c(\vec{k})$ annihilates a kaon. As discussed in Section 8.6, this implies that $d^\dagger(\vec{k})$ creates an anti-kaon, while $d(\vec{k})$ annihilates an anti-kaon. We denote kaons by K^+ and anti-kaons by K^-,

Let's calculate the probability amplitude for the process $K^+_{k_1}, K^+_{k_2} \to K^+_{k_3}, K^+_{k_4}$:

$$A(K^+_{k_1}, K^+_{k_2} \to K^+_{k_3}, K^+_{k_4}) = \langle K^+_{k_3}, K^+_{k_4} | \hat{S} | K^+_{k_1}, K^+_{k_2} \rangle \,. \tag{12.7}$$

We evaluate this amplitude by using the series expansion of the scattering operator $\hat{S}$ (Eq. 9.42)[4]

[4] This is completely analogous to what we did in Eq. 10.6. The only difference is that we're now dealing with a different interaction Hamiltonian H_i. In the previous chapter, we considered (Eq. 10.4)

$$H_i \equiv \int d^3x \left(\frac{1}{4!} \lambda \phi^4 \right)$$

while now we have (Eq. 12.5)

$$H_i = g \int d^3x \bar{\psi} \psi \phi \,.$$

$$\begin{aligned}
& A(K^+_{k_1}, K^+_{k_2} \to K^+_{k_3}, K^+_{k_4}) \\
& = \langle K^+_{k_3}, K^+_{k_4} | \hat{S} | K^+_{k_1}, K^+_{k_2} \rangle && \text{Eq. 10.5} \\
& = \langle K^+_{k_3}, K^+_{k_4} | T \Big(1 - i \int_{-\infty}^{\infty} dt_1 \, : H_i(t_1) : + \ldots \Big) | K^+_{k_1}, K^+_{k_2} \rangle && \text{Eq. 9.42} \\
& = T \, \langle K^+_{k_3}, K^+_{k_4} | K^+_{k_1}, K^+_{k_2} \rangle - iT \, \langle K^+_{k_3}, K^+_{k_4} | \int_{-\infty}^{\infty} dt_1 \, : H_i(t_1) : | K^+_{k_1}, K^+_{k_2} \rangle \\
& \quad - \frac{T}{2!} \langle K^+_{k_3}, K^+_{k_4} | \int_{-\infty}^{\infty} dt_1 \, : H_i(t_1) : \int_{-\infty}^{\infty} dt_2 \, : H_i(t_2) : | K^+_{k_1}, K^+_{k_2} \rangle \ldots \\
& \equiv A^{(0)} + A^{(1)} + A^{(2)} + \ldots \,. && \text{definition}
\end{aligned} \tag{12.8}$$

We want to evaluate this amplitude term-by-term. This is possible again by using Wick's theorem. Once we've applied Wick's theorem our formula contains all kinds of contractions. Thus it makes sense to calculate all possible elementary contractions that can occur first.

12.1.1 Important Contractions

As in Section 11.3, we can calculate all possible contractions that can appear in our Yukawa model by using the general formula (Eq. 11.20)

$$\overbrace{\phi(x) a^\dagger}(k) = \langle 0 | T \phi(x) a^\dagger(k) | 0 \rangle \,. \tag{12.9}$$

The results are completely analogous to what we found in Section 11.3 and the only non-vanishing contractions are[5]

[5] To understand why some contractions vanish, take note that a contraction is what is left over when we bring a time-ordered product into normal order. But if we consider a time-ordered product of two operators that commute, e.g. $[\phi, \psi]$ or $[c, \psi] = 0$, there is nothing left over and thus the contraction vanishes.

$$
\begin{aligned}
\overbracket{\phi(x)\phi(y)} &= D_F(x,y) \\
\overbracket{\psi(x)\psi^\dagger}(y) &= \tilde{D}_F(x,y) \\
\overbracket{\phi(x)|\pi^0_k}\rangle &= \mathrm{e}^{-i(kx)}\,|0\rangle \\
\overbracket{\psi(x)|K^+_k}\rangle &= \mathrm{e}^{-i(kx)}\,|0\rangle \\
\overbracket{\psi^\dagger(x)|K^-_k}\rangle &= \mathrm{e}^{-i(kx)}\,|0\rangle \\
\langle\overbracket{\pi^0_k|\phi}(x) &= \langle 0|\,\mathrm{e}^{i(kx)} \\
\langle\overbracket{K^+_k|\psi^\dagger}(x) &= \langle 0|\,\mathrm{e}^{i(kx)} \\
\langle\overbracket{K^-_k|\psi}(x) &= \langle 0|\,\mathrm{e}^{i(kx)} \\
\langle\overbracket{\pi^0_q|\ldots|\pi^0_k}\rangle &= \sqrt{2\omega_q}\sqrt{2\omega_k}(2\pi)^3\delta(\vec{q}-\vec{k}) \\
\langle\overbracket{K^+_q|\ldots|K^+_k}\rangle &= \sqrt{2\tilde{\omega}_q}\sqrt{2\tilde{\omega}_k}(2\pi)^3\delta(\vec{q}-\vec{k}) \\
\langle\overbracket{K^-_q|\ldots|K^-_k}\rangle &= \sqrt{2\tilde{\omega}_q}\sqrt{2\tilde{\omega}_k}(2\pi)^3\delta(\vec{q}-\vec{k})
\end{aligned}
\tag{12.10}
$$

where D_F is the Feynman propagator for a real scalar field and $\tilde{D}_F$ denotes the Feynman propagator for a complex scalar field (Eq. 8.121).

With these contractions at hand, we can evaluate the different terms in the perturbation series for the probability amplitude immediately.

12.1.2 Zeroth-Order Approximation

For the zeroth-order approximation of our probability amplitude (Eq. 12.8)

$$A^{(0)} = T\,\langle K^+_{k_3}, K^+_{k_4} | K^+_{k_1}, K^+_{k_2} \rangle \,, \tag{12.11}$$

there are only two non-vanishing contractions. Therefore, Wick's theorem tells us that[6]

[6] This calculation is completely analogous to what we did in Eq. 11.52.

$$\begin{aligned}
A^{(0)} &\equiv T\,\langle K^+_{k_3}, K^+_{k_4} | K^+_{k_1}, K^+_{k_2} \rangle \\
&\quad \text{(Wick's theorem)} \\
&=: \langle K^+_{k_3}, K^+_{k_4} | K^+_{k_1}, K^+_{k_2} \rangle : + \langle K^+_{k_3}, K^+_{k_4} | K^+_{k_1}, K^+_{k_2} \rangle \\
&\quad + \langle K^+_{k_3}, K^+_{k_4} | K^+_{k_1}, K^+_{k_2} \rangle + \langle K^+_{k_3}, K^+_{k_4} | K^+_{k_1}, K^+_{k_2} \rangle \\
&\quad \text{(Eq. 11.7, Eq. 11.46)} \\
&= \langle K^+_{k_3}, K^+_{k_4} | K^+_{k_1}, K^+_{k_2} \rangle + \langle K^+_{k_3}, K^+_{k_4} | K^+_{k_1}, K^+_{k_2} \rangle \\
&= \left(\sqrt{2\omega_{k_3}}\sqrt{2\omega_{k_1}}(2\pi)^3\delta(\vec{k}_3 - \vec{k}_1)\right)\left(\sqrt{2\omega_{k_4}}\sqrt{2\omega_{k_2}}(2\pi)^3\delta(\vec{k}_4 - \vec{k}_2)\right) \\
&\quad + \left(\sqrt{2\omega_{k_3}}\sqrt{2\omega_{k_2}}(2\pi)^3\delta(\vec{k}_3 - \vec{k}_2)\right)\left(\sqrt{2\omega_{k_4}}\sqrt{2\omega_{k_1}}(2\pi)^3\delta(\vec{k}_4 - \vec{k}_1)\right)
\end{aligned} \tag{12.12}$$

For the case that the final two particle have exactly the same momenta as the initial two states ($k_3, k_4 = k_1, k_2$) this reduces to

$$\begin{aligned}
A^{(0)} &= 2\omega_{k_1} 2\omega_{k_2} (2\pi)^6 \delta(\vec{k}_1 - \vec{k}_1)\delta(\vec{k}_2 - \vec{k}_2) \\
&= 4\omega_{k_1}\omega_{k_2}\left((2\pi)^3\delta(\vec{0})\right)^2 .
\end{aligned} \tag{12.13}$$

Thus at zeroth order, the result in our Yukawa model is exactly the same as in the ϕ^4 model we considered in the previous chapter. In diagrammatic form, the term here corresponds again to two lines that enter and leave the system without interaction with each other.

If we consider higher order terms, however, there are notable differences.

12.1.3 First-Order Approximation

The first order correction to our probability amplitude reads (Eq. 12.8)

$$A^{(1)} = -i \langle K^+_{k_3}, K^+_{k_4} | \int dt_1 T : H_i(t_1) : | K^+_{k_1}, K^+_{k_2} \rangle$$

↷ Eq. 12.5

$$= -i \langle K^+_{k_3}, K^+_{k_4} | \int dt_1 T : \left(g \int d^3x \bar{\psi}\psi\phi \right) : | K^+_{k_1}, K^+_{k_2} \rangle$$

↷

$$= -ig \langle K^+_{k_3}, K^+_{k_4} | \int d^4x \, T : \bar{\psi}\psi\phi : | K^+_{k_1}, K^+_{k_2} \rangle \, . \tag{12.14}$$

Before we apply Wick's theorem, we recall that whenever at least one field is left uncontracted, the term yields zero when we sandwich it between $\langle 0|$ and $|0\rangle$. This is necessarily the case because all remaining factors that are contracted can be pulled in front of the braket and we can then apply the normal-ordered remaining operators to the ground state (either to $\langle 0|$ or $|0\rangle$), which yields zero. Since there are an uneven number of fields (three) in the Yukawa interaction Hamiltonian and an even number of particles in the initial and final state (four in total), it's impossible to contract all operators at the same time. At least one operator always remains uncontracted. Thus we can immediately conclude that $A^{(1)} = 0$. We can interpret this result as follows. The interaction operator $\bar{\psi}\psi\phi$ connects three lines. Therefore, we can't build a diagram with two incoming and two outgoing lines using just one interaction vertex.

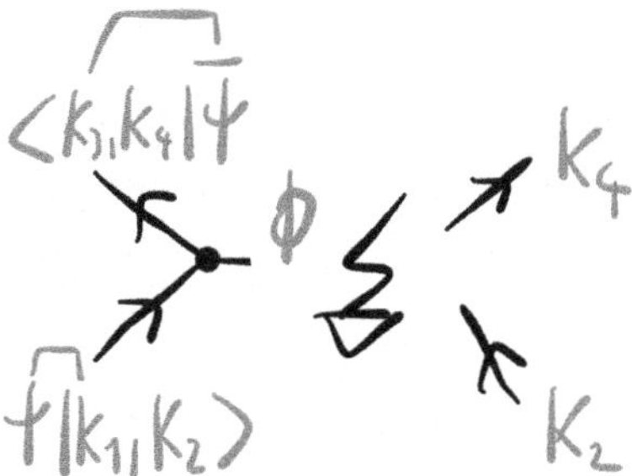

The situation is less trivial if we consider the next term in the Dyson series.

12.1.4 Second-Order Approximation

The second order correction to the probability amplitude reads (Eq. 12.8)

$$\begin{aligned}
A^{(2)} &= \frac{T}{2!}\langle K^+_{k_3}, K^+_{k_4}| \int_{-\infty}^{\infty} dt_1 : H_i(t_1) : \int_{-\infty}^{\infty} dt_2 : H_i(t_2) : |K^+_{k_1}, K^+_{k_2}\rangle \\
&\quad \text{Eq. 12.5} \\
&= \frac{T}{2!}\langle K^+_{k_3}, K^+_{k_4}| \left(\int_{-\infty}^{\infty} dt_1 : \left(g \int d^3x_1 \bar{\psi}(x_1)\psi(x_1)\phi(x_1)\right) : \right. \\
&\qquad \left. \times \int_{-\infty}^{\infty} dt_2 : \left(g \int d^3x_2 \bar{\psi}(x_2)\psi(x_2)\phi(x_2)\right) : \right) |K^+_{k_1}, K^+_{k_2}\rangle \\
&= \frac{g^2}{2}\int d^4x_1 d^4x_2 \, T\langle K^+_{k_3}, K^+_{k_4}| : \bar{\psi}(x_1)\psi(x_1)\phi(x_1) : \\
&\qquad \times : \bar{\psi}(x_2)\psi(x_2)\phi(x_2) : |K^+_{k_1}, K^+_{k_2}\rangle
\end{aligned} \tag{12.15}$$

If we now apply Wick's theorem to this term, we find that it's possible to find terms in which all operators are contracted at the same time. For example,

$$\langle K^+_{k_3}, K^+_{k_4}|\bar{\psi}(x_1)\psi(x_1)\phi(x_1)\bar{\psi}(x_2)\psi(x_2)\phi(x_2)|K^+_{k_1}, K^+_{k_2}\rangle \tag{12.16}$$

This term is non-vanishing since:

- ▷ All operators are contracted.
- ▷ The particles in the final state contract with $\bar{\psi}$. (A contraction of a particle in the final state with ψ or ϕ vanishes. This follows because the operator that generates a particle in the final state is $c(\vec{k})$ and ψ is an integral over $c(\vec{k})$ operators (Eq. 12.6). Since $[c,c] = 0$, this implies that the corresponding contraction vanishes. In contrast, $\psi^\dagger$ contains $c^\dagger$ and $[c,c^\dagger] \neq 0$ (Eq. 8.106). Therefore, a contraction of a particle in the final state with $\psi^\dagger$ is non-zero. In addition, take note that the situation is different if we consider anti-kaons in the final state.)

▷ The particles in the initial state contract with ψ.

Moreover, we take the term into account because there is no contraction of a field with itself at the same spacetime point (no self-loop). The only contraction of a field with itself $\phi(x_1)\phi(x_2)$ involves two different spacetime points.

As a Feynman diagram, the term in Eq. 12.16 looks like this:

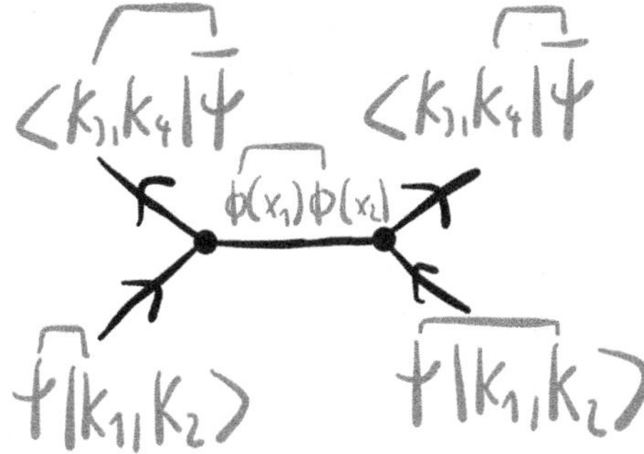

By looking at this diagram we can understand why there is a non-vanishing second order contribution. A second order term involves two vertices and since each vertex in the Yukawa model connects three lines, it's possible to construct a diagram with two incoming and two outgoing lines.

If we now use the explicit formulas for the transaction that are listed in Section 12.1.1, we find

$$
\begin{aligned}
&\langle K^+_{k_3}, K^+_{k_4}|\bar{\psi}(x_1)\psi(x_1)\phi(x_1)\bar{\psi}(x_2)\psi(x_2)\phi(x_2)|K^+_{k_1}, K^+_{k_2}\rangle \\
&\qquad \text{Eq. 12.10} \\
&= \langle 0|\,\mathrm{e}^{i(k_3x_1)}\,\langle 0|\,\mathrm{e}^{i(k_4x_2)}D_F(x_1,x_2)\mathrm{e}^{-i(k_1x_1)}\,|0\rangle\,\mathrm{e}^{-i(k_2x_2)}\,|0\rangle \\
&\qquad \langle 0|0\rangle = 1 \\
&= \mathrm{e}^{i(k_3x_1)}\mathrm{e}^{i(k_4x_2)}D_F(x_1,x_2)\mathrm{e}^{-i(k_1x_1)}\mathrm{e}^{-i(k_2x_2)} \\
&= \mathrm{e}^{i(k_3-k_1)x_1}\mathrm{e}^{i(k_4-k_2)x_2}D_F(x_1,x_2)\,.
\end{aligned}
\tag{12.17}
$$

This implies that this term contributes to our second order correction $A^{(2)}$ (Eq. 12.15) a factor of

$$
\begin{aligned}
& g^2 \int d^4x_1 d^4x_2 \, \mathrm{e}^{i(k_3-k_1)x_1} \mathrm{e}^{i(k_4-k_2)x_2} D_F(x_1,x_2) + \ldots \\
& = g^2 \int d^4x_1 d^4x_2 \left(\mathrm{e}^{i(k_3-k_1)x_1} \mathrm{e}^{i(k_4-k_2)x_2} \int \frac{d^4q}{(2\pi)^4} \frac{i\, e^{-iq(x_2-x_1)}}{q^2 - m_\phi^2 + i\epsilon} \right) && \text{Eq. 8.98} \\
& = i g^2 \int d^4x_1 d^4x_2 \frac{d^4q}{(2\pi)^4} \left(\mathrm{e}^{i(k_3-k_1+q)x_1} \mathrm{e}^{i(k_4-k_2-q)x_2} \frac{1}{q^2 - m_\phi^2 + i\epsilon} \right) \\
& = i g^2 \int \frac{d^4q}{(2\pi)^4} \left(\delta(k_3 - k_1 + q)\delta(k_4 - k_2 - q) \frac{1}{q^2 - m_\phi^2 + i\epsilon} \right) && \int \frac{d^4k}{(2\pi)^4} e^{-ik^\mu(x_\mu - y_\mu)} = \delta(x_\mu - y_\mu) \\
& = i g^2 \delta(k_3 - k_1 + (+k_4 - k_2)) \frac{1}{(k_4 - k_2)^2 - m_\phi^2 + i\epsilon} && \int dx' f(x')\delta(x - x') = f(x) \\
& = i g^2 \delta(k_3 + k_4 - k_1 - k_2) \frac{1}{t - m_\phi^2 + i\epsilon} \,. && t \equiv (k_4 - k_2)^2
\end{aligned}
\tag{12.18}
$$

Take note that $t \equiv (k_4 - k_2)^2$ is equal to $(k_3 - k_1)^2$ as a result of the delta distribution and describes the momentum transfer between the two particles.[7] Moreover, the delta distribution encodes momentum conservation.

[7] The quantity we called here t is a so-called Mandelstam variable and often appears in amplitudes.

There is one additional non-vanishing contraction:

$$
\langle K_{k_3}^+, K_{k_4}^+ | \overline{\psi}(x_1)\psi(x_1)\phi(x_1)\overline{\psi}(x_2)\psi(x_2)\phi(x_2) | K_{k_1}^+, K_{k_2}^+ \rangle \tag{12.19}
$$

This term is non-vanishing for exactly the same reasons listed above. In fact, the only difference is that in this process the particle that starts with momentum k_1 carries momentum k_4 at the end of the process whilst the particle with momentum k_2 carries the momentum k_3 at the end of the process. In short: $k_1 \to k_4, k_2 \to k_3$. This follows because here $K_{k_1}^+$ is contracted with $\psi(x_1)$ and $K_{k_4}^+$ is contracted to $\overline{\psi}(x_1)$. This implies that the transition $k_1 \to k_4$ happens at x_1. In contrast, the transition from $K_{k_2}^+$ to $K_{k_3}^+$ happens at x_2 since the corresponding operators are connected to the fields evaluated at x_2.[8]

[8] In the previous term (Eq. 12.16), we had $k_1 \to k_3, k_2 \to k_4$ since, for example, $K_{k_1}^+$ and $K_{k_3}^+$ are both contracted to fields evaluated at x_1.

The corresponding Feynman diagram looks like this

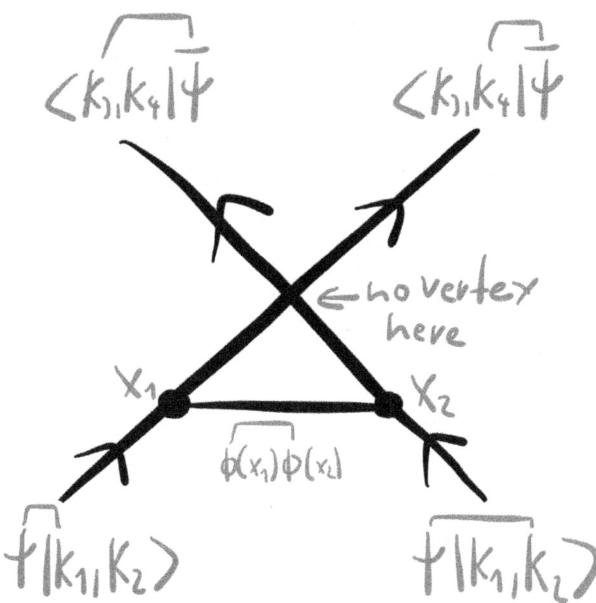

Moreover, we can again use the explicit formulas listed in Section 12.1.1, to rewrite the contraction as

$$\langle K^+_{k_3}, K^+_{k_4} | \overline{\psi}(x_1)\psi(x_1)\phi(x_1)\overline{\psi}(x_2)\psi(x_2)\phi(x_2) | K^+_{k_1}, K^+_{k_2} \rangle$$

Eq. 12.10

$$= e^{i(k_3-k_2)x_2} e^{i(k_4-k_1)x_1} D_F(x_1, x_2) \tag{12.20}$$

By following the same steps as in Eq. 12.18, we can calculate that this contraction contributes to our second order correction $A^{(2)}$ (Eq. 12.15) a factor of

$$ig^2\delta(k_3 + k_4 - k_1 - k_2)\frac{1}{u - m_\phi^2 + i\epsilon}, \tag{12.21}$$

where $u \equiv (k_4 - k_1)^2 = (k_3 - k_2)^2$.

Thus, we can conclude

$$
\begin{aligned}
A^{(2)} &\overset{12.15}{=} \frac{g^2}{2}\int d^4x_1 d^4x_2\, T\,\langle K^+_{k_3}, K^+_{k_4}| : \bar{\psi}(x_1)\psi(x_1)\phi(x_1) : \\
&\qquad\qquad \times : \bar{\psi}(x_2)\psi(x_2)\phi(x_2) : |K^+_{k_1}, K^+_{k_2}\rangle \\
&= \frac{g^2}{2}\int d^4x_1 d^4x_2 \Big(\langle K^+_{k_3}, K^+_{k_4}|\bar{\psi}(x_1)\psi(x_1)\phi(x_1)\bar{\psi}(x_2)\psi(x_2)\phi(x_2)|K^+_{k_1}, K^+_{k_2}\rangle \\
&\qquad + \langle K^+_{k_3}, K^+_{k_4}|\bar{\psi}(x_1)\psi(x_1)\phi(x_1)\bar{\psi}(x_2)\psi(x_2)\phi(x_2)|K^+_{k_1}, K^+_{k_2}\rangle \Big) \\
&\qquad\qquad \text{Eq. 12.17, Eq. 12.20} \\
&= \frac{g^2}{2}\int d^4x_1 d^4x_2 \Big(e^{i(k_3-k_1)x_1} e^{i(k_4-k_2)x_2} D_F(x_1,x_2) + e^{i(k_3-k_2)x_2} e^{i(k_4-k_1)x_1} D_F(x_1,x_2) \Big) \\
&\qquad\qquad \text{Eq. 12.18, Eq. 12.21} \\
&= i\frac{g^2}{2}\delta(k_3+k_4-k_1-k_2)\frac{1}{t-m_\phi^2+i\epsilon} + i\frac{g^2}{2}\delta(k_3+k_4-k_1-k_2)\frac{1}{u-m_\phi^2+i\epsilon}
\end{aligned}
\tag{12.22}
$$

12.1.5 The Non-Relativistic Limit

To understand the amplitude that we calculated in the previous section a bit better, let's assume that our particles move quite slowly ($\vec{p}^2 \ll m^2$). This is known as the non-relativistic limit. In this limit, we can write the four-momentum of each particle as

$$
\begin{aligned}
p_\mu = \begin{pmatrix} p_0 \\ \vec{p} \end{pmatrix} = \begin{pmatrix} E \\ \vec{p} \end{pmatrix} &\overset{2.13}{=} \begin{pmatrix} m\sqrt{1+\frac{\vec{p}^2}{m^2}} \\ \vec{p} \end{pmatrix} \\
&\qquad \sqrt{1+x} \approx 1 \text{ for } x \ll 1 \\
&\approx \begin{pmatrix} m \\ \vec{p} \end{pmatrix} .
\end{aligned}
\tag{12.23}
$$

Moreover, let's assume that the momenta of the two particles change during the process. This implies that the zeroth-order term (Eq. 12.12) yields zero and the first term in the perturbation series that contributes to the amplitude is the second-order term $A^{(2)}$ (Eq. 12.22). We focus on the first term in Eq. 12.22 for a moment:

$$A^{(2)} = i\frac{g^2}{2}\delta(k_3 + k_4 - k_1 - k_2)\frac{1}{t - m_\phi^2 + i\epsilon} + \dots . \qquad (12.24)$$

In the non-relativistic limit, the quantity $t \equiv (k_4 - k_2)^2$ simplifies to

$$t \equiv (k_4 - k_2)^2 \overset{12.23}{=} \left(\begin{pmatrix} m_\psi \\ \vec{k}_4 \end{pmatrix} - \begin{pmatrix} m_\psi \\ \vec{k}_2 \end{pmatrix} \right)^2 = \left(\begin{pmatrix} 0 \\ \vec{k}_4 - \vec{k}_2 \end{pmatrix} \right)^2$$

↷ Minkowski metric

$$= -(\vec{k}_4 - \vec{k}_2)^2 \equiv -\Delta\vec{k}^2 . \qquad (12.25)$$

Therefore, if we ignore the delta distribution, which only encodes the conservation of momentum and becomes important when we integrate over a specific momentum range for the final particles, and the factor $+i\epsilon$ which is not important in this context, we find that the amplitude reads

$$A(K^+_{k_1}, K^+_{k_2} \to K^+_{k_3}, K^+_{k_4}) \approx A^{(2)}$$

↷

$$= \frac{i\frac{g^2}{2}}{t - m_\phi^2} + \dots$$

↷ Eq. 12.25

$$= \frac{i\frac{g^2}{2}}{-\Delta\vec{k}^2 - m_\phi^2} + \dots . \qquad (12.26)$$

We learn here that the scattering amplitude is damped by a factor $\tilde{V}(\Delta\vec{k}) \equiv \frac{-g^2}{\Delta\vec{k}^2 + m^2}$.[9] This is exactly the Fourier transform of

$$V(\vec{r}) = -\frac{g^2}{4\pi|\vec{r}|}e^{-m_\phi|\vec{r}|} , \qquad (12.27)$$

which is the Yukawa potential (Eq. 6.20) that we discussed in Section 6.1.2. This is shown in Appendix B.3.

[9] The imaginary unit vanishes as soon as we calculate the absolute value, which is necessary to calculate the corresponding probability. Moreover, the dots indicate the contribution from the second contraction which, however, is similar.

12.1.6 Further Comments

In the previous sections, we've discussed one out of many possible scattering processes. For example, instead of $K^+_{k_1}, K^+_{k_2} \to$

$K^+_{k_3}, K^+_{k_4}$, we can consider $K^+_{k_1}, K^-_{k_2} \to K^+_{k_3}, K^-_{k_4}$ or $K^-_{k_1}, K^-_{k_2} \to K^-_{k_3}, K^-_{k_4}$ and, of course, also pion scattering. Moreover, we can again define Feynman rules as a map between terms in the perturbation series and Feynman diagrams.

▷ Each incoming external line corresponds to a factor of e^{-ipx}.

▷ Each outgoing external line corresponds to a factor of e^{ipx}.

▷ Each internal pion line corresponds to a factor of $D_F(x,y)$.

▷ Each internal kaon line corresponds to a factor of $\tilde{D}_F(x,y)$.

▷ Each vertex corresponds to a factor of $-ig$.

▷ Each line that enters and leaves the system without any interaction, contributes a factor $\sqrt{2\omega_q}\sqrt{2\omega_k}(2\pi)^3\delta(\vec{q}-\vec{k})$ (Eq. 11.42).

Using these building blocks we can create all Feynman diagrams with a given number of vertices and then translate them, using the Feynman rules, into the corresponding expressions that appear in the perturbation series.

At the beginning of this section, I've mentioned that we consider a simplified version of the "original" Yukawa model. In the "real" Yukawa model, we describe the interaction of a spinor field with a scalar field. The general features, however, are exactly the same. The only difference is that each incoming and outgoing spinor particle brings with it a spinor that we need to take into account. This is necessarily the case, because if we replace the complex scalar field ψ with a spinor field Ψ, we must use the expansions (Eq. 8.123)

$$\begin{aligned}\Psi &= \sum_{r=1}^{2}\int \frac{d^3k}{(2\pi)^3\sqrt{2\omega_k}}\left(c_r(\vec{k})u_r(k)\mathrm{e}^{-ik_\mu x^\mu} + d_r^\dagger(\vec{k})v_r(k)\mathrm{e}^{ik_\mu x^\mu}\right)\\ \bar{\Psi} \overset{5.55}{\equiv} \Psi^\dagger\gamma_0 &= \sum_{r=1}^{2}\int \frac{d^3k}{(2\pi)^3\sqrt{2\omega_k}}\left(c_r^\dagger(\vec{k})\bar{u}_r(k)\mathrm{e}^{ik_\mu x^\mu} + d_r(\vec{k})\bar{v}_r(k)\mathrm{e}^{-ik_\mu x^\mu}\right)\end{aligned} \tag{12.28}$$

for the fields that appear in the interaction Hamiltonian

$$H_{\text{interactions}} = g \int d^3x \bar{\Psi}\Psi\phi \,. \tag{12.29}$$

This implies that the Feynman rules become[10]

[10] There are a few subtleties we are glossing over here. For example, there are in some cases factors of -1 which occur because spinors anticommute.

- ▷ Every incoming external spinor particle with momentum p and spin r corresponds to a factor of $u_r(p)e^{-ipx}$. For example, $r = 1$ corresponds to a particle with spin up.
- ▷ Every outgoing external spinor particle with momentum p and spin r corresponds to a factor of $\bar{u}_r(p)e^{ipx}$.
- ▷ Every incoming external anti-spinor particle with momentum p and spin r corresponds to a factor of $\bar{v}_r(p)e^{-ipx}$.
- ▷ Every outgoing external anti-spinor particle with momentum p and spin r corresponds to a factor of $v_r(p)e^{ipx}$.
- ▷ Every internal spinor line corresponds to a factor of $\Delta_F(x,y)$, which we defined in Eq. 8.155.

For the sake of argument, let's call the spinor particle we consider here an electron. If we then consider an (electron + electron) $\to$ (electron + electron) scattering process, the result is almost exactly the same as in the (kaon + kaon) $\to$ (kaon + kaon) case that we considered above. If there is a non-zero momentum transfer, the first order term vanishes. Moreover, the first order correction yields zero because there are again three fields in the interaction Hamiltonian but four external particles. Thus it's impossible to contract all operators at the same time. The first non-vanishing contribution is therefore given by the second order term $A^{(2)}$, which reads analogous to what we found in Eq. 12.22[11]

[11] To unclutter the notation, I've left the factor $+i\epsilon$ out.

$$\begin{aligned} A^{(2)} &= i\frac{g^2}{2}\delta(k_3 + k_4 - k_1 - k_2)\bar{u}_r(k_3)u_s(k_1)\frac{1}{t - m_\phi^2}\bar{u}_{r'}(k_4)u_{s'}(k_2) \\ &\quad + i\frac{g^2}{2}\delta(k_3 + k_4 - k_1 - k_2)\bar{u}_{r'}(k_4)u_s(k_1)\frac{1}{u - m_\phi^2}\bar{u}_r(k_3)u_{s'}(k_2) \,, \end{aligned} \tag{12.30}$$

where r, r', s, s' label the spin configuration of the two incoming and outgoing particles. The corresponding Feynman diagrams are

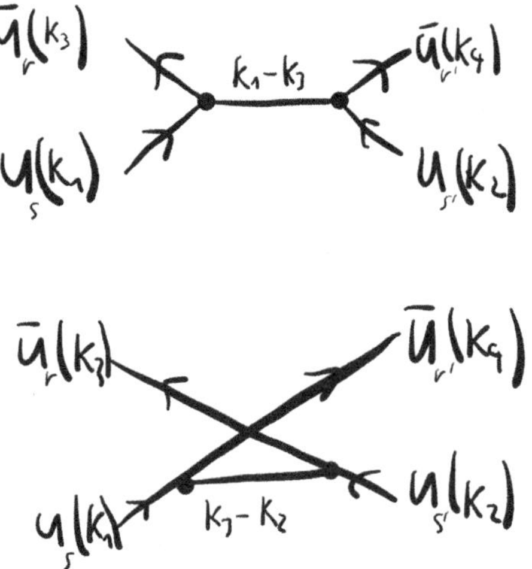

At this point, you've probably already noticed that the general story is always the same. Thus, let's quickly discuss just one additional model.

12.2 Gauge Interactions

In Section 6.4, we've already discussed the Lagrangian density that describes how a spinor field interacts with a massless gauge field (Eq. 6.60):

$$\mathcal{L} = \bar{\Psi}\Big(i\gamma^\mu\partial_\mu - m\Big)\Psi - \frac{1}{4}F_{\mu\nu}F^{\mu\nu} + e\bar{\Psi}\gamma^\mu A_\mu\Psi$$

↷ definitions

$$\equiv \mathcal{L}_{\rm f} + \mathcal{L}_{\rm i}\,. \qquad (12.31)$$

The free part of the Lagrangian density, $\mathcal{L}_f$, tells us that we can use the usual field expansions (Eq. 8.123, Eq. 5.156)

$$\Psi = \sum_{r=1}^{2}\int \frac{d^3k}{(2\pi)^3\sqrt{2\omega_k}}\Big(c_r(\vec{k})u_r(k)\mathrm{e}^{-ik_\mu x^\mu} + d_r^\dagger(\vec{k})v_r(k)\mathrm{e}^{ik_\mu x^\mu}\Big)$$

$$\bar{\Psi} \stackrel{5.55}{=} \Psi^\dagger\gamma_0 = \sum_{r=1}^{2}\int \frac{d^3k}{(2\pi)^3\sqrt{2\omega_k}}\Big(c_r^\dagger(\vec{k})\bar{u}_r(k)\mathrm{e}^{ik_\mu x^\mu} + d_r(\vec{k})\bar{v}_r(k)\mathrm{e}^{-ik_\mu x^\mu}\Big)$$

$$A_\mu(x) = \sum_{r=1}^{3}\int \frac{d^3p}{(2\pi)^3}\frac{1}{\sqrt{2k_0}}\Big(\epsilon_\mu^r a^r(\vec{k})e^{-ik_\mu x^\mu} + \epsilon_\mu^r a^{r\dagger}(\vec{k})e^{ik_\mu x^\mu}\Big)\,. \qquad (12.32)$$

The interaction term, $\mathcal{L}_i$, tells us that the interaction Hamiltonian reads

$$H_{\rm i} \stackrel{12.3}{=} -L_{\rm i}$$

↷ Eq. 12.31

$$= -e\int d^3x\bar{\Psi}\gamma^\mu A_\mu\Psi\,. \qquad (12.33)$$

Instead of going through the usual steps, let's just consider directly the Feynman rules for this model which are completely analogous to the rules that we discussed in the previous sections.

▷ Every incoming external spinor particle with momentum p and spin r corresponds to a factor of $u_r(p)e^{-ipx}$.

▷ Every outgoing external spinor particle with momentum p and spin r corresponds to a factor of $\bar{u}_r(p)e^{-ipx}$.

▷ Every incoming external anti-spinor particle with momentum p and spin r corresponds to a factor of $\bar{v}_r(p)e^{ipx}$.

▷ Every outgoing external anti-spinor particle with momentum p and spin r corresponds to a factor of $v_r(p)e^{ipx}$.

▷ Every incoming vector particle with momentum p and polarization r corresponds to a factor of $\epsilon^r_\mu(p)e^{-ipx}$.

▷ Every outgoing vector particle with momentum p and polarization r corresponds to a factor of $\epsilon^{r\star}_\mu(p)e^{ipx}$.

▷ Every internal vector line corresponds to a factor of $D^\perp_{ij}$, which we defined in Eq. 8.194.

▷ Every internal spinor line corresponds to a factor of $\Delta_F(x,y)$, which we defined in Eq. 8.155.

▷ Every vertex corresponds to a factor of $-ie\gamma^i$.

With these building blocks at hand, we can start drawing diagrams. For example, we can consider an (electron + positron) → (electron + positron) process, which we denote by $e^-_{k_1}, e^+_{k_2} \to e^-_{k_3}, e^+_{k_4}$. This is known as **Bhabha scattering**.[12] One of the simplest diagrams we can draw for this process includes two vertices and looks like this:

[12] In contrast, $e^-_{k_1}, e^-_{k_2} \to e^-_{k_3}, e^-_{k_4}$ is known as Møller scattering.

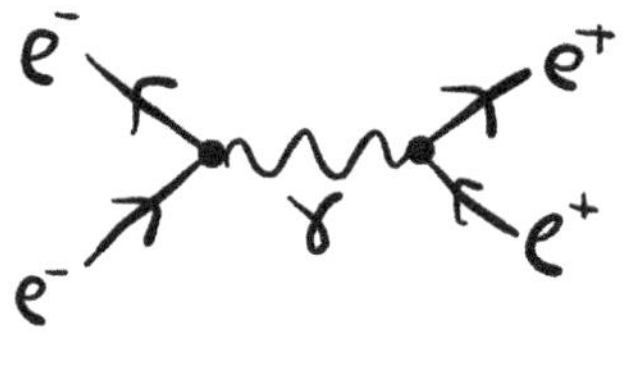

Using the Feynman rules, we can immediately write down the

corresponding contribution to the probability amplitude:

$$A(e^-_{k_1}, e^+_{k_2} \to e^-_{k_3}, e^+_{k_4}) \approx \int d^4x_1 d^4x_2 \, e^{-ik_2x_1} \bar{v}^{s'}(k_2)\Big(-ie\gamma^i\Big)u^s(k_1)e^{-ik_1x_1}$$
$$\times D^{\perp}_{ij}(x_1, x_2)\bar{u}^r(k_3)e^{ik_3x_2}\Big(-ie\gamma^j\Big)v^{r'}(k_4)e^{ik_4x_2}$$
$$+ \ldots . \tag{12.34}$$

12.2.1 The Non-Relativistic Limit

To evaluate this contribution further, let's introduce the notation

$$a^i \equiv \bar{v}^{s'}(k_2)\gamma^i u^s(k_1)$$
$$b^j \equiv \bar{u}^{r'}(k_3)\gamma^j v^s(k_4) . \tag{12.35}$$

These two factors describe the incoming spinor current and outgoing spinor current respectively. They depend on how we prepare the electron and positron at the beginning of the scattering experiment and which kind of final configuration we try to detect. Let's say we are working in the mass basis and that we start with an electron and positron in a spin-up configuration.[13] The spin-up electron and the spin-up positron are described by the spinors (Eq. 5.105)

[13] We discussed the mass basis in Section 5.2.3.

$$u_1 = \sqrt{\frac{\omega + m}{2m}} \begin{pmatrix} 1 \\ 0 \\ \frac{k_3}{\omega+m} \\ \frac{k_1+ik_2}{\omega+m} \end{pmatrix}$$
$$v_1 = \sqrt{\frac{\omega + m}{2m}} \begin{pmatrix} \frac{k_3}{\omega+m} \\ \frac{k_1+ik_2}{\omega+m} \\ 1 \\ 0 \end{pmatrix} . \tag{12.36}$$

Moreover, to simplify our calculation we assume that we are dealing with particles with very small momenta $\vec{k}^2 \ll m^2$, which implies that $\omega \approx m$ (see Eq. 12.23) and $\frac{k_i}{m} \approx 0$. In this non-relativistic limit, the spinors simplify to

$$u_1 \approx \sqrt{\frac{m+m}{2m}} \begin{pmatrix} 1 \\ 0 \\ 0 \\ 0 \end{pmatrix} = \begin{pmatrix} 1 \\ 0 \\ 0 \\ 0 \end{pmatrix}$$

$$v_1 = \sqrt{\frac{m+m}{2m}} \begin{pmatrix} 0 \\ 0 \\ 1 \\ 0 \end{pmatrix} = \begin{pmatrix} 0 \\ 0 \\ 1 \\ 0 \end{pmatrix} . \tag{12.37}$$

These formulas allow us to calculate each component of the incoming current a_i. For example, for $i = 3$, we find

$$\begin{aligned} a^3 &\equiv \bar{v}^{s'}(k_2)\gamma^3 u^s(k_1) \\ &= v^{s'\dagger}(k_2)\gamma^0\gamma^3 u^s(k_1) \\ &= \begin{pmatrix} 0 \\ 0 \\ 1 \\ 0 \end{pmatrix}^\dagger \begin{pmatrix} 1 & 0 & 0 & 0 \\ 0 & 1 & 0 & 0 \\ 0 & 0 & -1 & 0 \\ 0 & 0 & 0 & -1 \end{pmatrix} \begin{pmatrix} 0 & 0 & 1 & 0 \\ 0 & 0 & 0 & -1 \\ -1 & 0 & 0 & 0 \\ 0 & 1 & 0 & 0 \end{pmatrix} \begin{pmatrix} 1 \\ 0 \\ 0 \\ 0 \end{pmatrix} \\ &= 1 . \end{aligned} \tag{12.38}$$

$\bar{\Psi} \equiv \Psi^\dagger \gamma^0$ (Eq. 5.55)

Eq. 12.37, Eq. 5.99, Eq. 5.100

Similarly, we find that $a^1 = 0$, $a^2 = 0$.

Further, let's say that we are interested in the probability amplitude to detect at the end of the scattering process again a spin-up electron and a spin-up positron. This implies that we can use exactly the same basis spinors to calculate the outgoing current b^i and thus can calculate analogously that $b^1 = 0, b^2 = 0, b^3 = 1$. Thus in summary

$$\vec{a} = (0,0,1)^T, \quad \vec{b} = (0,0,1)^T . \tag{12.39}$$

With these results at hand, we can evaluate the complete contribution to the probability amplitude:

$$
\begin{aligned}
&A(e^-_{k_1}, e^+_{k_2} \to e^-_{k_3}, e^+_{k_4}) \\
&= -e^2 \int d^4x_1 d^4x_2 \, e^{-ik_2x_1} a^i e^{-ik_1x_1} D^{\perp}_{ij} e^{ik_3x_2} b^j e^{ik_4x_2} + \dots \\
&= -e^2 \int d^4x_1 d^4x_2 \, a^i e^{-i(k_2+k_1)x_1} \left(\int \frac{d^4k}{(2\pi)^4} \frac{i}{k^2+i\epsilon} \left(\delta_{ij} - \frac{k_ik_j}{k_lk_l}\right) e^{-ik(x_2-x_1)} \right) e^{i(k_3+k_4)x_2} b^j + \dots \\
&= -e^2 \left(\int \frac{d^4q}{(2\pi)^4} d^4x_1 d^4x_2 \, \frac{i}{q^2+i\epsilon} \left(\vec{a}\cdot\vec{b} - \frac{a_iq_iq_jb_j}{q_lq_l}\right) e^{-i(k_2+k_1-q)x_1} e^{i(k_3+k_4-q)x_2} \right) + \dots \\
&= -e^2 \left(\int \frac{d^4q}{(2\pi)^4} \frac{i}{q^2+i\epsilon} \left(\vec{a}\cdot\vec{b} - \frac{a_iq_iq_jb_j}{q_lq_l}\right) \delta(k_2+k_1-q)(2\pi)^4 \delta(k_3+k_4-q)(2\pi)^4 \right. \\
&\approx -e^2(2\pi)^4 \left(\int d^4q \, \frac{i}{q^2+i\epsilon} \left(1 - \frac{(q_3)(q_3)}{q_lq_l}\right) \delta(k_2+k_1-q)\delta(k_3+k_4-q) \right) + \dots \\
&= -\frac{ie^2(2\pi)^4}{s^2+i\epsilon} \left(1 - \frac{s_3^2}{s}\right) \delta\Big(k_3+k_4-(k_1+k_2)\Big) + \dots \\
&\approx -e^2(2\pi)^4 \frac{i}{s^2+i\epsilon} \delta(k_3+k_4-k_1-k_2), \qquad (12.40)
\end{aligned}
$$

Margin notes: Eq. 8.194; Eq. 12.39; $\vec{k}^2 \ll m^2 = k^2$

where $s^2 \equiv (k_1+k_2)^2 = (k_3+k_4)^2$, $\vec{s} \equiv \vec{k}_1 + \vec{k}_2$ and $s_3 \equiv (k_1+k_2)_3$. The delta distribution encodes, as usual, momentum conservation: the total four-momentum of the two incoming particles must be equal to the total four-momentum of the two outgoing particles. Moreover, if we assume that the two particles have no momentum component in the z-direction (e.g., move in the x-direction and $-x$-direction), we have $s_3 = 0$.[14] The quantity $s^2 \equiv (k_1+k_2)^2$ reads in more explicit terms

[14] The z-axis is singled out because we assumed that we deal with particles whose spin is aligned up with respect to the z-axis. We did this by using the spinors in Eq. 12.36. For spin up and spin down configurations with respect to different axes, different spinors must be used.

$$
\begin{aligned}
s^2 &\equiv (k_1+k_2)^2 = k_1^2 + k_2^2 + 2k_1k_2 = m_e^2 + m_e^2 + 2k_1k_2 \\
&= 2m_e^2 + 2\begin{pmatrix}\omega_{k_1} \\ \vec{k}_1\end{pmatrix}^T \begin{pmatrix}\omega_{k_2} \\ \vec{k}_2\end{pmatrix} = 2m_e^2 + 2\omega_{k_1}\omega_{k_2} + 2\vec{k}_1\cdot\vec{k}_2 \\
&= 2m_e^2 + 2\sqrt{m_e^2+\vec{k}_1^2}\sqrt{m_e^2+\vec{k}_2^2} + 2\vec{k}_1\cdot\vec{k}_2 \\
&\approx 2m_e^2 + 2m_e^2 \approx 4m_e^2 . \qquad (12.41)
\end{aligned}
$$

The total contribution to the probability amplitude is therefore

approximately

$$A(e^-_{k_1}, e^+_{k_2} \to e^-_{k_3}, e^+_{k_4}) \sim -\frac{ie^2}{4m_e^2} + \dots \quad (12.42)$$

12.2.2 Further Examples

There are many subtle aspects of gauge interactions that we haven't discussed. In fact, there are whole books dedicated to discussions of how gauge fields interact with other fields and it's impossible to summarize them on just a few pages. So if you want to learn more about gauge interactions, you are encouraged to pick up one of these dedicated books. You can find several reading recommendations in Chapter 19.

The general ideas, however, are always the same. We start with a Lagrangian, deduce the Feynman rules and then calculate probability amplitudes by drawing diagrams for specific processes. The following figure shows a few famous examples of scattering processes that involve electrons, positrons and the photon field.

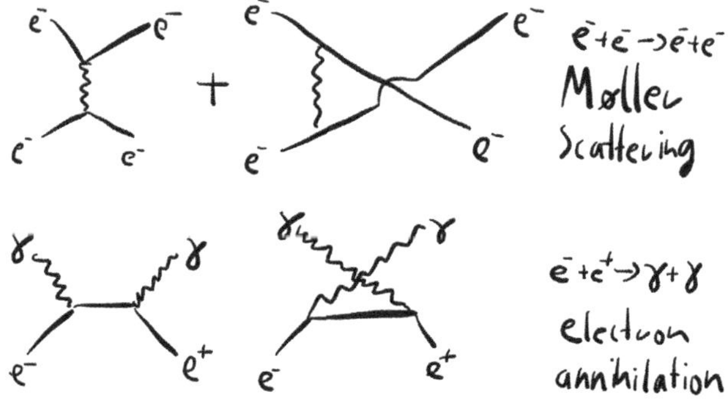

13

Scattered Comments

Applications of quantum field theory is a vast field and we've barely scratched the surface. So let's finish this part with various comments that should give you some orientation for your further studies.

Here's what we will discuss in the following section:

▷ People commonly use the concept of virtual particles to describe Feynman diagrams. We will discuss a few examples that demonstrate how this language can be useful.

▷ So far, we've only talked about the simplest terms in the perturbation series and the simplest kind of scattering processes. Thus it makes sense to discuss shortly what changes if we consider more complicated terms or processes.

▷ We will shortly go over a few conventions that are commonly used to describe scattering processes.

▷ We will revisit the topic of regularization and discuss its importance and meaning in more detail.

▷ Another topic that we've only briefly touched upon so far are renormalized couplings. Since this is an incredibly important topic, we will discuss their interpretation and implications.

With this rough plan in mind, let's dive right in.

13.1 Virtual Particles

It is certainly not mandatory that we use words to describe Feynman diagrams. But words can help to make sense of them, just as Feynman diagrams help us to make sense of the perturbation series.

Let's consider again, for example, the diagram that represents a contribution to the second order correction to the scattering amplitude $A(K^+_{k_1}, K^+_{k_2} \to K^+_{k_3}, K^+_{k_4})$.

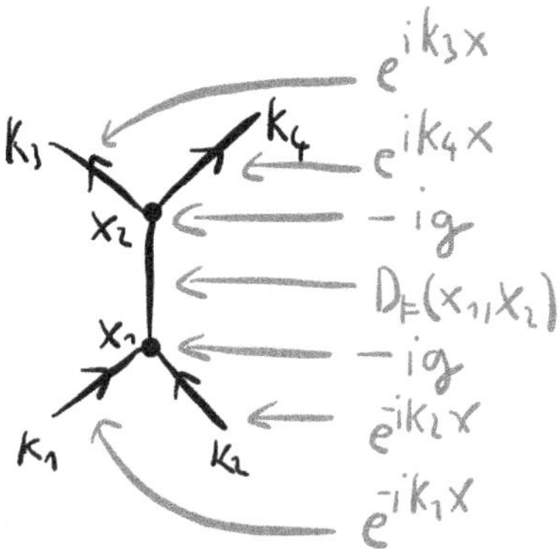

The corresponding term reads (Eq. 12.22)

$$A^{(2)} = g^2 \int d^4x_1 d^4x_2 \, e^{i(k_2-k_1)x_1} D_F(x_1,x_2) e^{i(k_4-k_3)x_2} \,. \qquad (13.1)$$

The external "legs" of the diagrams represent factors that describe the incoming and outgoing particles. The internal line represents the Feynman propagator $D_F(x_1, x_2)$.

We know already that Feynman propagators are Green's functions. Moreover, we know that Green's functions represent damping functions that encode how physical effects get weaker as we move farther away from a source (e.g. a particle). This alone is sufficient to interpret the Feynman diagram and the corresponding term in the perturbation series, analogously to how we interpreted the diagrams that we drew for a classical theory.

The incoming two particles are field excitations which influence each other. Each particle is described by a specific structure in the field. The trick that we exploit in perturbation theory is that we act as if the two particles were free and take modifications which occur as a result of the interaction as small corrections into account. In the first correction to the completely free approximation, we take into account how the non-zero field values that correspond to the second particle affect the field structure that describes the first particle and vice versa. Moreover, the Feynman propagator is the damping factor that tells us how strongly the non-zero field values at two specific locations x_1, x_2 affect each other depending on their distance.

A somewhat subtle aspect is that we are dealing with initial and final states with exactly known momenta. This implies that the particles are described by plane waves which are completely delocalized within the system. That's why we need to integrate over x_1 and x_2. In other words, both particles are described by field structures that spread out all over the system. Thus to investigate how they influence each other, we need to take the field values at all possible locations into account and damp them accordingly. In the context of quantum field theory, however, it is conventional to describe the diagram as follows. The two particles enter the system. They then interact by exchanging a virtual ϕ particle and leave the system again. In this story, the virtual ϕ particle is described by the propagator. This is an essential point. Virtual particles are not particles in the usual sense. They are just a convenient way to drape words around the Feynman propagator.[1] Real particles correspond to very different mathematical objects (plane waves in this context). Moreover, it is important to take note that this story is only complete if we say that the two particles exchange a virtual particle at each possible location x_1, x_2 of the two particles, since we integrate over x_1 and x_2.

[1] Now may be a good point to reread the meaning of the Feynman propagator discussed in Section 8.5.3.

The story gets even more interesting once we consider higher order corrections. For example, let's consider the diagram that corresponds to a second order correction:

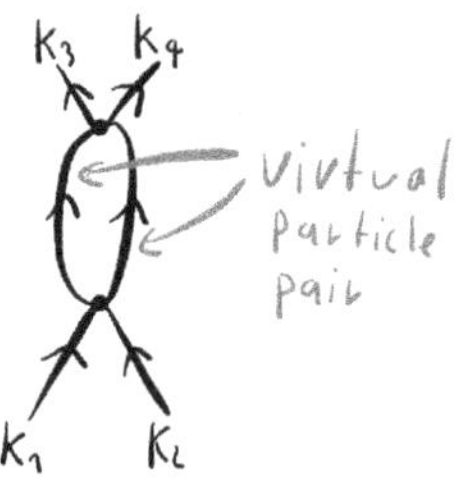

A popular interpretation of this kind of loop diagram is that the two particles that enter the system annihilate each other and create a virtual pair of ϕ particles. This pair of virtual ϕ particles annihilates quickly afterwards and produce a new particle pair.

An important feature of this virtual ϕ particle pair is that it doesn't play by the usual rules. We know that the four-momentum of a real particle fulfills the relation (Eq. 5.40)

$$m^2 = k^2 = \omega_0^2 - k_1^2 - k_2^2 - k_3^2 . \tag{13.2}$$

In this context this relation is also known as the **mass-shell condition**. This name is motivated by the observation that the formula

$$R^2 = x_0^2 - x_1^2 - x_2^2 - x_3^2 \tag{13.3}$$

is the condition that points which lie on a sphere of radius R in Minkowski space must fulfill.[2] But in the integral that describes the loop, we integrate over all possible momentum values without any restriction.[3] It is conventional to say that virtual particles can be off-shell, while real particles are necessarily on-shell. This is jargon for the observation that real particles fulfill Eq. 13.2, while virtual particles do not necessarily do so.

[2] In a four-dimensional Euclidean space, the correpsonding relation reads

$$R^2 = x_0^2 + x_1^2 + x_2^2 + x_3^2 \, , .$$

[3] We noticed this Section 11.6.3.

The question of how seriously we should take these kind of pictures remains a hotly debated topic and you're encouraged to read about the arguments on both sides. In any case, however, it is important to keep in mind that, first and foremost, stories involving virtual particles are useful mnemonics that allow us to put some meaning on the perturbation series. A Feynman diagram is just a convenient way to represent a term in the perturbation and is not a picture of the physical process.[4]

[4] It's often tempting and sometimes even illuminating to treat Feynman diagrams as actual pictures of the process. We will encounter a few instances where this is the case below.

13.2 Loops and Legs

As you've probably noticed by now, quantum field theory is really an infinite playground. There are infinitely many scattering processes that we can consider and for each process there are infinitely many terms in the perturbation series that we can evaluate. Whether it makes sense to consider these processes or terms is, of course, a different question.

To get some understanding of the phenomena that occur in a given model, it is often sufficient to consider $2 \to 2$ scattering processes and the first non-vanishing term in the perturbation series. However, there are hundreds of professional physicists all around the world who spend all of their time evaluating more complicated processes and higher order terms in the perturbation series. For many higher order corrections, these calculations are month-long projects and can only be done in team efforts using dedicated software tools. One reason is that there are hundreds and sometimes even thousands of Feynman diagrams that contribute to higher order corrections. The generation of all Feynman diagrams that contribute to a given order in perturbation theory can be automated and nowadays there are many tools available. So the more important reason that higher order corrections are hard to evaluate is that they involve complicated integrals that are hard to solve, even numerically. Thus in addition to dedicated computer clusters, clever new methods must be developed to bring the expressions into a more manageable form.

$$\mathcal{O}(\lambda) = c_0 + c_1\lambda + c_2\lambda^2 + \ldots$$

undergraduate students — graduate students — postdocs, faculty — computer clusters

The level of difficulty scales directly with the number of legs (external particles) and number of loops.

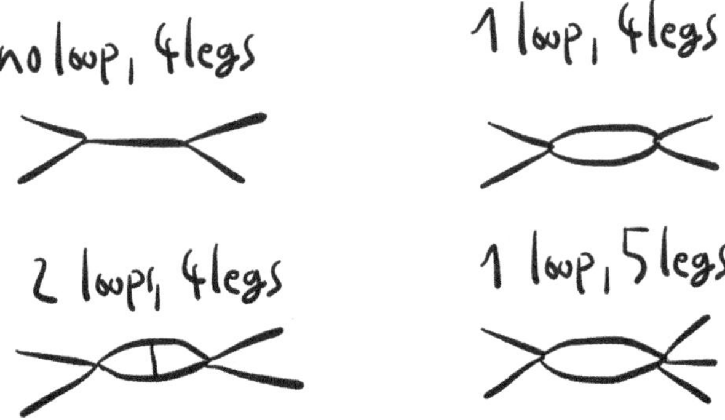

For many processes, two-loop corrections are the maximum that have been evaluated fully so far. However, partial results also exist for certain models and processes up to the five-loop level. Calculating multi-loop amplitudes is really an art in itself and requires a specialized set of tools. As far as I know, the only way to learn how to carry out the calculations is to join one of the research groups. But there are also dedicated textbooks that you can read to get at least some understanding of the general methods. One popular book is, for example, "Evaluating Feynman Integrals", by Vladimir A. A. Smirnov.

13.3 Scattering Conventions

There are many conventions and simplifications that are commonly used to describe scattering processes in quantum field theory. For example, it makes sense to factor out further factors that we encounter in every scattering amplitude. We've learned in the previous chapters that amplitudes always contain a delta distribution $\delta(p_1 + p_2 + \ldots - p_n)$ that encodes momentum conservation and a factor $(2\pi)^4$. Therefore, it is conventional to define

$$\hat{\mathcal{T}} \equiv (2\pi)^4 \delta(\sum p) \hat{\mathcal{M}}, \tag{13.4}$$

where $\sum p$ denotes a sum over the momenta of all initial particles minus a sum over the momenta of all final particles.

In addition, you should be aware that experimentalists usually don't talk about scattering probabilities or amplitudes but instead about cross sections. A cross section is directly proportional to the probability that a given process happens and the general concept stems from a time when particles were thought to be hard balls. There are many further conventions which are commonly used in the definition of cross sections and you are encouraged to pick up a dedicated particle physics book to learn more about them. My favorite is "Introduction to Elementary Particles" by David J. Griffiths. Another great choice is the "Introduction to Elementary Particle Physics" by Alessandro Bettini.

13.4 Regularization

In Section 11.6.3, we've briefly talked about regularization. We discovered that higher order corrections can yield an infinitely large contribution if we evaluate the integrals that we encounter naively. The reason for this divergence is that we integrate over all possible momentum values, all the way up to ∞. This motivated us to introduce a cutoff Λ. If we integrate from $-\Lambda$ to Λ instead of from $-\infty$ to ∞, we find finite contributions instead of diverging ones. Moreover, we learned that the actual value of Λ is not important since the cutoff drops out from quantities that we can measure in experiments. This implies that at the end of the calculation we can even take the limit $\Lambda \to \infty$ without encountering problems. Since this whole procedure surely seems a bit mysterious at first glance, it makes sense to discuss how the same procedure works in a more familiar setup.[5]

[5] The following discussion is based on

Fredrick Olness and Randall Scalise. Regularization, Renormalization, and Dimensional Analysis: Dimensional Regularization meets Freshman E&M. *Am. J. Phys.*, 79: 306, 2011. DOI: 10.1119/1.3535586

Let's say we want to calculate the electric potential that occurs in the vicinity of an infinitely long wire. We choose a coordinate system such that the wire points in the y-direction. Moreover, for simplicity we consider only two spatial dimensions (x, y) since this is sufficient to understand the main features of the system. We denote the constant charge density on the wire by

$$\lambda = \frac{dQ}{dy} . \tag{13.5}$$

In words this means that there is $\Delta Q = \lambda \Delta y$ Coulombs of charge on each Δy-long piece of the wire. We know that a point charge q generates the potential

$$V = \frac{q}{r} , \tag{13.6}$$

where $r \equiv \sqrt{x^2 + y^2}$ denotes the distance from the point charge. This implies that each infinitesimal charge dQ on the wire generates a potential

$$\begin{aligned} dV &= \frac{dQ}{r} \\ & \quad \text{(Eq. 13.5)} \\ &= \frac{\lambda dy}{r} . \end{aligned} \tag{13.7}$$

The wire as a whole therefore generates a potential

$$\begin{aligned} V(x) &= \int dV \\ & \quad \text{(Eq. 13.7)} \\ &= \int_{-\infty}^{\infty} \frac{\lambda dy}{r} \\ & \quad \left(r \equiv \sqrt{x^2 + y^2} \right) \\ &= \lambda \int_{-\infty}^{\infty} \frac{dy}{\sqrt{x^2 + y^2}} , \end{aligned} \tag{13.8}$$

where we integrate over the total length of the wire from $-\infty$ to ∞. Since for $y \gg x$

▷ $\sqrt{x^2+y^2} \approx y$, and additionally, we have

▷ $\int dy \, \frac{1}{y} = \ln(y)$,

▷ $\ln(\infty) = \infty$, and

▷ $\ln(-\infty) = \infty$,

the integral diverges

$$V(x) = \lambda \int_{-\infty}^{\infty} \frac{dy}{\sqrt{x^2+y^2}} = \infty \,. \tag{13.9}$$

This result is not necessarily problematic because the electric potential is not observable. Instead, it's only a tool that we use to calculate observable quantities like, for example, the work done if we move a charge e in the vicinity of the wire from x_1 to x_2:[6]

$$W(x_2, x_1) = q\Big(V(x_2) - V(x_1)\Big) \,. \tag{13.10}$$

[6] Another example of an observable quantity that we derive from the potential V is the electric field $\vec{E} = \nabla V$.

At first glance, however, it now seems as if the work done is always zero since Eq. 13.9 tells us that $V(x_2) = \infty$ and $V(x_1) = \infty$. This is clearly a wrong result. Energy is always necessary to move a charge in the vicinity of a charged wire, no matter how long it is.

The error we are making here is that infinity has some curious properties like $\infty + c = \infty$. This would imply that $\infty - \infty = c$, depending on how the two infinitely large numbers that appear in this formula are defined. This implies that the work formula can yield a correct non-zero result even though $V(x_2) = \infty$ and $V(x_1) = \infty$. The key question then is, of course, what number do we find in Eq. 13.10 if we subtract two infinitely large numbers?

This is a well-defined question that we can answer by regularizing the troublesome integral. We assume for a moment that our wire has a finite length $2L$. The formula for the electric potential then yields

$$V(x) = \lambda \int_{-L}^{L} \frac{dy}{\sqrt{x^2+y^2}}$$

$$\int dy \frac{1}{\sqrt{x^2+y^2}} = \ln\left(\sqrt{x^2+y^2}+y\right)$$

$$= \lambda \ln\left[\frac{+L+\sqrt{L^2+x^2}}{-L+\sqrt{L^2+x^2}}\right]. \tag{13.11}$$

This is a finite result, but yields infinity in the limit $L \to \infty$. However, if we plug the regularized potential into the work formula, we find that the result is finite even in the limit $L \to \infty$

$$W(x_2, x_1) \underset{L\to\infty}{\longrightarrow} q\lambda \ln\left[\frac{x_1^2}{x_2^2}\right]. \tag{13.12}$$

This is demonstrated in Appendix B.2.[7] Thus by introducing a cutoff L, we are indeed able to extract finite results for observable quantities. In other words, by regularizing infinitely large quantities we can answer questions like "$\infty - \infty = ?$" in a mathematically meaningful way.

[7] Similarly, it can be shown that the electric field is finite:

$$E(x) = \frac{-\partial V(x)}{\partial x} = \frac{\lambda}{x}\frac{L}{\sqrt{L^2+x^2}} \underset{L\to\infty}{\longrightarrow} \frac{\lambda}{x}.$$

Let's compare the steps that we used to make sense of the infinitely large wire with those discussed in Section 11.6.3. In both cases, we encountered an infinitely large number that occurs because we consider idealizations. We assumed that the wire is infinitely long although, of course, no infinitely long wire exists in nature. An infinitely long wire is a useful idealization that allows us to ignore boundary effects that occur for finite length wires.[8] In other words, saying that we consider an infinitely long wire is analogous to saying that we consider a wire that is so long that boundary effects do not matter.

[8] We encountered boundary effects when we introduced a finite length $2L$. All terms in the work formula that depend on L are a result of the finite length. For a long wire these effects become tiny but are still non-vanishing. Only in the limit $L \to \infty$ these terms vanish completely and this is why it often makes sense to consider such idealizations.

Similarly, we assume that infinitely large momenta are possible when we allow that the limits of the Feynman propagator integral are $-\infty$ and ∞. As for an infinitely large wire, a particle with infinitely large momentum doesn't exist in nature. But this doesn't matter because we only use $k \to \infty$ as a useful idealization. Of course, we have to be careful whenever we are dealing with infinitely large numbers. If we take the limit $k \to \infty$ too soon, we get nonsensical answers. Nevertheless, it's usually worth the extra effort to treat infinities that occur in our calculations carefully because, as for the wire, it allows us to avoid boundary effects.

Maybe you're wondering what the boundary effects are in this context. The short answer is that if there is a finite physical cutoff Λ, there are new terms in the Lagrangian that are proportional to inverse powers of Λ. For example, for a complex scalar field, we have[9]

$$\mathcal{L} = i\partial^\mu \psi^\dagger \partial_\mu \psi - m_\psi^2 \psi^\dagger \psi + \frac{g^2}{\Lambda^2} \psi^\dagger \psi \psi^\dagger \psi + \dots . \tag{13.13}$$

[9] This is discussed in a bit more detail in Chapter 17.

These terms describe the boundary effects that occur if there is a finite physical cutoff, analogous to how terms that depend on L describe boundary effects that occur for a finite length wire.

In fact, many physicists believe that there is a physical cutoff Λ that encodes the energy scale at which the Standard Model of particle physics becomes invalid.[10] But since no one knows for certain which value we should plug in for Λ, and we don't want to include additional terms in the Lagrangian that only become relevant at scales close to Λ anyway, we often work with $\Lambda \to \infty$.[11]

[10] There are various reasons why this should be the case like, for example, dark matter, neutrino masses or the baryon-antibaryon asymmetry.

[11] Popular contenders for physical cutoff scales are the Planck scale $m_P \approx 10^{18}$ GeV and the so-called unification scale $m_u \approx 10^{16}$ GeV. Moreover, take note that there are research groups that add all kinds of higher order terms to the Standard Model Lagrangian and then try to find hints for effects caused by these terms in collider data.

In summary, the main issue is that we encounter diverging integrals like

$$\int_0^\infty \frac{dx}{x+a} = [\ln(x+a)]_0^\infty = \infty . \tag{13.14}$$

We can regularize them by introducing a cutoff Λ:

$$\int_0^\Lambda \frac{dx}{x+a} = \ln \frac{(\Lambda + a)}{a} . \tag{13.15}$$

While this quantity is finite, it still diverges in the limit $\Lambda \to \infty$. However, we can take a look at

$$\int_0^\Lambda \frac{dx}{x+a} - \int_0^\Lambda \frac{dx}{x+b} \underset{\Lambda\to\infty}{\longrightarrow} \ln\frac{b}{a} \tag{13.16}$$

which is finite in the limit $\Lambda \to \infty$, although

$$\begin{aligned} \int_0^\Lambda \frac{dx}{x+a} &\underset{\Lambda\to\infty}{\longrightarrow} \infty \\ \int_0^\Lambda \frac{dx}{x+b} &\underset{\Lambda\to\infty}{\longrightarrow} \infty\,. \end{aligned} \tag{13.17}$$

As a final comment on this topic, take note that there are various ways to regularize an infinitely large quantity. An extremely popular alternative to the cutoff regularization discussed above is dimensional regularization. The main idea is that integrals which diverge in four-dimensions become finite in a different number of dimensions. Thus the integral is solved in $4+\epsilon$ dimensions which renders the result finite. This is a viable procedure as long as we take the limit $\epsilon \to 0$ at the end of the procedure. But this is really just a mathematical convenient trick, since the results are always the same no matter which regularization method we use.[12]

[12] You can find an illuminating discussion of dimensional regularization in

Fredrick Olness and Randall Scalise. Regularization, Renormalization, and Dimensional Analysis: Dimensional Regularization meets Freshman E&M. *Am. J. Phys.*, 79: 306, 2011. DOI: 10.1119/1.3535586

13.5 The Renormalization Group

A second important feature of quantum field theory that we stumbled upon in Section 11.6.3 is that the parameters that appear in the Lagrangian are not necessarily directly related to experimentally measurable coupling strengths. In particular, we argued that the Lagrangian parameter λ only describes the coupling between particles in a first order approximation, while experimental results always correspond to the complete amplitude and not just isolated approximation terms. Motivated by this observation we introduced the renormalized coupling

(Eq. 11.74)

$$\lambda_R(s_0) \equiv -\tilde{A}(s_0) = \lambda + \lambda^2 C \ln\left(\frac{s_0}{\Lambda^2}\right) + \ldots, \tag{13.18}$$

which can be extracted directly from the experimental scattering results at a specific scale s_0. With this definition, we can say that the two particle scattering process at the scale s_0 has amplitude $-\lambda_R(s_0)$ since, by definition, $\lambda_R(s_0)$ includes already all order corrections. In this sense, $\lambda_R(s_0)$ is the physical coupling that we measure in experiments.

We then discovered that if we rewrite our amplitude in terms of λ_R all dependence on the cutoff scale Λ drops out (Eq. 11.79)

$$\tilde{A}_0(s) = -\lambda_R(s_0) - C \ln\left(\frac{s}{s_0}\right) \lambda_R^2(s_0) + \ldots. \tag{13.19}$$

Let's try to understand a bit better what is going on here. We've argued that it doesn't matter which reference scale s_0 we choose. But what exactly happens if we choose a different scale s_1? The corresponding renormalized coupling reads

$$\lambda_R(s_1) \equiv -\tilde{A}(s_1) = \lambda + \lambda^2 C \ln\left(\frac{s_1}{\Lambda^2}\right) + \ldots. \tag{13.20}$$

Moreover, the amplitude in terms of $\lambda_R(s_1)$ reads

$$\tilde{A}_1(s) = -\lambda_R(s_1) - C \ln\left(\frac{s}{s_1}\right) \lambda_R^2(s_1) + \ldots. \tag{13.21}$$

This suggests that

$$\begin{aligned}
\tilde{A}_1(s) - \tilde{A}_0(s) &= \Big(-\lambda_R(s_1) - C \ln\left(\frac{s}{s_1}\right) \lambda_R^2(s_1) + \ldots \Big) \\
&\quad - \Big(-\lambda_R(s_0) - C \ln\left(\frac{s}{s_0}\right) \lambda_R^2(s_0) + \ldots \Big) \\
0 &= -\lambda_R(s_1) - C \ln\left(\frac{s}{s_1}\right) \lambda_R^2(s_1) \\
&\quad + \lambda_R(s_0) + C \ln\left(\frac{s}{s_0}\right) \lambda_R^2(s_0) + \ldots \\
\lambda_R(s_1) &= \lambda_R(s_0) + C \ln\left(\frac{s}{s_0}\right) \lambda_R^2(s_0) - C \ln\left(\frac{s}{s_1}\right) \lambda_R^2(s_1) + \ldots
\end{aligned} \tag{13.22}$$

Take note that $\lambda_R(s_1)$ still appears on both sides of the equation. However, we can solve the equation iteratively for $\lambda_R(s_1)$:

$$\begin{aligned}
\lambda_R(s_1) &= \lambda_R(s_0) + C\ln\left(\frac{s}{s_0}\right)\lambda_R^2(s_0) - C\ln\left(\frac{s}{s_1}\right)\lambda_R^2(s_1) + \dots \\
&\quad \text{Eq. 13.22} \\
&= \lambda_R(s_0) + C\ln\left(\frac{s}{s_0}\right)\lambda_R^2(s_0) \\
&\quad - C\ln\left(\frac{s}{s_1}\right)\Bigg(\lambda_R(s_0) + C\ln\left(\frac{s}{s_0}\right)\lambda_R^2(s_0) \\
&\qquad - C\ln\left(\frac{s}{s_1}\right)\lambda_R^2(s_1) + \dots\Bigg)^2 + \dots \\
&= \lambda_R(s_0) + C\ln\left(\frac{s}{s_0}\right)\lambda_R^2(s_0) - C\ln\left(\frac{s}{s_1}\right)\lambda_R^2(s_0) + \dots \\
&\quad \ln a - \ln b = \ln\frac{a}{b} \\
&= \lambda_R(s_0) + C\ln\left(\frac{s}{s_0}\left(\frac{s_1}{s}\right)\right)\lambda_R^2(s_0) + \dots \\
&= \lambda_R(s_0) + C\ln\left(\frac{s_1}{s_0}\right)\lambda_R^2(s_0) + \dots,
\end{aligned} \tag{13.23}$$

where we neglected all higher order terms $\propto \lambda_R^3$ which, however, can be rewritten similarly. Thus we can conclude that in a first order approximation, the equation

$$\lambda_R(s_1) \approx \lambda_R(s_0) + C\ln\left(\frac{s_1}{s_0}\right)\lambda_R^2(s_0) \tag{13.24}$$

describes how the renormalized coupling is modified if we change the scale from s_0 to s_1. This is an important result because it implies that the renormalized coupling depends on the energy scale at which we probe it. We say that couplings run with the energy scale and therefore are not constant. Formulated differently, the numerical value of the parameter that encodes how two particles interact depends on their momenta.[13] There is a beautiful way to understand how this comes about. But first, let's discuss how we can bring Eq. 13.24 into a more conventional form. If we take the derivative with respect to s_1,

[13] Reminder $s^2 = (k_1 + k_2)^2$ encodes roughly the energy scale at which the two particles interact.

we find

$$\begin{aligned}
\frac{d}{ds_1}\lambda_R(s_1) &\approx \frac{d}{ds_1}\left(\lambda_R(s_0) + C\ln\left(\frac{s_1}{s_0}\right)\lambda_R^2(s_0)\right) \\
&= \frac{d}{ds_1}\lambda_R(s_0) + C\left(\frac{d}{ds_1}\ln\left(\frac{s_1}{s_0}\right)\right)\lambda_R^2(s_0) \\
&= C\left(\frac{1}{s_1}\right)\lambda_R^2(s_0) \\
&= \frac{C}{s_1}\left(\lambda_R(s_1) + C\ln\left(\frac{s_0}{s_1}\right)\lambda_R^2(s_0) + \dots\right)^2 \\
&= \frac{C}{s_1}\lambda_R^2(s_1) + \dots
\end{aligned}$$

$\frac{d}{dx}\ln\left(\frac{x}{a}\right) = \frac{1}{x}$

Eq. 13.23

$\times s_1$

$$s_1\frac{d}{ds_1}\lambda_R(s_1) \approx C\lambda_R^2(s_1)\,. \tag{13.25}$$

where we again ignored higher order terms. This differential equation tells us how the coupling λ_R changes with the scale s_1. It's conventional to call the scale in this context μ and thus we write

$$\boxed{\mu\frac{d}{d\mu}\lambda_R(\mu) \approx C\lambda_R^2(\mu)\,.} \tag{13.26}$$

This is known as the **one-loop renormalization group equation of the ϕ^4 model**. This name is motivated by the observation that Eq. 13.26 allows us to calculate how the model behaves at a different scale μ given its behavior at some reference scale μ_0.[14] The switch from μ_0 to μ is a scaling transformation

[14] As usual, an initial value is necessary to get a unique solution of a differential equation.

$$\mu = a\mu_0\,, \tag{13.27}$$

where a is a real number. An important property of scaling transformations is that the combined action of two scaling transformations is again a scaling transformation:

$$\begin{aligned}
\mu_0 \to \mu_1 &= S_1(\mu_0) = a_1\mu_0 \\
\mu_1 \to \mu_2 &= S_2(\mu_1) = a_2\mu_1 \\
&= a_2(a_1\mu_0) \equiv \tilde{a}\mu_0 = \tilde{S}(\mu_0)\,.
\end{aligned} \tag{13.28}$$

In words, this means that the outcome of the scaling transformations from μ_0 to μ_1 to μ_2 is equivalent to a single scaling transformation μ_0 to μ_2. In mathematical terms

$$S_1 \circ S_2 = \tilde{S}\,, \tag{13.29}$$

where $\circ$ denotes the operator that allows us to connect transformations (here ordinary multiplication). This property of a set of transformations — called closure — is one of the hallmarks of a group. A group is a set of transformations that fulfill a special set of conditions (axioms) and closure is one of them. Analogously, it can be checked that scaling transformations fulfill the remaining group axioms and this motivates the name renormalization group equation.

13.5.1 The Meaning of the Renormalization Group Equation

To understand the running of the coupling $\lambda(\mu)$ a bit better, let's put some numbers into Eq. 13.24:[15]

[15] Equivalently, we could solve Eq. 13.26 with a specific initial value $\lambda_R(\mu_0)$ at a reference scale μ_0.

$$\begin{aligned} C &= \frac{3}{16\pi^2} \\ s_0 &= 10 \text{ GeV} \\ \lambda(s_0) &= 0.3\,. \end{aligned} \tag{13.30}$$

In this model, the change of λ_R as we move to higher energy scales s_1 looks schematically like this:

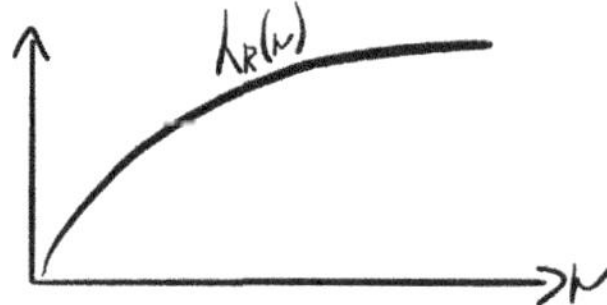

In words, this means that the physical coupling $\lambda_R(s_1)$ gets stronger at higher scales s_1. But it does so very slowly. By looking at Eq. 13.24, we can see that its growth is logarithmic. For example, at a scale $s_1 = 10000$ GeV it has only increased to $\lambda_R(10000 \text{ GeV}) \approx 0.312$. Here's one way to understand how this comes about.

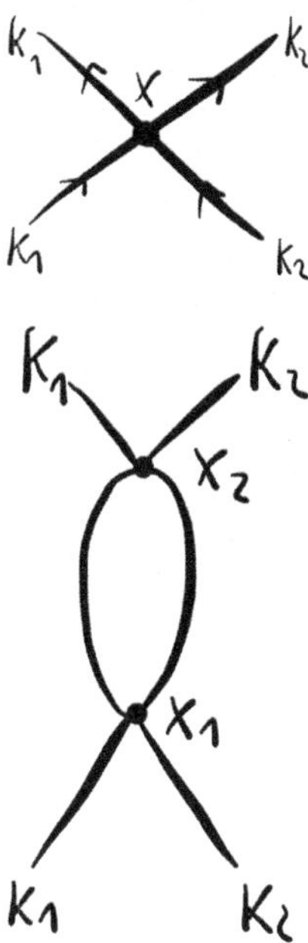

Recall that we want to describe how two particles that we interpret as field excitations of the scalar field ϕ interact with each other. For concreteness, we call these particles pions. In the lowest order approximation, the pions meet at a point and then scatter off again. If we take higher order corrections into account, we notice that the interaction between the two particles is far more complicated. For example, the two incoming particles can annihilate each other, produce a virtual pion pair which then annihilate and produce the final outgoing pion pair. Higher order corrections correspond to even more complicated ways in which the two particles can interact while they are in the system.

We have introduced the renormalized coupling $\lambda_R(s_0)$ at some reference scale s_0 in such a way that interactions can be described completely by the simple diagram with just one interaction vertex.

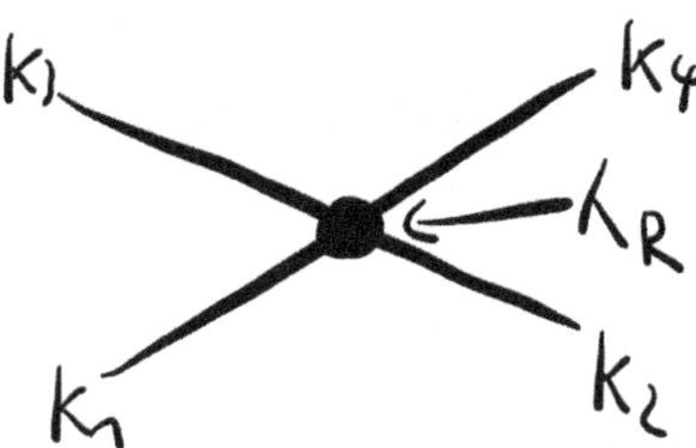

But if we move to another energy scale s_1, we must take correction terms into account which correspond to the more complicated diagrams given above. In our perturbation series with expansion parameter $\lambda_R(s_0)$, these corrections only yield zero for $s_1 = s_0$ since $\ln(1) = 0$ (see Eq. 13.24).[16] Moreover, higher order corrections become more and more important as we move to higher energy scales since for $s_1 = 2s_0$, we have

$$\ln\left(\frac{s_1}{s_0}\right) = \ln\left(\frac{2s_0}{s_0}\right) = \ln(2) \approx 0.7\,, \tag{13.31}$$

[16] For your convenience, Eq. 13.24 reads

$$\lambda_R(s_1) \approx \lambda_R(s_0) + C\ln\left(\frac{s_1}{s_0}\right)\lambda_R^2(s_0)\,.$$

while $s_1 = 10s_0$, we have

$$\ln\left(\frac{s_1}{s_0}\right) = \ln\left(\frac{10s_0}{s_0}\right) = \ln(10) \approx 2.3\,. \qquad (13.32)$$

We can therefore imagine that by investigating processes at higher energy scales s_1, we start to probe the more complicated ways in which the interaction can happen. At s_0, the interaction is described completely by the almost trivial Feynman diagram. At some slightly higher scale, e.g, $s_1 = 2s_0$, Feynman diagrams with two interaction vertices become noticeable, while at even higher scales , e.g, $s_1 = 10s_0$, more and more complicated diagrams start to contribute significant corrections.

A popular way to drape words around this observation is by saying that if we shoot particles into each other at higher energies, we probe the detailed substructure of the interaction. This, in turn, allows us to understand why $\lambda_R(s_1)$ gets larger at higher energy scales, s_1.

The diagrams that describe the first correction to the one-vertex interaction, involves one virtual pion pair. Higher order terms involve two or even more virtual pion pairs. Moreover, we imagine that each virtual pion carries the charge $\lambda_R(s_0)$. Thus at low energies, there are just the two incoming and outgoing particles.

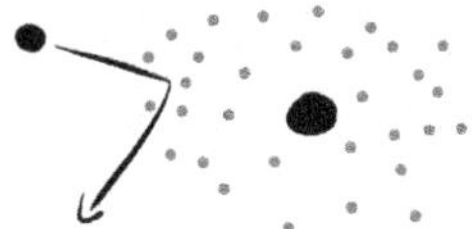

At higher energies, however, we start to see a cloud of virtual pions, each of which carries charge $\lambda_R(s_0)$.

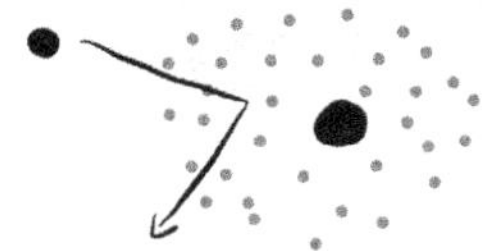

Thus the net charge involved in the process, $\lambda_R(s_1)$, is larger than $\lambda_R(s_0)$. As we move to higher energies, we start to see more and more virtual pion pairs and thus the net charge $\lambda_R(s_1)$ grows. This is known as **anti-screening** of the charge λ.

What we've discussed in this section is not a special feature of a scalar field with ϕ^4-self interaction term. Similar calculations lead to exactly the same conclusions in different models. In particular, running couplings are a general feature of quantum field models. But how exactly a given coupling changes with the scale at which we probe it, depends on the model at hand. Some coupling parameters get stronger as we move to higher energy scales, while others get weaker. A famous example is the electric charge e which is the coupling parameter that encodes how the electron field interacts with the electromagnetic field. Since the electron field is a complex spinor field, there are not just electrons but also anti-electrons known as positrons. Thus, when we probe the interaction of two electrons at high energies (again, relative to some reference scale), the effects of virtual electron-positron pairs become noticeable. Through the presence of the incoming electrons, the virtual electron-positron pairs are polarized, analogous to what happens in a dielectric medium.

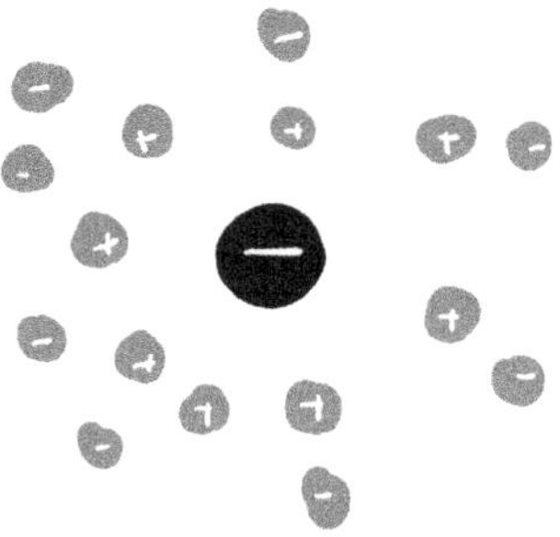

This leads to a **screening** of the charge. At higher energies, the effect of more and more virtual electron-positron pairs becomes noticeable and there is a more pronounced screening effect. This suggests that the electric charge gets weaker at higher energy scales, which is indeed observed in experiments.

Let's finish this section with a quick glance beyond. An exciting implication of the fact that charges run differently is that they can meet at a common point. In particular, the couplings associated with the three gauge forces (weak, strong, electromagnetic) meet approximately at around $M_{\text{GUT}} \approx 10^{15}$ GeV.[17]

[17] In the 1980s, when grand unification was first proposed the gauge couplings were not measured very precisely and it seemed plausible that the three couplings meet at a common point. Nowadays, the couplings are measured much more precisely and it is well known that there is a significant mismatch at all scales. This, however, can be interpreted as a hint for new particles between the electroweak and the unification scale. You can find a recent discussion in

Jakob Schwichtenberg. Gauge Coupling Unification without Supersymmetry. *Eur. Phys. J.*, C79(4):351, 2019a. DOI: 10.1140/epjc/s10052-019-6878-1

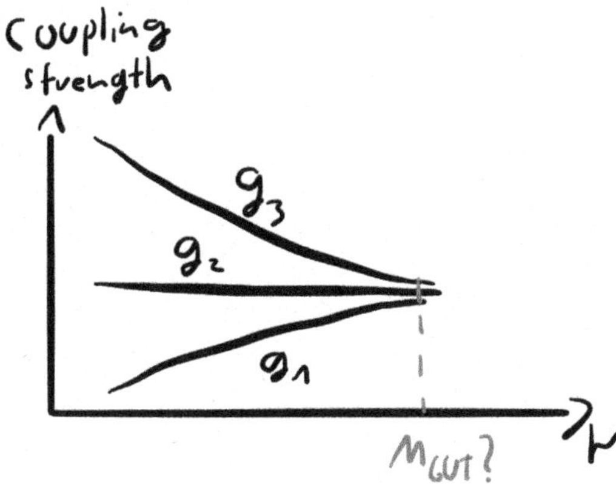

This has motivated the idea that the three gauge forces have a common origin. One popular framework to realize this idea is known as grand unification.

Now that we've developed some understanding of how we can use quantum field theory in practice, it's time to discuss several more advanced aspects.

Part III
Get an Understanding of Quantum Field Theory You Can Be Proud Of

"Is the purpose of theoretical physics to be no more than a cataloging of all the things that can happen when particles interact with each other and separate? Or is it to be an understanding at a deeper level in which there are things that are not directly observable (as the underlying quantized fields are) but in terms of which we shall have a more fundamental understanding?"

Julian Schwinger

PS: You can discuss the content of Part III with other readers and give feedback at `www.nononsensebooks.com/qft/bonus`.

In this final part of the book we will talk about several aspects of quantum field theory that go beyond the perturbative treatment of individual models discussed in the previous part:

▷ We will start with a discussion of symmetry breaking. In particular, we will see why spontaneous symmetry breaking leads to spontaneous mass generation.

▷ Afterwards, we will talk about the path integral formulation. We will discuss the main idea in the context of quantum mechanics and only afterwards discuss quickly the path integral formulation of quantum field theory.

▷ The path integral formulation is important because it allows us to describe phenomena that we miss in a perturbative treatment. As an explicit example of such non-perturbative phenomena we will discuss instantons which can be understood as a tunneling process from one ground state to another.

▷ Lastly, we will talk shortly about the origin of the Lagrangians that we used in the previous chapters.

14

The Living Vacuum

"Philosophers are people who know less and less about more and more until they know nothing about everything. Scientists are people who know more and more about less and less until they know everything about nothing." - Konrad Lorenz

"In classical mechanics three objects are already too difficult, in quantum mechanics two, in quantum field theory zero." - Unknown

"No point is more central than this, that empty space is not empty. It is the seat of the most rich and surprising physics." - John Wheeler

"Anatoly Larkin, posed a challenge to two outstanding undergraduate teenage theorists, Sacha Polyakov and Sasha Migdal: 'In field theory the vacuum is like a substance; what happens there?'" - from The Infinity Puzzle by Frank Close

---

One of the most interesting aspects of quantum field theory is the ground state of different quantum fields. Naively, we would imagine that the ground state of a field looks like a perfectly calm sea:

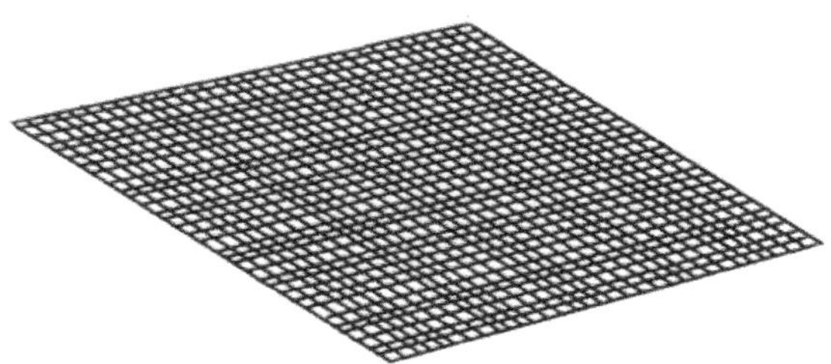

This is, in fact, true for classical fields which we can understand as networks of coupled classical oscillators. In contrast, for a network of quantum oscillators it is suggestive to imagine the configuration with the lowest amount of energy as something more similar to boiling water:

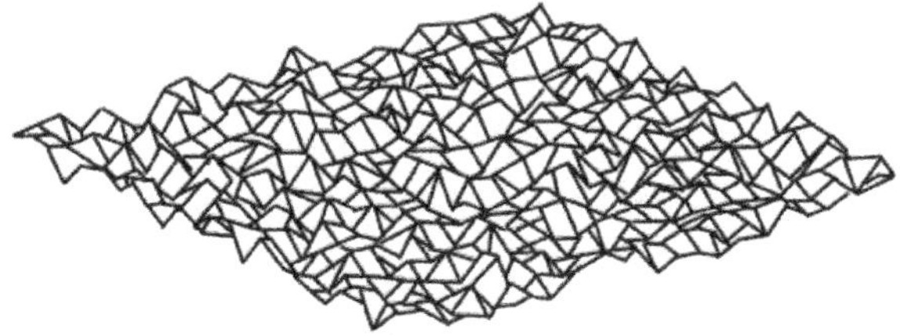

There is simply no way to make it any smoother since the ground state energy of each oscillator in the network is non-zero. Moreover, the standard deviation of observables like the position Δx and momentum Δp are always non-zero for a quantum oscillator. This is necessarily the case because otherwise the uncertainty relation $\Delta x \Delta p \geq \frac{\hbar}{2}$ would be violated. In words, this means that if we measure the location of a quantum oscillator in its ground state we don't always find it at its equilibrium position. Instead, sometimes we will find it a bit above and sometimes a bit below it.

We already stumbled upon this curious property of the ground state of quantum fields when we discovered that the energy of the ground state is infinitely large.[1] There are many, sometimes

[1] We calculated this in Eq. 8.19.

heated, discussions about how seriously we should take this result and what role is played by virtual particles. For example, it's very tempting to draw a connection between the vacuum bubble diagrams that we discarded by normal ordering our Hamiltonians and ground state fluctuations.[2] These vacuum bubble diagrams are usually described by stories along the lines of "particle-antiparticle pairs constantly pop in and out of existence". This language is problematic because even if we don't discard vacuum bubble diagrams altogether, internal lines in Feynman diagrams always correspond to Feynman propagators which is not what we use to describe particles.

[2] We discussed the need for normal-ordered Hamiltonians in Section 9.4 and discovered in Chapter 11 that the contractions that we remove this way correspond to self-loop diagrams.

Instead, Feynman propagators are damping factors that tell us how a non-zero field value affects the non-zero field value at a different location, while incoming and outgoing "real" particles are described by plane wave-like functions.

In addition, we only encounter an infinitely large energy because we start with the classical theory and then quantize it. But quantum theories are more fundamental than classical theories. Thus it makes more sense to start with a quantum theory that matches our observation and then dequantize it appropriately. In contrast, the quantization of a classical theory is necessarily plagued by ambiguities. To understand why, take note that the process of zooming out (quantum $\rightarrow$ classical) is usually possible without problems. But zooming in (classical $\rightarrow$ quantum) is often not possible in a unique way using theoretical methods alone.[3]

[3] Experiments can help to decide which fundamental model is the right one. But zooming in purely using mathematics leads to ambiguities.

There are many new details at a more fundamental level that are washed out when we zoom out. Thus there are usually many fundamental models that lead to the same less-fundamental model when we zoom out. The difference between these fundamental models are details that are washed out when we zoom out. This implies that the process of zooming in is not possible without ambiguities. In principle, we can end up with any of the more fundamental models that lead to the less-fundamental model after zooming out.

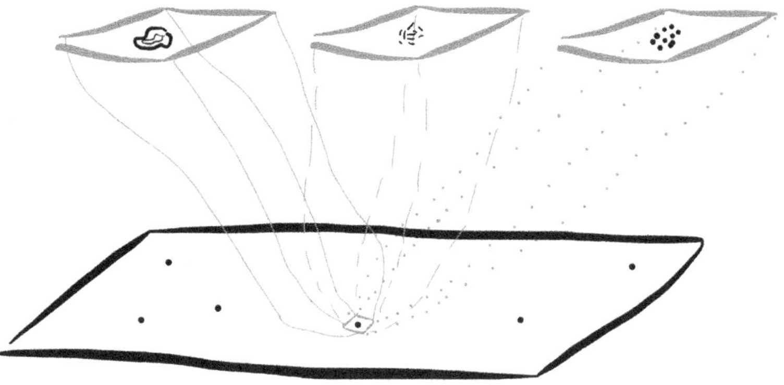

To make this a bit more concrete, recall how we ended up with the conclusion that the ground state energy in quantum field theory is infinitely large. We started with the classical Hamiltonian and the classical field expansion. We then promoted the coefficients $a(k)$, $a^\dagger(k)$ in the field expansion to operators by imposing the canonical commutation relations. Then we plugged the quantized field expansion into the formula for the Hamiltonian and, using the canonical commutation relations, found that

$$H = \int_V dk^3 \frac{\omega_k}{(2\pi)^3} a^\dagger(\vec{k}) a(\vec{k}) + \frac{1}{2} \int_V dk^3 \omega_k \delta(\vec{0}) \,. \tag{14.1}$$

But what if we rewrite the Hamiltonian first and then quantize it? We can plug the classical field expansion into the formula for the Hamiltonian and since in this context $a(k)$, $a^\dagger(k)$ are just ordinary functions that commute, we find

$$H = \int_V dk^3 \frac{\omega_k}{(2\pi)^3} a^\dagger(\vec{k}) a(\vec{k}) \,. \tag{14.2}$$

If we now quantize the field, there is no infinitely large term in

the Hamiltonian. In summary

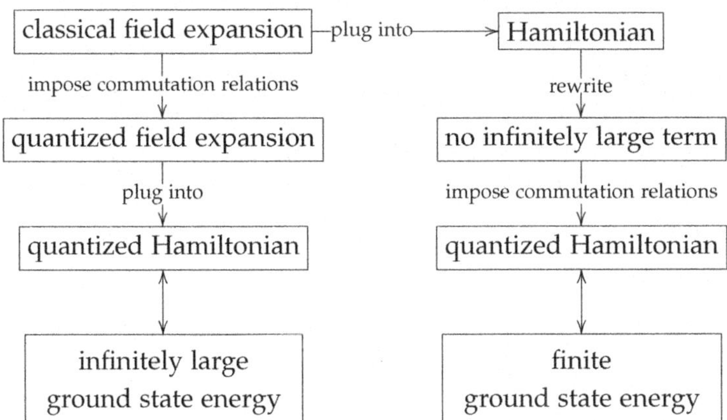

Which route is the right one? Or equivalently, which Hamiltonian describes energy in the quantum theory correctly? There is simply no way to answer these questions using purely theoretical arguments and thus it makes sense to work with the more convenient one until experiments tell us otherwise.[4]

[4] It is often argued that the experimentally confirmed Casimir effect demonstrates that the vacuum energy density is non-zero. The idea is to calculate the energy between and outside of two plates. Since they are not equal, there must be a force $F = -\frac{dE}{dr}$ that acts on the plates, which is known as Casimir force. This explanation is controversial because the Casimir force can also be understood as a van der Waals force. In particular, by saying that the electric field vanishes on the plates is analogous to saying that electronic fluctuations on the planes become synchronized. This is exactly how we describe the origin of the van der Waals force which has nothing to do with "vacuum fluctuations" or "vacuum pressure". For discussions see, for example,

Kimball A. Milton. The Casimir effect: Recent controversies and progress. *J. Phys.*, A37:R209, 2004. DOI: 10.1088/0305-4470/37/38/R01; R. L. Jaffe. The Casimir effect and the quantum vacuum. *Phys. Rev.*, D72:021301, 2005. DOI: 10.1103/PhysRevD.72.021301; and H. Nikolic. Proof that Casimir force does not originate from vacuum energy. *Phys. Lett.*, B761:197–202, 2016. DOI: 10.1016/j.physletb.2016.08.036

But luckily, there is also a lot of interesting physics associated with the ground state of quantum fields that is a lot less controversial.

One of the most important phenomena associated with the ground state of quantum fields is spontaneous symmetry breaking. Before we discuss *spontaneous* symmetry breaking, we should talk about symmetry breaking in more general terms first.

14.1 Symmetry Breaking

Speaking colloquially, a symmetry gets broken when an object becomes stiff. For example, let's consider a gas of molecules which is certainly not stiff. A result of the non-stiffness is that a gas is rotational symmetric and translational symmetric.

The situation changes if we cool the gas. At some point it will become fluid and eventually it will freeze and become solid. After each step the molecule system becomes more stiff. As a result, the system is no longer symmetric under all transformations.

For example, we can only rotate an ice crystal by very special angles like, say, 120 degrees or 240 degrees without inducing notable changes. In contrast, a gas can be rotated arbitrarily and always looks the same.

Here's one way of looking at the situation. Imagine that you want to perform an experiment with a substance that is located in a box. Before you perform the experiment, you hand the box to a friend who possibly rotates the substance within the box. If the substance in question is ice, the orientation of it inside the box can make a big difference. Therefore, you will immediately notice whether or not your friend rotated the substance. But if the substance in question is a gas, there isn't even a way to talk about it's orientation and hence it doesn't matter. In this sense, a block of ice has less symmetry than a gas.

The two rules of thumb to take away are:

▷ Objects are less symmetric if they are stiff.

▷ Objects become more stiff when we cool them.

If we combine these two observations, we can conclude that it's quite reasonable to expect that it is possible for symmetries to be broken when we cool a system. Moreover, if we increase the temperature within a system we typically expect that symmetries are restored.

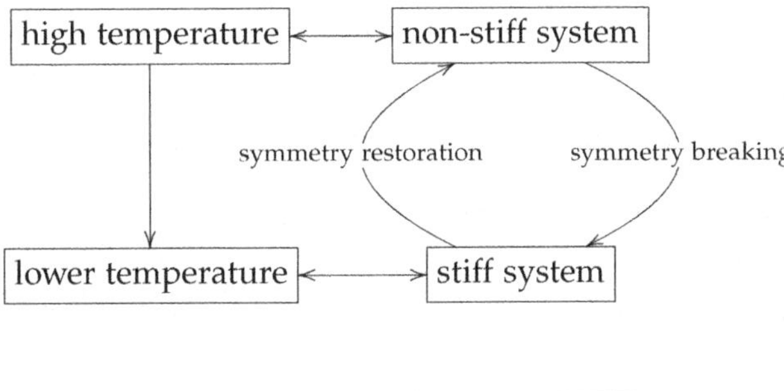

In the following section, we will discuss exactly the same ideas in the context of fields.

14.2 Explicit Symmetry Breaking

The Lagrangian that describes a free scalar field reads (Eq. 5.2)

$$\mathcal{L} = \frac{1}{2}(\partial_\mu \phi \partial^\mu \phi - m^2 \phi^2) . \tag{14.3}$$

An interesting observation is that if there is no mass term ($m = 0$), the Lagrangian is unchanged by field shifts

$$\phi \to \phi' = \phi + \epsilon , \tag{14.4}$$

where ϵ is a constant. We can check this explicitly:

$$\begin{aligned}\mathcal{L} &= \frac{1}{2}\partial_\mu\phi'\partial^\mu\phi' \\ &\quad \text{Eq. 14.4} \\ &= \frac{1}{2}\partial_\mu\Big(\phi+\epsilon\Big)\partial^\mu\Big(\phi+\epsilon\Big) \\ &\quad \partial_\mu\epsilon = 0 \\ &= \frac{1}{2}\partial_\mu\phi\partial^\mu\phi \quad \checkmark\end{aligned} \tag{14.5}$$

In contrast, the mass term is changed by a field shift

$$m^2\phi'^2 = m^2\Big(\phi+\epsilon\Big)^2 = m^2\Big(\phi^2+2\epsilon\phi+\epsilon^2\Big) \neq m^2\phi^2\,. \tag{14.6}$$

Thus we can summarize:

▷ If there is no mass term ($m = 0$) a field shift is a symmetry.

▷ If there is a mass term ($m \neq 0$) a field shift is not a symmetry.

This suggests that the mass parameter m describes the stiffness of the field. If we recall from Section 5.1.1 that we can understand a scalar field as a coupled network of oscillators, this interpretation makes perfect sense. In particular, we derived that the mass parameter m is directly related to the spring constant k associated with each oscillator ($m \equiv \frac{k}{Mc^2}$, Eq. 5.26).[5] For $m = 0$, we therefore have $k = 0$ which implies that the springs have zero stiffness. In other words, if $m = 0$ we are dealing with a network of coupled mass points. In the continuum limit, this network behaves like a rope (at least if we restrict ourselves to one spatial dimension).

[5] In the formula $m \equiv \frac{k}{Mc^2}$, the constant M describes the mass of the object attached at the end of the spring.

In contrast, for $m \neq 0$, we are dealing with a network of mass points which are attached to springs. In the continuum limit, this becomes a rope attached to springs

With these pictures in mind, we can understand why a scalar field is less symmetric if $m \neq 0$.

▷ If $m = 0$ we can raise or lower the rope as a whole (Eq. 14.4)

$$\phi \to \phi' = \phi + \epsilon \tag{14.7}$$

without changing anything.

▷ If $m \neq 0$, this is no longer possible. The springs keep track of the position of the rope and we must stretch them to move the rope.

In summary, the mass parameter m encodes the stiffness of a field. Moreover, if $m \neq 0$ the field shift symmetry (Eq. 14.4) is broken.

So far, we've tuned the parameter m by hand. But we can also imagine that the parameter m changes dynamically analogous to how a gas becomes more stiff if we cool it.

14.3 Spontaneous Symmetry Breaking

Let's consider once more a self-interacting scalar field which we describe by the Lagrangian (Eq. 6.26)[6]

$$\mathcal{L} = \frac{1}{2}\partial_\mu \phi \partial^\mu \phi - \frac{1}{2}\mu^2 \phi^2 - \frac{1}{4!}\lambda \phi^4 . \tag{14.8}$$

[6] We discussed this Lagrangian in Section 6.2. However, for reasons that will become clear in a minute we call the parameter in front of ϕ^2 now μ^2 instead of m^2.

The corresponding Hamiltonian reads (Eq. 10.2)

$$H = \int d^3x \left(\frac{1}{2} \partial_\mu \phi \partial^\mu \phi + \frac{1}{2} \mu^2 \phi^2 + \frac{1}{4!} \lambda \phi^4 \right) . \qquad (14.9)$$

In this formula, the first term encodes the kinetic energy while the second term encodes the potential energy:

$$V(\phi) \equiv \frac{1}{2} \mu^2 \phi^2 + \frac{1}{4!} \lambda \phi^4 . \qquad (14.10)$$

If we assume that potential parameters (μ^2, λ) are positive, the potential looks like this

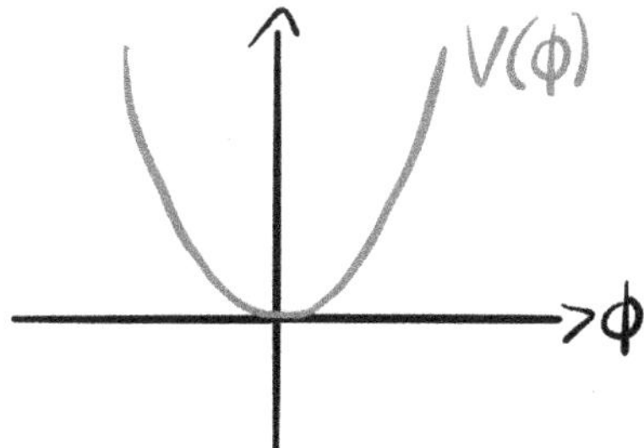

The minimum of the potential is at $\phi = 0$. While the model is not invariant under field shifts (Eq. 14.4), it is unchanged by the transformation

$$\phi \to \phi' = -\phi . \qquad (14.11)$$

In other words, this is a symmetry of the model.

The situation changes dramatically if we replace $\mu^2 \to -\mu^2$. The Lagrangian in this case reads

$$\mathcal{L} = \frac{1}{2} \partial_\mu \phi \partial^\mu \phi + \frac{1}{2} \mu^2 \phi^2 - \frac{1}{4!} \lambda \phi^4 . \qquad (14.12)$$

This implies that we are dealing with the potential

$$V(\phi) \equiv -\frac{1}{2} \mu^2 \phi^2 + \frac{1}{4!} \lambda \phi^4 , \qquad (14.13)$$

which looks like this

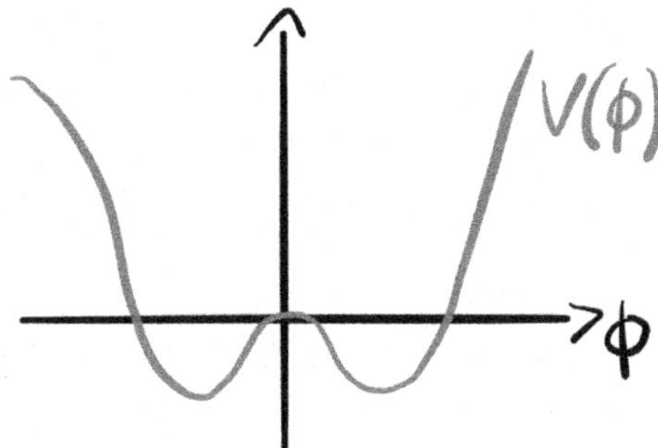

We can see that the minimum of the potential is no longer at $\phi = 0$. To calculate the new minima, we look at the zeroes of the derivative of the potential[7]

$$\begin{aligned}
0 &\stackrel{!}{=} \frac{dV(\phi)}{d\phi} \\
&\quad \text{Eq. 14.13} \\
&= \frac{d}{d\phi}\Big(-\frac{1}{2}\mu^2\phi^2 + \frac{1}{4!}\lambda\phi^4 \Big) \\
&\quad \frac{4}{4!} = \frac{1}{3!} \\
&= -\mu^2\phi + \frac{1}{3!}\lambda\phi^3 \\
&= \phi\Big(-\mu^2 + \frac{1}{3!}\lambda\phi^2 \Big) . \qquad (14.14)
\end{aligned}$$

[7] This is the standard method to calculate the maxima and minima of a function. The derivative describes the slope of the function and the defining feature of a maximum or minimum is that the slope is zero.

By looking at the figure above, we can see that while for $\phi = 0$ we also find $\frac{dV(\phi)}{d\phi} = 0$, this field value now corresponds to a maximum of the potential. The two minima correspond to the field values for which the expression between the brackets vanishes:

$$\begin{aligned}
0 &\stackrel{!}{=} -\mu^2 + \frac{1}{3!}\lambda\phi^2 \\
&\quad 3! = 3\cdot 2\cdot 1 = 6 \\
\frac{6}{\lambda}\mu^2 &\stackrel{!}{=} \phi^2 \\
&\quad \sqrt{\ } \\
\pm\sqrt{\frac{6\mu^2}{\lambda}} &\stackrel{!}{=} \phi . \qquad (14.15)
\end{aligned}$$

As shown in the figure above, there are two minima in this scenario. This result is important because we want to describe particles and we understand particles as field excitations above the ground state configuration. The ground state configuration is, by definition, the configuration with minimum energy. In the previous scenario with $+\mu^2$ in the potential there was no subtlety since the potential minimum corresponds to $\phi = 0$. As before, we can interpret the parameter μ as the mass associated with the field.

However, in the scenario with $-\mu^2$ in the potential we must be more careful. The minimum of the potential now corresponds to either $\phi = \sqrt{\frac{6\mu^2}{\lambda}}$ or $\phi = -\sqrt{\frac{6\mu^2}{\lambda}}$. This makes it difficult to think of particles as small excitations.

Moreover, formally the switch $\mu^2 \rightarrow -\mu^2$ implies that we are dealing with a field with an imaginary mass parameter:

$$\mu \rightarrow i\mu \quad \leftrightarrow \quad \mu^2 \rightarrow -\mu^2 . \tag{14.16}$$

These observations suggest that we are looking at the model in the wrong way. But it's not too hard to remedy the situation.

For concreteness, let's assume that the field ends up in the minimum at $\phi = \sqrt{\frac{6\mu^2}{\lambda}}$. We then define a new field by shifting the original field

$$\tilde{\phi} = \phi - \sqrt{\frac{6\mu^2}{\lambda}} . \tag{14.17}$$

This is a smart idea because the relevant minimum of the potential corresponds to $\tilde{\phi} = 0$. Moreover, we can check that the redefined field $\tilde{\phi}$ has a real mass parameter. To that end, we rearrange the terms in Eq. 14.17

$$\phi = \tilde{\phi} + \sqrt{\frac{6\mu^2}{\lambda}} \tag{14.18}$$

and plug this into the Lagrangian (Eq. 14.12)

$$\begin{aligned}
\mathcal{L} &= \frac{1}{2}\partial_\mu\phi\partial^\mu\phi + \frac{1}{2}\mu^2\phi^2 - \frac{1}{4!}\lambda\phi^4 \\
&= \frac{1}{2}\partial_\mu\Big(\tilde{\phi} + \sqrt{\frac{6\mu^2}{\lambda}}\Big)\partial^\mu\Big(\tilde{\phi} + \sqrt{\frac{6\mu^2}{\lambda}}\Big) + \frac{1}{2}\mu^2\Big(\tilde{\phi} + \sqrt{\frac{6\mu^2}{\lambda}}\Big)^2 \\
&\quad - \frac{1}{4!}\lambda\Big(\tilde{\phi} + \sqrt{\frac{6\mu^2}{\lambda}}\Big)^4 \\
&= \frac{1}{2}\partial_\mu\tilde{\phi}\partial^\mu\tilde{\phi} + \frac{1}{2}\mu^2\left(\tilde{\phi}^2 + \frac{6\mu^2}{\lambda} + 2\tilde{\phi}\sqrt{\frac{6\mu^2}{\lambda}}\right) \\
&\quad - \frac{1}{4!}\lambda\left(\tilde{\phi}^4 + 4\tilde{\phi}^3\sqrt{\frac{6\mu^2}{\lambda}} + 6\tilde{\phi}^2\frac{6\mu^2}{\lambda} + 4\tilde{\phi}\sqrt{\frac{6\mu^2}{\lambda}}^3 + \Big(\frac{6\mu^2}{\lambda}\Big)^2\right) \\
&= \frac{1}{2}\partial_\mu\tilde{\phi}\partial^\mu\tilde{\phi} + \frac{1}{2}\mu^2\tilde{\phi}^2 + \frac{3\mu^4}{\lambda} + \mu^2\tilde{\phi}\sqrt{\frac{6\mu^2}{\lambda}} \\
&\quad - \frac{1}{4!}\lambda\tilde{\phi}^4 - \frac{1}{3!}\lambda\tilde{\phi}^3\sqrt{\frac{6\mu^2}{\lambda}} - \frac{36}{4!}\mu^2\tilde{\phi}^2 - \frac{1}{3!}\lambda\tilde{\phi}\sqrt{\frac{6\mu^2}{\lambda}}^3 - \frac{36}{4!}\frac{\mu^4}{\lambda} \\
&= \frac{1}{2}\partial_\mu\tilde{\phi}\partial^\mu\tilde{\phi} - \mu^2\tilde{\phi}^2 + \frac{3\mu^4}{2\lambda} - \frac{1}{4!}\lambda\tilde{\phi}^4 - \frac{1}{3!}\lambda\tilde{\phi}^3\sqrt{\frac{6\mu^2}{\lambda}}. \qquad (14.19)
\end{aligned}$$

Eq. 14.18

$\partial_\mu\sqrt{\frac{6\mu^2}{\lambda}} = 0$

$\frac{36}{4!} = \frac{3}{2}$

We can see that the parameter in front of the $\tilde{\phi}^2$ term appears here with a minus sign which is the usual case and implies a real mass. Thus we conclude that if the mass term appears with a positive sign in the Lagrangian (= negative sign in potential), we should switch to a description in terms of the shifted field $\tilde{\phi}$ (Eq. 14.17).[8] This has many important implications. But before we discuss them, let's try to paint a bigger picture of what is going on here.

[8] Reminder: the relationship between the interaction Hamiltonian and the interaction Lagrangian is (Eq. 12.3)

$$H_{\text{interactions}} = -L_{\text{interactions}}\,.$$

Thus a negative sign in the interaction Lagrangian becomes a positive sign in the interaction Hamiltonian/potential.

According to the generally accepted big bang scenario, there was a time when the universe was extremely hot. As the universe expanded in the billions of years after the big bang, it gradually became cooler. This, in turn, suggests that fundamental systems like quantum fields became more stiff as the universe cooled down and gradually became less symmetric. If we imagine that the parameter μ^2 changes as the universe cools down, we can describe this idea in mathematical terms by using what we've just discussed.

In the early universe, the scalar field ϕ is properly described by a Lagrangian with a negative factor in front of the ϕ^2 term:

$$\mathcal{L} = \frac{1}{2}\partial_\mu\phi\partial^\mu\phi - \frac{1}{2}\mu^2\phi^2 - \frac{1}{4!}\lambda\phi^4 \,. \tag{14.20}$$

Then as the universe cools down, the factor μ^2 changes and eventually becomes negative.

This transformation is best described through the change of the potential (Eq. 14.10)

$$V(\phi) \equiv \frac{1}{2}\mu^2\phi^2 + \frac{1}{4!}\lambda\phi^4 \,. \tag{14.21}$$

The shape of the potential for different signs of the μ^2 term is shown in the following figure:

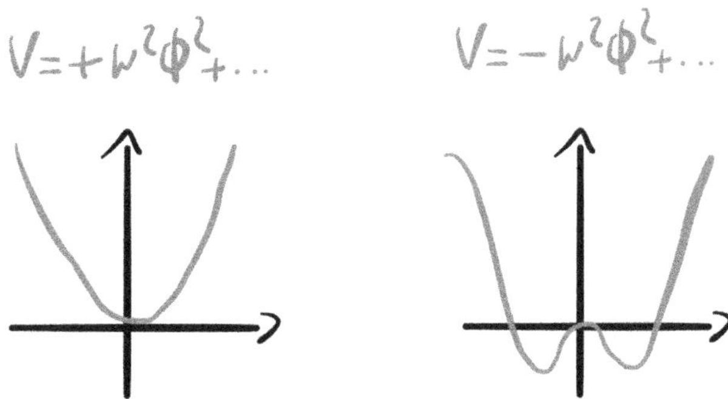

We can see that as long as there is a positive sign, there is just one minimum which corresponds to $\phi = 0$. For $\mu^2 < 0$, however, the shape of the potential is completely different and there are two different minima. What happens to the field ϕ if we assume that it was in its ground state ($\phi = 0$) in the early universe? Since the shape of the potential changes, the field will try to settle in one of the new minima. The previous minimum at $\phi = 0$ is no longer a minimum if there is a minus in front of μ^2

and the field spontaneously undergoes a phase transition into one of the new minimum energy configurations. In other words, we imagine that the field is pushed through the cooling process (as parametrized by the change of the μ^2 term) into one of the two new minima, analogous to how a marble rolls down if we put it on top of a sombrero.

Moreover, we imagine that particles are always field excitations above the ground state.

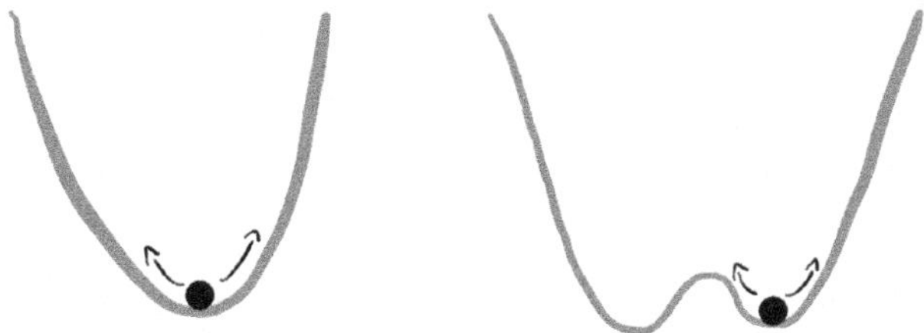

This explains why it's a good idea to use a description in terms of the shifted field $\tilde{\phi}$ after the phase transition.

An important observation is that as soon as the field leaves the previous ground state configuration ($\phi = 0$), the symmetry (Eq. 14.11)

$$\phi \to \phi' = -\phi \tag{14.22}$$

is broken by the new ground state configuration. The previous ground state was unchanged by this transformation because

$$\phi_{\text{min}} \equiv 0 = -0 \equiv -\phi_{\text{min}} \,. \tag{14.23}$$

But if the field settles in the minimum energy configuration $\phi_{\text{min}} = \sqrt{\frac{6\mu^2}{\lambda}}$, we have $\phi_{\text{min}} = \sqrt{\frac{6\mu^2}{\lambda}} \to -\sqrt{\frac{6\mu^2}{\lambda}} \neq \sqrt{\frac{6\mu^2}{\lambda}}$. Since the field ends up in one of the two minima, there is necessarily an element of the theory (the ground state) that does not respect the symmetry. We say, the symmetry is **spontaneously broken**.[9]

[9] Take note that the Lagrangian written in terms of $\tilde{\phi}$ (Eq. 14.19) is not invariant under the transformation $\tilde{\phi} \to -\tilde{\phi}$. However, it is still invariant under the original symmetry of the Lagrangian $\phi \to -\phi$, which implies for the shifted field $\tilde{\phi} \to -\phi - \sqrt{6\lambda\mu^2}$. It is conventional to say that the symmetry is only hidden in the Lagrangian but broken by the ground state. This is a defining feature of spontaneous symmetry breaking. A symmetry is explicitly broken if there is a term in the Lagrangian that isn't unchanged by the transformation.

Before we move on, let me emphasize the difference between spontaneous symmetry breaking and explicit symmetry breaking. One of the famous examples of spontaneous symmetry breaking is the bending of a rod. If we put no pressure on the rod, the system has a perfect rotational symmetry. However, if we apply a force in the longitudinal direction on the rod, it will bend and the symmetry is spontaneously broken.

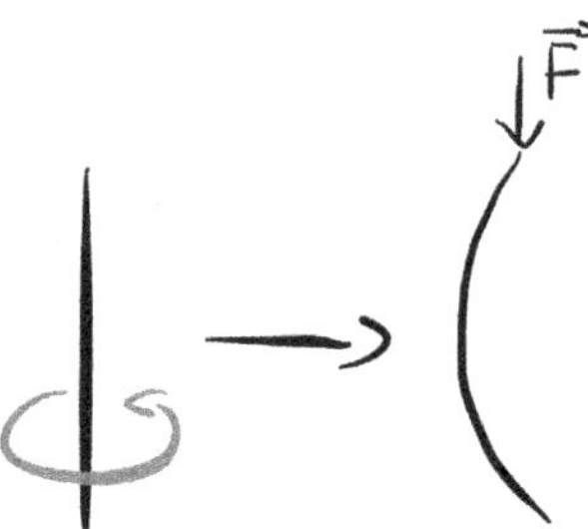

The key point here is that the rod and the force that we apply are both rotationally symmetric. Nevertheless, the system settles spontaneously in a new non-rotationally symmetric state.

We can, of course, also bend the rod by applying a force in the horizontal direction. In this case, the symmetry is broken explicitly by the non-symmetric force.

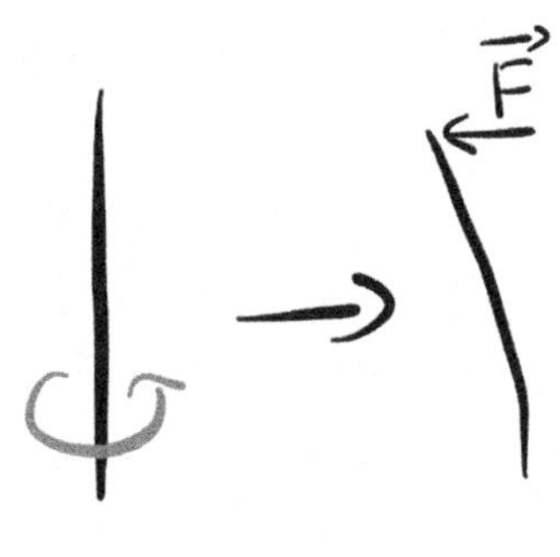

In the previous section, we've discussed that the stiffness of a field is encoded by the mass parameter and that the stiffness of a system is related to its symmetries. Moreover, we've seen in this section that changes in the stiffness parameter μ are directly related to the process of spontaneous symmetry breaking. In the following section, we will see that the situation becomes even more interesting if we consider how the phase transition of the scalar field ϕ affects other fields it interacts with.

14.4 Spontaneous Mass Generation

Let's consider once more the interaction between a real scalar field ϕ and a complex scalar field ψ. The Yukawa term in the Lagrangian that describes this interaction reads[10]

[10] We discussed Yukawa interactions in Section 6.3 and Section 12.1.

$$\mathcal{L}_{\text{Yukawa}} = -g\bar{\psi}\psi\phi\,. \tag{14.24}$$

We learned above that if the scalar field ϕ undergoes a phase transition, we should use the shifted field (Eq. 14.17)

$$\tilde{\phi} = \phi - \sqrt{\frac{6\mu^2}{\lambda}}\,. \tag{14.25}$$

The Yukawa term reads in terms of the shifted field

$$\begin{aligned}
\mathcal{L}_{\text{Yukawa}} &= -g\bar{\psi}\psi\phi \\
&\quad \text{Eq. 14.18} \\
&= -g\bar{\psi}\psi\left(\tilde{\phi} + \sqrt{\frac{6\mu^2}{\lambda}}\right) \\
&= -g\bar{\psi}\psi\tilde{\phi} - g\sqrt{\frac{6\mu^2}{\lambda}}\bar{\psi}\psi \,. \qquad (14.26)
\end{aligned}$$

On the one hand, this implies that the interaction between ψ and $\tilde{\phi}$ is described by the same coupling parameter g. On the other hand, we can see that there is an additional term which has exactly the structure as a mass term of the field ψ. Therefore, we conclude that if the field ψ is massless before the phase transition, it will be massive afterwards. Its mass

$$m_\psi \equiv g\sqrt{\frac{6\mu^2}{\lambda}} \qquad (14.27)$$

is directly related to its coupling strength g to the real field ϕ. This implies that the mass m_ψ is caused by interactions between ϕ and ψ. Therefore, we have here a dynamical model of how fields become massive. Analogous to how we say that a symmetry gets spontaneously broken, we say that we're dealing with a spontaneously generated mass, m_ψ.

It is again instructive to rephrase what we've discovered here in big picture terms. First of all, we imagine that in the early universe ψ was massless. Then as the universe cooled down, the field ϕ undergoes a phase transition. A byproduct of this phase transition is that the field ψ becomes massive. Moreover, we can imagine that there are other fields ψ_i that also interact with ϕ. To describe each of them appropriately after the phase transition of ϕ, we need to include a mass term for them in the Lagrangian. Each mass parameter that is generated through the phase transition can be written as

$$m_{\psi_i} \equiv g_i\sqrt{\frac{6\mu^2}{\lambda}} \,, \qquad (14.28)$$

where g_i encodes the coupling strength between ψ_i and ϕ. This implies that the stronger a field ψ_i interacts with ϕ, the bigger its mass will be after the phase transition.

Next, we want to understand better what a spontaneously generated mass really is. In the previous sections, we've treated the field ϕ entirely as classical and luckily, roughly the same conclusions apply to quantum field theory. An important hint is that the expectation values of quantum operators behave like classical variables.[11] In our context here, we write[12]

$$\langle 0|\phi|0\rangle = \phi_{c0} \,. \tag{14.29}$$

The expression $\langle 0|\phi|0\rangle$ is commonly called the **vacuum expectation value** of ϕ. In words, Eq. 14.29 tells us that ϕ_{c0} describes the field values that we expect on average if the field is in its ground state, $|0\rangle$.[13] Moreover, this formula implies that our (classical) conclusions from the previous sections apply in the quantum theory to the vacuum expectation value, $\langle 0|\phi|0\rangle$, of the field ϕ.

Before the phase transition we found that the minimum of the potential is at $\phi = 0$ and thus we have

$$\langle 0|\phi|0\rangle = 0 \,. \tag{14.30}$$

After the phase transition, the minimum is at $\phi = \pm\sqrt{\frac{6\mu^2}{\lambda}}$ and we can conclude[14]

$$\langle 0|\phi|0\rangle = \pm\sqrt{\frac{6\mu^2}{\lambda}} \,. \tag{14.31}$$

The existence of two minima implies that there are two different ground states of the field ϕ:

$$\begin{aligned}\langle 0^+|\phi|0^+\rangle &= \sqrt{\frac{6\mu^2}{\lambda}} \\ \langle 0^-|\phi|0^-\rangle &= -\sqrt{\frac{6\mu^2}{\lambda}} \,.\end{aligned} \tag{14.32}$$

[11] In quantum mechanics this is known as the Ehrenfest theorem.

[12] The following paragraph shouldn't be taken too seriously and is primarily a heuristic story, not a rigorous discussion. There are many subtleties that we are glossing over here. In particular, the vacuum expectation value is usually defined with respect to the interacting vacuum state $|\Omega\rangle$ which, in general, is different from the free vacuum state $|0\rangle$.

[13] Recall that $\langle\psi|\hat{O}|\psi\rangle$ denotes the expectation value of the operator $\hat{O}$ if we prepare the system in the state $|\psi\rangle$. Here, we prepare the field in its ground state, $|0\rangle$ and the field ϕ is the operator that we consider.

[14] Formally, this can be derived by considering the classical limit ($\hbar \to 0$) of the path integral

$$\begin{aligned}\langle 0|\phi|0\rangle &= \\ &= \lim_{\hbar\to 0}\int D\phi e^{\frac{i}{\hbar}\int d^4x\mathcal{L}[\phi]}\phi \\ &= \phi_{\text{min}} \,.\end{aligned}$$

We discuss the path integral in the next chapter.

Moreover, by looking at Eq. 14.31 we can conclude that, on average, we expect to find a non-zero field value if the field is in its ground state. One way to interpret this result is by saying that after the phase transition, the vacuum is filled with "$\tilde{\phi}$-substance". Before the phase transition we found $\langle 0|\phi|0\rangle = 0$ and thus we can imagine that vacuum was, on average, empty. After the phase transition, we are dealing with the shifted field $\tilde{\phi}$ and we found $\langle 0|\tilde{\phi}|0\rangle \neq 0$. This implies that the vacuum is no longer empty but filled with $\tilde{\phi}$ excitations.

We can use this to understand why other fields acquire a mass through the phase transition. Before the phase transition, $\langle 0|\phi|0\rangle = 0$ implies that a given field excitation (particle) can travel through space without being affected by ϕ.

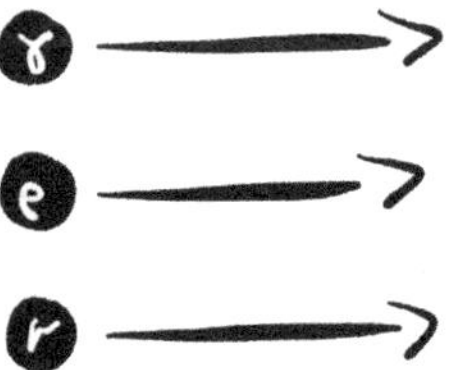

However, after the phase transition, each excitation of a field that interacts with $\tilde{\phi}$ is constantly affected by it since $\langle 0|\tilde{\phi}|0\rangle \neq 0$.

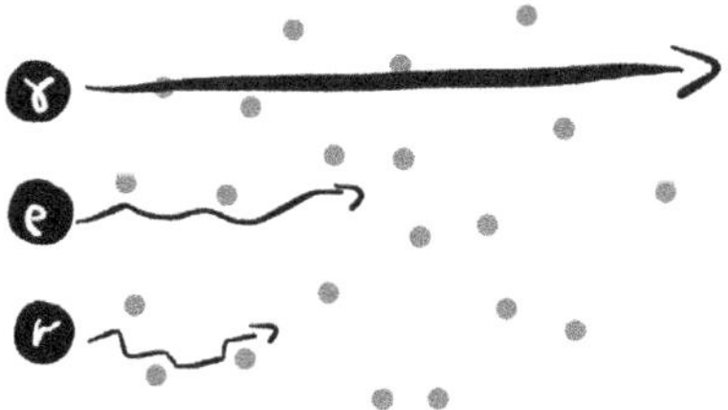

The constant interaction with the "$\tilde{\phi}$-substance" causes the particles to slow down, which we describe effectively through a non-zero mass.[15] Some particles have little problem moving in the "$\tilde{\phi}$-substance" since they couple only weakly to $\tilde{\phi}$. Therefore, we say that they have a small mass. Other particles interact

[15] Massless particles always travel with velocity c, while massive particles travel with a velocity $v < c$. This fact is closely related to our observations in Section 3.6 that all plane waves in a field without dispersion travel at the same velocity c.

strongly with the "$\tilde{\phi}$-substance" and therefore, effectively, have a large mass. Moreover, there are also particles that are not affected by the "$\tilde{\phi}$-substance" since they don't interact with $\tilde{\phi}$ (e.g., photons γ). These particles remain massless.

In this chapter, I've only sketched some of the key ideas behind symmetry breaking in quantum field theory. In particular, in addition to explicit and spontaneous symmetry breaking, there is anomalous symmetry breaking. This term is used to describe the phenomenon that a symmetry of the Lagrangian (a symmetry of the classical model) does not survive the quantization procedure. Moreover, we've only discussed the spontaneous breaking of the discrete symmetry $\phi \to -\phi$ (Eq. 14.11). Far more important in modern physics is the spontaneous breaking of continuous symmetries.[16] An interesting side-effect of the spontaneous breaking of a continuous symmetry is the emergence of massless particles, known as Goldstone bosons. This connection is formalized by the so-called Goldstone theorem. Moreover, there is a famous loophole in Goldstone's theorem that is known as the Higgs mechanism. In the Higgs mechanism the spontaneous breaking of global symmetry happens in the presence of long-ranged interactions. In this case, there are no Goldstone bosons and the long-ranged interaction becomes short-ranged. From a particle perspective this happens because the gauge bosons that are responsible for the interaction become massive.

[16] A continuous symmetry is a set of transformations that can be parametrized by a continuous parameter which leaves the model in question unchanged. A prototypical example are rotations which can be parameterized by a continuous rotation angle. Another important example is the phase shift symmetry (Eq. 4.53)

$$\psi \to \psi' = e^{-i\varphi}\psi$$

that we discussed in Section 4.3.2.

15

The Path Integral Formulation

An important feature of all fundamental theories of physics is that there is more than one formulation of them. For example, for classical mechanics there is the Newtonian formulation, the Lagrangian formulation and the Hamiltonian formulation. The status of alternative formulations of quantum field theory is not quite as clear as for the other theories. But one well-established alternative to the canonical formulation we have considered so far is known as the path integral formulation. The path integral formulation is in many regards a lot more complicated than the canonical formulation. In particular, it's extremely hard to evaluate the path integral for a given system explicitly and many sophisticated ideas are necessary to make progress. Nevertheless, it makes sense to understand at least the main idea behind the path integral formulation because it offers an alternative perspective that is invaluable in many applications.[1] In the following section, we discuss how the path integral formulation works in quantum mechanics. Afterwards we take a short look at the path integral in quantum field theory.

[1] We will discuss a concrete example in the next chapter.

15.1 The Path Integral in Quantum Mechanics

We start with a thought experiment that illustrates the general idea.[2]

[2] The following thought experiment is due to Anthony Zee and appears in his brilliant book titled *Quantum Field Theory in a Nutshell*. Moreover, this section is an excerpt from my book

Jakob Schwichtenberg. *No-Nonsense Quantum Mechanics*. No-Nonsense Books, Karlsruhe, Germany, 2018c. ISBN 978-1719838719

Our starting point is once more the double slit experiment. In the standard wave function formulation, we have a probability amplitude $\psi_1(B)$ that our particle travels from A through slit 1 and then ends up at the location B on our screen. Analogously, we have an amplitude $\psi_2(B)$ that it travels through slit 2 and we then detect it at the location B. The total probability is then the sum of the amplitudes squared[3]

[3] Take note that this is not the same as $|\psi_1(B)|^2 + |\psi_2(B)|^2$. The important difference is the interference term $\psi_1(B)\psi_2(B)$ which is responsible for the interference pattern.

$$P_{AB} = |\psi_{AB}| = |\psi_1(B) + \psi_2(B)|^2 . \tag{15.1}$$

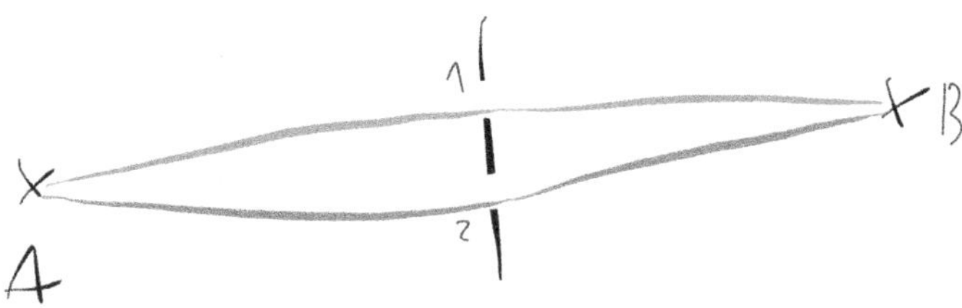

Now, here's a clever series of thoughts which starts with the question: What happens if we drill another slit into our wall?

Well, in this case we simply have

$$P_{AB} = |\psi_{AB}| = |\psi_1(B) + \psi_2(B) + \psi_3(B)|^2 . \tag{15.2}$$

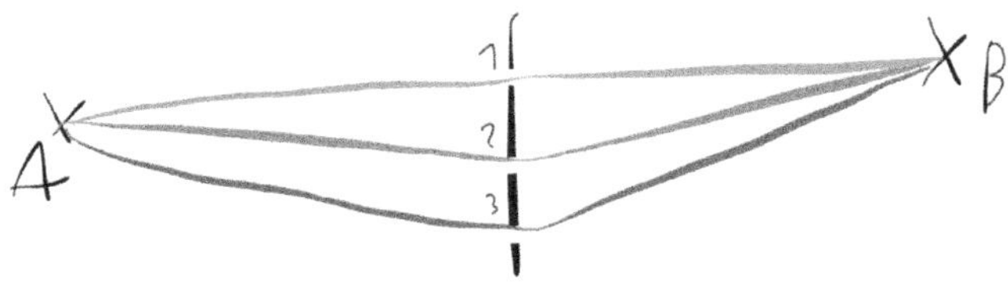

The next clever question is: What happens if we add another wall with holes in it behind the first one?

Again, we need to include all of the possible ways that the particle can get from A to B. For example, we now have an amplitude for the path from slit 1 in the first wall to the slit $1'$ in the second wall, another amplitude for the path from slit 1 in the first wall to slit $2'$ in the second wall and so on.

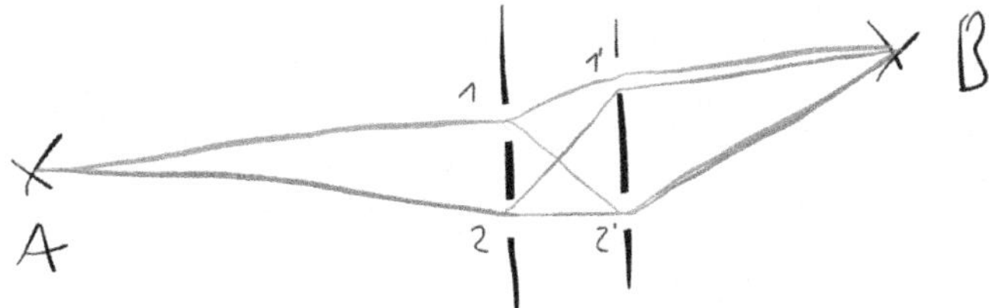

The crazy thing is what happens when we take this game to the extreme: We add more and more walls and drill more and more holes into them. At some point there will be no walls left since we drilled so many holes into them. However, our discussion from above suggests how we have to calculate the probability that the particle starts at A and ends up at B: we have to add the amplitudes for all possible paths to get from A to B. This is true even though there are no longer any walls since we drilled so many holes into them. The final lesson is therefore that in empty space without any physical walls, we have to consider the probabilities of the particle taking *all* possible paths from one point to another instead of just one path. This is the basic idea behind the path integral formulation of quantum mechanics.

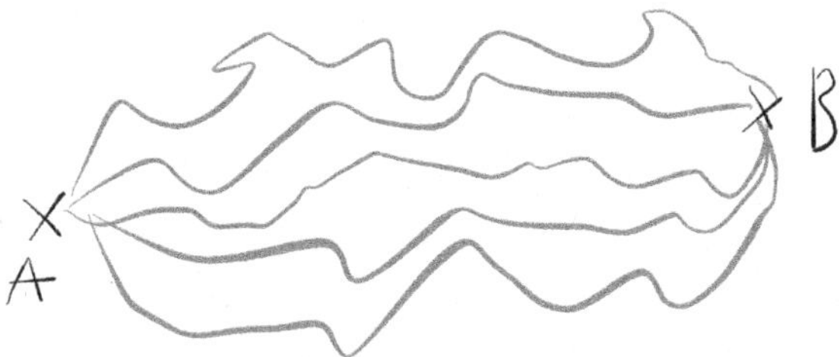

We will translate exactly this idea into a mathematical form and then see how the name *path integral* comes about.

What we are interested in is the probability that a particle that starts at a point A ends up after some time T at another point B. Using the standard quantum framework, we can immediately write down the corresponding probability amplitude[4]

[4] We discussed the quantum framework in Chapter 7.

$$\langle B|\Psi(A,T)\rangle \,. \tag{15.3}$$

Using the time evolution operator (Eq. (7.27)) we can write this as[5]

[5] We use the shorthand notation $|\psi(q)\rangle \equiv |q\rangle$ and, for simplicity assume that the Hamiltonian is time-independent, which is the case for a free particle. Otherwise, we have to write the integral all the time: $U(t) = e^{-\frac{i}{\hbar}\int_0^t dt' H(t')}$. Also, we neglect the factor $\hbar$ to unclutter the notation.

$$\begin{aligned}\langle B|\Psi(A,T)\rangle &= \langle B|U(T)|A\rangle \\ &= \langle B|e^{-iHT}|A\rangle \,.\end{aligned}$$

The thought experiment from above suggests how we can calculate this: We slice the spatial region between A and B and the time-interval $[0,T]$ into many many pieces. Then, to calculate the probability that the particle moves from A to B, we have to sum over the amplitudes for all possible paths between A and B.

For example, let's consider one specific path where the particle travels from A via some intermediate point q_1 to B.

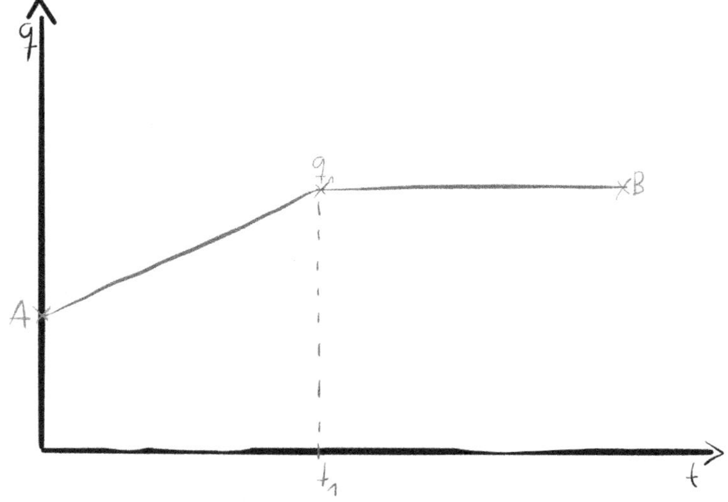

The corresponding probability amplitude is

$$\langle B|e^{-iH(T-t_1)}|q_1\rangle \langle q_1|e^{-iHt_1}|A\rangle ,$$

where t_1 is the time the particle needs to travel from A to the intermediate point q_1.

However, according to our thought experiment, it is not enough to consider one specific path. Instead, we must add the amplitudes for *all* possible paths. This means that we need to take into account the probability amplitudes that after t_1 seconds the particle is at *any* possible locations q

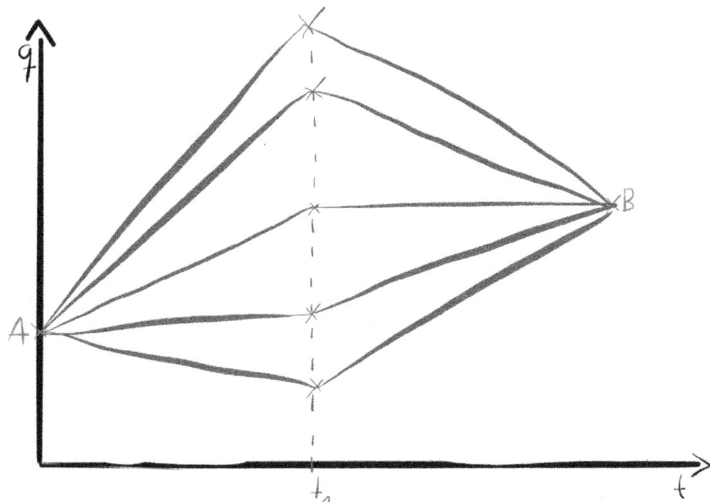

And mathematically this means that

$$\sum_{q_1} \langle B|e^{-iH(T-t_1)}|q_1\rangle \langle q_1|e^{-iHt_1}|A\rangle . \qquad (15.4)$$

In general, there is not just a discrete set of possible locations after t_1 seconds but instead a continuum. Therefore, we have to replace the sum with an integral

$$\text{Eq. (15.4)} \to \int dq_1 \langle B|e^{-iH(T-t_1)}|q_1\rangle \langle q_1|e^{-iHt_1}|A\rangle . \qquad (15.5)$$

So far we've only taken the probability amplitudes into account that the particle is at some specific point in time t_1 at all possible locations. However, to consider *all* possible paths we have to do the same thing for all points in time between 0 and T. For this purpose, we slice the interval $[0, T]$ into N equally sized pieces: $\delta = T/N$. The time evolution operator between two points in time is then $U(\delta) = \mathrm{e}^{-iH\delta}$ and we have to sum after each time evolution step over all possible locations:

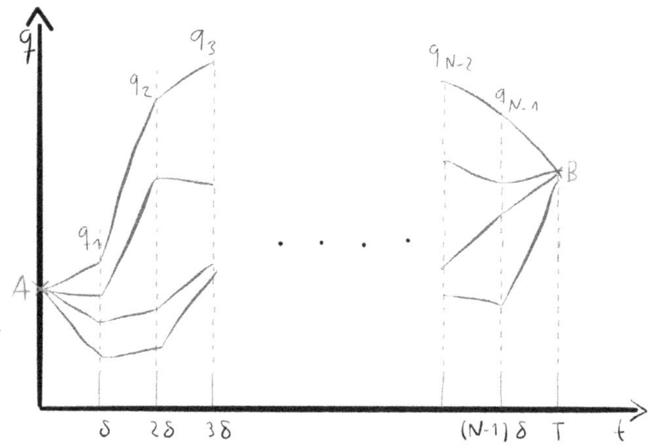

Mathematically, we have completely analogous to Eq. (15.5) for the amplitude $\psi_{A\to B}$ that we want to calculate

$$\psi_{A\to B} = \int dq_1 \cdots dq_{N-1} \langle B| e^{-iH\delta} |q_{N-1}\rangle \langle q_{N-1}| e^{-iH\delta} |q_{N-2}\rangle \cdots \\ \cdots \langle q_1| e^{-iH\delta} |A\rangle \,. \tag{15.6}$$

Our task is therefore to calculate the products of the form

$$\langle q_{j+1}| e^{-iH\delta} |q_j\rangle \equiv K_{q_{j+1},q_j}.$$

We expand the exponential function in a series since δ is tiny[6]

$$K_{q_{j+1},q_j} = \langle q_{j+1}| \left(1 - iH\delta - \frac{1}{2}H^2\delta^2 + \cdots\right) |q_j\rangle \\ = \langle q_{j+1}| q_j\rangle - i\delta \langle q_{j+1}| H |q_j\rangle + \ldots. \tag{15.7}$$

[6] Once more we use the series expansion $\mathrm{e}^x = \sum_{n=0}^{\infty} \frac{x^n}{n!}$.

The further evaluation of the propagator is quite complicated and needs many tricks that look extremely fishy at first glance. So don't worry if some steps are not perfectly clear since, as often happens, you simply need to get used to them.[7] If you're not in the mood for a long calculation, it also makes sense to jump directly to the final result in Eq. (15.13).

[7] The following quote by John von Neumann seems quite fitting here: "Young man, in mathematics you don't understand things. You just get used to them."

With this said, let's continue. The first term in the sum is a delta distribution since our eigenstates are orthogonal

$$\langle q_{j+1} | q_j \rangle = \delta(q_{j+1} - q_j) = \int \frac{dp_j}{2\pi} e^{ip_j(q_{j+1}-q_j)} . \tag{15.8}$$

In the last step we rewrote the delta distribution in terms of its explicit integral representation[8].

[8] This can be motivated as follows: recall that we construct a wave packet as a linear combination of plane waves. The delta distribution is, in a sense, an extreme wave packet which is infinitely thin but at the same time infinitely high. To construct such a wave packet using plane waves we have to use every plane wave that exists. This is basically what we wrote down here. For more on this, see Appendix E.

Next, we evaluate the second term in Eq. (15.7). The crucial idea is to recall the explicit form of $H \propto \hat{p}^2/2m + \hat{V}(x)$. To get rid of the operator $\hat{p}$, we need to switch to the momentum basis[9]

[9] This is analogous to how we switched from an abstract $|\Psi\rangle$ to the explicit position basis in Section 7.1.6.

$$\begin{aligned}
-i\delta \langle q_{j+1} | H | q_j \rangle &= -i\delta \langle q_{j+1} | \left(\frac{\hat{p}^2}{2m} + V(\hat{q}) \right) | q_j \rangle \\
&= -i\delta \langle q_{j+1} | \left(\frac{\hat{p}^2}{2m} + V(\hat{q}) \right) \underbrace{\int \frac{dp_j}{2\pi} | p_j \rangle \langle p_j |}_{=1} q_j \rangle \\
&= -i\delta \int \frac{dp_j}{2\pi} \left(\frac{p_j{}^2}{2m} + V(q_{j+1}) \right) \langle q_{j+1} | p_j \rangle \langle p_j | q_j \rangle \\
&= -i\delta \int \frac{dp_j}{2\pi} \left(\frac{p_j{}^2}{2m} + V(q_{j+1}) \right) e^{ip_j(q_{j+1}-q_j)} ,
\end{aligned} \tag{15.9}$$

$\curvearrowright$

$\curvearrowright$

$\curvearrowright$ $\langle p_j | q_j \rangle = e^{-ip_j q_j}$

where we again used the orthogonality of the basis states and the explicit integral representation of the delta distribution.

So in summary, our propagator (Eq. 15.7) reads

$$
\begin{aligned}
K_{q_{j+1},q_j} &= \langle q_{j+1}|\, q_j\rangle - i\delta \langle q_{j+1}|\, H\, |q_j\rangle + \ldots \\
&\quad \text{Eq. 15.8} \\
&= \int \frac{dp_j}{2\pi} e^{ip_j(q_{j+1}-q_j)} - i\delta \langle q_{j+1}|\, H\, |q_j\rangle + \ldots \\
&\quad \text{Eq. 15.9} \\
&= \int \frac{dp_j}{2\pi} e^{ip_j(q_{j+1}-q_j)} \\
&\quad - i\delta \int \frac{dp_j}{2\pi} \left(\frac{p_j^2}{2m} + V(q_{j+1}) \right) e^{ip_j(q_{j+1}-q_j)} + \ldots \\
&= \int \frac{dp_j}{2\pi} e^{ip_j(q_{j+1}-q_j)} \underbrace{\left(1 - i\delta \left(\frac{p_j^2}{2m} + V(q_{j+1}) \right) + \ldots \right)} \\
&= \int \frac{dp_j}{2\pi} e^{ip_j(q_{j+1}-q_j)} \exp\left(-i\delta \left(\frac{p_j^2}{2m} + V(q_{j+1}) \right) \right) \\
&= \int \frac{dp_j}{2\pi} e^{ip_j(q_{j+1}-q_j)} \exp\left(-i\delta H(p_j, q_{j+1}) \right)
\end{aligned}
\tag{15.10}
$$

With this at hand, we are finally ready to go back to Eq. (15.6) and evaluate the amplitude $\psi_{A\to B}$. In total, we get N times such a propagator K_{q_{j+1},q_j}.

$$
\begin{aligned}
\psi_{A\to B} &= \int \prod_{j=1}^{N-1} dq_j K_{q_{j+1},q_j} \\
&\quad \text{Eq. 15.10} \\
&= \int \prod_{j=1}^{N-1} dq_j \int \frac{dp_j}{2\pi} \exp\left(i\delta \sum_{j=0}^{N-1} \left(p_j \frac{(q_{j+1}-q_j)}{\delta} - H(p_j, \bar{q}_j) \right) \right).
\end{aligned}
\tag{15.11}
$$

Now, in the limit $N \to \infty$ our interval δ becomes infinitesimal. Therefore, in this limit the term $\frac{(q_{j+1}-q_j)}{\delta}$ becomes the velocity $\dot{q}$.[10] So the term in the exponent reads $p\dot{q} - H$. If we then execute the integration over dp and recall that the Lagrangian L is exactly the Legendre transform of the Hamiltonian, we can

[10] This is the definition of the derivative as the difference quotient.

rewrite the amplitude as

$$\psi_{A\to B} = \left(\frac{m}{2\pi i\delta}\right)^{N/2} \int \prod_{j=1}^{N-1} dq_j \exp\left(i\delta \sum_{j=0}^{N-1} \left(L(q_j)\right)\right). \quad (15.12)$$

It is conventional to then write the amplitude in the following more compact form[11]

$$\boxed{\psi_{A\to B} = \int \mathcal{D}q(t) e^{iS[q(t)]/\hbar}} \quad (15.13)$$

[11] We have included the so-far neglected $\hbar$ again in this final formula.

where $S[q(t)]$ is the action that we always use in the Lagrangian formalism and $\mathcal{D}q(t)$ is the so-called path integral measure.

In words, this equation tells us that in quantum mechanics we can calculate the probability amplitude that a particle goes from A to B by summing over all possible paths between A and B and *weight each path by the corresponding action*. This is in stark contrast to what we do in classical mechanics. In classical mechanics, we also calculate the path an object takes between two fixed points A and B by considering all paths and using the action. But in classical mechanics, there is only one correct path: the path with minimal action[12].

[12] This is the whole point of the Lagrangian formalism. For each path between two points, we can calculate the corresponding action. Since Nature is lazy, she always takes the path with minimal action. The paths with minimal action correspond to solutions of the Euler-Lagrange equations, which are therefore our equations of motion. (In some cases the action is not minimal and a more correct statement would be to talk about paths with stationary action.)

Now, in quantum mechanics we act as if the particle takes all possible paths and the classical path with minimal action is therefore only one path out of many.

Take note that the path integral formulation not only works for the probabilities of a particle which travels between two points. Instead, we can use the same method to calculate the probability that a system in a given configuration evolves into another configuration at a later point in time. In this case, we are talking about paths in configuration space.

The explicit evaluation of the path integral (Eq. 15.13) for concrete systems is notoriously difficult. For almost any system, clever approximation schemes are needed to get any information out of it. For this reason, we will not talk about any details here.

Instead, we will discuss a helpful visual way to understand the path integral which was popularized mainly by Richard Feynman. The main idea is that the action is just a number for any given path. Some paths require a lot of action (i.e., $S[q(t)]$ is large for these paths between A and B) while others require only a little action. The action appears as the argument of the complex exponential function: $e^{iS[q(t)]}$.

In general, since the action $S[q(t)]$ is an ordinary number this is a complex number with absolute value 1. In the complex plane, these numbers lie on the unit circle[13].

[13] Once more we can understand this using Euler's formula

$$\begin{aligned} z &= e^{i\phi} \\ &= \cos(\phi) + i\sin(\phi) \\ &= \text{Re}(z) + i\text{Im}(z) \end{aligned}$$

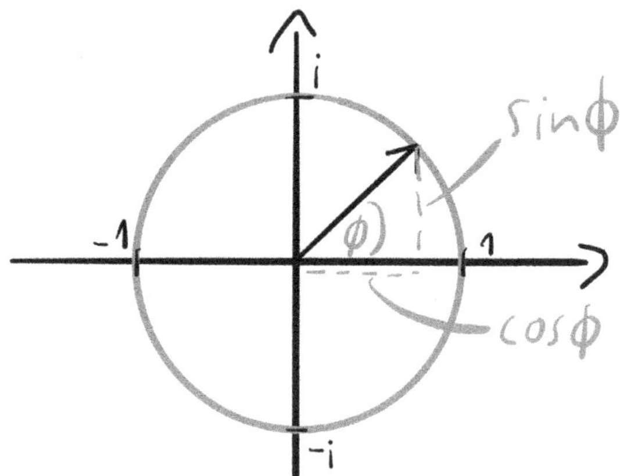

The contribution of each path to the total path integral is therefore simply a unit complex number. The total path integral is a sum over infinitely many unit complex numbers.

Therefore, it is useful to imagine that there is a little stopwatch attached to the particle as it travels a given path. At the beginning of each path the dial points directly to the right[14]. In the complex plane this corresponds to $z = 1 = e^{i0}$. Now, the clocks move as the particle travels. At the end of each path, the dial points to one specific number on the clock.

[14] On a real clock it would point to the 3.

For example, for one path the situation may look like this:

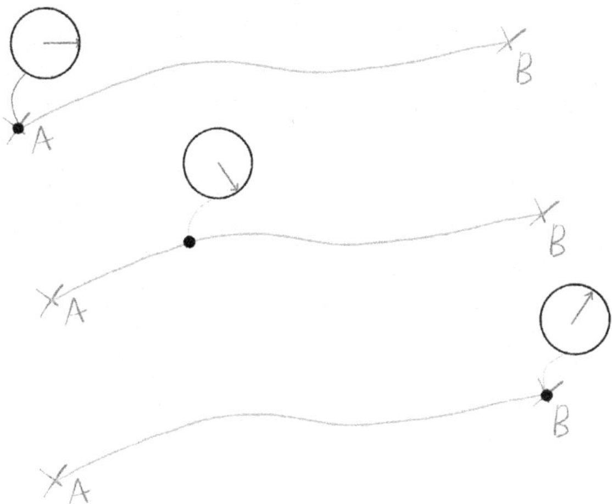

While for another path we have

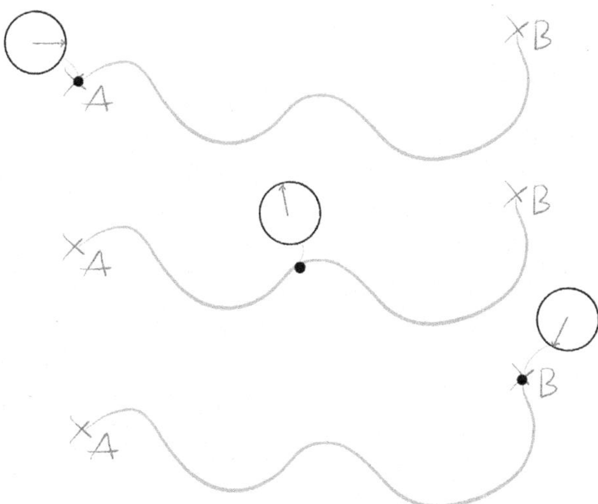

To calculate the path integral, we have to add the little arrows for each path like we would add vectors. The total value of the path integral is then the resulting arrow.

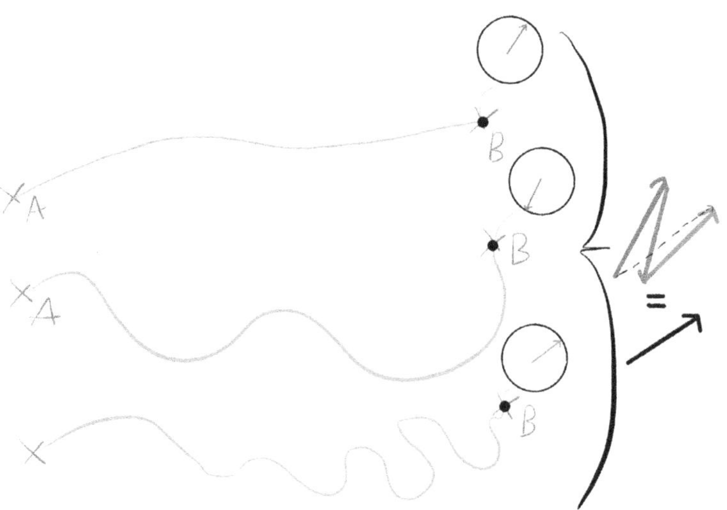

The black arrow here is what we get if we connect the starting point of the first gray arrow with the final point of the third gray arrow.

Since the resulting arrows do not necessarily all point in the same direction, the resulting arrow can be quite small. Here, we have three paths but to get the final result we have to include all possible paths, not just three. The final result depends on the points A and B. For some final point B most of the arrows cancel each other. The resulting arrow is tiny. In physical terms this means that the probability to find the particle at this location is tiny. For a different final point, lots of arrows point in the same direction and the resulting arrow is large. This means that it is quite probable that we find the particle at this location at the end of our time interval.

15.1.1 The Classical Path

What we have learned above is that the probability of a given final position depends crucially on the relative positions of the final arrows. If the arrows point mostly in the same direction, we get a long final arrow. In such a situation we say that we have **constructive interference**. If the final arrows point wildly in different directions, they mostly average out and we end up with a short total arrow. This is known as **destructive interference**.

This observation allows us to understand why the path of least action is so important in classical mechanics.

In our quantum context, the classical path is just one path out of many. But we can understand why the classical path is so important in classical mechanics by exploring the contributions of neighboring paths. For concreteness, let's consider two neighboring paths $q(t)$ and $q'(t)$ where the second path is a variation of the first one $q'(t) = q(t) + \eta(t)$, and where $\eta(t)$ denotes a small variation.

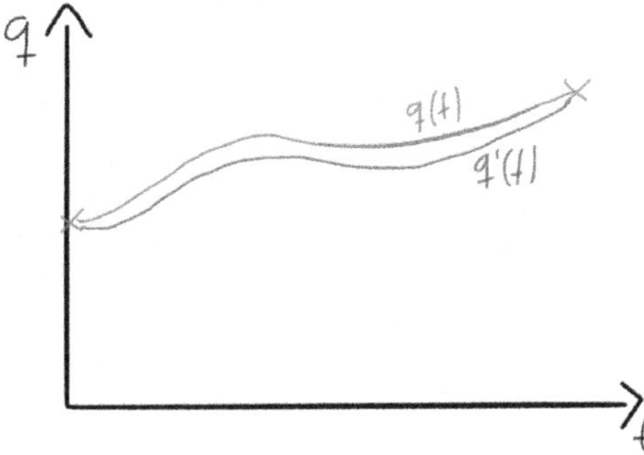

The first path contributes $e^{iS[q(t)]/\hbar}$ while the second path contributes $e^{iS'[q'(t)]/\hbar}$. We can expand the action of the second path around the first one

$$S[q'] = S[q+\eta] = S[q] + \int dt\, \eta(t) \frac{\delta S[q]}{\delta q(t)} + O(\eta^2).$$

Now, if $q(t)$ is the path with minimal action $q_{cl}(t)$, the first order variation vanishes[15]

[15] Reminder: the minimum of the action functional is characterized by a vanishing first order variation. We discussed this in Section 4.1.1.

$$S[q'] = S[q_{cl} + \eta] = S[q_{cl}] + \underbrace{\int dt\, \eta(t) \frac{\delta S[q]}{\delta q(t)}}_{=0 \text{ for } q(t)=q_{cl}(t)} + O(\eta^2)$$
$$= S[q_{cl}] + O(\eta^2)\,.$$

The physical implication for our path integral is that paths in the neighborhood of the path with minimal action $q_{cl}(t)$ yield arrows that point in approximately the same direction since $S[q'] \approx S[q_{cl}]$. In other words, paths around the classical path interfere constructively.

This is why the classical path is important. In contrast, for an arbitrary path far away from the classical path, the resulting arrows of neighboring paths vary wildly, and we get destructive interference.

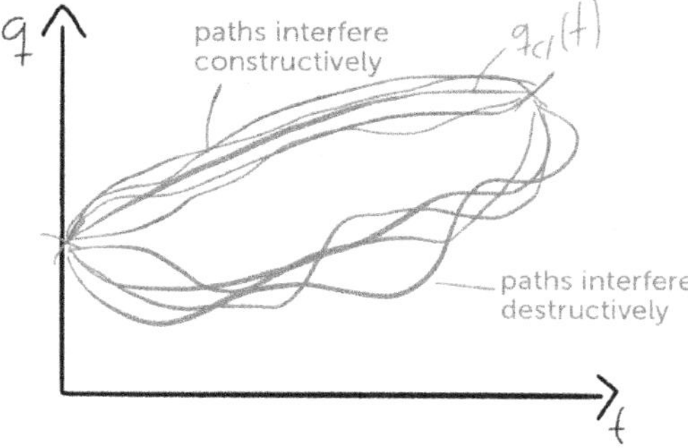

This effect becomes even more dominant if we consider systems in which the action of each path is much larger than Planck's constant $S[q(t)] \gg \hbar$.[16] Since the probability amplitude associated with each path is

[16] This is the case for macroscopic objects which we describe in classical mechanics.

$$\Psi = e^{iS[q(t)]/\hbar}, \tag{15.14}$$

we can see that for $S[q(t)] \gg \hbar$ even tiny differences in the action of neighboring paths lead to vastly different probability amplitudes.[17] And paths with vastly different probability amplitudes interfere destructively.

[17] In some sense, by dividing the term in the exponent by a, in comparison, tiny number $\hbar$ differences become especially significant. (Dividing by a tiny number is equal to multiplying by a huge number.)

Therefore, for systems for which $S[q(t)] \gg \hbar$, the only paths which interfere constructively are those surrounding the classical paths of least action. The limit $S[q(t)] \gg \hbar$ is known as the **classical limit** because for macroscopic objects, the energies involved are much higher than for elementary particles and therefore lead to much larger values for the action functional $S[q(t)]$.

15.2 The Path Integral in Quantum Field Theory

Completely analogously to how we are able to describe quantum mechanical systems using path integrals, we can also describe quantum fields using path integrals. In quantum field theory we primarily want to describe how fields evolve in time. Thus the most basic question we can ask is: given a field in a specific configuration $\phi_0(\vec{x})$ at t_0 what does it look like at a later point in time τ? In the quantum framework, we answer questions like this by calculating probability amplitudes like

$$\langle \phi(\vec{x}), \tau | \phi_0(\vec{x}), t_0 \rangle \,, \tag{15.15}$$

where $\phi_\tau(\vec{x})$ is a specific final configuration. In the path integral formulation of quantum field theory, we calculate the amplitude by evaluating a path integral

$$\boxed{\langle \phi(\vec{x}, \tau) | \phi(\vec{x}, 0) \rangle = \int_{\phi(0,\vec{x})=\phi_0(\vec{x})}^{\phi(\tau,\vec{x})=\phi_\tau(\vec{x})} \mathcal{D}\phi(t, \vec{x})\; e^{\frac{i}{\hbar} S[\phi(t,\vec{x})]} \,.} \tag{15.16}$$

This formula is completely analogous to the path integral formula that we derived for quantum mechanics in Eq. 15.13.[18] In words it tells us that to find the probability amplitude that a specific initial field configuration $\phi_0(\vec{x})$ evolves into a specific final configuration $\phi_\tau(\vec{x})$, we have to consider all sequences of field configurations that connect the two.

[18] For your convenience: Eq. 15.13 reads

$$\psi_{A\to B} = \int \mathcal{D}q(t) e^{iS[q(t)]/\hbar}$$

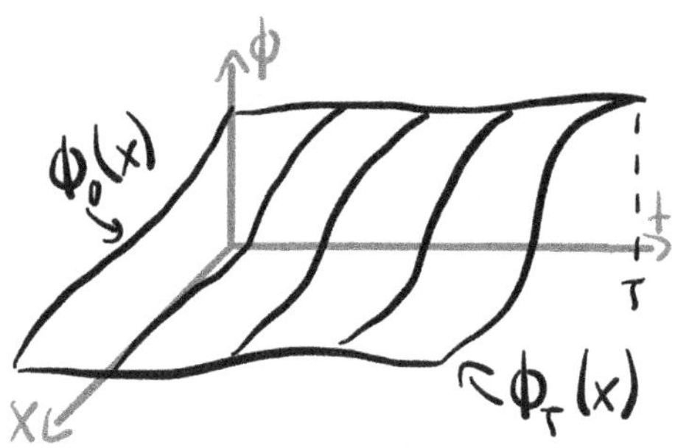

This is analogous to how we have to consider all paths that are possible between a fixed initial position A and a fixed final position B for a single particle in quantum mechanics. Moreover, we still consider paths but not in physical space but in configuration space.[19] Each point in configuration space corresponds to a specific configuration the field can be in.

[19] You can find a discussion of configuration space and how it relates to other mathematical arenas like path space and Hilbert space in

Jakob Schwichtenberg. *No-Nonsense Classical Mechanics : a student-friendly introduction.* No-Nonsense Books, Karlsruhe, Germany, 2019b. ISBN 9781096195382

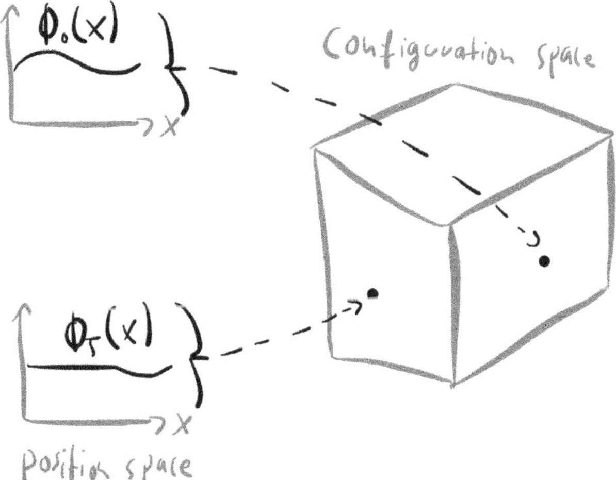

In Eq. 15.16, we integrate over all possible paths in configuration space that connect the configuration space points $\phi_0(\vec{x})$ and $\phi_T(\vec{x})$.

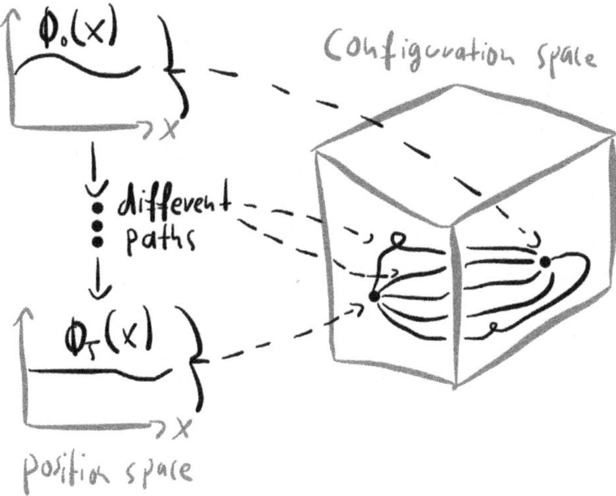

Moreover, as was the case in quantum mechanics, each possible path contributes a phase factor to the total path integral.

The path integral in quantum field theory is extremely difficult to evaluate. We can find much quicker answers to most questions by using the canonical formulation of quantum field theory that we considered so far in this book. However, one reason why the path integral is nevertheless useful is that it allows us to understand phenomena that cannot be described in the perturbative canonical approach. We will discuss these "non-perturbative" phenomena in the next chapter.

16

Non-Perturbative Phenomena

So far, we've calculated amplitudes by using a perturbative approach. Schematically, we have

$$\mathcal{O} = \sum_n c_n \lambda^n \,, \tag{16.1}$$

where λ is coupling constant. We've discovered that some of the terms that show up in this series are infinitely large if we evaluate them naively. Moreover, we've learned that we can solve this problem through regularization and renormalization of the model. Interestingly, the story of infinities in quantum field theory does not end here. Even if we handle all terms appropriately such that each of them yields a finite contribution, the series as a whole diverges

$$\sum_n^\infty c_n \lambda^n \sim \infty \,. \tag{16.2}$$

In particular, the series only converges up to order $n \sim \frac{1}{\lambda}$. For example, if $\lambda = 0.2$, terms beyond the fifth term ($n = \frac{1}{0.2} = 5$) in the series give increasingly large contributions.

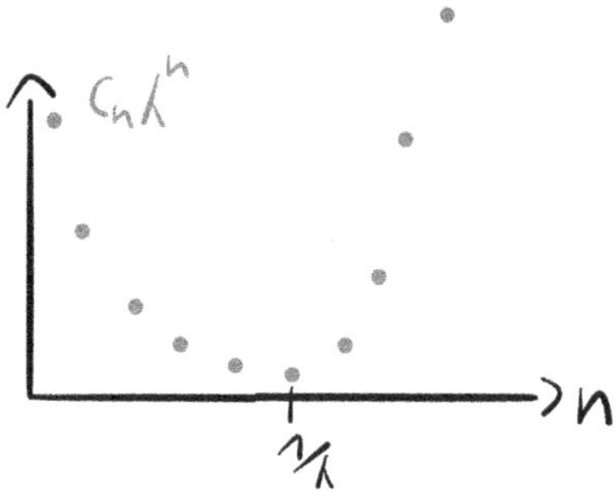

In mathematical terms, a series with this kind of behavior is known as an asymptotic series. The argument for why the perturbation series in quantum field theory is an asymptotic series is subtle and would lead us too far astray here.[1] Far more interesting for us is the physical reason why we find yet another infinity in quantum field theory.

[1] You can find a discussion at www.jakobschwichtenberg.com/divergence-perturbation-series-qft.

As usual, the occurrence of an infinitely large result indicates that we're doing something wrong. The problem in this case is that the perturbative approach is unable to describe all physical phenomena that can occur in quantum field theory. In particular, there are interesting field configurations that require a different approach. While we often get away with ignoring these configurations, we ultimately have to pay the price for this negligence in the form of yet another divergence.

One way to see that we are missing something in the perturbative approach is by calculating the Taylor series expansion of the function $e^{-\frac{1}{\lambda}}$ around $\lambda = 0$. The general formula yields

$$\begin{aligned} e^{-\frac{1}{\lambda}} &= e^{-\frac{1}{\lambda}}\Big|_{\lambda=0} + \left(\frac{d}{d\lambda}e^{-\frac{1}{\lambda}}\right)\lambda\Big|_{\lambda=0} + \frac{1}{2}\left(\frac{d^2}{d\lambda^2}e^{-\frac{1}{\lambda}}\right)\lambda^2\Big|_{\lambda=0} + \ldots \\ &= e^{-\frac{1}{\lambda}}\Big|_{\lambda=0} + \frac{e^{-\frac{1}{\lambda}}}{\lambda^2}\lambda\Big|_{\lambda=0} + \frac{1}{2}\frac{e^{-\frac{1}{\lambda}}(1-2\lambda)}{\lambda^4}\lambda^2\Big|_{\lambda=0} \\ &= 0+0+0+\ldots \end{aligned} \tag{16.3}$$

$\curvearrowright$ $e^{-1/0} = e^{-\infty} = 0$

Here we used that $e^{-\frac{1}{\lambda}}$ goes much faster to zero as the contribution from the polynomial in the denominator grows in the limit $\lambda \to 0$.[2] This implies that the Taylor series method fails for functions of the form $e^{-\frac{1}{\lambda}}$. If we trust the series expansion, we say that the function contributes nothing for small values of λ. But this is wrong since if we consider the function directly, we find that it's clearly non-zero for every $\lambda \neq 0$.

[2] This can also be shown in rigorous terms, but as usual we assume that a trustworthy mathematician confirms that each term in this Taylor series expansion yields zero.

This observation is important because each sequence of field configurations in the path integral contributes a factor $e^{\frac{i}{\hbar}S[\phi(t,\vec{x})]}$, where $S[\phi(t,\vec{x})]$ denotes the action.[3] Therefore, if there are sequences of field configurations that contribute something proportional to $\frac{1}{\lambda}$ to the action, their contribution is completely lost if we use a perturbative approach.

[3] Reminder: the path integral (Eq. 15.16) reads

$$\langle\phi(\vec{x},_T)|\phi(\vec{x},0)\rangle = \int_{\phi(0,\vec{x})=\phi_0(\vec{x})}^{\phi(T,\vec{x})=\phi_T(\vec{x})} \mathcal{D}\phi(t,\vec{x})\, e^{\frac{i}{\hbar}S[\phi(t,\vec{x})]}\,.$$

In general, we call phenomena that contribute a factor to the action with a vanishing Taylor expansion (e.g. $\sim -\frac{1}{\lambda}$ or $\sim \frac{1}{\lambda^2}$) **non-perturbative phenomena**. The question now is, of course, are there really non-perturbative phenomena? And if yes, how can we interpret them?

16.1 Instantons

In quantum theories, factors of the form $\sim \mathrm{e}^{-\frac{1}{\lambda}}$ are usually associated with tunneling phenomena. The easiest way to understand this is by considering a concrete example. Therefore, let's take another look at a self-interacting scalar field. To simplify the following discussion we now write the Lagrangian density a bit differently:

$$\begin{aligned}\mathcal{L} &= \frac{1}{2}\partial_\mu\phi\partial^\mu\phi - \frac{\lambda}{4}(v^2-\phi^2)^2 \\ &= \frac{1}{2}\partial_\mu\phi\partial^\mu\phi - \frac{\lambda}{4}\left(v^4+\phi^4-2v^2\phi^2\right) \\ &= \frac{1}{2}\partial_\mu\phi\partial^\mu\phi - \frac{\lambda}{4}v^4 - \frac{\lambda}{4}\phi^4 + \frac{\lambda}{2}v^2\phi^2 \,. \end{aligned} \tag{16.4}$$

This is almost exactly the ϕ^4-Lagrangian that we've already discussed several times. The only differences are that we are using slightly different symbols for the parameters and that there is an additional constant term $-\frac{\lambda}{4}v^4$. However, constant terms in the Lagrangian do not change the physics described by it and therefore, the model described by this Lagrangian is equivalent to the physics described by the ϕ^4 Lagrangian we considered previously (Eq. 6.26):

$$\mathcal{L} = \frac{1}{2}\partial_\mu\phi\partial^\mu\phi - \frac{1}{2}\mu^2\phi^2 + \frac{1}{4!}\tilde{\lambda}\phi^4 \,.$$

By comparing this Lagrangian with the one in Eq. 16.4, we see that $\mu^2 \equiv -\lambda v^2$. This implies $v^2 = -\frac{\mu^2}{\lambda}$. Moreover, we have

$$\begin{aligned} -\frac{\lambda}{4} &= \frac{\tilde{\lambda}}{4!} \\ &\quad \left(\frac{4}{4!} = \frac{1}{3!}\right) \\ \lambda &= -\frac{\tilde{\lambda}}{3!} \end{aligned} \tag{16.5}$$

and therefore $v^2 = \frac{6\mu^2}{\tilde{\lambda}}$. This explains why we introduce v in Eq. 16.4 since $\phi_{\min} = \pm v = \pm\sqrt{\frac{6\mu^2}{\tilde{\lambda}}}$ are exactly the minima of the potential that we found in Eq. 14.15.

As usual, we call the first term in Eq. 16.4 the kinetic term and the remaining terms the potential

$$V(\phi) \equiv \frac{\lambda}{4}(v^2 - \phi^2)^2 . \tag{16.6}$$

This potential has its minima at $\phi = \pm v$.

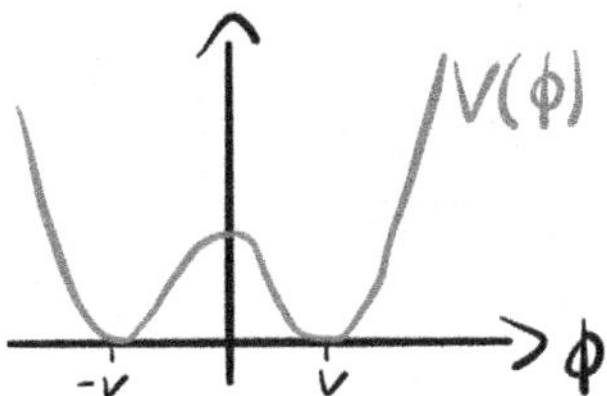

We've discussed in Chapter 14 that (classically) the scalar field's ground state corresponds to these two minimum potential energy configurations. Therefore, let's assume that the scalar field is in the ground state $\phi(\vec{x}) = -v$ everywhere at $t = -\infty$.

An interesting question is if it might be possible that the field undergoes a sequence of field configurations such that it is in the second ground state $\phi(\vec{x}) = +v$ everywhere at $t = +\infty$. In other words, is it possible that the field tunnels through the potential barrier that separates the two minima? This is in fact possible and exactly the kind of process that we miss if we use a perturbative approach.

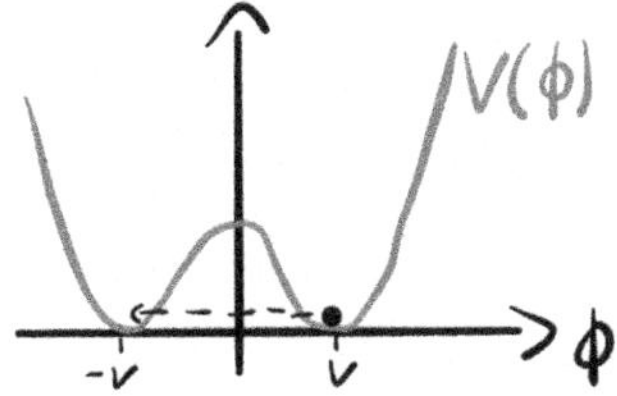

The standard method for analyzing these kinds of problems is based on the observation that tunneling processes correspond to classical paths in configuration space if we use an imaginary time variable. This surely seems like a wild idea, so let's discuss the individual puzzle pieces involved here:

▷ The first ingredient in our analysis is that we perform a **Wick rotation** $t \to -i\tau$. While this transformation might look quite suspicious, the motivation behind it from a physical point of view is that it flips the potential upside down.

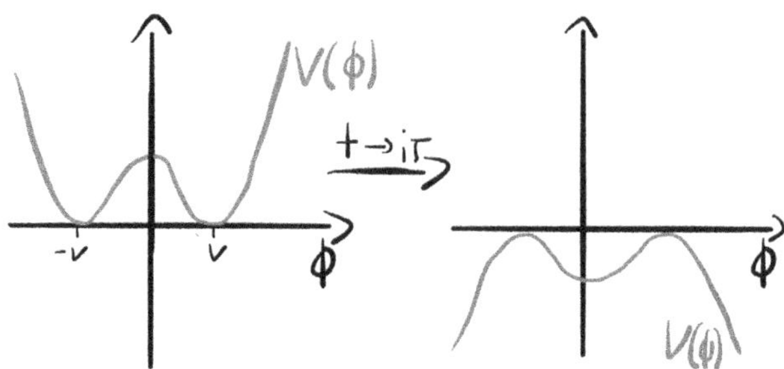

To understand why, consider the classical action

$$S[x]_{t_1}^{t_2} = \int_{t_1}^{t_2} \left[\frac{m}{2} \left(\frac{dx}{dt} \right)^2 - V(x) \right] dt.$$

If we perform a Wick rotation, we find

$$\begin{aligned} S[x] &= \int \left[\frac{m}{2} \left(\frac{dx}{dt} \right)^2 - V(x) \right] dt \\ & \quad \text{↷ } t \to -i\tau \\ &= \int \left[\frac{m}{2} \left(\frac{dx}{-id\tau} \right)^2 - V(x) \right] (-id\tau) \\ & \quad \text{↷ } i^2 = -1 \\ &= i \int \left[\frac{m}{2} \left(\frac{dx}{d\tau} \right)^2 + V(x) \right] (d\tau) \\ & \quad \text{↷ } S_E[x] \equiv -iS[x] \\ S_E[x] &= \int \left[\frac{m}{2} \left(\frac{dx}{d\tau} \right)^2 + V(x) \right] d\tau \,, \end{aligned} \tag{16.7}$$

where we call S_E the **Euclidean action**.[4] We can see that switching to an imaginary time variable has the effect of flipping the potential.

[4] This name is motivated by the observation that a Wick rotation implies for the spacetime distance between two events (Eq. 2.4):

$$\begin{aligned} \Delta s^2 &= c^2 \Delta t^2 - \Delta x^2 - \Delta y^2 - \Delta z^2 \\ &= c^2 (i\Delta\tau)^2 - \Delta x^2 - \Delta y^2 - \Delta z^2 \\ &= -c^2 \Delta\tau^2 - \Delta x^2 - \Delta y^2 - \Delta z^2 \\ \Delta \tilde{s}^2 &= c^2 \Delta\tau^2 + \Delta x^2 + \Delta y^2 + \Delta z^2 \,. \end{aligned}$$

In words, this means that a Wick rotation turns Minkowski space into Euclidean space.

▷ As soon as the potential is flipped, there is a classical path in configuration space that connects the two points which were the minima of the potential before the Wick rotation:

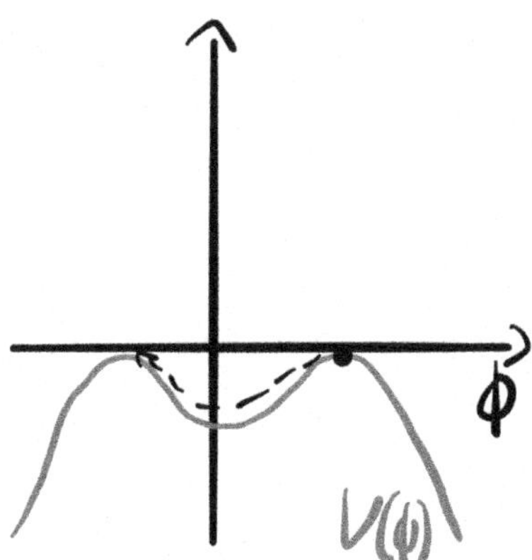

This suggests that we can find the sequence of field configurations that connects the two minima by solving the classical equation of motion that follows from the Wick rotated action.

With these ideas in mind, let's return to our self-interacting scalar field. After the Wick rotation, we are dealing with the Lagrangian density (Eq. 16.4 with $V \to -V$)

$$\mathcal{L} = \frac{1}{2}\partial_\mu\phi\partial^\mu\phi + V(\phi), \tag{16.8}$$

where $V(\phi)$ is defined in Eq. 16.6.[5] As usual, we calculate the equation of motion by plugging the Lagrangian density into the Euler-Lagrange equation (Eq. 4.25):

[5] For your convenience: Eq. 16.6 reads $V(\phi) \equiv \frac{\lambda}{4}(v^2 - \phi^2)^2$

$$\frac{\partial \mathcal{L}}{\partial \phi} = \partial_\mu \left(\frac{\partial \mathcal{L}}{\partial(\partial_\mu \phi)} \right)$$

$\quad \curvearrowright$ Eq. 16.8

$$\frac{\partial\left(\frac{1}{2}\partial_\mu\phi\partial^\mu\phi + V(\phi)\right)}{\partial\phi} = \partial_\mu \left(\frac{\partial\left(\frac{1}{2}\partial_\mu\phi\partial^\mu\phi + V(\phi)\right)}{\partial(\partial_\mu\phi)} \right)$$

$\quad \curvearrowright$

$$\frac{\partial V(\phi)}{\partial \phi} = \partial_\mu\partial^\mu\phi \tag{16.9}$$

For simplicity, we assume that ϕ has the same constant value everywhere. This implies that $\partial_i\phi = 0$ and therefore $\partial_\mu\partial^\mu\phi =$

$\partial_0^2\phi$. The equation of motion for this special case therefore reads

$$\frac{\partial V(\phi)}{\partial \phi} = \partial_0^2 \phi \,. \tag{16.10}$$

Instead of solving the second order equation in Eq. 16.10, it is sufficient to solve the first order equation

$$2V(\phi) = (\partial_0 \phi)^2 \,. \tag{16.11}$$

This follows because each solution of Eq. 16.11 is automatically a solution of Eq. 16.10 since

$$\begin{aligned}
2V(\phi) &= (\partial_0 \phi)^2 && \quad \text{$\frac{d}{d\tau}$} \\
2\frac{dV(\phi)}{d\tau} &= \frac{d}{d\tau}(\partial_0 \phi)^2 && \quad \text{chain rule} \\
2\frac{\partial V(\phi)}{\partial \phi}\partial_0 \phi &= 2\partial_0^2 \phi \partial_0 \phi && \quad \text{$\cancel{2\partial_0\phi}$} \\
\frac{\partial V(\phi)}{\partial \phi} &= \partial_0^2 \phi \,.
\end{aligned} \tag{16.12}$$

If we plug the explicit form of the potential into Eq. 16.11, we find

$$\begin{aligned}
2V(\phi) &= (\partial_0 \phi)^2 && \quad \text{Eq. 16.6} \\
2\Big(\frac{\lambda}{4}(v^2 - \phi^2)^2\Big) &= (\partial_0 \phi)^2 && \quad \sqrt{} \\
\sqrt{\frac{\lambda}{2}}(v^2 - \phi^2) &= \partial_0 \phi \,.
\end{aligned} \tag{16.13}$$

To solve this equation, we separate the variables

$$\begin{aligned}
\sqrt{\frac{\lambda}{2}}(v^2 - \phi^2) &= \frac{d\phi}{d\tau} \\
&\quad \curvearrowleft \\
\sqrt{\frac{\lambda}{2}} d\tau &= \frac{d\phi}{(v^2 - \phi^2)} \\
&\quad \curvearrowleft \int \\
\sqrt{\frac{\lambda}{2}} \int d\tau &= \int \frac{d\phi}{(v^2 - \phi^2)} \\
&\quad \curvearrowleft \\
\sqrt{\frac{\lambda}{2}} \tau &= \frac{\tanh^{-1}(\frac{\phi}{v})}{v} \\
&\quad \curvearrowleft \\
\tanh\left(v\sqrt{\frac{\lambda}{2}}\tau\right) &= \frac{\phi}{v} \\
&\quad \curvearrowleft \\
v \tanh\left(v\sqrt{\frac{\lambda}{2}}\tau\right) &= \phi . \qquad (16.14)
\end{aligned}$$

This solution describes a sequence of field configurations that starts at $\tau = -\infty$ with $\phi(-\infty) = -v$ and ends at $\tau = \infty$ with $\phi(-\infty) = v$:

$$\begin{aligned}
\phi(-\infty) &= v \tanh\left(v\sqrt{\frac{\lambda}{2}}(-\infty)\right) \\
&\quad \curvearrowleft \ \tanh(-\infty) = -1 \\
&= -v \quad \checkmark \\
\phi(\infty) &= v \tanh\left(v\sqrt{\frac{\lambda}{2}}(\infty)\right) \\
&\quad \curvearrowleft \ \tanh(\infty) = 1 \\
&= v \quad \checkmark \qquad (16.15)
\end{aligned}$$

Thus we can conclude that tunneling processes from one ground state to the other can happen. We call the sequence of field configurations described by Eq. 16.14 an instanton solution or simply an **instanton**.

This name is motivated by the observation that the energy associated with the solution is localized in time but not in space. During a short period in time, the energy becomes non-zero as the field undergoes a transition from $-v$ to v. At $\tau = -\infty$ and $\tau = \infty$ the energy of the field is zero since it is in its ground state. Moreover, since the transition happens everywhere equally, we are dealing with a lump of energy that is localized in time but not in space.[6]

[6] Take note that in an instanton process the field tunnels through the potential barrier that separates different ground states. Nevertheless, the field energy becomes non-zero during the process which can be calculated by considering the field energy explicitly. If a field carries sufficient energy it can also move *across* the potential barrier instead of right through it. Such ground state to ground state transitions are known as sphaleron processes.

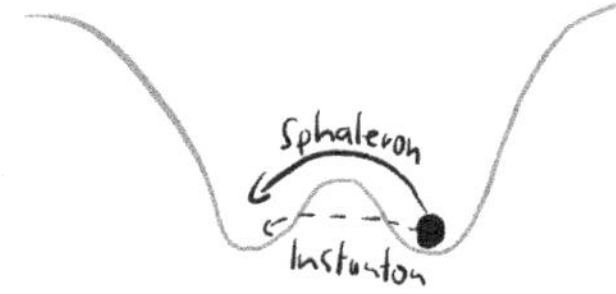

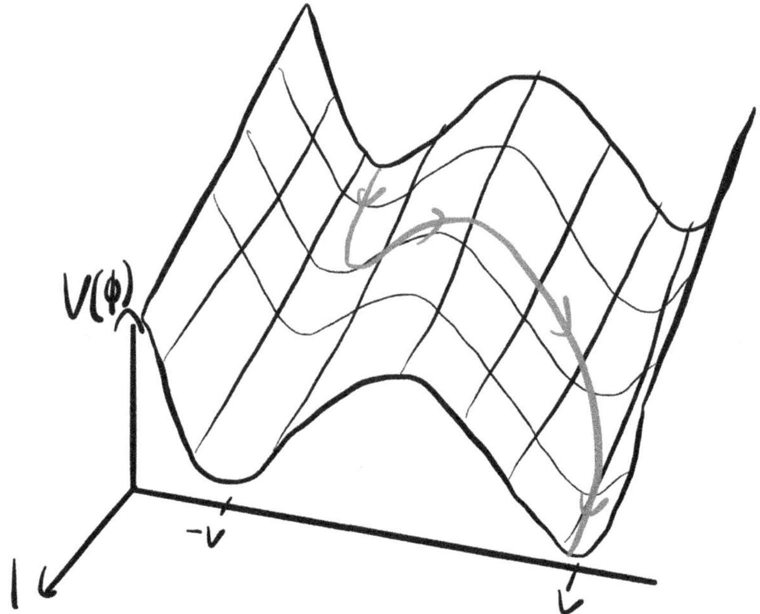

For the solution given in Eq. 16.14 the instanton is localized around $t = 0$. However, this is not necessarily always the case. This follows because there can be a non-zero integration constant in the third line of Eq. 16.14. This constant determines the location of the instanton in time, i.e. when exactly the transition from $-v$ to v happens.

As a final step, let's check that this is indeed a non-perturbative phenomenon. To that end, we calculate the contribution of the sequence of field configurations described by Eq. 16.14 to the total action. Since we assume that ϕ has the same constant value everywhere, the spatial part of the action integral will simply yield the total spatial volume of our system, Ω.[7] The only non-

[7] We use here the symbol Ω for the spatial volume to avoid confusion with the potential $V(\phi)$.

trivial part is therefore the $d\tau$ integration

$$S_E[\phi] = \int d^4x\, \mathcal{L}$$

$$= \int d^4x \left(\frac{1}{2}\partial_\mu\phi\partial^\mu\phi + V(\phi)\right) \qquad \text{Eq. 16.8}$$

$$= \int d^4x \left(\frac{1}{2}(\partial_0\phi)^2 + V(\phi)\right) \qquad \phi = \phi(t)$$

$$= \Omega \int d\tau \left(\frac{1}{2}(\partial_0\phi)^2 + V(\phi)\right) \qquad \phi = \phi(t)$$

$$= \Omega \int d\tau \left(\frac{1}{2}(\partial_0\phi)^2 + \frac{1}{2}(\partial_0\phi)^2\right) \qquad \text{Eq. 16.11}$$

$$= \Omega \int d\tau\, (\partial_0\phi)^2$$

$$= \Omega \int d\tau \left(\frac{d\phi}{d\tau}\right)^2 \qquad \partial_0 = \frac{d}{d\tau}$$

$$= \Omega \int d\phi\, \frac{d\phi}{d\tau} \qquad \cancel{d\tau}$$

$$= \Omega \int d\phi\, \sqrt{2V(\phi)} \qquad 2V(\phi) = (\partial_0\phi)^2,\ \text{Eq. 16.11}$$

$$= \Omega \int d\phi\, \sqrt{2\frac{\lambda}{4}(v^2-\phi^2)^2} \qquad \text{Eq. 16.6}$$

$$= \Omega \int d\phi\, \sqrt{\frac{\lambda}{2}}(v^2-\phi^2)$$

$$= \Omega\sqrt{\frac{\lambda}{2}}\left(v^2\phi - \frac{\phi^3}{3}\right)\Bigg|_{\phi=-v}^{\phi=v} \qquad \int d\phi$$

$$= \Omega\sqrt{\frac{\lambda}{2}}\left(v^2\big(v-(-v)\big) - \frac{(v^3-(-v)^3)}{3}\right)$$

$$= \Omega\sqrt{\frac{\lambda}{2}}\left(2v^3 - \frac{2v^3}{3}\right)$$

$$= \Omega\sqrt{\frac{\lambda}{2}\frac{4}{3}v^3}$$

$$= \frac{4}{3}\Omega\sqrt{\frac{\lambda}{2}}\left(\sqrt{\frac{6\mu^2}{\lambda}}\right)^3 \qquad v \equiv \sqrt{\frac{6\mu^2}{\lambda}}$$

$$= 8\sqrt{3}\Omega\frac{\mu^3}{\lambda}. \qquad (16.16)$$

We can see here that the contribution to the action is in fact proportional to $\frac{1}{\lambda}$. This, in turn, implies that the corresponding contribution to the path integral is $\sim e^{\frac{1}{\lambda}}$ and is therefore invisible if we use a perturbative approach. In other words, the transition from $-v$ to v is indeed a non-perturbative phenomenon.

In summary, we've learned in this chapter that there are phenomena that we cannot describe using the methods discussed in Part II. These phenomena are non-perturbative since their contribution is invisible in a perturbative approach. This follows because the Taylor series method fails for functions of the form $\sim e^{\frac{1}{\lambda}}$. Moreover, we've discussed an explicit example of a non-perturbative phenomenon: the tunnelling of a scalar field from one ground state configuration to another. While the contributions of such phenomena to observables are often quite small, they are still an essential part of quantum field theory.[8]

[8] A famous example that demonstrates why non-perturbative phenomena are important is the strong CP problem. You can find a discussion at `http://jakobschwichtenberg.com/demystifying-the-qcd-vacuum-part-1/`

17

Effective Field Models and the Origin of Simplicity

The Lagrangians that we use to describe elementary fields are astonishingly simple. For example, the Lagrangian for a single scalar field reads (Eq. 5.2)

$$\mathcal{L} = \frac{1}{2}(\partial_\mu \phi \partial^\mu \phi - m^2\phi^2)\,. \tag{17.1}$$

In principle, there are infinitely many additional terms that we could add to it:

$$\tilde{\mathcal{L}} = \frac{1}{2}(\partial_\mu \phi \partial^\mu \phi - m^2\phi^2) + a\phi^3 + b\phi^4 + c\phi^5 + d\phi^6 + \dots\,. \tag{17.2}$$

But for some reason, the simplest non-trivial terms for each type of field are already sufficient.

Nowadays, most theoretical physicists are convinced that at higher energy scales (= smaller length scales) the correct Lagrangian contains lots of additional terms.[1] However, these higher-order terms become less and less important as we zoom out. Therefore, no matter how complicated and ugly the Lagrangian is at high energy scales, at the low energy scales that we can probe using present-day technology, we are left with simple Lagrangians.[2]

[1] When two particles collide at higher energies, they sometimes create heavier particles. As mentioned before, in this sense, colliders are essentially large microscopes which allow us to look deeper. The higher the energy of the colliding particles, the deeper we can look.

[2] The following figure should not be understood as a subtle promotion of string theory.

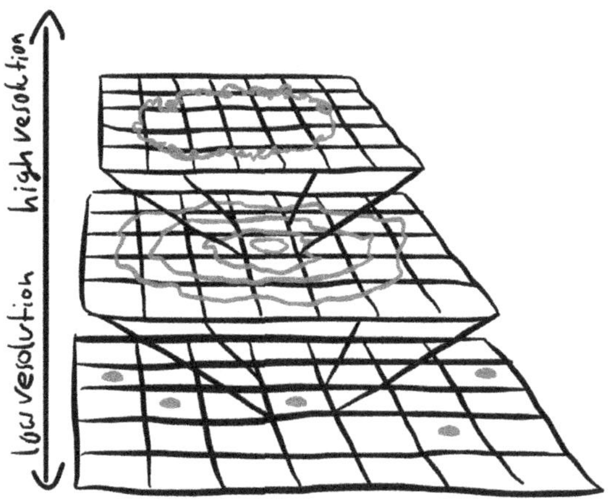

So the reason that simple and beautiful Lagrangians work so well is not that Nature prefers simplicity for some magical reason, but instead, that if we look at something from a distance it usually appears simpler.

To make this a bit more concrete, we consider a complex scalar field ψ that interacts with a real scalar field ϕ which has an incredibly large mass parameter m_ϕ compared to m_ψ. As in Section 12.1, the Lagrangian density reads[3]

$$\mathcal{L} = \partial^\mu \bar{\psi} \partial_\mu \psi - m_\psi^2 \bar{\psi}\psi - g\bar{\psi}\psi\phi + \frac{1}{2}(\partial_\mu \phi)^2 - \frac{m_\phi^2}{2}\phi^2 \,. \qquad (17.3)$$

The key idea is that as long as we consider processes at energy scales far below m_ϕ, we can safely ignore the effects of the real scalar field because there is simply not enough energy in the system to disturb it.[4] To use this idea mathematically, we calculate the equation of motion for the heavy field ϕ.

As usual, we do this by plugging the Lagrangian density into the Euler-Lagrange equation (Eq. 4.25):[5]

[3] For simplicity, we again use the notation $\psi^\dagger = \bar{\psi}$.

[4] Recall that roughly, the mass parameter associated with a field describes a minimum energy threshold that is necessary to excite a given field.

[5] The following discussion is very sketchy. Everything stated here can be shown in much more rigorous terms and the study of effective field models is a beautiful and important subfield in itself. Some great resources are listed below.

$$
\begin{aligned}
0 &= \frac{\partial \mathcal{L}}{\partial \phi} - \partial_\mu \left(\frac{\partial \mathcal{L}}{\partial(\partial_\mu \phi)} \right) \\
&\quad \text{Eq. 17.3} \\
&= -m_\phi^2 \phi - g\bar{\psi}\psi - \partial_\mu \partial^\mu \phi \\
-g\bar{\psi}\psi &= (m_\phi^2 + \partial_\mu \partial^\mu)\phi \,. \qquad (17.4)
\end{aligned}
$$

This equation is formally solved by

$$
\phi = -g \frac{1}{m_\phi^2 + \partial_\mu \partial^\mu} \bar{\psi}\psi \qquad (17.5)
$$

as we can check

$$
\begin{aligned}
-g\bar{\psi}\psi &= (m_\phi^2 + \partial_\mu \partial^\mu)\phi \\
&\quad \text{Eq. 17.5} \\
&= (m_\phi^2 + \partial_\mu \partial^\mu) \left(-g \frac{1}{m_\phi^2 + \partial_\mu \partial^\mu} \bar{\psi}\psi \right) \\
&\quad \cancel{(m_\phi^2 + \partial_\mu \partial^\mu)} \\
&= -g\bar{\psi}\psi \quad \checkmark \qquad (17.6)
\end{aligned}
$$

For small energies, the kinetic term $(\partial_\mu \partial^\mu)$ is much smaller than the mass term (m_ϕ^2) of this expression and we can use the formula

$$
\frac{1}{a+b} = \frac{1}{a(1+\frac{b}{a})} = \frac{1}{a} \frac{1}{1+\frac{b}{a}} \approx \frac{1}{a} \left(1 - \frac{b}{a} + \left(\frac{b}{a} \right)^2 + \ldots \right), \qquad (17.7)
$$

which is valid for $a \gg b$. For our formal solution this implies

$$
\begin{aligned}
\phi &= -g \frac{1}{m_\phi^2 + \partial_\mu \partial^\mu} \bar{\psi}\psi \\
&\approx -g \left(\frac{1}{m_\phi^2} - \frac{1}{m_\phi^2} \frac{\partial_\mu \partial^\mu}{m_\phi^2} + \ldots \right) \bar{\psi}\psi \\
&= -g \left(\frac{1}{m_\phi^2} - \frac{\partial_\mu \partial^\mu}{m_\phi^4} + \ldots \right) \bar{\psi}\psi \,. \qquad (17.8)
\end{aligned}
$$

We can use this formula to remove the field ϕ from the Lagrangian (Eq. 17.3):

$$
\mathcal{L}_{\text{eff}} = \partial^\mu \bar{\psi} \partial_\mu \psi - m_\psi^2 \bar{\psi}\psi - g\bar{\psi}\psi \left(-g \left(\frac{1}{m_\phi^2} - \frac{\partial_\mu \partial^\mu}{m_\phi^4} + \ldots \right) \bar{\psi}\psi \right) + \ldots \qquad (17.9)
$$

where the dots denote the mass term and kinetic term of the ϕ field that we no longer care about. What we are left with here, is an **effective Lagrangian density** that only depends on the light field ψ. The only remaining trace of the heavy field ϕ are additional terms which, however, are suppressed by inverse powers of m_ϕ. In particular, in the limit $m_\phi \to \infty$, we end up with the much simpler Lagrangian

$$\mathcal{L}_{\text{eff}} = \partial^\mu \bar{\psi} \partial_\mu \psi - m_\psi^2 \bar{\psi} \psi \,. \tag{17.10}$$

We say that the Lagrangian in Eq. 17.10 describes an effective model that remains valid as long as we consider processes at scales far below m_ϕ. If we consider processes at scales close to m_ϕ we must include at least some of the additional terms given in Eq. 17.9. In other words, m_ϕ is a physical cutoff scale for the effective model above which it must be replaced by a more complete description that involves the additional field ϕ.

17.1 Dimensional Analysis

In the discussion above we assumed that new physical effects that occur above the cutoff scale can be described by additional heavy particles. Moreover, we assumed that it's again sufficient to only include the simplest non-trivial terms to describe these heavy particles. But it's also plausible that the physics above some cutoff scale is much weirder. Maybe our framework is simply no longer feasible above the cutoff scale. For example, we can imagine that infinitely many (possibly much more complicated) higher-order terms in the Lagrangian would be necessary to incorporate all the effects.

An interesting observation is that even if this is the case, we can understand why the simple Lagrangians that we use at low energies work so well. This follows from dimensional arguments. In the following, we discuss how this comes about.

The action is defined as the spacetime integral over the Lagrangian density

$$S = \int d^4x\, \mathcal{L}\,. \tag{17.11}$$

What can we say about the units of the action? In the path integral formulation, the action appears as the argument of the exponential function $\sim e^{iS}$. The argument of the exponential function has to be dimensionless. This follows from the definition of the exponential function in terms of a series:

$$e^{iS} = 1 + iS + \frac{(iS)^2}{2} + \ldots\,. \tag{17.12}$$

The first term in this series has no dimension. Therefore all other terms must be dimensionless too since otherwise we would be adding apples to oranges. Therefore, we can conclude that (in natural units) the action is dimensionless.[6]

By looking at Eq. 17.11, we can then conclude that the Lagrangian density has units L^{-4}, where L is the unit we measure lengths in (e.g. meters). In natural units, lengths are measured in inverse powers of energy:[7]

$$[x_\mu] = E^{-1}\,. \tag{17.13}$$

Since dx means "a little bit of x", it also has units E^{-1} and d^4x has units E^{-4}. Therefore,

$$[\mathcal{L}] = E^4 \tag{17.14}$$

such that $[S] = 1$:

$$[S] = \int [d^4x]\,[\mathcal{L}] = E^{-4}E^4 = 1 \quad \checkmark \tag{17.15}$$

This allows us to deduce the dimensions of a field. For example, let's have a look at the Lagrangian for a free scalar field (Eq. 5.2)

$$\mathcal{L} = \frac{1}{2}(\partial_\mu\phi\partial^\mu\phi - m^2\phi^2)\,. \tag{17.16}$$

The derivative operator $\partial_\mu = \frac{\partial}{\partial x^\mu}$ has the same units as $\frac{1}{x^\mu}$ since ∂x^μ also means "a little bit of x^μ" :

$$[\partial_\mu] = \frac{\partial}{[\partial x_\mu]} \overset{17.13}{=} \frac{1}{E^{-1}} = E. \tag{17.17}$$

[6] In non-natural units, we have factors of the form $\sim e^{iS/\hbar}$. This implies that S has the same units as the Planck constant $\hbar$.

[7] The notation [quantity] is used to denote the units of the quantity.

In natural units we have by definition $c = \hbar = 1$. To derive the units of a quantity in natural units, we start by observing that

$$[c] = \frac{[\text{length}]}{[\text{time}]} \equiv \frac{[L]}{[T]}$$

implies

$$[L] = [T].$$

Moreover, the (reduced) Planck constant $\hbar$ has units

$$[\hbar] = \frac{[M][L]^2}{[T]}$$

which, using $[L] = [T]$, yields

$$[\hbar] = [M][L]\,.$$

Since by definition $\hbar = 1$ this implies

$$[L] = \frac{1}{[M]}\,.$$

The final step is to use the energy momentum relation $E^2 = \vec{p}^2 + m^2c^4$ (Eq. 2.43) to deduce

$$[E] = [M] = [\vec{p}]\,.$$

Therefore, lengths are measured in inverse powers of energy

$$[L] = \frac{1}{[E]}\,.$$

This allows us to deduce the dimension of ϕ:

$$
\begin{aligned}
[\mathcal{L}] &= ([\partial_\mu][\phi][\partial^\mu][\phi] + \dots \\
&\quad \text{Eq. 17.14, Eq. 17.17} \\
\mathrm{E}^4 &= \mathrm{E}[\phi][\phi]\mathrm{E} \\
\mathrm{E}^2 &= [\phi][\phi] \\
\mathrm{E} &= [\phi] \,.
\end{aligned}
\tag{17.18}
$$

This also makes sense if we look at the second term in the Lagrangian, $m^2\phi^2$, and use that the dimension of a mass parameter m in natural units is E.[8] The result in Eq. 17.18 is extremely useful. For example, let's imagine that we want to add higher order terms to the Lagrangian density:[9]

[8] As mentioned above, this follows from the relativistic energy momentum relation $E^2 = \vec{p}^2 + m^2c^4$ (Eq. 2.43) which, in natural units ($c = \hbar = 1$), yields

$$[E] = [M] = [\vec{p}] \,.$$

[9] Take note that by using the same arguments we can deduce that the constant λ in front of a ϕ^4 term is dimensionless and a constant in front of a ϕ^3 term has units E.

$$\mathcal{L} = \frac{1}{2}(\partial_\mu\phi\partial^\mu\phi - m^2\phi^2) + c_1\phi^5 + c_2\phi^6 + c_3\phi^7 + \dots \tag{17.19}$$

Since all terms must have the same dimensions, we can immediately conclude that the constants c_1, c_2, c_2, must be measured in inverse powers of E:

$$
\begin{aligned}
[\mathcal{L}] &= \dots + [c_1][\phi]^5 + [c_2][\phi]^6 + [c_3][\phi]^7 + \dots \\
&\quad \text{Eq. 17.14, Eq. 17.18} \\
\mathrm{E}^4 &= \dots + [c_1]\mathrm{E}^5 + [c_2]\mathrm{E}^6 + [c_3]\mathrm{E}^7 + \dots \,.
\end{aligned}
\tag{17.20}
$$

We can conclude:

$$
\begin{aligned}
[c_1] &= \mathrm{E}^{-1} \\
[c_2] &= \mathrm{E}^{-2} \\
[c_3] &= \mathrm{E}^{-3} \,.
\end{aligned}
\tag{17.21}
$$

That's how far we can get using dimensional analysis alone. But if we additionally use some physical understanding, we can go further. What we learn in Eq. 17.21 is that there must be at least one additional constant with dimension E that is responsible for the dimensions of the coefficients. This constant must be somehow related to these higher order terms and it is thus very tempting to identify it with a cutoff scale Λ. The cutoff scale Λ encodes the boundary above which new physical phenomena can no longer be ignored and from which these higher order terms originate.[10] We therefore write

[10] We learned above that if there is a cuttoff scale (which in this case is denoted by m_Φ), we find that effects from "higher scale physics" are suppressed by inverse powers of

$$m_\Phi$$

at lower scales (Eq. 17.9).

$$c_1 = \frac{\lambda_1}{\Lambda}$$
$$c_2 = \frac{\lambda_2}{\Lambda^2}$$
$$c_3 = \frac{\lambda_3}{\Lambda^3}, \tag{17.22}$$

where $\lambda_1, \lambda_2, \lambda_3$ are dimensionless. The Lagrangian then reads

$$\mathcal{L} = \frac{1}{2}(\partial_\mu\phi\partial^\mu\phi - m^2\phi^2) + c_1\phi^5 + c_2\phi^6 + c_3\phi^7 + \dots$$

$\rightarrow$ Eq. 17.22

$$= \frac{1}{2}(\partial_\mu\phi\partial^\mu\phi - m^2\phi^2) + \frac{\lambda_1}{\Lambda}\phi^5 + \frac{\lambda_2}{\Lambda^2}\phi^6 + \frac{\lambda_3}{\Lambda^3}\phi^7 + \dots \tag{17.23}$$

We can see here that higher order terms are suppressed by inverse powers of the cutoff scale Λ. If we assume that Λ is some large number, we can understand why at low energies only the simplest terms in the Lagrangian play a role.

In summary, using dimensional analysis we discovered that higher order terms are necessarily related to at least one new energy scale. The discussion in the previous section motivated us to interpret the new energy scale as a cutoff scale. Thus, higher order terms are strongly suppressed and we can understand why simple Lagrangians work so well.

A downside of what we've just discovered is that the implications of high-scale physics are extremely hidden at lower energy scales. The effects of all higher order terms that could hint towards particular new phenomena are strongly suppressed by inverse powers of the cutoff scale. Thus, on the one hand it's certainly great that high energy phenomena decouple from phenomena at lower energies because this allows us to describe Nature in relatively simple terms. But on the other hand, it implies that we must come up with much more powerful methods to accelerate particles before we can hope to see first glimpses of phenomena that happen beyond the cutoff scale.

For example, a popular contender for a physical cutoff scale is the Planck scale $m_P \sim 10^{18}$ GeV. In contrast, the most powerful collider that we presently have, the LHC, is only able to probe processes up to $\sim 10^4$ GeV. Moreover, using present-day technology, a collider that could probe particle collisions at $\sim 10^{18}$ GeV would need to span the entire solar system. To end this discussion on a positive note, take note that the authors of [Chen and Noble, 1997] argue that this is "*not an inconceivable task for an advanced technological society.*"

17.2 The Origin of "Fundamental" Lagrangians

In Chapter 5, we assumed that someone hands us the Klein-Gordon Lagrangian, the Dirac Lagrangian and the Proca Lagrangian and then talked about the corresponding equations of motion and their solutions. By using what we've learned in the previous section, we can understand a bit better how we end up with these Lagrangians.

In general, writing down a Lagrangian description of a physical model is a two step process:

▷ First of all, we need to clarify which mathematical objects we should use.

▷ Afterwards, we need to answer the question: Which terms involving these objects do we write into the Lagrangian?

The most powerful tools that we can use to answer these questions are symmetries. For example, we know that our models should respect the laws of special relativity. Jean-Marc Levy-Leblond once summarized this nicely as follows[11]:

[11] Jean-Marc Levy-Leblond. One more derivation of the Lorentz transformation. *American Journal of Physics*, 44(3):271–277, 1976. DOI: 10.1119/1.10490

"We believe that special relativity at the present time stands as a universal theory describing the structure of a common space-time arena in which all fundamental processes take place. All the laws of physics are constrained by special relativity acting as a sort of 'super law'."

We've discussed in Section 2.8 that this implies that our fundamental models should be unchanged by Poincaré transformations (rotations, boosts and translations). Thus the first step is to identify objects with well-defined transformation behavior under Poincaré transformations.

This is possible through a branch of mathematics known as group theory. A cornerstone of group theory is representation theory which allows us to deduce which kinds of objects a given set of symmetries can act on. Applying representation theory to the Poincaré group allows us to derive that the simplest objects Poincaré transformations can act on are: scalars, spinors and four-vectors.[12] This is the answer to the first problem outlined above.

[12] You can learn more about how this works in detail in my book

Jakob Schwichtenberg. *Physics from Symmetry*. Springer, Cham, Switzerland, 2018b. ISBN 978-3319666303

The second step is that we need to determine which terms involving scalars, spinors and vectors we can write into a Lagrangian. Again, the most important restriction is that our model should respect the laws of special relativity. For the Lagrangian this implies that we are only allowed to write down terms that are invariant under Poincaré transformations. If the Lagrangian is unchanged by a given set of transformations, the model described by it respects the corresponding symmetries.

However, there are still infinitely many terms that fulfill this requirement. This is where what we learned in the previous section becomes important. Usually, we only include the simplest possible, nontrivial terms in the Lagrangian. In summary:

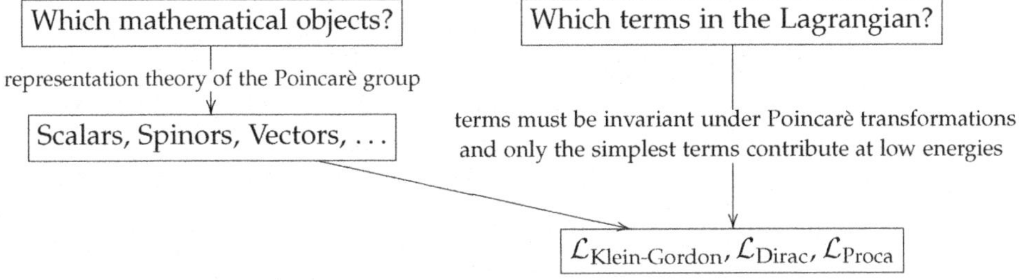

To understand a bit better how this works, let's consider a single real scalar field ϕ. A scalar field is left unchanged by all transformations and thus we can write down all kinds of terms into

the Lagrangian:

$$\mathcal{L}(\phi, \dot{\phi}, t) = a\phi + b\phi^2 + c\phi^3 + \ldots \tag{17.24}$$

What about derivatives? A term like $\partial_\mu \phi$ is certainly not invariant.[13]

[13] Whenever an object remains unchanged by a transformation, we say it's invariant. The derivative operator $\frac{\partial}{\partial x_\mu}$, just as x_μ itself, is changed by rotations.

For example, under a rotation it becomes (Eq. 3.22)

$$\partial_\mu \phi \to R^{(vx)}_{\mu\nu} \partial^\nu \phi \,. \tag{17.25}$$

A term that remains unchanged, however, is the scalar product of such a term with itself $\partial_\mu \phi \partial^\mu \phi$.[14] Therefore, we can also include additional terms that include derivatives of the scalar field into the Lagrangian:

[14] We checked this explicitly in Eq. 2.57. In contrast, a term like $\partial_\mu \phi \partial_\nu \phi$ would not be invariant.

$$\mathcal{L}(\phi, \dot{\phi}, t) = a\phi + b\phi^2 + c\phi^3 + d\partial_\mu \phi \partial^\mu \phi + e(\partial_\mu \phi \partial^\mu \phi)^2 + \ldots \tag{17.26}$$

This may not seem particularly helpful. While we were able to exclude a few terms from the Lagrangian, there are still infinitely many that are allowed. So symmetries are not enough and we need a second guiding principle. However, as we've discussed in the previous section, higher order terms are suppressed by inverse powers of an energy scale and can therefore usually be neglected if we only want to describe Nature at low energy scales.

The final question we therefore need to answer is: which terms are the simplest non-trivial terms? The simplest term $a\phi$ has no influence on the dynamics since it only yields a constant if we plug it into the Euler-Lagrange equation:

$$\begin{aligned} &\frac{\partial \mathcal{L}}{\partial \phi} - \partial_\mu \left(\frac{\partial \mathcal{L}}{\partial(\partial_\mu \phi)} \right) \\ &= \frac{\partial(a\phi)}{\partial \phi} - \partial_\mu \left(\frac{\partial(a\phi)}{\partial(\partial_\mu \phi)} \right) && \text{↷ } \mathcal{L} = a\phi \\ &= a && \text{↷ } \frac{\partial(\phi)}{\partial \phi} = 1, \ \frac{\partial \phi}{\partial(\partial_\mu \phi)} = 0 \end{aligned} \tag{17.27}$$

A constant has no real effect in the equations of motions and therefore, the term $a\phi$ can be neglected from the Lagrangian. The terms quadratic in ϕ and its derivative $\partial_\mu\phi$, however, have something more exciting to offer. So let's assume that our Lagrangian density reads

$$\mathcal{L} = b\phi^2 + d\partial_\mu\phi\partial^\mu\phi\,, \tag{17.28}$$

and that we can ignore all higher order terms. If we plug this Lagrangian into the Euler-Lagrange equation, we find

$$\begin{aligned} 0 &= \frac{\partial\mathcal{L}}{\partial\phi} - \partial_\mu\left(\frac{\partial\mathcal{L}}{\partial(\partial_\mu\phi)}\right) \\ &= \frac{\partial(b\phi^2 + d\partial_\mu\phi\partial^\mu\phi)}{\partial\phi} - \partial_\mu\left(\frac{\partial(b\phi^2 + d\partial_\mu\phi\partial^\mu\phi)}{\partial(\partial_\mu\phi)}\right) \\ &= 2b\phi - d\partial_\mu\phi\partial^\mu\phi\,. \end{aligned} \tag{17.29}$$

↷ Eq. 17.28

↷

A final important observation is that we are always free to multiply the Lagrangian by a constant $\mathcal{L} \to \text{const.} \times \mathcal{L}$ since such a constant cancels in the equation of motion.[15] This implies that only one of the two constants in the Lagrangian is really necessary. If we then give the remaining constant its conventional name m^2 and introduce a conventional factor of $1/2$, the Lagrangian reads

[15] This can be seen because we have a zero on the right-hand side of the Euler-Lagrange equation. Therefore, if we plug const. $\times\,\mathcal{L}$ into it, we can cancel const. immediately.

$$\mathcal{L} = \frac{1}{2}(\partial_\mu\phi\partial^\mu\phi - m^2\phi^2)\,. \tag{17.30}$$

The corresponding equation of motion becomes

$$\begin{aligned} 0 &= \frac{\partial\mathcal{L}}{\partial\phi} - \partial_\mu\left(\frac{\partial\mathcal{L}}{\partial(\partial_\mu\phi)}\right) \\ 0 &= \frac{\partial}{\partial\phi}\left(\frac{1}{2}(\partial_\mu\phi\partial^\mu\phi - m^2\phi^2)\right) - \partial_\mu\left(\frac{\partial}{\partial(\partial_\mu\Phi)}\left(\frac{1}{2}(\partial_\mu\phi\partial^\mu\phi - m^2\phi^2)\right)\right) \\ 0 &= (\partial_\mu\partial^\mu + m^2)\phi\,. \end{aligned} \tag{17.31}$$

↷ Eq. 17.30

↷

This is the Klein-Gordon equation in its conventional form.

Similarly, we can also derive the Dirac equation. All we have to do is to identify the simplest possible non-trivial terms that respect our fundamental symmetries.[16] The Proca Lagrangian, however, is a bit more subtle since we are not interested in ordinary vector fields but in gauge fields.[17]

[16] As mentioned before, this story is discussed in detail in

Jakob Schwichtenberg. *Physics from Symmetry*. Springer, Cham, Switzerland, 2018b. ISBN 978-3319666303

[17] One hint of why it contains the term $F_{\mu\nu}F^{\mu\nu}$ is our discovery in Section 3.9 that it's the field strength tensor $F_{\mu\nu}$ which encodes imperfections in the "exchange" rates between different local coordinate systems. You can find a more extensive discussion of gauge models in

Jakob Schwichtenberg. *Physics from Finance*. No-Nonsense Books, Karlsruhe, Germany, 2019c. ISBN 978-1795882415

18

Outlook

An often recounted piece of physics history is that Lord Kelvin declared around 1900 that[1]

> "There is nothing new to be discovered in physics now. All that remains is more and more precise measurement."

What followed shortly afterwards were the revolutionary discoveries of special relativity, quantum mechanics, and general relativity.

Even though this story is well-known, the general attitude of most physicist nowadays is not too different. The only difference is that Newton's theory of mechanics has been replaced by quantum field theory as the supposedly ultimate and final theory of nature. The details that still need to be worked out are a few smaller puzzles like the strong CP puzzle or the dark matter puzzle. The standard strategy to tackle these puzzles is to add one or several new fields to the standard model of particle physics. However, it shouldn't be surprising that with sufficient ingenuity it's possible to tackle almost any puzzle within a given framework.

[1] There is actually no evidence that Lord Kelvin ever said or wrote this. Instead, it is now believed that the quote is misattributed to Lord Kelvin and is a paraphrase of Nobel laureate Albert A. Michelson who stated in 1884: "..."it seems probable that most of the grand underlying principles have been firmly established ... An eminent physicist remarked that the future truths of physical science are to be looked for in the sixth place of decimals." Either way, these quotes are often used to summarize the general attitude at that time.

A useful analogy is the epicycle model of the solar system. The idea is that if we add enough epicycles to the geocentric model of the solar system, we can explain many of the planetary motion puzzles that we can observe. But this doesn't mean that planets move in epicycles. Ultimately, the epicycle model has been replaced by a much simpler model with the sun at the center and no epicycles are necessary. Of course, I can't predict the future but maybe quantum fields will turn out to be the epicycles of our time.

Quantum field theory is a beautiful and extremely flexible framework. However, it also has severe limitations. The most famous example is that no generally accepted theory of quantum gravity exists. Moreover, there are still problems in putting various aspects of quantum field theory on a mathematically precise basis.[2]

[2] One example is a rigorous definition of the path integral. Another example is Haag's theorem which roughly states that the interaction picture of quantum field theory cannot be consistently defined. For a readable discussion of Haag's theorem see

John Earman and Doreen Fraser. Haag's theorem and its implications for the foundations of quantum field theory, December 2005. URL `http://philsci-archive.pitt.edu/2673/`

Moreover, one of the most important lessons in physics is that different frameworks are necessary to describe nature at different scales:

▷ At galactic scales ($l_{\text{milky way}} \sim 10^{20}$ m), we need general relativity.

▷ At everyday scales (~ 1 m) , classical mechanics works perfectly.

▷ At atomic scales ($l_a \approx 10^{-10}$ m), we need quantum mechanics.

▷ At present-day collider scales ($l_{\text{LHC}} \sim 10^{-19}$ m), quantum field theory is a suitable framework.

Thus it seems reasonable to assume that to describe nature at even smaller scales, for example, around the Planck scale ($l_P \sim 10^{-35}$ m), we need to invent at least one additional framework. In particular, take note that between everyday scales and atomic length scales there are "just" 10 orders of magnitude and we need completely different frameworks to describe what happens at these scales (classical mechanics and quantum mechanics). In contrast, between the Planck scale and the scales that we can presently probe in colliders there are roughly 16 orders of magnitude. Thus I would say it's quite optimistic to assume that quantum field theory remains the best suited framework across these 16 orders of magnitude.

In other words, in my humble opinion, it's quite unlikely that we have already discovered the ultimate framework to describe nature at fundamental scales. But please don't ask me which framework will eventually supersede quantum field theory. Unfortunately, details get lost when we zoom out and thus the inner workings of nature at the Planck scale are hidden from us. This is demonstrated by the fact that there are infinitely many models that yield the standard model of particle physics in the low energy limit.[3] Thus it's impossible to deduce from low energy data alone what is really going on at smaller scales.

[3] This follows from the observations discussed in Chapter 17.

To quote Howard Georgi:[4]

[4] http://www.people.fas.harvard.edu/~hgeorgi/weak.pdf

> "Local field theory is a useful idealization. The only way we know to describe the quantum mechanical interactions of a finite number of types of particles in ordinary space-time is in a local quantum field theory characterized by a local Lagrangian density, with the interactions described by products of fields at the same space-time point. We strongly suspect that this picture is only approximate. It would be astonishing if our naive picture of the space-time continuum, or quantum mechanics, or anything else that the human mind can imagine, continued to make sense down to arbitrarily small distances."

Of course, we can try to guess which framework will supersede quantum field theory. While there are several contenders (string theory, Xiao-Gang Wen's qubit theory, "pointless" frameworks like twistor theory, the noncommutative geometry framework, ...), there is currently no experimental evidence that one of them is the correct one. In fact, I don't think that the odds are very high that someone will guess the correct next framework without new experimental data. But it's certainly not impossible as demonstrated by Einstein and his discovery of general relativity.

In summary, quantum field theory is the best provisional description of nature at scales that we can currently probe. At some point in the future, new experimental data will probably force us to adopt a new framework. But until this happens, it certainly makes sense to focus on quantum field theory. There are still many aspects of nature that we can explore using quantum field theory and there remains much to be learned about the framework itself. At the same time, it's important to avoid "*to be trapped by the formalism and to become a 'slave' to the formalism*" as Xiao-Gang Wen puts it[5]. To make truly revolutionary advances, we must allow for the possibility that quantum field theory is not the ultimately theory of nature.

[5] Xiao-Gang Wen. *Quantum field theory of many-body systems : from the origin of sound to an origin of light and electrons*. Oxford University Press, Oxford New York, 2004. ISBN 9780199227259

I personally think there is still much to come. Future developments will be extremely interesting and I hope you will continue to follow the story and maybe contribute something yourself.

19

Further Reading Recommendations

There are many amazing books on quantum field theory. Besides the usual textbooks that discuss the general ideas, there are lots of books that focus on special topics. But let's start with a few comments on books you can read to get alternative perspectives on the topics discussed in this book.

Textbooks written in the same spirit as this book are

▷ Student Friendly Quantum Field Theory by Klauber,

▷ Quantum Field Theory for the Gifted Amateur by Lancaster and Blundell.

These books should be your first choices if you want to get a second opinion on the topics discussed in this book.

More advanced but still readable textbooks are

▷ Quantum Field Theory and the Standard Model by Schwartz, which is a new and extremely authoritative reference that is often my first choice if I want get a second opinion on a topic.

- Quantum Field Theory by Srednicki is very well-organized and useful as a reference.

Additionally, there are various lecture notes that are freely available online and can also be quite helpful. Two noteworthy examples are

- David Tong's lecture notes[1], and
- Sidney Coleman's lecture notes[2].

[1] http://www.damtp.cam.ac.uk/user/tong/qft.html

[2] https://arxiv.org/abs/1110.5013

Further textbooks that are often mentioned but are far less student-friendly are An Introduction To Quantum Field Theory by Peskin and Schröder and The Quantum Theory of Fields by Steven Weinberg. The book by Peskin and Schröder primarily focuses on how to carry out calculations, while Weinberg focuses on the "Whys" behind quantum field theory.

Great places to start learning about the path integral formulation of quantum field theory are

- Quantum Field Theory in a Nutshell by Zee. However, take note that it's quite difficult to understand most of Zee's arguments unless you have already a solid grasp on what quantum field theory is all about.
- Quantum Field Theory by Ryder.

Regarding non-perturbative phenomena, my favorite books are

- ▷ Solitons and Instantons by Rajaraman,
- ▷ Topological Solitons by Manton and Sutcliff,
- ▷ Classical Solutions in Quantum Field Theory: Solitons and Instantons by Weinberg,
- ▷ Classical Theory of Gauge Fields by Rubakov.

To learn more about effective field models, try

- ▷ Effective Field Theory by Georgi[3],
- ▷ Section 9 in Grossman's Lectures on Flavor Physics[4]

[3] http://www.people.fas.harvard.edu/~hgeorgi/review.pdf

[4] https://www.physics.uci.edu/~tanedo/files/notes/FlavorNotes.pdf

---

Last but not least, there are great books to learn more about the history of quantum field theory. My favorites are

- ▷ The Infinity Puzzle by Frank Close,
- ▷ QED and the Men Who Made It by Silvan Schweber.

One Last Thing

It's impossible to overstate how important reviews are for an author. Most book sales, at least for books without a marketing budget, come from people who find books through the recommendations on Amazon. Your review helps Amazon figure out what types of people would like my book and makes sure it's shown in the recommended products.

I'd never ask anyone to rate my book higher than they think it deserves, but if you like my book, please take the time to write a short review and rate it on Amazon. This is the biggest thing you can do to support me as a writer.

Each review has an impact on how many people will read my book and, of course, I'm always happy to learn about what people think about my writing.

PS: If you write a review, I would appreciate a short email with a link to it or a screenshot to Jakobschwich@gmail.com. This helps me to take note of new reviews. And, of course, feel free to add any comments or feedback that you don't want to share publicly.

Part IV
Appendices

A

Cumbersome Calculations from Part 0 and Part I

A.1 Rewriting the Proca Lagrangian

$$
\begin{aligned}
\mathcal{L} &= \frac{1}{4}F^{\mu\nu}F_{\mu\nu} \\
&\quad \text{Eq. 3.103} \\
&= \frac{1}{4}(\partial^\mu A^\nu - \partial^\nu A^\mu)(\partial_\mu A_\nu - \partial_\nu A_\mu) \\
&= \frac{1}{4}(\partial^\mu A^\nu \partial_\mu A_\nu - \partial^\mu A^\nu \partial_\nu A_\mu \\
&\quad - \partial^\nu A^\mu \partial_\mu A_\nu + \partial^\nu A^\mu \partial_\nu A_\mu) \\
&\quad \text{renaming dummy indices} \\
&= \frac{1}{4}(\partial^\mu A^\nu \partial_\mu A_\nu - \partial^\mu A^\nu \partial_\nu A_\mu \\
&\quad - \partial^\mu A^\nu \partial_\nu A_\mu + \partial^\mu A^\nu \partial_\mu A_\nu) \\
&= \frac{1}{4}(2\partial^\mu A^\nu \partial_\mu A_\nu - 2\partial^\mu A^\nu \partial_\nu A_\mu) \\
&= \frac{1}{2}(\partial^\mu A^\nu \partial_\mu A_\nu - \partial^\mu A^\nu \partial_\nu A_\mu) \quad \checkmark
\end{aligned}
\tag{A.1}
$$

A.2 Noether Current for a Complex Field

In this appendix, we want to show that if the Lagrangian density depends on a complex field ϕ, the Noether current is given by the sum

$$J^\mu \equiv J_1^\mu + J_2^\mu , \tag{A.2}$$

where

$$J_1^\mu \equiv \frac{\partial \mathcal{L}}{\partial(\partial_\mu \phi)} \Delta\phi$$
$$J_2^\mu \equiv \frac{\partial \mathcal{L}}{\partial(\partial_\mu \phi^\dagger)} \Delta\phi^\dagger \tag{A.3}$$

are the currents that would follow if we consider ϕ and $\phi^\dagger$ in isolation. The steps here are completely analogous to what we did in Eq. 4.44 and Eq. 4.45. The only difference is that we now have to consider the variations of ϕ and of $\phi^\dagger$. We treat the field ϕ and $\phi^\dagger$ as independent fields and thus must consider the variations of them separately. This is really just a shortcut to consider two scalar fields at once. Instead of ϕ and $\phi^\dagger$ we could treat the real and imaginary parts as independent fields.

[1] Reminder: the Euler-Lagrange equation for a field ϕ reads (Eq. 4.25)

$$\frac{\partial \mathcal{L}}{\partial \phi} = \partial_\mu \left(\frac{\partial \mathcal{L}}{\partial(\partial_\mu \phi)} \right) .$$

Analogously the Euler-Lagrange equation for the field $\phi^\dagger$ reads

$$\frac{\partial \mathcal{L}}{\partial \phi^\dagger} = \partial_\mu \left(\frac{\partial \mathcal{L}}{\partial(\partial_\mu \phi^\dagger)} \right) .$$

We start again by using the symmetry condition.

$$\begin{aligned} 0 &= \mathcal{L}(\phi, \partial_\mu \phi, \phi^\dagger, \partial_\mu \phi^\dagger) - \mathcal{L}\Big(\phi + \Delta\phi, \partial_\mu(\phi + \Delta\phi), \phi^\dagger + \Delta\phi^\dagger, \partial_\mu(\phi^\dagger + \Delta\phi^\dagger)\Big) \\ &\quad \text{Taylor expansion} \\ &= \mathcal{L} - \Big(\mathcal{L} + \frac{\partial \mathcal{L}}{\partial \phi}\Delta\phi + \frac{\partial \mathcal{L}}{\partial(\partial_\mu \phi)}\Delta\partial_\mu\phi + \frac{\partial \mathcal{L}}{\partial \phi^\dagger}\Delta\phi^\dagger + \frac{\partial \mathcal{L}}{\partial(\partial_\mu \phi^\dagger)}\Delta\partial_\mu\phi^\dagger\Big) \\ &\quad \Delta\partial_\mu\phi = \partial_\mu\Delta\phi \\ &= -\frac{\partial \mathcal{L}}{\partial \phi}\Delta\phi - \frac{\partial \mathcal{L}}{\partial(\partial_\mu \phi)}\partial_\mu\Delta\phi - \frac{\partial \mathcal{L}}{\partial \phi^\dagger}\Delta\phi^\dagger - \frac{\partial \mathcal{L}}{\partial(\partial_\mu \phi^\dagger)}\partial_\mu\Delta\phi^\dagger . \end{aligned} \tag{A.4}$$

We can simplify this formula by using the Euler-Lagrange equation and the product rule:[1]

$$\begin{aligned} 0 &= -\frac{\partial \mathcal{L}}{\partial \phi}\Delta\phi - \frac{\partial \mathcal{L}}{\partial(\partial_\mu \phi)}\partial_\mu\Delta\phi - \frac{\partial \mathcal{L}}{\partial \phi^\dagger}\Delta\phi^\dagger - \frac{\partial \mathcal{L}}{\partial(\partial_\mu \phi^\dagger)}\partial_\mu\Delta\phi^\dagger \\ &\quad \text{EL equation (Eq. 4.25)} \\ &= -\partial_\mu\left(\frac{\partial \mathcal{L}}{\partial(\partial_\mu \phi)}\right)\Delta\phi - \frac{\partial \mathcal{L}}{\partial(\partial_\mu \phi)}\partial_\mu\Delta\phi - \partial_\mu\left(\frac{\partial \mathcal{L}}{\partial(\partial_\mu \phi \dagger)}\right)\Delta\phi^\dagger - \frac{\partial \mathcal{L}}{\partial(\partial_\mu \phi^\dagger)}\partial_\mu\Delta\phi^\dagger \\ &\quad (\partial_x f)g + f(\partial_x g) = (\partial_x fg) \\ &= \partial_\mu\left(\frac{\partial \mathcal{L}}{\partial(\partial_\mu \phi)}\Delta\phi\right) + \partial_\mu\left(\frac{\partial \mathcal{L}}{\partial(\partial_\mu \phi^\dagger)}\Delta\phi^\dagger\right) \\ &\quad \text{definition} \\ &\equiv \partial_\mu J^\mu \equiv \partial_\mu J_1^\mu + \partial_\mu J_2^\mu . \end{aligned} \tag{A.5}$$

We can therefore see that the total Noether current is given by the sum of the two contributions coming from the variation of ϕ and $\phi^\dagger$.

A.3 Rewriting the General Solution of the Klein-Gordon Equation

First of all it is conventional to use the short-hand notation $kx \equiv k_\mu x^\mu$. Our general solution in Eq. 5.49 then reads

$$\phi(x) = \int \frac{dk^4}{(2\pi)^4} \left(a(k)e^{-i(kx)} + a^\dagger(k)e^{i(kx)} \right) . \tag{A.6}$$

Secondly, take note that the notation in Eq. A.6 is still quite sloppy. A general solution of the Klein-Gordon equation doesn't include an integral over all wave vectors k_μ. Instead, only four-vectors are permitted that fulfill the dispersion relation (Eq. 5.40)

$$k_\mu k^\mu = m^2 , \tag{A.7}$$

where m is the mass parameter that appears in the Klein-Gordon equation. In field theory, Eq. A.7 is known as the mass-shell condition. We can understand why by noting that Eq. A.7 is exactly the defining condition of a sphere of radius m in Minkowski space.[2]

[2] In Euclidean space, a sphere is defined by the condition $x^2 + y^2 + z^2 = R^2$. Here, we have the condition $k_0^2 - k_1^2 - k_2^2 - k_3^2 = m^2$.

A mathematical tool that allows us to incorporate the condition in Eq. A.6 is Dirac's delta distribution $\delta(k^2 - m^2)$:[3]

[3] If you're unfamiliar with the delta distribution, have a look at Appendix E.

$$\phi(x)_{\text{physical}} = \int \frac{dk^4}{(2\pi)^4} 2\pi\delta(k^2 - m^2) \left(a(k)e^{-i(kx)} + a^\dagger(k)e^{i(kx)} \right) . \tag{A.8}$$

The delta distribution makes sure that only wave vectors k_μ that fulfill the condition in Eq. A.6 make a non-zero contribution to the total wave form $\phi(x)_{\text{physical}}$.

Another physical constraint is that only positive energy solutions are physical.[4] We will learn later that in quantum field

[4] From a purely mathematical point of view, negative energy solutions are solutions of the Klein-Gordon equation too. They are just not useful to describe the physical systems that we observe in nature.

theory there is a close connection between frequency and energy: $k_0 = \omega = \frac{E}{\hbar}$. For our wave four-vector components this implies that we have the condition $k_0 > 0$. The mathematical tool that allows us to include this condition in our formula for the general solution is the Heaviside function. The Heaviside function is defined as follows:

$$\Theta(x) = \begin{cases} 1 & \text{if } x \geq 0 \\ 0 & \text{if } x < 0 \end{cases} \tag{A.9}$$

Therefore, we can include the positive energy condition by introducing $\Theta(k_0)$ into the expression for the general solution:

$$\phi(x)_{\text{physical}} = \int \frac{1}{(2\pi)^3} \mathrm{d}k^4 \delta(k^2 - m^2)\Theta(k_0) \left(a(k)\mathrm{e}^{-i(kx)} + a^\dagger(k)\mathrm{e}^{i(kx)}\right) \tag{A.10}$$

This expression looks quite ugly and therefore it makes sense to massage it a bit using a few mathematical tricks. In particular, we rewrite the factor $\mathrm{d}k^4\delta(k^2 - m^2)\Theta(k_0)$ as follows:

$$\begin{aligned}
\mathrm{d}k^4\delta(k^2 - m^2)\Theta(k_0) &\equiv \mathrm{d}k^4\delta(k_\mu k^\mu - m^2)\Theta(k_0) \\
&\quad \text{⤸ } k_\mu k^\mu = k_0^2 - \vec{k}^2 \\
&= \mathrm{d}k^4\delta(k_0^2 - \vec{k}^2 - m^2)\Theta(k_0) \\
&\quad \text{⤸ } \omega_k^2 \equiv \vec{k}^2 + m^2 \text{ (definition)} \\
&= \mathrm{d}k^4\delta(k_0^2 - \omega_k^2)\Theta(k_0) \\
&\quad \text{⤸ } (a-b)(a+b) = a^2 - b^2 \\
&= \mathrm{d}k^4\delta\Big((k_0 - \omega_k)(k_0 + \omega_k)\Big)\Theta(k_0) \\
&\quad \text{⤸ } \delta(f(x)) = \sum_i \frac{\delta(x - a_i)}{\left|\frac{df}{dx}(a_i)\right|} \text{ with } f(a_i) = 0 \\
&= \mathrm{d}k^4 \frac{1}{2k_0}\big(\delta(k_0 - \omega_k) + \delta(k_0 + \omega_k)\big)\Theta(k_0) \\
&\quad \text{⤸ } (k_0 + \omega_k) \neq 0 \text{ for } k_0 > 0 \\
&= \mathrm{d}k^4 \frac{1}{2k_0}\delta(k_0 - \omega_k) \\
&\quad \text{⤸ } \mathrm{d}k^4 = \mathrm{d}k^3\mathrm{d}k_0 \\
&= \mathrm{d}k^3\mathrm{d}k_0 \frac{1}{2k_0}\delta(k_0 - \omega_k) \\
&\quad \text{⤸ } \int \\
\int \mathrm{d}k^4\delta(k^2 - m^2)\Theta(k_0) &= \int \mathrm{d}k^3\mathrm{d}k_0 \frac{1}{2k_0}\delta(k_0 - \omega_k) \\
&\quad \text{⤸ } \int \mathrm{d}x\, \delta(x-a)f(x) = f(a) \\
&= \int \mathrm{d}k^3 \frac{1}{2\omega_k}\,.
\end{aligned} \tag{A.11}$$

Using this formula, we arrive at the following expression for a general solution of the Klein-Gordon equation:

$$\begin{aligned}
\phi(x)_{\text{physical}} &= \int \frac{dk^4}{(2\pi)^3}\delta(k^2-m^2)\Theta(k_0)\left(a(k)e^{-i(kx)} + a^\dagger(k)e^{i(kx)}\right) && \text{this is Eq. A.10} \\
&\quad \text{(Eq. A.11)} \\
&= \int \frac{dk^3}{(2\pi)^3}\frac{1}{2\omega_k}\left(a(k)e^{-i(kx)} + a^\dagger(k)e^{i(kx)}\right) . && \text{(A.12)}
\end{aligned}$$

In addition, it is conventional to absorb a factor of $1/\sqrt{2\omega_k}$ into the definitions of $a(k)$ and $a^\dagger(k)$:[5]

[5] This step has no deeper meaning but leads to easier formulas in the following chapters.

$$\begin{aligned}
a(\vec{k}) &\equiv \frac{a(k)}{\sqrt{2\omega_k}} \\
a^\dagger(\vec{k}) &\equiv \frac{a^\dagger(k)}{\sqrt{2\omega_k}} .
\end{aligned} \tag{A.13}$$

Our general solution then reads

$$\begin{aligned}
\phi(x)_{\text{physical}} &= \int \frac{dk^3}{(2\pi)^3}\frac{1}{2\omega_k}\left(a(k)e^{-i(kx)} + a^\dagger(k)e^{i(kx)}\right) \\
&\quad \left(\sqrt{2\omega_k}\sqrt{2\omega_k} = 2\omega_k\right) \\
&= \int \frac{dk^3}{(2\pi)^3}\frac{1}{\sqrt{2\omega_k}\sqrt{2\omega_k}}\left(a(k)e^{-i(kx)} + a^\dagger(k)e^{i(kx)}\right) \\
&= \int \frac{dk^3}{(2\pi)^3}\frac{1}{\sqrt{2\omega_k}}\left(\frac{a(k)}{\sqrt{2\omega_k}}e^{-i(kx)} + \frac{a^\dagger(k)}{\sqrt{2\omega_k}}e^{i(kx)}\right) \\
&\quad \text{(Eq. A.13)} \\
&= \int \frac{dk^3}{(2\pi)^3}\frac{1}{\sqrt{2\omega_k}}\left(a(\vec{k})e^{-i(kx)} + a^\dagger(\vec{k})e^{i(kx)}\right) .
\end{aligned} \tag{A.14}$$

Thus we end up with

$$\phi(x) = \int dk^3 \frac{1}{(2\pi)^3\sqrt{2\omega_k}}\left(a(\vec{k})e^{-i(kx)} + a^\dagger(\vec{k})e^{i(kx)}\right) . \tag{A.15}$$

A.4 Verifying the $a(k)$, $a^\dagger(k)$ commutation relations

In this appendix, we verify that if the coefficients $a(k)$, $a^\dagger(k)$ fulfill the commutation relation in Eq. 8.14, the canonical commutation relations (Eq. 8.6) are automatically fulfilled:

$$
\begin{aligned}
i\delta(\vec{x}-\vec{y}) &= [\phi(t,\vec{x}),\pi(t,\vec{y})] \\
&= \phi(t,\vec{x})\pi(t,\vec{y}) - \pi(t,\vec{y})\phi(t,\vec{x}) \\
&= \left(\int dk^3 \frac{1}{(2\pi)^3\sqrt{2\omega_k}}\left(a_k e^{-i(\omega_k t-\vec{k}\cdot\vec{x})} + a_k^\dagger e^{i(\omega_k t-\vec{k}\cdot\vec{x})}\right)\right) \\
&\qquad \times \left(\int dk'^3 \frac{-i\sqrt{\omega_k}}{(2\pi)^3\sqrt{2}}\left(a_{k'} e^{-i(\omega_{k'} t-\vec{k}'\cdot\vec{y})} - a_{k'}^\dagger e^{i((\omega_{k'} t-\vec{k}'\cdot\vec{y}))}\right)\right) \\
&\quad - \left(\int dk'^3 \frac{-i\sqrt{\omega_k}}{(2\pi)^3\sqrt{2}}\left(a_{k'} e^{-i(\omega_{k'} t-\vec{k}'\cdot\vec{y})} - a_{k'}^\dagger e^{i(\omega_{k'} t-\vec{k}'\cdot\vec{y})}\right)\right) \\
&\qquad \times \left(\int dk^3 \frac{1}{(2\pi)^3\sqrt{2\omega_k}}\left(a_k e^{-i(\omega_k t-\vec{k}\cdot\vec{x})} + a_k^\dagger e^{(\omega_k t-\vec{k}\cdot\vec{x})}\right)\right) \\
&= \int dk^3 dk'^3 \Big(\frac{-i}{(2\pi)^6 2} a_k a_{k'} e^{-i(\omega_k+\omega_{k'})t} e^{i(\vec{k}\cdot\vec{x}+\vec{k}'\cdot\vec{y})}\Big) \\
&\quad - \int dk^3 dk'^3 \Big(\frac{-i}{(2\pi)^6 2} a_k a_{k'}^\dagger e^{-i(\omega_k-\omega_{k'})t} e^{i(\vec{k}\cdot\vec{x}-\vec{k}'\cdot\vec{y})}\Big) \\
&\quad + \int dk^3 dk'^3 \Big(\frac{-i}{(2\pi)^6 2} a_k^\dagger a_{k'} e^{i(\omega_k-\omega_{k'})t} e^{i(-\vec{k}\cdot\vec{x}+\vec{k}'\cdot\vec{y})}\Big) \\
&\quad - \int dk^3 dk'^3 \Big(\frac{-i}{(2\pi)^6 2} a_k^\dagger a_{k'}^\dagger e^{i(\omega_k+\omega_{k'})t} e^{-i(\vec{k}\cdot\vec{x}+\vec{k}'\cdot\vec{y})}\Big) \\
&\quad - \left(\int dk^3 dk'^3 \Big(\frac{-i}{(2\pi)^6 2} a_{k'} a_k e^{-i(\omega_{k'}+\omega_k)t} e^{i(\vec{k}'\cdot\vec{y}+\vec{k}\cdot\vec{x})}\Big)\right. \\
&\quad + \int dk^3 dk'^3 \Big(\frac{-i}{(2\pi)^6 2} a_{k'} a_k^\dagger e^{-i(\omega_{k'}-\omega_k)t} e^{i(\vec{k}'\cdot\vec{y}-\vec{k}\cdot\vec{x})}\Big) \\
&\quad - \int dk^3 dk'^3 \Big(\frac{-i}{(2\pi)^6 2} a_{k'}^\dagger a_k e^{i(\omega_{k'}-\omega_k)t} e^{i(-\vec{k}'\cdot\vec{y}+\vec{k}\cdot\vec{x})}\Big) \\
&\quad \left. - \int dk^3 dk'^3 \Big(\frac{-i}{(2\pi)^6 2} a_{k'}^\dagger a_k^\dagger e^{i(\omega_{k'}+\omega_k)t} e^{-i(\vec{k}'\cdot\vec{y}+\vec{k}\cdot\vec{x})}\Big)\right)
\end{aligned}
$$

this is Eq. 8.6

↷ $[A,B] \equiv AB - BA$

↷ Eq. 5.51 , Eq. 8.12

↷

↷ $AB - BA \equiv [A,B]$ (see next page)

$$
\begin{aligned}
&= \int dk^3 dk'^3 \Big(\frac{-i}{(2\pi)^6 2} [a_k, a_{k'}] e^{-i(\omega_k+\omega_{k'})t} e^{i(\vec{k}\cdot\vec{x}+\vec{k}'\cdot\vec{y})} \Big) \\
&\quad - \int dk^3 dk'^3 \Big(\frac{-i}{(2\pi)^6 2} [a_k, a^\dagger_{k'}] e^{-i(\omega_k-\omega_{k'})t} e^{i(\vec{k}\cdot\vec{x}-\vec{k}'\cdot\vec{y})} \Big) \\
&\quad + \int dk^3 dk'^3 \Big(\frac{-i}{(2\pi)^6 2} [a^\dagger_k, a_{k'}] e^{i(\omega_k-\omega_{k'})t} e^{i(-\vec{k}\cdot\vec{x}+\vec{k}'\cdot\vec{y})} \Big) \\
&\quad - \int dk^3 dk'^3 \Big(\frac{-i}{(2\pi)^6 2} [a^\dagger_k, a^\dagger_{k'}] e^{i(\omega_k+\omega_{k'})t} e^{-i(\vec{k}\cdot\vec{x}+\vec{k}'\cdot\vec{y})} \Big) \\
&= \int dk^3 dk'^3 \Big(\frac{-i}{(2\pi)^6 2} \Big(0\Big) e^{-i(\omega_k+\omega_{k'})t} e^{i(\vec{k}\cdot\vec{x}+\vec{k}'\cdot\vec{y})} \Big) \\
&\quad - \int dk^3 dk'^3 \Big(\frac{-i}{(2\pi)^6 2} \Big((2\pi)^3 \delta(\vec{k}-\vec{k}')\Big) e^{-i(\omega_k-\omega_{k'})t} e^{i(\vec{k}\cdot\vec{x}-\vec{k}'\cdot\vec{y})} \Big) \\
&\quad + \int dk^3 dk'^3 \Big(\frac{-i}{(2\pi)^6 2} \Big(-(2\pi)^3 \delta(\vec{k}-\vec{k}')\Big) e^{i(\omega_k-\omega_{k'})t} e^{i(-\vec{k}\cdot\vec{x}+\vec{k}'\cdot\vec{y})} \Big) \\
&\quad - \int dk^3 dk'^3 \Big(\frac{-i}{(2\pi)^6 2} \Big(0\Big) e^{i(\omega_k+\omega_{k'})t} e^{-i(\vec{k}\cdot\vec{x}+\vec{k}'\cdot\vec{y})} \Big) \\
&= -\int dk^3 \Big(\frac{-i}{(2\pi)^3 2} e^{-i(\omega_k-\omega_k)t} e^{i(\vec{k}\cdot\vec{x}-\vec{k}\cdot\vec{y})} \Big) - \int dk^3 \Big(\frac{-i}{(2\pi)^3 2} e^{i(\omega_k-\omega_k)t} e^{i(-\vec{k}\cdot\vec{x}+\vec{k}\cdot\vec{y})} \Big) \qquad \text{↷ } e^0 = 1 \\
&= \int dk^3 \Big(\frac{i}{(2\pi)^3 2} e^{i(\vec{k}\cdot\vec{x}-\vec{k}\cdot\vec{y})} \Big) + \int dk^3 \Big(\frac{i}{(2\pi)^3 2} e^{i(-\vec{k}\cdot\vec{x}+\vec{k}\cdot\vec{y})} \Big) \\
&= \frac{i}{2}\delta(\vec{x}-\vec{y}) + \frac{i}{2}\delta(\vec{y}-\vec{x}) \\
&= i\delta(\vec{x}-\vec{y}) \quad \checkmark
\end{aligned}
\tag{A.16}
$$

A.5 Rewriting the Scalar Field Energy

In this appendix we want to demonstrate that the energy stored in a scalar field (Eq. 8.16)

$$H = \frac{1}{2}\int d^3x \left(\pi^2 + (\partial_i\phi)^2 + m^2\phi^2\right) \tag{A.17}$$

can be rewritten as (Eq. 8.17)

$$H = \frac{1}{2}\int \mathrm{d}k^3 \frac{1}{(2\pi)^3}\omega_k \left(a^\dagger(\vec{k})a(\vec{k}) + a(\vec{k})a^\dagger(\vec{k})\right) . \tag{A.18}$$

To that end, we plug the explicit formulas for the conjugate momentum density π (Eq. 8.12) and the scalar field ϕ (Eq. 5.51) into Eq. A.17. To unclutter the discussion, we look at the three terms in Eq. A.17 in isolation and combine the results afterwards.

$$\frac{1}{2}\int d^3x\pi^2$$

▹ Eq. 8.12

$$= \frac{1}{2}\int d^3x\left(\int \mathrm{d}k^3 \frac{-i\sqrt{\omega_k}}{(2\pi)^3\sqrt{2}}\left(a(\vec{k})\mathrm{e}^{-i(kx)} - a^\dagger(\vec{k})\mathrm{e}^{i(kx)}\right)\right)^2$$

▹ $i^2 = -1$

$$= \frac{1}{4}\int d^3x \frac{-\mathrm{d}k^3\mathrm{d}q^3}{(2\pi)^6}\sqrt{\omega_k}\sqrt{\omega_q}\left(a(\vec{k})\mathrm{e}^{-i(kx)} - a^\dagger(\vec{k})\mathrm{e}^{i(kx)}\right)\left(a(\vec{q})\mathrm{e}^{-i(qx)} - a^\dagger(\vec{q})\mathrm{e}^{i(qx)}\right)$$

▹

$$= \frac{1}{4}\int d^3x \frac{-\mathrm{d}k^3\mathrm{d}q^3}{(2\pi)^6}\sqrt{\omega_k}\sqrt{\omega_q}\Big(a(\vec{k})\mathrm{e}^{-i(kx)}a(\vec{q})\mathrm{e}^{-i(qx)} - a^\dagger(\vec{k})\mathrm{e}^{i(kx)}a(\vec{q})\mathrm{e}^{-i(qx)}$$
$$- a(\vec{k})\mathrm{e}^{-i(kx)}a^\dagger(\vec{q})\mathrm{e}^{i(qx)} + a^\dagger(\vec{k})\mathrm{e}^{i(kx)}a^\dagger(\vec{q})\mathrm{e}^{i(qx)}\Big)$$

▹ see next page

$$= \frac{1}{4}\int d^3x \frac{-\mathrm{d}k^3\mathrm{d}q^3}{(2\pi)^6}\sqrt{\omega_k}\sqrt{\omega_q}\bigg(a(\vec{k})a(\vec{q})\mathrm{e}^{-ix(k+q)} - a^\dagger(\vec{k})a(\vec{q})\mathrm{e}^{ix(k-q)}$$

$$- a(\vec{k})a^\dagger(\vec{q})\mathrm{e}^{-ix(k-q)} + a^\dagger(\vec{k})a^\dagger(\vec{q})\mathrm{e}^{ix(k+q)}\bigg)$$

$\rightsquigarrow \int d^3x$

$$= \frac{1}{4}\int \frac{-\mathrm{d}k^3\mathrm{d}q^3}{(2\pi)^3}\sqrt{\omega_k}\sqrt{\omega_q}\bigg(a(\vec{k})a(\vec{q})\delta(k+q)\mathrm{e}^{-ix_0(\omega_k+\omega_q)} - a^\dagger(\vec{k})a(\vec{q})\delta(k-q)\mathrm{e}^{ix_0(\omega_k-\omega_q)}$$

$$- a(\vec{k})a^\dagger(\vec{q})\delta(k-q)\mathrm{e}^{-ix_0(\omega_k-\omega_q)} + a^\dagger(\vec{k})a^\dagger(\vec{q})\delta(k+q)\mathrm{e}^{ix_0(\omega_k+\omega_q)}\bigg)$$

$\rightsquigarrow \int d^3q$

$$= \frac{1}{4}\int \frac{-\mathrm{d}k^3}{(2\pi)^3}\sqrt{\omega_k}\sqrt{\omega_k}\bigg(a(\vec{k})a(-\vec{k})\mathrm{e}^{-ix_0(\omega_k+\omega_k)} - a^\dagger(\vec{k})a(\vec{k})\mathrm{e}^{ix_0(\omega_k-\omega_k)}$$

$$- a(\vec{k})a^\dagger(\vec{k})\mathrm{e}^{-ix_0(\omega_k-\omega_k)} + a^\dagger(\vec{k})a^\dagger(-\vec{k})\mathrm{e}^{ix_0(\omega_k+\omega_k)}\bigg)$$

$\rightsquigarrow e^0 = 1$

$$= \frac{1}{4}\int \frac{-\mathrm{d}k^3}{(2\pi)^3}\omega_k\bigg(a(\vec{k})a(-\vec{k})\mathrm{e}^{-i2x_0\omega_k} - a^\dagger(\vec{k})a(\vec{k})$$

$$- a(\vec{k})a^\dagger(\vec{k}) + a^\dagger(\vec{k})a^\dagger(-\vec{k})\mathrm{e}^{i2x_0\omega_k}\bigg) \tag{A.19}$$

Analogously, we find

$$\int d^3x(\partial_i\phi)^2$$

$\rightsquigarrow$ Eq. 5.51

$$= \int \frac{\mathrm{d}k^3}{(2\pi)^3}\frac{\vec{k}^2}{4\omega_k}\bigg(a(\vec{k})a(-\vec{k})\mathrm{e}^{-i2x_0\omega_k} + a^\dagger(\vec{k})a(\vec{k})$$

$$+ a(\vec{k})a^\dagger(\vec{k}) + a^\dagger(\vec{k})a^\dagger(-\vec{k})\mathrm{e}^{i2x_0\omega_k}\bigg) \tag{A.20}$$

and

$$\int d^3xm^2\phi^2$$

$\rightsquigarrow$ Eq. 5.51

$$= \int \frac{\mathrm{d}k^3}{(2\pi)^3}\frac{m^2}{4\omega_k}\bigg(a(\vec{k})a(-\vec{k})\mathrm{e}^{-i2x_0\omega_k} + a^\dagger(\vec{k})a(\vec{k})$$

$$+ a(\vec{k})a^\dagger(\vec{k}) + a^\dagger(\vec{k})a^\dagger(-\vec{k})\mathrm{e}^{i2x_0\omega_k}\bigg). \tag{A.21}$$

If we put these puzzle pieces together, we find

$$
\begin{aligned}
H &= \frac{1}{2}\int d^3x \left(\pi^2 + (\partial_i\phi)^2 + m^2\phi^2\right) \\
&= \frac{1}{4}\int \frac{-dk^3}{(2\pi)^3}\omega_k \Big(a(\vec{k})a(-\vec{k})e^{-i2x_0\omega_k} - a^\dagger(\vec{k})a(\vec{k}) \\
&\qquad - a(\vec{k})a^\dagger(\vec{k}) + a^\dagger(\vec{k})a^\dagger(-\vec{k})e^{i2x_0\omega_k}\Big) \\
&\quad + \int \frac{dk^3}{(2\pi)^3}\frac{\vec{k}^2}{4\omega_k}\Big(a(\vec{k})a(-\vec{k})e^{-i2x_0\omega_k} + a^\dagger(\vec{k})a(\vec{k}) \\
&\qquad + a(\vec{k})a^\dagger(\vec{k}) + a^\dagger(\vec{k})a^\dagger(-\vec{k})e^{i2x_0\omega_k}\Big) \\
&\quad + \int \frac{dk^3}{(2\pi)^3}\frac{m^2}{4\omega_k}\Big(a(\vec{k})a(-\vec{k})e^{-i2x_0\omega_k} + a^\dagger(\vec{k})a(\vec{k}) \\
&\qquad + a(\vec{k})a^\dagger(\vec{k}) + a^\dagger(\vec{k})a^\dagger(-\vec{k})e^{i2x_0\omega_k}\Big) \\
&= \int \frac{dk^3}{(2\pi)^3}\frac{1}{4\omega_k}\left(\omega_k^2 + \vec{k}^2 + m^2\right)\left(a^\dagger(\vec{k})a(\vec{k}) + a(\vec{k})a^\dagger(\vec{k})\right) \\
&\quad + \int \frac{dk^3}{(2\pi)^3}\frac{1}{4\omega_k}\left(-\omega_k^2 + \vec{k}^2 + m^2\right)\left(a(\vec{k})a(-\vec{k})e^{-i2x_0\omega_k} + a^\dagger(\vec{k})a^\dagger(-\vec{k})e^{i2x_0\omega_k}\right) \\
&= \int \frac{dk^3}{(2\pi)^3}\frac{1}{4\omega_k}\left(2\omega_k^2\right)\left(a^\dagger(\vec{k})a(\vec{k}) + a(\vec{k})a^\dagger(\vec{k})\right) \\
&= \int \frac{dk^3}{(2\pi)^3}\frac{\omega_k}{2}\left(a^\dagger(\vec{k})a(\vec{k}) + a(\vec{k})a^\dagger(\vec{k})\right)
\end{aligned} \tag{A.22}
$$

↷ Eq. A.19, Eq. A.20, Eq. A.21

↷

↷ $\vec{k}^2 + m^2 = \omega_k^2$

↷

This is exactly Eq. A.18.

A.6 Rewriting the Scalar Field Momentum

In this appendix we want to check that the formula which we derived for the scalar field momentum (Eq. 8.39)

$$\hat{P}_i = \int d^3x\; \pi\partial_i\phi \tag{A.23}$$

can be rewritten as (Eq. 8.40)

$$\hat{P}_i = \int \frac{d^3k}{(2\pi)^3}\; k_i a^\dagger(\vec{k})a(\vec{k}) \tag{A.24}$$

if we use the explicit expansions of the conjugate momentum density π (Eq. 8.12) and ϕ (Eq. 5.51):

$$\hat{P}_i = \int d^3x \, \pi \partial_i \phi$$

↷ Eq. 8.12, Eq. 5.51

$$= \int d^3x \left(\int dk^3 \frac{-i\sqrt{\omega_k}}{(2\pi)^3\sqrt{2}} \left(a(\vec{k})e^{-i(kx)} - a^\dagger(\vec{k})e^{i(kx)} \right) \right)$$
$$\times \partial_i \left(\int dq^3 \frac{1}{(2\pi)^3\sqrt{2\omega_q}} \left(a(\vec{q})e^{-iqx} + a^\dagger(\vec{q})e^{ikq} \right) \right)$$

↷

$$= \int d^3x \left(\int dk^3 \frac{-i\sqrt{\omega_k}}{(2\pi)^3\sqrt{2}} \left(a(\vec{k})e^{-i(kx)} - a^\dagger(\vec{k})e^{i(kx)} \right) \right)$$
$$\times \left(\int dq^3 \frac{1}{(2\pi)^3\sqrt{2\omega_q}} \left(a(\vec{q})(-iq_i)e^{-iqx} + a^\dagger(\vec{q})(iq_i)e^{ikq} \right) \right)$$

↷

$$= \frac{1}{2} \int d^3x \frac{dk^3dq^3}{(2\pi)^6} q_i \left(a(\vec{k})e^{-i(kx)} - a^\dagger(\vec{k})e^{i(kx)} \right) \left(-a(\vec{q})e^{-iqx} + a^\dagger(\vec{q})e^{ikq} \right)$$

↷

$$= \frac{1}{2} \int d^3x \frac{dk^3dq^3}{(2\pi)^6} q_i \Big(-a(\vec{k})e^{-i(kx)}a(\vec{q})e^{-iqx} + a^\dagger(\vec{k})e^{i(kx)}a(\vec{q})e^{-iqx}$$
$$+ a(\vec{k})e^{-i(kx)}a^\dagger(\vec{q})e^{ikq} - a^\dagger(\vec{k})e^{i(kx)}a^\dagger(\vec{q})e^{ikq} \Big)$$

↷

$$= \frac{1}{2} \int d^3x \frac{dk^3dq^3}{(2\pi)^6} q_i \Big(-a(\vec{k})a(\vec{q})e^{-ix(k+q)} + a^\dagger(\vec{k})a(\vec{q})e^{ix(k-q)}$$
$$+ a(\vec{k})a^\dagger(\vec{q})e^{-ix(k-q)} - a^\dagger(\vec{k})a^\dagger(\vec{q})e^{ix(k+q)} \Big)$$

↷ $\int d^3x$

$$= \frac{1}{2} \int \frac{dk^3dq^3}{(2\pi)^3} q_i \Big(-a(\vec{k})a(\vec{q})\delta(k+q)e^{-ix_0(\omega_k+\omega_q)} + a^\dagger(\vec{k})a(\vec{q})\delta(k-q)e^{ix_0(\omega_k-\omega_q)}$$
$$+ a(\vec{k})a^\dagger(\vec{q})\delta(k-q)e^{-ix_0(\omega_k-\omega_q)} - a^\dagger(\vec{k})a^\dagger(\vec{q})\delta(k+q)e^{ix_0(\omega_k+\omega_q)} \Big)$$

↷ $\int d^3q$

$$= \frac{1}{2} \int \frac{dk^3}{(2\pi)^3} k_i \Big(-a(\vec{k})a(-\vec{k})e^{-ix_0(\omega_k+\omega_k)} + a^\dagger(\vec{k})a(\vec{k})e^{ix_0(\omega_k-\omega_k)}$$
$$+ a(\vec{k})a^\dagger(\vec{k})e^{-ix_0(\omega_k-\omega_k)} - a^\dagger(\vec{k})a^\dagger(-\vec{k})e^{ix_0(\omega_k+\omega_k)} \Big)$$

↷ $e^0 = 1$

$$= \frac{1}{2} \int \frac{dk^3}{(2\pi)^3} k_i \Big(-a(\vec{k})a(-\vec{k})e^{-i2x_0\omega_k} + a^\dagger(\vec{k})a(\vec{k}) + a(\vec{k})a^\dagger(\vec{k}) - a^\dagger(\vec{k})a^\dagger(-\vec{k})e^{i2x_0\omega_k} \Big) \tag{A.25}$$

To simplify this expression, we note that $k_i a(\vec{k})a(-\vec{k})$ and $k_i a^\dagger(\vec{k})a^\dagger(-\vec{k})$ are antisymmetric with respect to $k_i \rightarrow -k_i$. Therefore, the integral over $k_i a(\vec{k})a(-\vec{k})$ and $k_i a^\dagger(\vec{k})a^\dagger(-\vec{k})$ vanishes since we have a symmetric integration interval. If we use this in Eq. A.25, we find

$$\begin{aligned}
\hat{P}_i &= \frac{1}{2}\int \frac{dk^3}{(2\pi)^3} k_i \left(a^\dagger(\vec{k})a(\vec{k}) + a(\vec{k})a^\dagger(\vec{k}) \right) \\
&\quad \text{↷ } AB = BA + [A,B] \\
&= \frac{1}{2}\int \frac{dk^3}{(2\pi)^3} k_i \left(2a^\dagger(\vec{k})a(\vec{k}) + [a(\vec{k}), a^\dagger(\vec{k})] \right) \\
&\quad \text{↷ Eq. 8.14} \\
&= \int \frac{dk^3}{(2\pi)^3} k_i a^\dagger(\vec{k})a(\vec{k}) + \frac{1}{2}\int dk^3\, \vec{k}\delta(0)\,. \qquad \text{(A.26)}
\end{aligned}$$

The first term is exactly what we wanted to derive (Eq. 8.40). The second term is an infinite constant contribution that we choose to ignore, analogous to what we did for the energy.

A.7 Demonstration that the Feynman Propagator is a Green's Function

In this appendix we want to check if the Feynman propagator (Eq. 8.93)

$$D_F(t',\vec{x}',t,\vec{x}) \equiv \Theta(t'-t)D(t',\vec{x}',t,\vec{x}) + \Theta(t-t')D(t,\vec{x},t',\vec{x}') \qquad \text{(A.27)}$$

is indeed a Green's function of the Klein-Gordon equation. This is true if we find a delta distribution when we plug the Feynman propagator into the Klein-Gordon equation since this is the defining condition of a Green's function (Eq. 8.94):

$$\left(\partial_\mu \partial^\mu + m^2\right) D_F(y_\mu, x_\mu) = i\delta(x_\mu - y_\mu)\,. \qquad \text{(A.28)}$$

We need several puzzle pieces in the following calculation:

▷ The derivative of the Heaviside function $\Theta(x)$ (Eq. A.9) is exactly the delta distribution

$$\frac{d\Theta(x)}{dx} = \delta(x)\,. \qquad \text{(A.29)}$$

Intuitively this follows because the slope of $\Theta(x)$ is only non-zero at $x = 0$ where it is infinity since the jump is discontinuous.

▷ The "fundamental" propagator $D(t', \vec{x}', t, \vec{x})$ (Eq. 8.82) is a solution of the free Klein-Gordon equation. We can check this explicitly

$$\begin{aligned}
0 &= \left(\partial_\mu \partial^\mu + m^2\right) D(y_\mu, x_\mu) \\
&\quad \text{Eq. 8.82} \\
&= \left(\partial_\mu \partial^\mu + m^2\right) \left(\int \frac{dk^3}{(2\pi)^3 2\omega_k} e^{ik^\mu (y_\mu - x_\mu)} \right) \\
&\quad \partial_x^2 e^{ikx} = -k^2 e^{ikx} \\
&= \int \frac{dk^3}{(2\pi)^3 2\omega_k} \left(-k_\mu k^\mu + m^2\right) e^{ik^\mu (y_\mu - x_\mu)} \\
&\quad k_\mu k^\mu = m^2 \text{ (Eq. 5.40)} \\
&= \int \frac{dk^3}{(2\pi)^3 2\omega_k} \left(-m^2 + m^2\right) e^{ik^\mu (y_\mu - x_\mu)} \\
&\quad -m^2 + m^2 = 0 \\
&= 0 \quad \checkmark
\end{aligned} \tag{A.30}$$

▷ The product rule for double derivatives reads

$$\begin{aligned}
\frac{d^2}{dx^2} fg &= \frac{d}{dx} \left(\frac{d}{dx} fg \right) \\
&= \frac{d}{dx} \left(f'g + fg'\right) \\
&\quad \text{product rule} \\
&= \frac{d}{dx} f'g + \frac{d}{dx} fg' \\
&\quad \text{product rule} \\
&= f''g + f'g' + f'g' + fg'' \\
&= f''g + 2f'g' + fg'',
\end{aligned} \tag{A.31}$$

where $f' \equiv \frac{df}{dx}$ and $f'' \equiv \frac{d^2 f}{dx^2}$.

▷ Distributions like $\delta(x)$ are always only defined under an integral. This becomes important when we want to evaluate the expression $\frac{d\delta(x)}{dx} f(x)$, where we assume that $f(x)$ vanishes at infinity.[6]

If we introduce the necessary integral and then integrate by parts, we find

[6] In mathematical terms, we assume that $f(x)$ has compact support. This means $f(x)$ is only non-zero within a finite region.

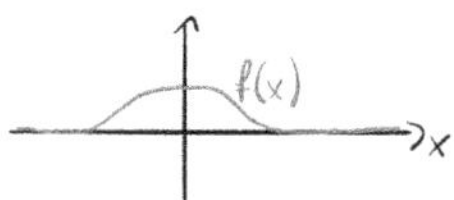

From a physical point of view, this can be motivated by saying that physical fields have to vanish at infinity. This requirement follows from the observation that an infinitely large amount of energy would be necessary to create a field excitation that spreads all the way to infinity.

$$\int_{-\infty}^{\infty} dx\, \frac{d\delta(x)}{dx} f(x) = \delta(x) f(x)\Big|_{-\infty}^{\infty} - \int_{-\infty}^{\infty} dx\, \delta(x) \frac{df(x)}{dx}$$

↷ $f(\infty) = f(-\infty) = 0$

$$= -\int_{-\infty}^{\infty} dx\, \delta(x) \frac{df(x)}{dx} . \qquad \text{(A.32)}$$

If we then go back to our usual sloppy physics notation, we can write

$$\frac{d\delta(x)}{dx} f(x) = -\delta(x) \frac{df(x)}{dx} . \qquad \text{(A.33)}$$

▷ The relation in Eq. A.33 is important when we want to calculate the second derivative of the Heaviside function which appears if we put the Feynman propagator into the Klein-Gordon equation.

If we assume again that we are dealing with a function $f(x)$ that vanishes at infinity, we can calculate:

$$\Big(\frac{d^2}{dx^2}\Theta(x)\Big) f(x) \overset{\text{Eq. A.29}}{=} \Big(\frac{d}{dx}\delta(x)\Big) f(x)$$

↷ Eq. A.33

$$= -\delta(x) \frac{df(x)}{dx} . \qquad \text{(A.34)}$$

▷ To unclutter the notation, we introduce the following shorthand notations:

$$\begin{aligned} D^{yx} &\equiv D(y_\mu, x_\mu) \\ D^{xy} &\equiv D(x_\mu, y_\mu) \\ \Theta^{t't} &\equiv \Theta(t'-t) \\ \Theta^{tt'} &\equiv \Theta(t-t') . \end{aligned} \qquad \text{(A.35)}$$

With these puzzle pieces in place, we are ready to check if the Feynman propagator is indeed a Green's function.

$$
\begin{aligned}
i\delta(x_\mu - y_\mu) &\stackrel{!}{=} \left(\partial_\mu\partial^\mu + m^2\right) D_F(y_\mu, x_\mu) && \text{this is Eq. 8.94} \\
&= \partial_\mu\partial^\mu D_F(y_\mu, x_\mu) + m^2 D_F(y_\mu, x_\mu) && \partial_\mu\partial^\mu = \partial_0^2 - \partial_i^2 \\
&= (\partial_0^2 - \partial_i^2) D_F(y_\mu, x_\mu) + m^2 D_F(y_\mu, x_\mu) && \text{Eq. 8.93, Eq. A.35} \\
&= (\partial_0^2 - \partial_i^2)\left(\Theta^{t't} D^{yx} + \Theta^{tt'} D^{xy}\right) + m^2 D_F(y_\mu, x_\mu) && \partial_i \Theta^{t't} = 0 \\
&= \partial_0^2 \Theta^{t't} D^{yx} - \Theta^{t't}\partial_i^2 D^{yx} + \partial_0^2 \Theta^{tt'} D^{xy} - \Theta^{tt'}\partial_i^2 D^{xy} + m^2 D_F(y_\mu, x_\mu) && \text{Eq. A.31} \\
&= \left(\partial_0^2\Theta^{t't}\right) D^{yx} + \Theta^{t't}\left(\partial_0^2 D^{yx}\right) + 2\left(\partial_0\Theta^{t't}\right)\left(\partial_0 D^{yx}\right) \\
&\quad + \left(\partial_0^2\Theta^{tt'}\right) D^{xy} + \Theta^{tt'}\left(\partial_0^2 D^{xy}\right) + 2\left(\partial_0\Theta^{tt'}\right)\left(\partial_0 D^{xy}\right) \\
&\quad - \Theta^{t't}\partial_i^2 D^{yx} - \Theta^{tt'}\partial_i^2 D^{xy} + m^2 D_F(y_\mu, x_\mu) && \partial_\mu\partial^\mu = \partial_0^2 - \partial_i^2 \\
&= \left(\partial_0^2\Theta^{t't}\right) D^{yx} + \Theta^{t't}\left(\partial_\mu\partial^\mu D^{yx}\right) + 2\left(\partial_0\Theta^{t't}\right)\left(\partial_0 D^{yx}\right) \\
&\quad + \left(\partial_0^2\Theta^{tt'}\right) D^{xy} + \Theta^{tt'}\left(\partial_\mu\partial^\mu D^{xy}\right) + 2\left(\partial_0\Theta^{tt'}\right)\left(\partial_0 D^{xy}\right) \\
&\quad + m^2 D_F(y_\mu, x_\mu) && \text{Eq. A.30} \\
&= \left(\partial_0^2\Theta^{t't}\right) D^{yx} + \Theta^{t't}\left(-m^2 D^{yx}\right) + 2\left(\partial_0\Theta^{t't}\right)\left(\partial_0 D^{yx}\right) \\
&\quad + \left(\partial_0^2\Theta^{tt'}\right) D^{xy} + \Theta^{tt'}\left(-m^2 D^{xy}\right) + 2\left(\partial_0\Theta^{tt'}\right)\left(\partial_0 D^{xy}\right) \\
&\quad + m^2 D_F(y_\mu, x_\mu) && \text{Eq. 8.93} \\
&= \left(\partial_0^2\Theta^{t't}\right) D^{yx} + 2\left(\partial_0\Theta^{t't}\right)\left(\partial_0 D^{yx}\right) \\
&\quad + \left(\partial_0^2\Theta^{tt'}\right) D^{xy} + 2\left(\partial_0\Theta^{tt'}\right)\left(\partial_0 D^{xy}\right) \\
&\quad + m^2 D_F(y_\mu, x_\mu) - m^2 D_F(y_\mu, x_\mu) && m^2 - m^2 = 0 \\
&= \left(\partial_0^2\Theta^{t't}\right) D^{yx} + 2\left(\partial_0\Theta^{t't}\right)\left(\partial_0 D^{yx}\right) \\
&\quad + \left(\partial_0^2\Theta^{tt'}\right) D^{xy} + 2\left(\partial_0\Theta^{tt'}\right)\left(\partial_0 D^{xy}\right) . && \text{(A.36)}
\end{aligned}
$$

We can simplify this further by using the facts about the derivatives of the Heaviside functions that we discussed above:

$$\begin{aligned}
&\Big(\partial_0^2\Theta^{t't}\Big)D^{yx} + 2\Big(\partial_0\Theta^{t't}\Big)\Big(\partial_0 D^{yx}\Big) && \text{this is Eq. A.36}\\
&\quad + \Big(\partial_0^2\Theta^{tt'}\Big)D^{xy} + 2\Big(\partial_0\Theta^{tt'}\Big)\Big(\partial_0 D^{xy}\Big) && \text{Eq. A.29}\\
&= \Big(\partial_0^2\Theta^{t't}\Big)D^{yx} + 2\Big(\delta(t'-t)\Big)\Big(\partial_0 D^{yx}\Big)\\
&\quad + \Big(\partial_0^2\Theta^{tt'}\Big)D^{xy} + 2\Big(\delta(t-t')\Big)\Big(\partial_0 D^{xy}\Big) && \text{Eq. A.34}\\
&= -\Big(\delta(t'-t)\Big)\partial_0 D^{yx} + 2\Big(\delta(t'-t)\Big)\Big(\partial_0 D^{yx}\Big)\\
&\quad - \Big(\delta(t-t')\Big)\partial_0 D^{xy} + 2\Big(\delta(t-t')\Big)\Big(\partial_0 D^{xy}\Big) && 2-1=1\\
&= \delta(t'-t)\partial_0 D^{yx} + \delta(t-t')\partial_0 D^{xy} && \text{Eq. 8.82}\\
&= \delta(t'-t)\partial_0\Big(\int \frac{dk^3}{(2\pi)^3 2\omega_k} e^{ik^\mu(y_\mu - x_\mu)}\Big)\\
&\quad + \delta(t-t')\partial_0\Big(\int \frac{dk^3}{(2\pi)^3 2\omega_k} e^{ik^\mu(x_\mu - y_\mu)}\Big) && \partial_t e^{i\omega t} = i\omega e^{i\omega t},\ k_0 = \omega_k\\
&= \delta(t'-t)\int \frac{dk^3}{(2\pi)^3 2\omega_k} i\omega_k e^{ik^\mu(y_\mu - x_\mu)}\\
&\quad + \delta(t-t')\int \frac{dk^3}{(2\pi)^3 2\omega_k} i\omega_k e^{ik^\mu(x_\mu - y_\mu)} && \cancel{\omega_k}\\
&= \delta(t'-t)\int \frac{dk^3\, i}{(2\pi)^3 2} e^{ik^\mu(y_\mu - x_\mu)}\\
&\quad + \delta(t-t')\int \frac{dk^3\, i}{(2\pi)^3 2} e^{ik^\mu(x_\mu - y_\mu)} && \delta(t'-t) \leftrightarrow t = t'\\
&= \delta(t'-t)\int \frac{dk^3\, i}{(2\pi)^3 2} e^{i\vec{k}\cdot(\vec{y}-\vec{x})}\\
&\quad + \delta(t-t')\int \frac{dk^3\, i}{(2\pi)^3 2} e^{i\vec{k}\cdot(\vec{x}-\vec{y})} && \delta(\vec{y}-\vec{x}) \equiv \int \frac{dk^3}{(2\pi)^3} e^{i\vec{k}\cdot(\vec{y}-\vec{x})}\ \text{(Eq. 8.80)}\\
&= \delta(t'-t)\frac{i}{2}\delta(\vec{y}-\vec{x}) + \delta(t-t')\frac{i}{2}\delta(\vec{x}-\vec{y}) && \delta(t'-t) = \delta(t-t'),\ \delta(\vec{y}-\vec{x}) = \delta(\vec{x}-\vec{y})\\
&= \delta(t'-t)\frac{i}{2}\delta(\vec{y}-\vec{x}) + \delta(t-t')\frac{i}{2}\delta(\vec{x}-\vec{y}) && \frac{1}{2}+\frac{1}{2} = 1\\
&= i\delta(t'-t)\delta(\vec{x}-\vec{y}) && \\
&= i\delta(x_\mu - y_\mu) \quad \checkmark && \text{(A.37)}
\end{aligned}$$

A.8 Total Charge in Terms of Creation and Annihilation Operators

In this appendix, we want to demonstrate that the electric charge (Eq. 4.61)

$$\tilde{Q}_q = iq \int d^3x \left(\frac{\partial \mathcal{L}}{\partial(\partial_0 \phi^\dagger)} \phi^\dagger - \frac{\partial \mathcal{L}}{\partial(\partial_0 \phi)} \phi \right) . \tag{A.38}$$

can be written as

$$\tilde{Q}_q = q \int \frac{dk^3}{(2\pi)^3} \left(a^\dagger(k)a(k) - b^\dagger(k)b(k) \right) . \tag{A.39}$$

if we use the Lagrangian (Eq. 8.102) and the explicit expansions of ϕ and $\phi^\dagger$.

First of all, we calculate

$$\begin{aligned} &\frac{\partial \mathcal{L}}{\partial(\partial_0 \phi)} \\ &\quad \text{Eq. 8.102} \\ &= \frac{\partial\Big(\big(\partial_\mu \phi^\dagger \partial^\mu \phi - m^2 \phi^\dagger \phi \big) \Big)}{\partial(\partial_0 \phi)} \\ &= \partial_0 \phi^\dagger \equiv \pi \end{aligned} \tag{A.40}$$

and

$$\begin{aligned} &\frac{\partial \mathcal{L}}{\partial(\partial_0^\dagger \phi)} \\ &\quad \text{Eq. 8.102} \\ &= \frac{\partial\Big(\big(\partial_\mu \phi^\dagger \partial^\mu \phi - m^2 \phi^\dagger \phi \big) \Big)}{\partial(\partial_0^\dagger \phi)} \\ &= \partial_0 \phi \equiv \pi^\dagger , \end{aligned} \tag{A.41}$$

where π is the conjugate momentum density (Eq. 8.104). The charge operator therefore reads

$$\tilde{Q}_q = iq \int d^3x \left(\pi^\dagger \phi^\dagger - \pi\phi \right) . \tag{A.42}$$

Moreover, the conjugate momentum density reads in more explicit terms

$$\begin{aligned}
\pi^\dagger &\equiv \partial_0 \phi \\
&= \partial_0 \Big(\int dk^3 \frac{1}{(2\pi)^3 \sqrt{2\omega_k}} \Big(a(\vec{k}) e^{-ikx} + b^\dagger(\vec{k}) e^{ikx} \Big) \Big) \\
&= \int dk^3 \frac{1}{(2\pi)^3 \sqrt{2\omega_k}} \Big(a(\vec{k})(-ik_0) e^{-ikx} + b^\dagger(\vec{k})(ik_0) e^{ikx} \Big) \\
&= \int dk^3 \frac{i\sqrt{\omega_k}}{(2\pi)^3 \sqrt{2}} \Big(-a(\vec{k}) e^{-ikx} + b^\dagger(\vec{k}) e^{ikx} \Big) . \qquad \text{(A.43)}
\end{aligned}$$

↷ Eq. 8.100

↷

↷ $k_0 \equiv \omega_k$

This implies

$$\begin{aligned}
\pi &\equiv \partial_0 \phi^\dagger \\
&= \int dk^3 \frac{i\sqrt{\omega_k}}{(2\pi)^3 \sqrt{2}} \Big(a^\dagger(\vec{k}) e^{ikx} - b(\vec{k}) e^{-ikx} \Big) . \qquad \text{(A.44)}
\end{aligned}$$

↷

Let's focus on the last term in Eq. A.42:

$$\begin{aligned}
&\int d^3x \, \pi\phi \\
&= \int d^3x \left(\int dk^3 \frac{i\sqrt{\omega_k}}{(2\pi)^3 \sqrt{2}} \Big(a^\dagger(\vec{k}) e^{ikx} - b(\vec{k}) e^{-ikx} \Big) \right) \\
&\qquad \times \left(\int dq^3 \frac{1}{(2\pi)^3 \sqrt{2\omega_q}} \Big(a(\vec{q}) e^{-iqx} + b^\dagger(\vec{q}) e^{iqx} \Big) \right) \\
&= \int d^3x \, \frac{i dk^3 dq^3}{(2\pi)^6} \frac{\sqrt{\omega_k}}{2\sqrt{\omega_q}} \left(\Big(a^\dagger(\vec{k}) e^{ikx} - b(\vec{k}) e^{-ikx} \Big) \Big(a(\vec{q}) e^{-iqx} + b^\dagger(\vec{q}) e^{iqx} \Big) \right) \\
&= \int d^3x \, \frac{i dk^3 dq^3}{(2\pi)^6} \frac{\sqrt{\omega_k}}{2\sqrt{\omega_q}} \Big(a^\dagger(\vec{k}) a(\vec{q}) e^{ix(k-q)} - b(\vec{k}) a(\vec{q}) e^{-ix(k+q)} \\
&\qquad + a^\dagger(\vec{k}) b^\dagger(\vec{q}) e^{ix(k+q)} - b(\vec{k}) b^\dagger(\vec{q}) e^{-ix(k-q)} \Big)
\end{aligned}$$

↷

↷

↷

↷ (see next page)

$$= \int \frac{idk^3dq^3}{(2\pi)^3} \frac{\sqrt{\omega_k}}{2\sqrt{\omega_q})} \Big(a^\dagger(\vec{k})a(\vec{q})e^{ix_0(\omega_k-\omega_q)}\delta(\vec{k}-\vec{q}) - b(\vec{k})a(\vec{q})e^{-ix_0(\omega_k+\omega_q)}\delta(\vec{k}+\vec{q})$$
$$+ a^\dagger(\vec{k})b^\dagger(\vec{q})e^{ix_0(\omega_k+\omega_q)}\delta(\vec{k}+\vec{q}) - b(\vec{k})b^\dagger(\vec{q})e^{-ix_0(\omega_k-\omega_q)}\delta(\vec{k}-\vec{q})\Big)$$

$$= \int \frac{idk^3}{(2\pi)^3} \frac{\sqrt{\omega_k}}{2\sqrt{\omega_k}} \Big(a^\dagger(\vec{k})a(\vec{k})e^{-ix_0(\omega_k-\omega_k)} - b(\vec{k})a(-\vec{k})e^{ix_0(\omega_k+\omega_k)}$$
$$+ a^\dagger(\vec{k})b^\dagger(-\vec{k})e^{ix_0(\omega_k+\omega_k)} - b(\vec{k})b^\dagger(\vec{k})e^{-ix_0(\omega_k-\omega_k)}\Big)$$

$$= \int \frac{idk^3}{(2\pi)^3} \frac{1}{2} \Big(a^\dagger(\vec{k})a(\vec{k}) - b(\vec{k})a(-\vec{k})e^{-i2x_0\omega_k} + a^\dagger(\vec{k})b^\dagger(-\vec{k})e^{i2x_0\omega_k} - b(\vec{k})b^\dagger(\vec{k})\Big) \tag{A.45}$$

Analogously, we find

$$\int d^3x\, \pi^\dagger\phi^\dagger$$

$$= \int d^3x \left(\int dk^3 \frac{i\sqrt{\omega_k}}{(2\pi)^3\sqrt{2}} \Big(-a(\vec{k})e^{-ikx} + b^\dagger(\vec{k})e^{ikx}\Big) \right)$$
$$\times \left(\int dq^3 \frac{1}{(2\pi)^3\sqrt{2\omega_q}} \Big(a^\dagger(\vec{q})e^{iqx} + b(\vec{q})e^{-iqx}\Big) \right)$$

$$= \int \frac{idk^3}{(2\pi)^3} \frac{1}{2} \Big(-a(\vec{k})a^\dagger(\vec{k}) + b^\dagger(\vec{k})a^\dagger(-\vec{k})e^{i2x_0\omega_k}$$
$$- a(\vec{k})b(-\vec{k})e^{-i2x_0\omega_k} + b^\dagger(\vec{k})b(\vec{k})\Big)\,. \tag{A.46}$$

Therefore we can rewrite Eq. A.42 as

$$\tilde{Q}_q = iq \int d^3x\, \big(\pi^\dagger\phi^\dagger - \pi\phi\big)$$

$$= iq \Bigg(\int \frac{idk^3}{(2\pi)^3} \frac{1}{2} \Big(-a(\vec{k})a^\dagger(\vec{k}) + b^\dagger(\vec{k})a^\dagger(-\vec{k})e^{i2x_0\omega_k}$$
$$- a(\vec{k})b(-\vec{k})e^{-i2x_0\omega_k} + b^\dagger(\vec{k})b(\vec{k})\Big)$$
$$- \int \frac{idk^3}{(2\pi)^3} \frac{1}{2} \Big(a^\dagger(\vec{k})a(\vec{k}) - b(\vec{k})a(-\vec{k})e^{-i2x_0\omega_k}$$
$$+ a^\dagger(\vec{k})b^\dagger(-\vec{k})e^{i2x_0\omega_k} - b(\vec{k})b^\dagger(\vec{k})\Big)\Bigg)$$

see below

$$= q \int \frac{dk^3}{(2\pi)^3} \frac{1}{2} \Big(a^\dagger(\vec{k})a(\vec{k}) + a(\vec{k})a^\dagger(\vec{k}) - b^\dagger(\vec{k})b(\vec{k}) - b(\vec{k})b^\dagger(\vec{k}) \Big)$$

$\quad AB = BA + [A, B]$

$$= q \int \frac{dk^3}{(2\pi)^3} \frac{1}{2} \Big(2a^\dagger(\vec{k})a(\vec{k}) + [a(\vec{k}), a^\dagger(\vec{k})] - 2b^\dagger(\vec{k})b(\vec{k}) - [b(\vec{k}), b^\dagger(\vec{k})] \Big)$$

$$= q \int \frac{dk^3}{(2\pi)^3} \frac{1}{2} \Big(2a^\dagger(\vec{k})a(\vec{k}) - 2b^\dagger(\vec{k})b(\vec{k}) + [a(\vec{k}), a^\dagger(\vec{k})] + [b(\vec{k}), b^\dagger(\vec{k})] \Big) . \qquad (A.47)$$

The first two terms here are exactly what we wanted to derive. The remaining two terms yield an infinitely large constant offset that we already encountered for other Noether charges like momentum or energy. Thus if we ignore these constant terms, we find

$$\tilde{Q}_q = q \int \frac{dk^3}{(2\pi)^3} \Big(a^\dagger(k)a(k) - b^\dagger(k)b(k) \Big) . \qquad (A.48)$$

Take note that we used in the calculation above that

$$\int \frac{dk^3}{(2\pi)^3} b^\dagger(\vec{k})a^\dagger(-\vec{k})e^{i2x_0\omega_k} - \int \frac{dk^3}{(2\pi)^3} a^\dagger(\vec{k})b^\dagger(-\vec{k})e^{i2x_0\omega_k}$$

$\quad \vec{k} \to -\vec{k}$

$$= \int \frac{dk^3}{(2\pi)^3} b^\dagger(\vec{k})a^\dagger(-\vec{k})e^{i2x_0\omega_k} - \int \frac{dk^3}{(2\pi)^3} a^\dagger(-\vec{k})b^\dagger(\vec{k})e^{i2x_0\omega_k}$$

$\quad [a^\dagger, b^\dagger] = 0$

$$= \int \frac{dk^3}{(2\pi)^3} b^\dagger(\vec{k})a^\dagger(-\vec{k})e^{i2x_0\omega_k} - \int \frac{dk^3}{(2\pi)^3} b^\dagger(\vec{k})a^\dagger(-\vec{k})e^{i2x_0\omega_k}$$

$$= 0 . \qquad (A.49)$$

Moreover, by the same argument $b(\vec{k})a(-\vec{k})e^{-i2x_0\omega_k}$ and $a(\vec{k})b(-\vec{k})e^{-i2x_0\omega_k}$ cancel.

B

Cumbersome Calculations from Part II and Part III

B.1 Validating Wick's Theorem For Three Field Products

To build some confidence in the validity of Wick's theorem, we want to bring $\phi(x)\phi(y)\phi(z)$ into normal order by hand and then compare the result to what we get by applying Wick's theorem (Eq. 11.24). First of all, take note that, without losing generality, we can assume that $x_0 > y_0 > z_0$. This is possible because in quantum field theory, we always integrate over our spacetime variables. Therefore, we could write the time ordered product by using theta functions. However, since we integrate over our spacetime variables, we can then relabel these spacetime variables such that we are only left with one time ordered term. Formulated differently, the terms with different time ordering ($y_0 > x_0 > z_0$, etc) yield exactly the same result. Thus it is sufficient to consider the case $x_0 > y_0 > z_0$. To simplify the calculation, we introduce the notation $\phi(x) \equiv \phi_x$, $\phi(y) \equiv \phi_y$, $\phi(z) \equiv \phi_z$. We then find

$$
\begin{aligned}
T\phi_x\phi_y\phi_z &= \phi_x T\phi_y\phi_z \\
&= \phi_x\Big(: \phi_y\phi_z : + \overbracket{\phi_y\phi_z}\Big) \\
&= \phi_x : \phi_y\phi_z : + \phi_x\overbracket{\phi_y\phi_z}\,.
\end{aligned}
\tag{B.1}
$$

(Eq. 11.17)

In the first line we used that $y_0 > z_0$ which implies $T\phi_y\phi_z = \phi_y\phi_z$. The second term in the final line is already one of the terms that we expect from applying Wick's theorem (Eq. 11.24). Thus let's focus on the first term, which we still need to bring into normal order. This is possible by using the explicit field splitting in terms of creation and annihilation terms (Eq. 10.13):[1]

[1] Reminder: in Eq. 10.13 we defined $\phi \equiv \phi^- + \phi^+$, where ϕ^- is an integral over annihilation operators and ϕ^+ is an integral over creation operators.

$$
\begin{aligned}
\phi_x : \phi_y\phi_z : &= \phi_x : \Big((\phi_y^- + \phi_y^+)(\phi_z^- + (\phi_z^+)\Big) : \\
&= \phi_x : \Big(\phi_y^-\phi_z^- + \phi_y^-\phi_z^+ + \phi_y^+\phi_z^- + \phi_y^+\phi_z^+\Big) : \\
&= \phi_x\Big(\phi_y^-\phi_z^- + \phi_z^+\phi_y^- + \phi_y^+\phi_z^- + \phi_y^+\phi_z^+\Big) \\
&= (\phi_x^- + \phi_x^+)\Big(\phi_y^-\phi_z^- + \phi_z^+\phi_y^- + \phi_y^+\phi_z^- + \phi_y^+\phi_z^+\Big) \\
&= \phi_x^-\phi_y^-\phi_z^- + \phi_x^-\phi_z^+\phi_y^- + \phi_x^-\phi_y^+\phi_z^- + \phi_x^-\phi_y^+\phi_z^+ \\
&\quad + \phi_x^+\phi_y^-\phi_z^- + \phi_x^+\phi_z^+\phi_y^- + \phi_x^+\phi_y^+\phi_z^- + \phi_x^+\phi_y^+\phi_z^+ \\
&= \phi_x^-\phi_y^-\phi_z^- + \Big(\phi_z^+\phi_x^- + [\phi_x^-, \phi_z^+]\Big)\phi_y^- \\
&\quad + \Big(\phi_y^+\phi_x^- + [\phi_x^-, \phi_y^+]\Big)\phi_z^- + \Big(\phi_y^+\phi_x^- + [\phi_x^-, \phi_y^+]\Big)\phi_z^+ \\
&\quad + \phi_x^+\phi_y^-\phi_z^- + \phi_x^+\phi_z^+\phi_y^- + \phi_x^+\phi_y^+\phi_z^- + \phi_x^+\phi_y^+\phi_z^+ \\
&= \phi_x^-\phi_y^-\phi_z^- + \phi_z^+\phi_x^-\phi_y^- + [\phi_x^-, \phi_z^+]\phi_y^- \\
&\quad + \phi_y^+\phi_x^-\phi_z^- + [\phi_x^-, \phi_y^+]\phi_z^- \\
&\quad + \phi_y^+\Big(\phi_z^+\phi_x^- + [\phi_x^-, \phi_z^+]\Big) + [\phi_x^-, \phi_y^+]\phi_z^+ \\
&\quad + \phi_x^+\phi_y^-\phi_z^- + \phi_x^+\phi_z^+\phi_y^- + \phi_x^+\phi_y^+\phi_z^- + \phi_x^+\phi_y^+\phi_z^+
\end{aligned}
$$

see next page

$$
\begin{aligned}
&= [\phi_x^-, \phi_y^+](\phi_z^- + \phi_z^+) + [\phi_x^-, \phi_z^+](\phi_y^- + \phi_y^+) \\
&\quad + \phi_x^- \phi_y^- \phi_z^- + \phi_z^+ \phi_x^- \phi_y^- + \phi_y^+ \phi_x^- \phi_z^- \\
&\quad + \phi_y^+ \phi_z^+ \phi_x^- + \phi_x^+ \phi_y^- \phi_z^- + \phi_x^+ \phi_z^+ \phi_y^- \\
&\quad + \phi_x^+ \phi_y^+ \phi_z^- + \phi_x^+ \phi_y^+ \phi_z^+ \\
&= [\phi_x^-, \phi_y^+]\phi_z + [\phi_x^-, \phi_z^+]\phi_y + :\phi_x\phi_y\phi_z: \\
&= \overline{\phi(x)\phi(y)}\phi_z + \overline{\phi(x)\phi(z)}\phi_y + :\phi_x\phi_y\phi_z: \, .
\end{aligned}
\tag{B.2}
$$

Eq. 11.15

If we plug this back into Eq. B.1, we find

$$
\begin{aligned}
T\phi_x\phi_y\phi_z &= \phi_x : \phi_y\phi_z : + \phi_x\overline{\phi_y\phi_z} \\
&= \overline{\phi(x)\phi(y)}\phi_z + \overline{\phi(x)\phi(z)}\phi_y + :\phi_x\phi_y\phi_z: + \phi_x\overline{\phi_y\phi_z} \, .
\end{aligned}
\tag{B.3}
$$

Eq. B.2

This is exactly what we get if we use Wick's theorem (Eq. 11.24).

B.2 Work in the Vicinity of an Infinitely Long Wire

In this appendix, we want to show that if we plug the regularized potential (Eq. 13.11)

$$V(x) = \lambda \int_{-L}^{L} \frac{dy}{\sqrt{x^2+y^2}}$$

$$\int dy \frac{1}{\sqrt{x^2+y^2}} = \ln\left(\sqrt{x^2+y^2}+y\right)$$

$$= \lambda \ln\left[\frac{+L+\sqrt{L^2+x^2}}{-L+\sqrt{L^2+x^2}}\right] . \tag{B.4}$$

into the work formula (Eq. 13.10)

$$W(x_2,x_1) = q\Big(V(x_2)-V(x_1)\Big) \tag{B.5}$$

we get a finite result, even in the limit $L \to \infty$. Thus we start by plugging the regularized potential into the work formula:

$$\begin{aligned}
W(x_2,x_1) &\overset{13.10}{=} q\Big(V(x_2)-V(x_1)\Big) \\
&= q\left(\lambda \ln\left[\frac{+L+\sqrt{L^2+x_2^2}}{-L+\sqrt{L^2+x_2^2}}\right] - \lambda \ln\left[\frac{+L+\sqrt{L^2+x_1^2}}{-L+\sqrt{L^2+x_1^2}}\right]\right) \\
&= q\lambda\left(\ln\left[\frac{L\left(1+\sqrt{1+\frac{x_2^2}{L^2}}\right)}{L\left(-1+\sqrt{1+\frac{x_2^2}{L^2}}\right)}\right] - \ln\left[\frac{L\left(1+\sqrt{1+\frac{x_1^2}{L^2}}\right)}{L\left(-1+\sqrt{1+\frac{x_1^2}{L^2}}\right)}\right]\right) \\
&= q\lambda\left(\ln\left[\frac{1+\sqrt{1+\frac{x_2^2}{L^2}}}{-1+\sqrt{1+\frac{x_2^2}{L^2}}}\right] - \ln\left[\frac{1+\sqrt{1+\frac{x_1^2}{L^2}}}{-1+\sqrt{1+\frac{x_1^2}{L^2}}}\right]\right) .
\end{aligned} \tag{B.6}$$

To understand why this is finite in the limit $L \to \infty$, take note that in the limit $L \to \infty$, we have $L^2 \gg x_1^2$ and $L^2 \gg x_1^2$. Therefore, we can use the approximation $\sqrt{1+\epsilon} \approx 1+\frac{\epsilon}{2}$, which is valid for $\epsilon \ll 1$. In our case, $\frac{x_1^2}{L^2} \ll 1$ and $\frac{x_2^2}{L^2} \ll 1$ and we therefore find

$$W(x_2,x_1) = q\lambda\Big(\ln\left[\frac{1+\sqrt{1+\frac{x_2^2}{L^2}}}{-1+\sqrt{1+\frac{x_2^2}{L^2}}}\right] - \ln\left[\frac{1+\sqrt{1+\frac{x_1^2}{L^2}}}{-1+\sqrt{1+\frac{x_1^2}{L^2}}}\right]\Big)$$

$\curvearrowright \quad \sqrt{1+\epsilon} \approx 1 + \frac{\epsilon}{2},$

$$\approx q\lambda\Big(\ln\left[\frac{1+\left(1+\frac{x_2^2}{2L^2}\right)}{-1+\left(1+\frac{x_2^2}{2L^2}\right)}\right] - \ln\left[\frac{1+\left(1+\frac{x_1^2}{2L^2}\right)}{-1+\left(1+\frac{x_1^2}{2L^2}\right)}\right]\Big)$$

$\curvearrowright$

$$= q\lambda\Big(\ln\left[\frac{2+\frac{x_2^2}{2L^2}}{\frac{x_2^2}{2L^2}}\right] - \ln\left[\frac{2+\frac{x_1^2}{2L^2}}{\frac{x_1^2}{2L^2}}\right]\Big)$$

$\curvearrowright \quad \ln a - \ln b = \ln\frac{a}{b}$

$$= q\lambda \ln\left[\frac{2+\frac{x_2^2}{2L^2}}{\frac{x_2^2}{2L^2}}\left(\frac{\frac{x_1^2}{2L^2}}{2+\frac{x_1^2}{2L^2}}\right)\right]$$

$\curvearrowright$

$$= q\lambda \ln\left[\frac{2+\frac{x_2^2}{2L^2}}{2+\frac{x_1^2}{2L^2}}\left(\frac{\frac{x_1^2}{2L^2}}{\frac{x_2^2}{2L^2}}\right)\right]$$

$\curvearrowright \quad \cancel{2L^2}$

$$= q\lambda \ln\left[\frac{2+\frac{x_2^2}{2L^2}}{2+\frac{x_1^2}{2L^2}}\left(\frac{x_1^2}{x_2^2}\right)\right]. \tag{B.7}$$

In the limit $L \to \infty$, we have $\frac{x_2^2}{2L^2} \to 0$ and $\frac{x_1^2}{2L^2} \to 0$ and the work formula therefore reads

$$W(x_2,x_1) \approx q\lambda \ln\left[\frac{2}{2}\left(\frac{x_1^2}{x_2^2}\right)\right] = q\lambda \ln\left[\frac{x_1^2}{x_2^2}\right], \tag{B.8}$$

which is indeed finite.

B.3 Fourier Transform of the Yukawa Potential

In this appendix, we want to show that[2]

[2] We stumbled upon this factor in Eq. 12.26.

$$\tilde{V}(\vec{k}) \equiv \frac{-g^2}{\vec{k}^2 + m_\phi^2} \tag{B.9}$$

is the Fourier transform of the Yukawa potential (Eq. 6.20)

$$V(\vec{x}) = \frac{g^2}{4\pi|\vec{x}|} e^{-m_\phi|\vec{x}|} . \tag{B.10}$$

To see this, we use that the Fourier transform $\tilde{f}(k)$ of a function $f(x)$ is defined as

$$\tilde{f}(k) \equiv \int dx\, e^{-ixk} f(x) . \tag{B.11}$$

For the Yukawa potential, this formula yields

$$\begin{aligned}
\tilde{V}(\vec{k}) &= \int d^3x\, e^{-i\vec{x}\cdot\vec{k}} V(\vec{x}) && \text{Eq. B.10} \\
&= \int d^3x\, e^{-i\vec{x}\cdot\vec{k}} \Big(\frac{g^2}{4\pi|\vec{x}|} e^{-m_\phi|\vec{x}|} \Big) && \text{spherical coordinates} \\
&= \int dr\, d\theta\, d\phi\, r^2 \sin(\theta)\, e^{-i|\vec{k}||\vec{x}|\cos(\theta)} \Big(\frac{g^2}{4\pi|\vec{x}|} e^{-m_\phi|\vec{x}|} \Big) && |x| \equiv r \\
&= \frac{g^2}{4\pi} \int dr\, d\theta\, d\phi\, r \sin(\theta)\, e^{-i|\vec{k}|r\cos(\theta)} e^{-m_\phi r} && \int d\phi \\
&= \frac{g^2}{4\pi} 2\pi \int dr\, d\theta\, r \sin(\theta)\, e^{-i|\vec{k}|r\cos(\theta)} e^{-m_\phi r} && \int d\theta \text{ (see next page)}
\end{aligned}$$

$$= \frac{g^2}{2} \frac{1}{i|\vec{k}|} \int dr\, e^{-i|\vec{k}|r\cos(\theta)} e^{-m_\phi r} \Big|_{\theta=0}^{\theta=\pi}$$

↷ $\cos 0 = 1, \cos\pi = -1$

$$= \frac{g^2}{2i|\vec{k}|} \int dr \left(e^{i|\vec{k}|r} - e^{-i|\vec{k}|r} \right) e^{-m_\phi r}$$

↷ $\sin(x) = \frac{1}{2i}(e^{ix} - e^{-ix})$

$$= \frac{g^2}{|\vec{k}|} \int dr \, \sin(|\vec{k}|r) e^{-m_\phi r}$$

↷ $\int dr$

$$= \frac{g^2}{|\vec{k}|} \frac{e^{-m_\phi r}\left(m_\phi \sin(|\vec{k}|r) - |\vec{k}|\cos(|\vec{k}|r)\right)}{m_\phi^2 + |\vec{k}|^2} \Bigg|_{r=0}^{r=\infty}$$

↷ $e^{-\infty} = 0, e^0 = 1, \cos(0) = 1, \sin(0) = 0$

$$= \frac{-g^2}{|\vec{k}|} \frac{|\vec{k}|}{m_\phi^2 + |\vec{k}|^2}$$

↷ $\cancel{|\vec{k}|}$

$$= \frac{-g^2}{m_\phi^2 + |\vec{k}|^2} . \tag{B.12}$$

This is exactly Eq. B.9.

C

Wave Properties

In this appendix, we talk about the various quantities $(\vec{k}, \omega, \pm, \vec{E}_0, \delta)$ which appear in solutions of the wave equation

$$f(x) = A\cos(kx \pm \omega t + \delta)\,. \qquad \text{(C.1)}$$

▷ We typically call the argument $\varphi \equiv (kx \pm \omega t)$ of our periodic function $\cos\varphi$ the **phase** of the wave. A phase of zero $\varphi = 0$ means we are at the top of our waveform since $\cos(0) = 1$ If the phase is $\varphi = \pi$, we are at the bottom since $\cos(\pi) = -1$.

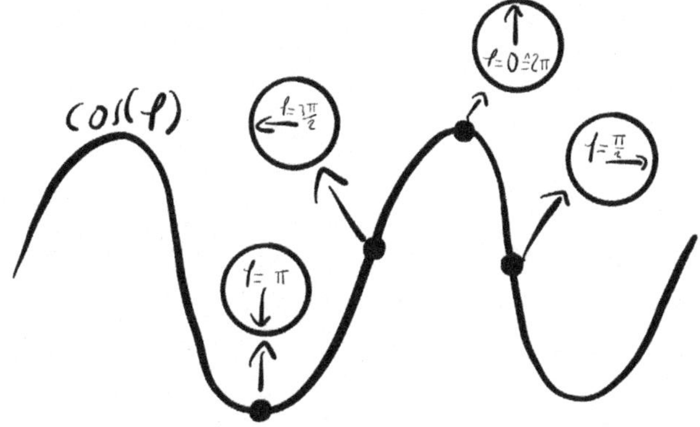

One full wave cycle starts at $\varphi = 0$ and goes on until $\varphi = 2\pi$.

A periodic wave repeats itself after 2π since $\cos(\varphi + 2\pi) = \cos(\varphi)$.[1]

[1] Take note that it is conventional in theoretical physics to measure angles in multiples of π, e.g. $180° \leftrightarrow \pi$ and for a full circle $360° \leftrightarrow 2\pi$.

▷ If we are dealing, with a three-dimensional system, our solution reads

$$f(x) = A\cos(\vec{k} \cdot \vec{x} \pm \omega t + \delta) . \qquad \text{(C.2)}$$

The vector $\vec{k}$ is usually called the **wave vector**. The direction of $\vec{k}$ tells us in which direction the wave is traveling.

The length of the wave vector $|\vec{k}|$ describes how many oscillations there are *per meter*. To understand this, imagine that we could stop the time, i.e. keep t fixed and then move through space. As we move along the axis defined by $\vec{k}$ we count how many full wave shapes we encounter per meter. This number is the wave number. One full oscillation is over as soon as the phase of the wave has increased by 2π. Hence, we can say a bit more precisely that $|\vec{k}|$ measures how many 2π cycles there are per meter.[2] For this reason, $|\vec{k}|$ is known as spatial angular frequency or **wave number**.[3]

[2] Formulated differently, $|\vec{k}|$ tells us how much the phase changes as we move one meter along the wave at one fixed point in time.

[3] This is in contrast to the *temporal* angular frequency ω, which tells us how many oscillations there are per second.

For example, if we move 2 meters and observe that the phase changes by 20π, we know that the wave number is 10π radians per meter.[4]

[4] $20\pi/2\text{ m} = 10\pi/\text{ m}$

The wave number is directly related to the **wavelength** λ:

$$\lambda = \frac{2\pi}{|\vec{k}|} . \qquad \text{(C.3)}$$

The wavelength is defined as the spatial distance that we need to move until the phase of the wave has changed by 2π:[5]

[5] Formulated differently, the wavelength is the distance between adjacent identical parts of the wave.

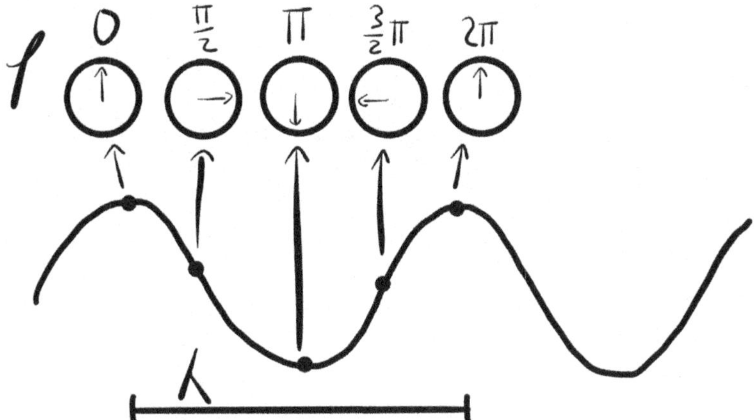

▷ The constant ω is known as temporal angular frequency or simply **angular frequency**. The angular frequency describes how many oscillations there are *per second*. To understand it, imagine that we are at one fixed point in space and time moves on. We now observe how the wave moves up and down at this one particular point. We count how often it undergoes a full oscillation, i.e. from maximum to maximum.

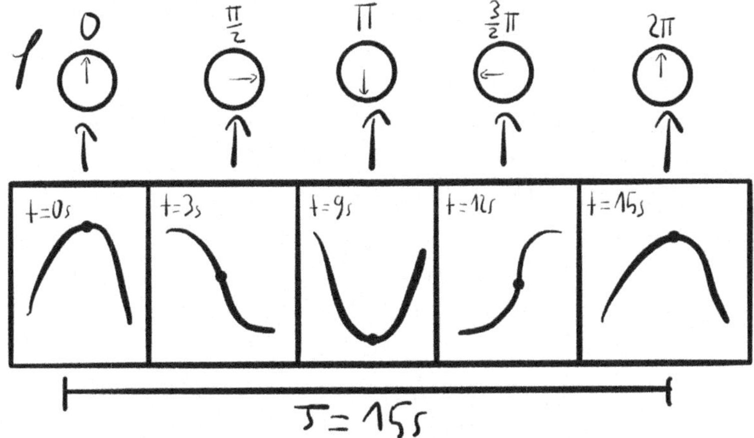

The result is the angular frequency of the wave. Formulated differently, ω tells us how much the phase changes during one second. For example, if we observe the wave for two seconds and the phase changes by 20π, i.e. we observe 10 full wave cycles, we know the angular frequency is 10π radians per second.

The angular frequency is directly related to the **period** τ and ordinary **frequency** f of the wave

$$\omega = \frac{2\pi}{\tau} = 2\pi f \,. \tag{C.4}$$

The period τ is the time the wave needs for one full oscillation.

The factor A in front of the oscillating function encodes the **peak magnitude of the oscillation**:

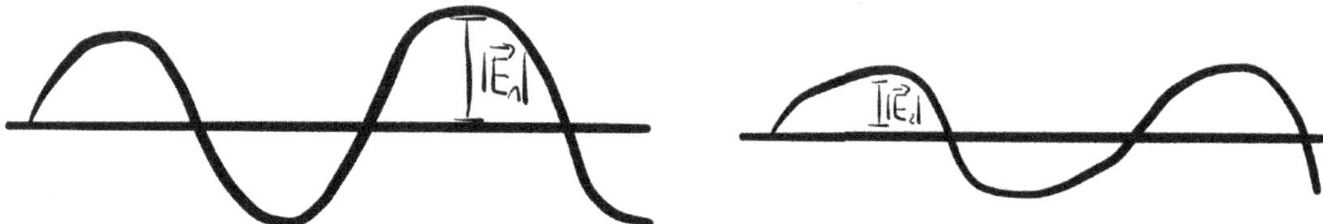

▷ The sign between the two terms in the cosine function determines whether our wave moves up or down on the axis defined by $\vec{k}$. For example, a solution of the form $\vec{E} = \vec{E}(x - ct)$ describes a wave which moves to the right on our x-axis, while a solution of the form $\vec{E} = \vec{E}(x + ct)$ describes a wave which moves to the left. This interpretation comes about since if we focus on a fixed point in our wave shape $\vec{E}(x - ct)$ and t increases, x also has to increase in order to keep $\vec{E}(x - ct)$ at the same value. In other words, this means that if we focus on a specific point in our wave shape, at a later point in time (a larger t), we will find it at a larger x.

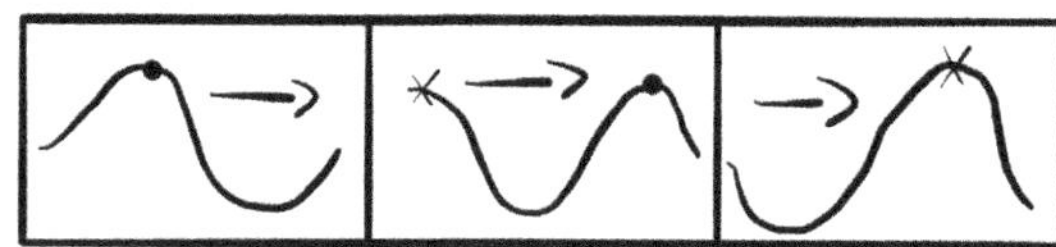

Analogously, a solution of the form $E = E(z - ct)$ describes a wave that moves up on our z-axis.

▷ The **absolute phase** δ encodes the phase of the wave at $\vec{r} = 0$ and $t = 0$.

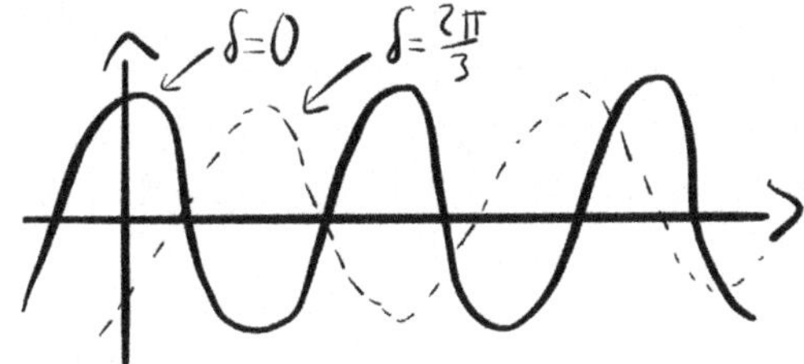

This quantity isn't measurable since it depends on how we choose our coordinate system. However, it is still important if we consider superposition of waves. If we add two waves, their relative absolute phase crucially determines if the amplitude of the resulting wave is larger

in which case we speak of **constructive interference** or smaller

in which case we speak of **destructive interference**.

Now that we have a rudimentary understanding of the basic quantities associated with waves, we can talk about the most important of the more advanced properties.

C.1 Advanced properties

▷ An extremely important question that we haven't answered so far is: how fast are waves traveling?
Let's focus on a specific point on our wave. In particular, to determine the velocity of the wave, we follow the movement of a point.

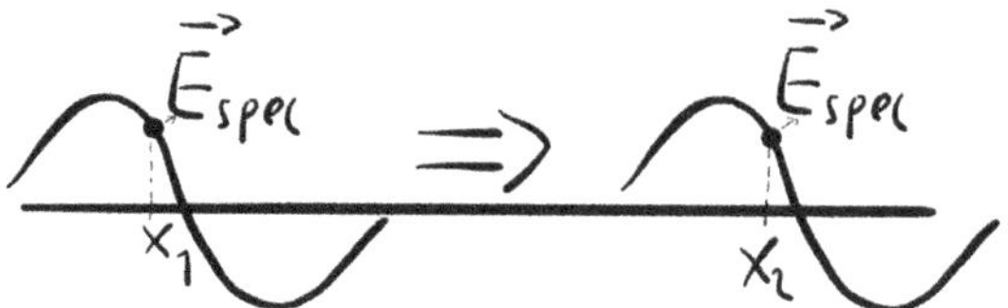

To simplify the discussion, we restrict ourselves to a wave that moves in one-dimension. With this in mind, we can calculate the velocity by using a basic solution

$$\vec{E} = \vec{A}\cos\Big(kx - \omega t\Big) = \vec{E}_0 \cos\Big(k(x - \frac{\omega}{k}t)\Big) . \tag{C.5}$$

We assume that the specific point in our waveform $\vec{E}_{\text{spec}}$ we are interested in is at $t = t_1$ at $x = x_1$:

$$\vec{E}_{\text{spec}} = \vec{A}\cos\Big(k(x_1 - \frac{\omega}{k}t_1)\Big) . \tag{C.6}$$

At a later point in time $t = t_2$, we will find our specific point $\vec{E}_{\text{spec}}$ at some new location $x = x_2$:

$$\vec{E}_{\text{spec}} = \vec{A}\cos\Big(k(x_2 - \frac{\omega}{k}t_2)\Big) . \tag{C.7}$$

This means that in the interval $\Delta t = t_2 - t_1$ our specific point has traveled the distance $\Delta x = x_2 - x_1$. Therefore, our point travels with velocity

$$v = \frac{\Delta x}{\Delta t} = \frac{x_2 - x_1}{t_2 - t_1} . \tag{C.8}$$

Since we are considering the same specific point $\vec{E}_{\text{spec}}$ in Eq. C.6 and Eq. C.7, we can conclude

$$x_2 - \frac{\omega}{k}t_2 = x_1 - \frac{\omega}{k}t_1$$

$$\therefore \quad \frac{\omega}{k} = \frac{x_2 - x_1}{t_2 - t_1} . \tag{C.9}$$

By comparing Eq. C.8 with Eq. C.9, we can conclude

$$v = \frac{\omega}{k}. \tag{C.10}$$

In words, the velocity of each point in our wave form is given by the ratio of the angular frequency ω and the wave number k.

We can also understand this from a different perspective. A velocity has units of meters per second. The only combination of our basic wave quantities discussed in the previous section with units meter per second is[6]

$$v = \frac{\lambda}{\tau} \tag{C.11}$$

since the wavelength λ is measured in meters and the period in seconds. In words, this equation tells us that a wave travels one wavelength λ per period τ. We can rewrite the velocity of the wave v in terms of the angular frequency ω and wave number $k \equiv |\vec{k}|$ as follows

$$v = \frac{\lambda}{\tau} = \frac{2\pi/k}{2\pi/\omega} = \frac{\omega}{k}. \tag{C.12}$$

This is exactly the equation, we already derived above (Eq. C.10).

[6] To be a bit more precise: the velocity we talk about here is the **phase velocity**. This name is used to make clear that it's also possible to associate a different kind of velocity, called **group velocity**, to wave packets. The group velocity is the speed at which the envelope moves forward, while the phase velocity is the speed of the individual plane waves inside the packet. The group velocity and phase velocity are not always the same.

D

Gauge Symmetry in Classical Electrodynamics

Interpreting the actual meaning of a massless gauge field $A_\mu(x_\mu)$ is a delicate and subtle business. There are various ways to understand why. In this section, however, we will restrict ourselves to just one explanation which nicely illustrates the most important ideas.

The first key fact is that we can't observe gauge fields directly. This is something that is well-known from classical electrodynamics although the terminology used is a bit different. In electrodynamics we call A_μ the electromagnetic four-potential:

$$A_\mu = \begin{pmatrix} \frac{\phi}{c} \\ \vec{A} \end{pmatrix} = \begin{pmatrix} \frac{\phi}{c} \\ A_1 \\ A_2 \\ A_3 \end{pmatrix}, \tag{D.1}$$

where ϕ is the electric potential and $\vec{A}$ the magnetic potential. Neither the electric potential ϕ nor the magnetic potential $\vec{A}$ are directly observable.[1] Instead, what is measurable is the electric field $\vec{E}$ and the magnetic field $\vec{B}$. These three-vector fields are related to A_μ (in natural units with $c = 1$) by[2]

[1] Here's an alternative perspective: Only potential differences are measurable. But potential differences remain unchanged by shifts of the potential

$$\begin{aligned} \phi(x_\mu) &\to \phi(x_\mu) + A \\ \Delta\phi &= \phi(a_\mu) - \phi(b_\mu) \\ \to \Delta\phi' &= \big(\phi(a_\mu) + A\big) - \big(\phi(b_\mu) + A\big) \\ &= \phi(a_\mu) - \phi(b_\mu) \\ &= \Delta\phi, \end{aligned} \tag{D.2}$$

where a_μ and b_μ denote two different spacetime points and we shifted the electric potential by a constant amount A.

[2] It is often more convenient to write equations in index notation. In index notation, the cross product $\vec{A} \times \vec{B}$ reads $\epsilon_{ijk} A_i B_j$, where ϵ_{ijk} is the Levi-Civita symbol. In vector notation, these formulas read

$$\vec{E} = -\nabla A_0 - \partial_t \vec{A}$$
$$\vec{B} = \nabla \times \vec{A}.$$

$$E_i = -\partial_i A_0 - \partial_0 A_i$$
$$B_i = \epsilon_{ijk}\partial_j A_k \,. \tag{D.3}$$

If we combine these puzzle pieces, we discover that there are many different four-potentials A_μ that lead to exactly the same electric and magnetic field configurations and thus describe exactly the same physical situation. In particular, we can shift the potentials by a constant amount

$$A_0 \to A_0' = A_0 + \eta$$
$$A_i \to A_i' = A_i + \xi_i \tag{D.4}$$

without altering the electric field and the magnetic field. Let's check this explicitly:

$$\begin{aligned} E_i = -\partial_i A_0 - \partial_0 A_i \to E_i' &= -\partial_i A_0' - \partial_0 A_i' \\ &\quad \text{(Eq. D.4)} \\ &= -\partial_i (A_0 + \eta) - \partial_0 (A_i + \xi_i) \\ &= -\partial_i A_0 - \partial_i \eta - \partial_0 A_i - \partial_0 \xi_i \\ &\quad (\partial_i \eta = \partial_0 \xi_i = 0) \\ &= -\partial_i A_0 - \partial_0 A_i \\ &\quad \text{(Eq. D.3)} \\ &= E_i \quad \checkmark \end{aligned} \tag{D.5}$$

where we used that ξ_i and η are constants. Analogously, we find

$$\begin{aligned} B_i = \epsilon_{ijk}\partial_j A_k \to B_i' &= \epsilon_{ijk}\partial_j A_k' \\ &\quad \text{(Eq. D.4)} \\ &= \epsilon_{ijk}\partial_j (A_k + \xi_k) \\ &= \epsilon_{ijk}\partial_j A_k + \epsilon_{ijk}\partial_j \xi_k \\ &\quad (\partial_j \xi_k = 0) \\ &= \epsilon_{ijk}\partial_j A_k \\ &\quad \text{(Eq. D.3)} \\ &= B_i \quad \checkmark \end{aligned} \tag{D.6}$$

Motivated by this discovery, we can try to find even more complicated transformations of the four potential A_μ that leave the electric and magnetic field unchanged. If we look at the formulas for a while, we can discover that we can not only add constants to the potentials but also derivatives of an arbitrary scalar function $\eta(x_\mu)$. In particular, the electric and magnetic field strengths remain completely unaltered by the transformations[3]

$$\begin{aligned} A_0(x_\mu) &\to A_0(x_\mu) + \partial_0\eta(x_\mu) \\ A_i(x_\mu) &\to A_i(x_\mu) - \partial_i\eta(x_\mu) . \end{aligned} \tag{D.7}$$

[3] Take note that we only have this freedom for massless vector fields. For a massive vector field, only transformations of the from Eq. D.4 are permitted. The electromagnetic field, however, is a massless vector field since the corresponding particles (photons) are massless. Therefore, we have this freedom in classical electrodynamics. We will discuss this later in more detail.

Again, we can check this explicitly:

$$\begin{aligned} E_i = -\partial_i A_0 - \partial_0 A_i \to \tilde{E}_i &= -\partial_i(A_0 + \partial_0\eta) - \partial_0(A_i - \partial_i\eta) \\ &= -\partial_i A_0 - \partial_i\partial_0\eta - \partial_0 A_i + \partial_0\partial_i\eta \\ &= -\partial_i A_0 - \cancel{\partial_0\partial_i\eta} - \partial_0 A_i + \cancel{\partial_0\partial_i\eta} \\ &= -\partial_i A_0 - \partial_0 A_i \\ &= E_i \quad \checkmark \end{aligned} \tag{D.8}$$

and

$$\begin{aligned} B_i = \epsilon_{ijk}\partial_j A_k \to \tilde{B}_i &= \epsilon_{ijk}\partial_j(A_k + \partial_k\eta) \\ &= \epsilon_{ijk}\partial_j A_k + \underbrace{\epsilon_{ijk}\partial_j\partial_k\eta}_{=0} \\ &= \epsilon_{ijk}\partial_j A_k \\ &= B_i \quad \checkmark \end{aligned} \tag{D.9}$$

where we used that ϵ_{ijk} is antisymmetric but $\partial_j\partial_k$ is symmetric under the switching of the indices $j \leftrightarrow k$.[4]

[4] As mentioned above, every time we have a sum over something symmetric in its indices multiplied by something antisymmetric in the same indices, the result is zero:

$$\sum_{ij} a_{ij} b_{ij} = 0$$

if $a_{ij} = -a_{ji}$ and $b_{ij} = b_{ji}$ holds for all i, j.

The fact that everything we can measure remains completely unchanged by the transformations in Eq. D.7 is known as **gauge freedom**.[5]

[5] As mentioned above, a symmetry always refers to a set of transformations which leaves our system unchanged.

D.1 Partial Gauge Fixing

By choosing to work with configurations that fulfill the Lorenz condition we have not exhausted our gauge freedom completely.

There are, in fact, still infinitely many members in each equivalence class that describe the situation at hand and that fulfill the Lorenz condition. Here's why.

Let's assume that we've found one configuration A_μ that describes the situation (i.e. solves the Maxwell equation) and fulfills the Lorenz condition. We can now write down infinitely many new configurations A'_μ that fulfill these two criteria:

$$A'_\mu(x_\mu) = A_\mu(x_\mu) + \partial_\mu \tilde{\eta}(x_\mu)\,, \tag{D.10}$$

where $\tilde{\eta}(x_\mu)$ is no longer completely arbitrary but has to fulfill the condition[6]

$$\partial_\mu \partial^\mu \tilde{\eta} = 0\,. \tag{D.11}$$

[6] Mathematicians call a function $f(x,y,z,\ldots)$ that fulfills the condition

$$\partial_i^2 f(x) = \partial_x^2 f(x) + \partial_y^2 f(x) + \ldots = 0$$

a harmonic function. Moreover, the condition $\partial_\mu \partial^\mu \tilde{\eta} = 0$ is sometimes called the d'Alembert condition. Since there are infinitely many functions $\tilde{\eta}$ that fulfill this condition, there are infinitely many field configurations that fulfill the Lorenz condition and solve the Maxwell equation for a specific system.

Let's check this explicitly:

$$\begin{aligned}
\partial_\mu A'^\mu &\overset{\text{Eq. D.10}}{=} \partial_\mu (A^\mu + \partial^\mu \tilde{\eta}) \\
&= \partial_\mu A^\mu + \partial_\mu \partial^\mu \tilde{\eta} && \text{$\partial_\mu \partial^\mu \tilde{\eta} = 0$ (Eq. D.11)} \\
&= \partial_\mu A^\mu && \text{initial A_μ fulfills the Lorenz condition} \\
&= 0\,.
\end{aligned} \tag{D.12}$$

We can see here, as promised above, that as long as we restrict ourselves to gauge functions $\tilde{\eta}(x_\mu)$ that fulfill the condition $\partial_\mu \partial^\mu \tilde{\eta} = 0$ we can still write down lots of physically equivalent gauge field configurations $A'_\mu(x_\mu)$ that also fulfill the Lorenz condition.[7]

[7] The configurations describe the same physical situations because A_μ and A'_μ are related by a gauge transformation. In particular, take note that the transformation in Eq. D.10 is a gauge transformation (Eq. 5.137) , although a special one since the gauge function has to fulfill an additional condition.

In technical terms, we say that the Lorenz condition only partially fixes the gauge and that there is still residual gauge freedom.

E

Delta Distribution

The delta distribution was invented as a tool that allows us to describe point sources. For example, in electrodynamics, an electron is a point source of the electromagnetic field. Usually, in electrodynamics, we describe the locations of charges using a quantity called charge density $\rho(\vec{x})$. A charge density encodes the amount of charge per unit volume. Hence, if we integrate it over some volume, we get the total charge contained in the volume

$$\text{total charge inside } V = \int_V \rho(\vec{x}) dV \,. \tag{E.1}$$

Now, how can we describe that there is only a single charge at one particular location? In other words: what's the charge density for a single point charge? We write the charge density of a point charge as

$$\rho_{\mathrm{P}}(\vec{x}) = q\delta(\vec{x} - \vec{x}_0) \,, \tag{E.2}$$

where q is the charge of the point charge, $\vec{x}_0$ its location and $\delta(\vec{x} - \vec{x}_0)$ the delta distribution. The defining property of the delta distribution is that *any* integral over a volume V_1 which contains the location of the point charge, yields exactly q:

$$\text{total charge inside } V_1 = \int_{V_1} \rho_{\mathrm{P}}(\vec{x}) dV = \int_{V_1} q\delta(\vec{x} - \vec{x}_0) dV = q \tag{E.3}$$

but an integral over a different volume V_2 which does not contain the point $\vec{x}_0$ yields exactly zero:

$$\text{total charge inside } V_2 = \int_{V_2} \rho_{\text{P}}(\vec{x})dV = \int_{V_2} q\delta(\vec{x}-\vec{x}_0)dV = 0\,. \tag{E.4}$$

This means that the $\delta(\vec{x}-\vec{x}_0)$ yields zero for all $\vec{x}$, except for $\vec{x}=\vec{x}_0$.

A good way to understand the delta distribution[1] (also known as the Dirac delta) is to recall a simpler but analogous mathematical object: the **Kronecker delta** δ_{ij}, which is defined as follows:

[1] The delta distribution is not really a function in the strict mathematical sense and therefore a new word was invented: distributions.

$$\delta_{ij} = \begin{cases} 1 & \text{if } i=j \\ 0 & \text{if } i\neq j \end{cases} \tag{E.5}$$

In matrix form, the Kronecker delta is simply the unit matrix[2]. The Kronecker delta δ_{ij} is useful because it allows us to pick one specific term of any sum. For example, let's consider the sum

[2] For example, in two-dimensions

$$1_{(2\times 2)} = \begin{pmatrix} 1 & 0 \\ 0 & 1 \end{pmatrix}. \tag{E.6}$$

$$\sum_{i=1}^{3} a_i b_j = a_1 b_j + a_2 b_j + a_3 b_j \tag{E.7}$$

and let's say we want to extract only the second term. We can do this by multiplying the sum by the Kronecker delta δ_{2i}:

$$\sum_{i=1}^{3} \delta_{2i} a_i b_j = \underbrace{\delta_{21}}_{=0} a_1 b_j + \underbrace{\delta_{22}}_{=1} a_2 b_j + \underbrace{\delta_{23}}_{=0} a_3 b_j = a_2 b_j. \tag{E.8}$$

In general, we have

$$\sum_{i=1}^{3} \delta_{ik} a_i b_j = a_k b_j. \tag{E.9}$$

The **delta distribution** $\delta(x-y)$ is a generalization of this idea for integrals instead of sums.[3] This means that we can use the delta distribution to extract specific terms from any given integral:[4]

$$\int dx f(x)\delta(x-y) = f(y). \tag{E.10}$$

[3] To unclutter the notation, we restrict ourselves to one-dimension.

[4] Take note that this implies the statement made above for $f(x) = q$:

$$\int dx q\delta(x-y) = q\,.$$

In words, this means that the delta distribution allows us to extract exactly one term - the term $x = y$ - from the infinitely many terms which we sum over as indicated by the integral sign. For example,

$$\int dx f(x)\delta(x-2) = f(2)\,.$$

Now, one example where the Kronecker delta appears is

$$\frac{\partial x_i}{\partial x_j} = \delta_{ij}\,. \tag{E.11}$$

The derivative of $\partial_x x = 1$, whereas $\partial_x y = 0$ and $\partial_x z = 0$.

Completely analogously, the delta distribution appears as follows:

$$\frac{\partial f(x_i)}{\partial f(x_j)} = \delta(x_i - x_j). \tag{E.12}$$

The delta distribution is also often introduced by the following definition:

$$\delta(x-y) = \begin{cases} \infty & \text{if } x = y, \\ 0 & \text{if } x \neq y \end{cases}, \tag{E.13}$$

which is somewhat analogous to the definition of the Kronecker delta in Eq. E.5. Moreover, when we use a constant function in Eq. E.10, for example, $f(x) = 1$, we get the following remarkable equation:

$$\int dx 1\delta(x-y) = 1. \tag{E.14}$$

The thing is that Eq. E.10 tells us that if we have the delta distribution $\delta(x-y)$ together with a function under an integral, the result is the value of the function at $y = x$. Here, we have a constant function and its value at $y = x$ is simply 1.

In words, these properties mean that the delta distribution is infinitely thin (only non-zero at $y = x$) and also an infinitely high function that yields exactly one if we integrate it over all space.

E.1 Integral Representation of the Delta Distribution

In this appendix we want to derive the integral representation of the delta distribution

$$\delta(x-y) = \frac{1}{2\pi}\int_{-\infty}^{\infty} e^{i(x-y)t}\,\mathrm{d}t\,. \tag{E.15}$$

The two puzzle pieces that we need are the formula for the Fourier transform of a function $f(t)$

$$F(x) = \int f(t)e^{-ixt}\mathrm{d}t \tag{E.16}$$

and the formula for the inverse Fourier transform

$$f(t) = \frac{1}{2\pi}\int F(x)e^{ixt}\mathrm{d}x\,. \tag{E.17}$$

By combining these two formulas, we find

$$\begin{aligned}
F(y) &= \int_{-\infty}^{\infty} f(t)e^{-iyt}\mathrm{d}t && \text{this is Eq. E.16} \\
&\quad \text{Eq. E.17} \\
&= \int_{-\infty}^{\infty}\frac{1}{2\pi}\int_{-\infty}^{\infty} F(x)e^{ixt}\mathrm{d}x\, e^{-iyt}\,\mathrm{d}t \\
&\quad \text{rearranging} \\
&= \frac{1}{2\pi}\int_{-\infty}^{\infty} F(x)\int_{-\infty}^{\infty} e^{ixt}\, e^{-iyt}\,\mathrm{d}t\,\mathrm{d}x \\
&\quad e^a e^{-b} = e^{a-b} \\
&= \frac{1}{2\pi}\int_{-\infty}^{\infty} F(x)\int_{-\infty}^{\infty} e^{i(x-y)t}\,\mathrm{d}t\,\mathrm{d}x\,.
\end{aligned} \tag{E.18}$$

The defining property of the delta distribution is

$$F(y) = \int_{-\infty}^{\infty} F(x)\delta(x-y)\mathrm{d}x\,. \tag{E.19}$$

If we compare this formula with Eq. E.18, we can read off

$$\delta(x-y) = \frac{1}{2\pi}\int_{-\infty}^{\infty} e^{i(x-y)t}\,\mathrm{d}t\,, \tag{E.20}$$

which is exactly what we set out to prove.

F

Statistics

F.1 Mean

One of the simplest but at the same time most important statistical tools is the so-called **mean**. Alternative names for the mean are: *expected value, expectation value* or simply the *average*.

The mean of a quantity is the average value we obtain when we repeat a given experiment many times. We use it whenever we are forced to make probabilistic predictions.[1]

[1] Think: flipping a coin, or tossing a die.

For example, imagine the following situation: A friend offers to play a game. She flips a coin. If it lands on tails, she pays you $1.5. But if it lands on heads, you have to pay her $1. By calculating the expectation value for the outcome, you can decide whether or not you should play this game.

▷ The probability that a coin lands on heads is $p_1 = 50\%$. In this case, the outcome for you is: $x_1 = -\$1$

▷ Equally, the probability that a coin lands on tails is $p_2 = 50\%$. In this case the outcome for you is: $x_2 = +\$1.5$

The mean is defined as the sum over each outcome times the probability of the outcome

$$\begin{aligned} \text{mean} &= \sum_i x_i P_i = x_1 P_1 + x_2 P_2 \\ &= -\$1 \times 50\% + \$1.5 \times 50\% = \$0.25\,. \end{aligned} \tag{F.1}$$

So, if you play this game many times, you will make a profit. On average, you make $0.25 per game. For example, let's say you play the game only twice: you win the first time and lose the second time. For the win in the first game, you get $1.5. For the loss in the second game, you lose $1. In total, you therefore win $0.5 in two games. This equals $0.25 per game.

Of course, the system here is so simple that we could have guessed this without calculating anything. But for more complicated systems the situation quickly becomes messy.

To summarize: the mean is the average of the outcomes if we play the game many, many times. A common mathematical notation for the mean of a quantity x looks like this: $\langle x \rangle$.

Bibliography

Pisin Chen and Robert J. Noble. Crystal channel collider: Ultrahigh-energy and luminosity in the next century. *AIP Conf. Proc.*, 398(1):273–285, 1997. DOI: 10.1063/1.53055.

John Earman and Doreen Fraser. Haag's theorem and its implications for the foundations of quantum field theory, December 2005. URL http://philsci-archive.pitt.edu/2673/.

Daniel Fleisch. *A student's guide to Maxwell's equations*. Cambridge University Press, Cambridge, UK New York, 2008. ISBN 978-0521701471.

David Hestenes. The zitterbewegung interpretation of quantum mechanics. *Foundations of Physics*, 20(10):1213–1232, Oct 1990. ISSN 1572-9516. DOI: 10.1007/BF01889466. URL https://doi.org/10.1007/BF01889466.

R. L. Jaffe. The Casimir effect and the quantum vacuum. *Phys. Rev.*, D72:021301, 2005. DOI: 10.1103/PhysRevD.72.021301.

Jean-Marc Levy-Leblond. One more derivation of the Lorentz transformation. *American Journal of Physics*, 44(3):271–277, 1976. DOI: 10.1119/1.10490.

Kimball A. Milton. The Casimir effect: Recent controversies and progress. *J. Phys.*, A37:R209, 2004. DOI: 10.1088/0305-4470/37/38/R01.

Luca Guido Molinari. Notes on Wick's theorem in many-body theory, 2017.

H. Nikolic. Proof that Casimir force does not originate from vacuum energy. *Phys. Lett.*, B761:197–202, 2016. DOI: 10.1016/j.physletb.2016.08.036.

H. C. Ohanian. What is spin? *Am. J. Phys.*, 54:501–505, 1986.

Fredrick Olness and Randall Scalise. Regularization, Renormalization, and Dimensional Analysis: Dimensional Regularization meets Freshman E&M. *Am. J. Phys.*, 79:306, 2011. DOI: 10.1119/1.3535586.

T. Padmanabhan. Obtaining the Non-relativistic Quantum Mechanics from Quantum Field Theory: Issues, Folklores and Facts. *Eur. Phys. J.*, C78(7):563, 2018. DOI: 10.1140/epjc/s10052-018-6039-y.

Jakob Schwichtenberg. *No-Nonsense Electrodynamics*. No-Nonsense Books, Karlsruhe, Germany, 2018a. ISBN 978-1790842117.

Jakob Schwichtenberg. *Physics from Symmetry*. Springer, Cham, Switzerland, 2018b. ISBN 978-3319666303.

Jakob Schwichtenberg. *No-Nonsense Quantum Mechanics*. No-Nonsense Books, Karlsruhe, Germany, 2018c. ISBN 978-1719838719.

Jakob Schwichtenberg. Gauge Coupling Unification without Supersymmetry. *Eur. Phys. J.*, C79(4):351, 2019a. DOI: 10.1140/epjc/s10052-019-6878-1.

Jakob Schwichtenberg. *No-Nonsense Classical Mechanics : a student-friendly introduction*. No-Nonsense Books, Karlsruhe, Germany, 2019b. ISBN 9781096195382.

Jakob Schwichtenberg. *Physics from Finance*. No-Nonsense Books, Karlsruhe, Germany, 2019c. ISBN 978-1795882415.

Xiao-Gang Wen. *Quantum field theory of many-body systems : from the origin of sound to an origin of light and electrons*. Oxford University Press, Oxford New York, 2004. ISBN 9780199227259.

Index

action functional, 146
  Euclidean, 558
angular frequency, 621
  spatial, 620
  temporal, 621
anti-screening, 505
anticommutation relations, 360
antiparticle, 354

bandwidth theorem, 329
basis change, 289
basis expansion, 274

canonical commutation relations, 309
  gauge field, 378
canonical momentum, 151
chirality, 106
classical limit, 546, 549
classical path, 546
commutator, 282
completeness relation, 370
conjugate momentum, 151
connection, 127
constructive interference, 548
contraction, 426
coordinate transformation
  bookkeepers, 127
  global, 126
  local, 126
covariant derivative, 129
creation operator, 318
curvature, 132
  source, 135

delta distribution, 238, 631
  integral representation, 634
  transverse, 378
destructive interference, 548
Dirac equation, 198
  Lagrangian, 195
  Meaning, 199
  solution, 205
Dirac spinor, 86
Dirac spinor field, 94
dispersion relation, 221
dotted index, 96
double slit experiment, 536
Dyson series, 393

electromagnetic potential, 81
energy operator, 280
energy-momentum relation
  non-relativistic, 60
  relativistic, 59
Euclidean metric, 54
Euler formula, 113
Euler's formula, 543
Euler-Lagrange equation, 149
expectation value, 635

Feynman diagram, 441
  loops, 445
  self-loop, 444

tree-level, 443
Feynman rules, 442
ϕ^4 model, 447
gauge model, 482
Yukawa, 479
field
as-if mattress, 110, 171
Dirac spinor, 94
quantum, 304
scalar, 73
space, 122
spinor, 94
vector, 74
Weyl spinor, 94
field strength tensor, 132
fundamental solution, 245

gauge choice, 229
Lorenz, 229
radiation, 374
temporal, 373
gauge field, 134
massive
polarizations, 223
massless, 226
polarizations, 230
gauge symmetry, 225
fixing, 229
generalized momentum, 151
generator, 279
Green's function, 245
Dirac equation, 257
Klein-Gordon equation, 240
Maxwell equation, 266
group theory, 277

Hamiltonian density, 315
Hamiltonian operator, 285
Heisenberg picture, 383

inhomogenous Maxwell equation, 216
instanton, 561
interaction picture, 384
interactions
gauge
classical, 264
quantum, 481
self
classical, 246
quantum, 407, 437, 448
Yukawa
classical, 253
quantum, 467

Klein-Gordon equation, 170
derivation, 179
general solution, 192
higher order terms, 188
Lagrangian, 170
solution, 189

Lagrangian density, 154
dimensional analysis, 568
effective, 568
Lagrangian formalism, 137
Levi-Civita symbol, 14
Lorentz transformation
Dirac spinor
boost, 88
parity, 89
left-chiral spinor
boost, 86
rotation, 85
right-chiral spinor
boost, 86
rotation, 86
scalar
boost, 84
rotation, 84
vector
boost, 85
rotation, 85
Lorentz transformations, 62
vector
boost, 64
rotation, 63
Lorenz condition, 218
Lorenz gauge, 229

mass basis, 211
mass term, 120

mass-shell condition, 490
Maxwell equation
  general solution, 233
  meaning, 216
Minkowski metric, 54
Minkowski space
  scalar product, 55
    invariant, 66
momentum operator, 280

Noether's theorem, 155, 275
  internal symmetry, 161
    field shift, 161
    phase shift, 163
  spacetime symmetry, 157
non-perturbative phenomena, 555
normal ordering, 399

particle
  free, 291
Path Integral, 541
path integral
  quantum field theory, 549
Pauli exclusion principle, 364
phase, 619
Planck constant, 281
plane wave, 113, 329
  superposition, 117
Poincaré transformations, 62
polarization, 78
  massive gauge field, 79
  massless gauge field, 79
Proca equation, 216
  general solution, 233
  Lagrangian, 214
  meaning, 216
  solutions, 218
propagator, 337
  advanced, 340
  fermion, 366
  Feynman, 341
    complex scalar field, 357
    spinor field, 366
  retarded, 340
proper time, 51

radiation gauge, 374
regularization, 456
renormalization group, 565
  interpretation, 503
renormalization group equation
  ϕ^4 model, 501
renormalized coupling, 454

scalar, 80
scalar field, 73
scalar product
  spinors, 97
  vectors, 55
Schrödinger equation, 285
  stationary, 294
  time-independent, 294
Schrödinger picture, 382
screening, 506
spacetime, 39
  Euclidean, 41
  event, 39
  interval, 52
  Minkowski, 41
speed of light, 43
spin, 102
spinor, 85
  left-chiral, 85
spinor field, 94
  example, 94
spinor metric, 97
spinor scalar product, 97
symmetry, 276
  continuous, 277
  discrete, 277
symmetry breaking
  explicit, 528
  spontaneous, 521, 528

temporal gauge, 373
time dilation, 47
time evolution operator, 286
transition amplitude, 382
transverse delta, 378

vacuum expectation value, 531
variation, 144

variational calculus, 142
vector, 80
vector field, 74
virtual particles, 489

wave equation, 113
  dispersion, 115
  solution, 113
wave number, 620
wave packet, 118
  dispersion, 116
  superposition, 117
wave vector, 620
wavelength, 620
Weyl spinor, 85
Weyl spinor field, 94
Wick rotation, 558
Wick's theorem, 428

Yukawa potential, 243, 477

Made in the USA
Las Vegas, NV
24 February 2022

44486528R00352